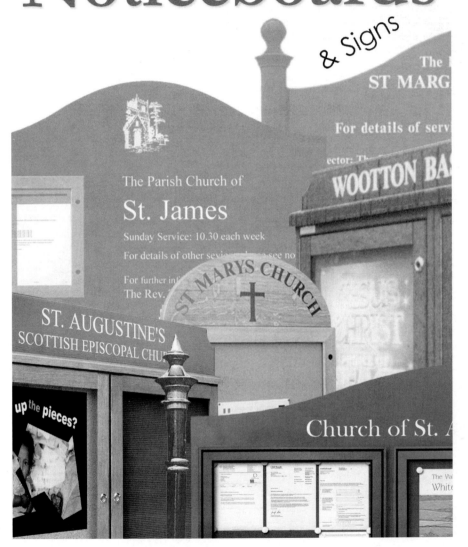

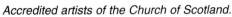

SCOTTISH CHRISTIAN PRESS

Scottish Christian Press is an imprint of the Board of Parish Education.
We have provided the Church with educational resources in the areas of
children's, youth and adult ministry for over fifty years.

New Books for 2005 include:

YOU'RE AN ANGEL! Being Yourself and Sharing your Faith
by Peter Neilson and David Currie

PRACTICAL CARING - a handbook for the pastoral visitor
by Sheilah Steven

WAKE UP TO YOUR DREAMS - exploring ability and disability through dreams
by Dr Jean C Morrison, with original art work by John Lowrie Morrison

And announcing our new Internet imprint:
the **Covenanters' Press** www.covenanters.co.uk

PRAYING ON THE EDGE - Bible studies for
concerned Christians by Bryan Owen

KEEPING IT CHEERY - the history of Church
House and Bridgeton Youth Club in Glasgow
by Bill Shackleton

MOTHMILK AND MOONDUST - reflections
on lives lived in the grace of God
by Karen McDonald,
benefiting Strathcarron Hospice.

THE BACK TO FRONT BOY - the true
story of adopting a child with
attachment disorder
by Rebecca Wright

For details of all new books check out our
websites www.scottishchristianpress.org.uk
and www.covenanters.co.uk. Or phone
0131 260 3120 and request a catalogue!

Dr Alison Elliot OBE

MODERATOR

The Church of Scotland
YEAR BOOK
2004/2005

Editor
Rev. Ronald S. Blakey
MA BD MTh

Published on behalf of
THE CHURCH OF SCOTLAND
BOARD OF COMMUNICATION
by SAINT ANDREW PRESS
121 George Street, Edinburgh EH2 4YN

THE OFFICES OF THE CHURCH

121 George Street
Edinburgh EH2 4YN

Tel: 0131-225 5722
Fax: 0131-220 3113
Internet: http://www.churchofscotland.org.uk/

Office Hours:
Office Manager:

Monday–Friday 9.00 am–5.00 pm
Mrs Dorothy H. Woodhouse

PARISH EDUCATION
21 Young Street, Edinburgh EH2 4HU

Tel: 0131-260 3110

SOCIAL RESPONSIBILITY
Charis House   47 Milton Road East, Edinburgh EH15 2SR
[E-mail: info@charis.org.uk]

Tel: 0131-657 2000
Fax: 0131-657 5000

NATIONAL MISSION
Glasgow Office   59 Elmbank Street, Glasgow G2 4PQ
Kirkcaldy Office   St Bryce Kirk Centre,
St Brycedale Avenue, Kirkcaldy KY1 1ET

Tel: 0141-333 1948

Tel/Fax: 01592 646406

(Youth Adviser: Presbytery of Glasgow)
110 St James Road, Glasgow G4 0PS

Tel: 0141-400 7788

QUICK DIRECTORY

A.C.T.S. 01786 823588
Badenoch Centre 01540 651373
Board of Communication 0131-240 2236
Bridgeton, St Francis-in-the-East Church House 0141-554 8045
Carberry 0131-665 3135/7604
Christian Aid London 020 7620 4444
Christian Aid Scotland 0131-220 1254
Glasgow Lodging House Mission 0141-552 0285
Kirk Care 0131-225 7246
Netherbow 0131-556 9579/2647
Media Relations Unit (Press Office) 0131-240 2243
Pathway Media 0131-225 5722
Scottish Churches Parliamentary Office 0131-622 2278
Society, Religion and Technology Project 0131-556 2953

First published in 2004 by SAINT ANDREW PRESS, 121 George Street, Edinburgh EH2 4YN on behalf of the
BOARD of COMMUNICATION of the CHURCH of SCOTLAND

Copyright © The BOARD of COMMUNICATION of the CHURCH of SCOTLAND, 2004

ISBN 0 86153 356 9

British Library Cataloguing in Publication Data
A catalogue record for this book is available from the British Library.

Printed and bound by Bell and Bain Ltd, Glasgow

CONTENTS

All correspondence regarding the *Year Book* should be sent to
The Editor, *Church of Scotland Year Book*,
Saint Andrew Press, 121 George Street, Edinburgh EH2 4YN
Fax: 0131-220 3113
[E-mail: yearbookeditor@cofscotland.org.uk]

GENERAL ASSEMBLY OF 2005
The General Assembly of 2005 will convene on
Saturday, 21st May 2005

FROM THE MODERATOR

Collecting data and then interpreting them used to be an important part of my life. The enjoyable part was devising and carrying out tests into how children learned their native language. This involved identifying what could be recorded and then counted in structured conversations with young children, so as to crack the code of how they performed the everyday miracle of turning from being babbling infants into talkative youngsters.

But then there was also the time I spent giving lectures in statistics to some hapless science students. It was a fairly dismal business travelling across Edinburgh on cold winter mornings to an old-fashioned, echoing lecture theatre in a different part of the university, trying to persuade reluctant students that statistics was an interesting subject, not just a course requirement.

Two lessons from these days. Data are only as useful as the accuracy with which they have been collected. So we are greatly in the debt of Rev. Ron Blakey and those who have helped him in the painstaking task of putting together this *Year Book*.

And the interpretation of data is only as interesting as the imagination you bring to discovering the story that they embody. There are many interesting stories hidden in this book, stories of trends and distributions that are waiting to be discovered. As well as lots of useful telephone numbers!

I am happy to commend this *Year Book* for 2004/2005 to you.

Alison Elliot
July 2004

FROM THE EDITOR

James Hamilton, later to be minister of London's Regent Square Church, wrote in his student day-book in 1838: 'Some preachers use their text as a louping-on-stane: if by help of it they can only get mounted, they do not care how far they go from it or if they ever see it again'. The freedom of such an approach is attractive, the more so if one is not rationed to a single text. Thus it is that there are offered here a line from James Thurber together with three proverbs culled, let it be admitted, not from the Scriptural Solomon but from the Penguin Dictionary.

Beauty is in the eye of the beholder. What was simultaneously commended as 'attractive and appealing' and condemned as "dreadful" with an appearance that looks at best 'dyslexic' at worst 'illiterate'? The answer of course is last year's – and this year's – *Year Book* cover.

You can't tell a book by its cover. Last year's Editorial promised that, whatever the changed appearance of the *Year Book*'s new cover, 'for the peace of the Church, the colour is sacrosanct'. The correspondent who subsequently opined that the finished article was not red enough and not enough red was clearly unconvinced. The front cover was grudgingly accepted as being a kind of inferior red albeit with an intrusive dash of blue; the back cover was dismissed as totally redless; the spine gained a bare 50 per cent pass mark. Elsewhere, the Editor was treated to a whistle-stop tour of other 'red books'. Chairman Mao's 'Little Red Book', Michael Aspel's 'Big Red Book', that essential football fixture almanack of many of our childhoods, 'The Wee Red Book', and Webster's 'Royal Red Book' of the nobility first published in 1847 were all paraded as red books which required for their proper identity a descriptive adjective. The Church of Scotland, on the other hand, or so it was implied, had always had the definitive Red Book. It was clearly inconceivable that its future could be anything other than totally secure.

There is no safety in numbers. These untypically pessimistic words of James Thurber might well be adopted as the motto of those who find it 'illogical', 'confusing' and 'frustrating' that, already bereft of Presbyteries with the numbers fifteen, twenty and twenty-one, even more gaps in our numerical system are a definite possibility for the future. One caller appeared to be speaking on behalf of, or even on the instruction of, her computer, whose habits of a lifetime were such that it refused point blank to recognise such untidiness and had in effect declared UDI, numbering all remaining Presbyteries in strict numerical sequence and so branding everyone else out of step – a situation that will doubtless continue until a suitably trained counsellor can be found to rebuild its self-confidence.

A nod is as good as a wink. It probably is in matters of political intrigue, in affairs of the heart, in the sensitivities of insider share-dealing and of course, as the originator of these words knew well, when communicating with a blind horse. It is not so when recording an e-mail address, where absolute accuracy is required if the address is to function. Put another way, a - is not as good as a _: an l will not suffice where a 1 is required: an 8 is very different from a B, a c is no substitute for an e, while an o is truly as nothing when what is wanted is a 0. It is for this reason that the request is made each year for e-mail addresses to be submitted in some printed form. For whatever reason, a number of clerks, secretaries and individuals decline or ignore this request and offer instead a scruffy ball-point scrawl which tests the imagination, ingenuity and patience of the Editor. With 433 new or altered e-mail addresses to be incorporated this year, errors will doubtless have occurred.

As far as this year's volume is concerned, thanks are due to the Board of World Mission for a considerably more comprehensive list (List 6-L) of resigned and retired mission partners who have given ten or more years' service. The index of former parishes and congregations has further been amended and updated. The section giving information about the Assembly's Boards and Committees takes due account of the newcomers on the block – the Council of Assembly, the Central Services Committee, the Panel on Review and Reform, the Parish Development Fund Committee and the Committee Planning the Church Without Walls Celebration.

It is next year's edition, however, which is likely to see more major changes. As is reported in the section of this volume which reflects on the General Assembly of 2004, the Boards, Committees and Panels which fall within the definition of Agencies of the General Assembly are to be organised and reconstituted within six new Councils. Some familiar names will disappear altogether; others will seem to have disappeared but will in fact still be there, albeit housed within one of the new Councils. The 'numbers game' associated with the amalgamation of Presbyteries will have a no doubt equally popular sequel as the Boards and Committees appear in a whole new order. Beyond that, and of rather greater long-term significance, the Church Solicitor will shortly be advising Saint Andrew Press on the implications of the Data Protection Act for publications such as the *Year Book*.

As far as the ongoing work of the Editor is concerned, what has been personally most rewarding over the past twelve months have been the many words of appreciation expressed for the inclusion last year of the tribute to Andrew Herron. With these have come stories and reminiscences which are treasured. At a time when many ministers feel undervalued, seeming to hear more of criticism than of commendation, it is perhaps worth retelling Andrew's story 'in praise of the silent majority'. He linked it to words of advice allegedly offered by a Lanarkshire church officer to the newly inducted minister, but it is sufficiently in keeping with our national temperament to have originated anywhere, even in Andrew's own fertile mind: 'Remember, son, if we like you we say nothing; if we don't, we tell you'.

Ronald S. Blakey
July 2004

SECTION 1

Assembly Boards
and Committees

MEETINGS OF BOARDS AND COMMITTEES

The following Boards and Committees have indicated that they plan to meet on the dates listed.

BOARD OF NATIONAL MISSION

Board (Wednesdays, 10:30am)
2004   1 December
2005   2 February

Committee on Parish Appraisal (Tuesdays, 10:30am)
2004   19 October, 16 November, 21 December
2005   15 February, 15 March

Committee on New Charge Development (Wednesdays, 10:30am)
2004   17 November
2005   19 January, 16 March

Congregational Mission Development (Thursdays, 10:30am)
2004   28 October
2005   13 January

Committee on Chaplaincies (Wednesdays, 11am)
2004   3 November
2005   26 January

Hospitals, Healthcare and Universities Sub-Committee (Tuesdays, 10:30am)
2004   16 November
2005   18 January, 15 March

Church and Industry Sub-Committee (Wednesdays, 6pm)
2004   17 November
2005   19 January, 20 April

Prison Chaplaincies Sub-Committee (Wednesdays, 10:30am)
2004   6 October
2005   12 January

Joint Faiths Advisory Board on Criminal Justice (Wednesdays, 2pm)
2004   8 December
2005   9 March

Committee on Priority Areas
2004   17 November
2005   18 January, 12 April

BOARD OF WORLD MISSION
2004   24–25 November
2005   2 February, 20 April, 15–16 June

CHURCH OF SCOTLAND GUILD
National Executive Committee
2004   2 November
2005   8 February, 15 March

COMMITTEE ON ARTISTIC MATTERS
2004   7 October, 4 November, 9 December
2005   3 February, 3 March, 7 April, 5 May, 2 June, 7 July, 1 September

COMMITTEE ON ECUMENICAL RELATIONS
2005   27 January, 24 March, 22–23 September

COMMITTEE ON EDUCATION
2004   17 November
2005   9 February, 15 June

GENERAL TRUSTEES
General Trustees
2004   26 October, 23 November, 21 December
2005   25 January, 22 February, 22 March, 26 April, 31 May, 5 July, 27 September

Committees
2004   12 October, 9 November, 7 December
2005   11 January, 8 February, 8 March, 5 April, 10 May, 14 June, 26 July,
        6 September

HOUSING AND LOAN FUND
2004   14 December
2005   22 February, 19 April, 21 June, 20 September

PANEL ON DOCTRINE
2004   1 December
2005   2 February, 1 June

PANEL ON WORSHIP
2004   18 November
2005   17 February, 9 June, 15 September

INDEX OF ASSEMBLY BOARDS AND COMMITTEES

[Note: Years, where given, indicate the year of appointment]

(1) COUNCIL OF ASSEMBLY

MEMBERSHIP

(a) Convener, Vice Convener and eight members appointed by the General Assembly; the General Treasurer and the Solicitor of the Church; the Principal Clerk as Secretary to the Council; together with:

(b) *Until 31 May 2005*: the Conveners of the Boards of Ministry, National Mission, Parish Education, Stewardship and Finance, Social Responsibility and World Mission, together with the Convener of the Church and Nation Committee *or* the Education Committee, as agreed between the two Committees; the General Secretaries of the Boards of Ministry, National Mission, Parish Education, Social Responsibility and World Mission, together with the Secretary of the Church and Nation Committee *or* the Education Committee, as agreed between the two Committees.

(c) *From 1 June 2005*: the Conveners of the Councils, namely Church and Society, Ministries, Mission and Discipleship, Social Care, Services and Support, and World Mission; the Secretaries of the following Councils, namely Church and Society, Ministries, Mission and Discipleship, Social Care and World Mission.

Convener:	Mrs Helen McLeod MA (2004)
Vice Convener:	Rev. Gilbert Nisbet CA BD (2004)
Secretary:	The Principal Clerk

REMIT

1. To implement the plan of reorganisation and structural change of the Agencies of the General Assembly as formulated by the Assembly Council and approved by the General Assembly of 2004.

2. To monitor, evaluate and co-ordinate the work of the Agencies of the General Assembly, within the context of policy determined by the Assembly.

3. To advise the General Assembly on the relative importance of work being undertaken by its various Agencies.

4. To receive reports from, offer guidance to and issue instructions to Agencies of the General Assembly as required from time to time on matters of management, organisation and administration.

5. To bring recommendations to the General Assembly concerning the total amount of the Church's Co-ordinated Budget for the following financial year and the disposition thereof among Local Mission, Parish Staffing and the Mission and Renewal Fund.

6. To determine the allocation of the total budgets for the following financial year for Parish Staffing and the Mission and Renewal Fund among the relevant Agencies of the General Assembly and Ecumenical Bodies.

7. To prepare and present to the General Assembly an indicative Rolling Budget for the following five financial years.

8. To receive and distribute unrestricted legacies and donations among the Agencies of the General Assembly with power to specify the use to which the same are to be applied.

9. To consider and decide on proposals from Agencies of the General Assembly to purchase heritable property or any other asset (except investments) valued in excess of £50,000 or lease any heritable property where the annual rental exceeds £10,000 per annum, declaring that no Agency save those referred to in section 17 hereof shall proceed to purchase or lease such property without prior approval from the Council.

10. To consider and decide on proposals from Agencies of the General Assembly, save those referred to in Section 17 hereof, to sell or lease for a period in excess of five years or otherwise dispose of any heritable property, or sell or otherwise dispose of any asset (except investments) valued in excess of £50,000, held by or on behalf of that Agency, with power to allocate all or part of the sale or lease proceeds to another Agency or Agencies in terms of section 11 hereof.

11. To reallocate following upon consultation with the Agency or Agencies affected unrestricted funds held by or on behalf of any of the Agencies of the General Assembly to another Agency or Agencies with power to specify the use to which the same are to be applied.

12. To determine staffing and resourcing requirements of Agencies of the General Assembly, including inter-Departmental sharing or transfer of staff, in accordance with policies drawn up by the Council of Assembly in line with priorities approved by the General Assembly, it being declared that the term 'staffing' shall not include those appointed or employed to serve either in particular Parishes or overseas.

13. To keep under review the central administration of the Church, with particular regard to resolving issues of duplication of resources.

14. To attend to the general interests of the Church in matters which are not covered by the remit of any other Agency.

15. To deal with urgent issues arising between meetings of the General Assembly, provided that:
    (a) these do not fall within the jurisdiction of the Commission of Assembly or of any Presbytery or Kirk Session,
    (b) they are not of a legislative or judicial nature and
    (c) any action taken in terms of this clause shall be reported to the next General Assembly.

16. To encourage all Agencies of the General Assembly to work ecumenically wherever possible and to have regard to the international, evangelical and catholic nature of the Church.

17. For the avoidance of doubt, sections 9 and 10 shall not apply to the Church of Scotland General Trustees, the Church of Scotland Housing and Loan Fund for Retired Ministers and Widows and Widowers of Ministers and the New Charge Development Committee and its successor body, all of which may deal with heritable property and other assets without the approval of the Council.

---

(2) PRACTICE AND PROCEDURE

MEMBERSHIP
BOARD OF PRACTICE AND PROCEDURE
(38 members: 32 appointed by the Assembly, plus Moderator, Moderator Designate, Clerks, Procurator and Law Agent *ex officiis*)

Convener:	Rev. William C. Hewitt BD DipPS (2004)
Vice Convener:	Rev. Alastair H. Symington MA BD (2002)
Secretary:	The Principal Clerk

COMMITTEE TO NOMINATE THE MODERATOR
(54 members: three surviving immediate past Moderators, three elders appointed through the Nomination Committee and one member from each Presbytery)

Convener: The earliest serving former Moderator present and willing to act
Secretary: The Principal Clerk

JUDICIAL COMMISSION OF THE GENERAL ASSEMBLY
Chairman: Rev. Alistair G.C. McGregor QC BD
Vice Chairman: Mr C. Noel Glen BL NP
Secretaries: The Clerks of Assembly

STAFF
Principal Clerk: Very Rev. Finlay A.J. Macdonald MA BD PhD DD
Depute Clerk: Rev. Marjory A. MacLean LLB BD PhD
Principal Administration Officer: Mrs Alison Murray MA

REMIT: BOARD OF PRACTICE AND PROCEDURE
1. To advise the General Assembly on questions of Church Law and of Constitutional Law affecting the relationship between Church and State.
2. To advise and assist Committees of the General Assembly in the preparation of proposed legislation and on questions of interpretation, including interpretation of and proposed changes to their remits.
3. To make all necessary arrangements for the General Assembly each year.
4. To advise the Moderator anent his or her official duties, if so required.
5. To be responsible to the General Assembly for the care and maintenance of all Assembly buildings and its other property.
6. To compile the statistics of the Church, except Youth and Finance; and to supervise on behalf of the General Assembly all arrangements for care of Church Records and for Presbytery Visits.

---

(3) CENTRAL SERVICES COMMITTEE

MEMBERSHIP
(11 members: seven appointed by the General Assembly, and four *ex officiis* and non-voting, namely the Principal Clerk, the Solicitor of the Church, the General Treasurer and the Personnel Manager)
Convener: Mr Leon Marshall CA (2001)
Vice Convener: Mr John Neil OBE

STAFF
Administrative Secretary: Mrs Pauline Wilson BA
                                 (E-mail: pwilson@cofscotland.org.uk)

REMIT
1. To be responsible for the proper maintenance and insurance of the Church Offices at 117–123 George Street, Edinburgh ('the George Street Offices').
2. To be responsible for matters relating to Health and Safety within the George Street Offices.

3.   To be responsible for matters relating to Data Protection within the George Street Offices and with respect to the General Assembly Boards and Committees based elsewhere.
4.   To be responsible for the allocation of accommodation within the George Street Offices and the annual determination of rental charges to the Boards, Committees and other parties accommodated therein.
5.   To oversee the delivery of central services to Departments within the George Street Offices and to the General Assembly Boards and Committees based elsewhere, namely:
   •   those facilities directly managed by the Office Manager
   •   information technology (including the provision of support services to Presbytery Clerks)
   •   insurance
   •   purchasing and travel
   •   personnel services
   •   financial services (as delivered by the General Treasurer's Department)
   •   legal services (as delivered by the Law Department and subject to such oversight not infringing principles of 'client/solicitor' confidentiality).
6.   To provide an internal audit function to the General Assembly Boards, Statutory Corporations and Committees (other than the Board of Social Responsibility).
7.   The Committee shall act as one of the five employing agencies of the Church.

---

(4) GENERAL TREASURER'S DEPARTMENT

STAFF

General Treasurer:	Mr Donald F. Ross MA CA
Senior Deputy Treasurer:	Mr Iain W. Grimmond BAcc CA
Deputy General Treasurers:	Mr Alexander F. Gemmill BAcc CA
	Mr John S. Steven CA
	Mr William J. McKean BAcc CA
Assistant Treasurer:	Mrs Anne Macintosh BA CA
Accountants:	Mr Ross Donaldson
	Mr Derek Cant FCCA

Responsibilities of the General Treasurer's Department include:
•   payroll processing for the Board of Ministry, Board of National Mission and Central Co-ordinating Committee
•   calculating congregational Mission and Renewal Fund allocations
•   issuing to congregations their annual requirement figures for the National Stipend Fund and the Mission and Renewal Fund
•   receiving payments from congregations towards their central requirements
•   making Gift Aid tax recoveries on behalf of Boards, Committees and Statutory Corporations
•   making VAT returns and tax recoveries on behalf of Boards, Committees and Statutory Corporations and providing VAT information to congregations
•   providing support, training and advice on financial matters to congregational treasurers
•   receiving and discharging legacies and bequests on behalf of Boards, Committees and Statutory Corporations

- providing banking arrangements and operating a central banking system for Boards, Committees and Statutory Corporations
- providing accountancy systems and services for Boards, Committees, Statutory Corporations and the Trustees of the Church's Pension Schemes
- providing Finance Departments for the Boards of World Mission and Parish Education.

(5) INFORMATION TECHNOLOGY DEPARTMENT

STAFF

Information Technology Manager: Alastair Chalmers
Depute Information Technology Manager: Veronica Hay

The Department provides computing facilities for Boards and Departments within 121 George Street, Presbytery Clerks, National Mission personnel outwith George Street, the Scottish Churches Parliamentary Office and the Moderator's house. It is also responsible for the telephone services within the George Street Offices.

The facilities provided include:
- the provision and maintenance of networks for both data and voice
- the purchase and installation of hardware and software
- support for problems and guidance on the use of software
- development of in-house software
- maintenance of data within the central databases and finance systems.

(6) THE LAW DEPARTMENT

STAFF

Solicitor of the Church
  and of the General Trustees: Mrs Janette S. Wilson LLB NP
Depute Solicitor: Miss Mary E. Macleod LLB NP
Assistant Solicitors: Mr Ian K. Johnstone MA LLB
                      Mrs Elizabeth M. Kemp MA LLB
                      Mrs Jennifer M. Hamilton BA NP
                      Mrs Elspeth Annan LLB NP
                      Miss Susan Killean LLB NP

The Law Department of the Church was created in 1937/38. The Department acts in legal matters for the Church and all of its Courts, Boards, Committees, the Church of Scotland General Trustees, the Church of Scotland Trust and the Church of Scotland Investors Trust. It also acts for individual congregations and is available to give advice on any legal matter arising.

The Department is under the charge of the Solicitor of the Church, a post created at the same time as the formation of the Department and a post which is now customarily held along with the traditional posts of Law Agent of the General Assembly and the Custodier of former United Free Church titles (E-mail: lawdept@cofscotland.org.uk).

---

(7) OFFICE MANAGER'S DEPARTMENT

STAFF

Office Manager: Mrs Dorothy Woodhouse
                                   (E-mail: dwoodhouse@cofscotland.org.uk)

The responsibilities of the Office Manager's Department include:
* management of a maintenance budget for the upkeep of the Church Offices at 121 George Street, Edinburgh
* responsibility for all aspects of health and safety for staff, visitors and contractors working in the building
* managing a team of staff providing the Offices with security, reception, mail room, print room, switchboard, day-to-day maintenance services and Committee room bookings
* overseeing all sub-contracted services to include catering, cleaning, boiler-room maintenance, intruder alarm, fire alarms and lifts
* maintaining building records in accordance with the requirements of statutory legislation
* overseeing all alterations to the building and ensuring, where applicable, that they meet Planning and Building Control regulations.

---

(8) THE PERSONNEL DEPARTMENT

STAFF

Personnel Manager:	Mr George B.B. Eadie BA
Deputy Personnel Manager:	Miss Angela Brady MCIPD
Personnel Officer:	Miss Maria Carena
Personnel Assistant:	Mrs Dorothy Menzies

REMIT

The Personnel Committee was set up in 1978 on the Report of the Advisory Board to determine salaries, length of service and conditions generally for Secretaries and Members of Office Staff. In 1991, and again in 1996, the General Assembly made certain minor adjustments to the remit, including a requirement that the Personnel Committee should conduct an annual salary review of those members of staff for which it is the employing agency.

In recognition of the aim that the Personnel Committee may in time operate as the co-ordinating body for the Church in respect of the salaries and conditions of employment of all persons employed by the five employing agencies, the other four employing agencies are required to provide all information on such matters as requested by the Personnel Committee.

As from 1 September 2001, this remit passed to the new Central Co-ordinating Committee, which has been renamed the Central Services Committee following the 2004 General Assembly.

---

(9) GENERAL TRUSTEES

MEMBERSHIP
(New Trustees are appointed, as required, by the General Assembly, on the recommendation of the General Trustees)

Chairman: Rev. James H. Simpson BD LLB (2003)
Vice Chairman: Mr W. Findlay Turner CA (2003)
Secretary and Clerk: Mr David D. Robertson LLB NP
Depute Secretary and Clerk: Mr T.R.W. Parker LLB

COMMITTEES:
Fabric Committee
Convener: Rev. Angus T. Stewart MA BD PhD (2003)

Chairman's Committee
Convener: Rev. James H. Simpson BD LLB (2003)

Glebes Committee
Convener: Rev. William Paterson BD (2003)

Finance Committee
Convener: Mr R.G. Burnett BComm CA FCMA (1999)

Law Committee
Convener: Mr C. Noel Glen BL NP (2004)

STAFF
Secretary and Clerk: Mr. David D. Robertson LLB NP
Depute Secretary and Clerk: Mr T.R.W. Parker LLB
Assistants: Mr Keith J. Fairweather LLB (Glebes)
                                   Mr Keith S. Mason LLB NP (Ecclesiastical Buildings)
Treasurer: Mr Donald F. Ross MA CA
Deputy Treasurer: Mr W.J. McKean BAcc CA

REMIT
The General Trustees are a Property Corporation created and incorporated under the Church of Scotland (General Trustees) Order Confirmation Act 1921. Their duties, powers and responsibilities were greatly extended by the Church of Scotland (Property & Endowments) Acts and Orders 1925 to 1995, and they are also charged with the administration of the Central Fabric Fund (see below) and the Consolidated Fabric Fund and the Consolidated Stipend Fund in which monies held centrally for the benefit of individual congregations are lodged.

The scope of the work of the Trustees is broad, covering all facets of property administration, but particular reference is made to the following matters:

1. **ECCLESIASTICAL BUILDINGS.** The Trustees' Fabric Committee considers proposals for work at buildings, regardless of how they are vested, and plans of new buildings. Details of all such projects should be submitted to the Committee before work is commenced. The Committee also deals with applications for the release of fabric monies held by the General Trustees for individual congregations, and considers applications for assistance from the Central Fabric Fund from which grants and/or loans may be given to assist congregations faced with expenditure on fabric. Application forms relating to consents for work and possible financial assistance from the Central Fabric Fund are available from the Secretary of the Trustees and require to be submitted through Presbytery with its approval. The Committee normally meets on the first or second Tuesday of each month, apart from July, when it meets on the last Tuesday, and August, when there is no meeting.

2. **SALE, PURCHASE AND LETTING OF PROPERTIES.** All sales or lets of properties vested in the General Trustees fall to be carried out by them in consultation with the Financial Board of the congregation concerned, and no steps should be taken towards any sale or let without prior consultation with the Secretary of the Trustees. Where property to be purchased is to be vested in the General Trustees, it is essential that contact be made at the earliest possible stage with the Solicitor to the Trustees, who is responsible for the lodging of offers for such properties and all subsequent legal procedure.

3. **GLEBES.** The Trustees are responsible for the administration of Glebes vested in their ownership. All lets fall to be granted by them in consultation with the minister concerned. It should be noted that neither ministers nor Kirk Sessions may grant lets of Glebe land vested in the General Trustees. As part of their Glebe administration, the Trustees review regularly all Glebe rents.

4. **INSURANCE.** Properties vested in the General Trustees must be insured with the Church of Scotland Insurance Co. Ltd, a company wholly owned by the Church of Scotland whose profits are applied for Church purposes. Insurance enquiries should be sent directly to the Company at 67 George Street, Edinburgh EH2 2JG (Tel: 0131-220 4119; Fax: 0131-220 4120; E-mail: enquiries@cosic.co.uk).

---

(10) NOMINATION

MEMBERSHIP – NOMINATION COMMITTEE
(44 members)

Convener:	Rev. Keith F. Hall BD (2002)
Vice Convener:	Rev. Iain D. Cunningham MA BD (2002)
Secretary:	The Principal Clerk

REMIT
To bring before the General Assembly names of persons to serve on the Boards and Standing Committees of the General Assembly.

(11) CHURCH OF SCOTLAND INVESTORS TRUST

MEMBERSHIP
(Trustees are appointed by the General Assembly, on the nomination of the Investors Trust)
Chairman: Mr D.M. Simpson BA FFA
Vice Chairman: Mrs I.J. Hunter MA
Treasurer: Mr D.F. Ross MA CA
Secretary: Mr F.E. Marsh MCIBS

REMIT
The Church of Scotland Investors Trust, established in 1994 by Act of Parliament, offers to Boards, Committees and congregations of the Church a simple and economical medium for the investment of their funds. Investors are at liberty to invest in the Church of Scotland Investors Trust to an unlimited extent, and it is felt that the facilities afforded thereby are preferable to the powers of investment offered by the Trustee Investments Act 1961, with all the attendant restrictions and conditions. The Church of Scotland Investors Trust provides three Funds for Church investors:

1.   **THE DEPOSIT FUND** is intended for short-term investment and aims to provide a high rate of interest. Deposits are repayable on demand. Interest is calculated quarterly in arrears and paid gross on 15 May and 15 November. The Fund is invested mainly in short-term loans to Banks, Building Societies and Licensed Deposit-Taking Institutions. The Deposit Fund is professionally managed by Noble Grossart Limited, Edinburgh.

2.   **THE GROWTH FUND** is very largely equity-based and is intended for long-term investment. The Fund is operated on a unitised basis and aims to provide capital growth. Units can be purchased or sold monthly. Income is distributed gross on 15 May and 15 November. The Growth Fund is professionally managed by Henderson Global Investors Limited, London.

3.   **THE INCOME FUND** is intended for medium-term investment and aims to provide immediate high income. The Fund is invested predominantly in fixed-interest securities and is operated on a unitised basis. Units can be purchased or sold monthly. Income is distributed gross on 15 March and 15 September. The Income Fund is professionally managed by Baillie Gifford & Company, Edinburgh.

Application Forms for investment and further information may be had from the Secretary of the Church of Scotland Investors Trust, 121 George Street, Edinburgh EH2 4YN.

---

(12) THE CHURCH OF SCOTLAND
HOUSING AND LOAN FUND FOR RETIRED MINISTERS
AND WIDOWS AND WIDOWERS OF MINISTERS

MEMBERSHIP
(The Board of Trustees has a maximum limit of 11: three appointed by the General Assembly on the nomination of the Board, three appointed by the Baird Trust, four appointed by the Board of Ministry

(three ministers and one member) and the General Secretary of the Board of Ministry *ex officio*)
Chairman: Mr William McVicar RD CA
Secretary: Miss Lin J. Macmillan MA

STAFF
Property Manager: Miss Hilary J. Hardy

REMIT
The Fund, as established by the General Assembly, facilitates the provision of housing accommodation for retired ministers and widow(er)s of ministers. When provided, help may take the form of either a house to rent or a house-purchase loan.

The Trustees may grant tenancy of one of their existing houses or they may agree to purchase for rental occupation an appropriate house of an applicant's choosing. Leases are normally on very advantageous terms as regards rental levels. Alternatively, the Trustees may grant a housing loan of up to 70 per cent of a house-purchase price but with an upper limit. Favourable rates of interest are charged.

The Trustees are also prepared to consider assisting those who have managed to house themselves but are seeking to move to more suitable accommodation. Those with a mortgaged home on retirement may be granted a loan to enable them to repay such a mortgage and thereafter to enjoy the favourable rates of interest charged by the Fund.

Ministers making application within five years of retirement, upon their application being approved, will be given a fairly firm commitment that, in due course, either a house will be made available for renting or a house-purchase loan will be offered. Only within nine months of a minister's intended retiral date will the Trustees initiate steps to find a suitable house; only within one year of that date will a loan be advanced. Preliminary applications submitted about ten years prior to retirement have the benefit of initial review and, if approved, a place on the waiting-list for appropriate decision in due time.

Donations and legacies over the years have been significant in building up this Fund, and the backbone has been provided by congregational contributions.

The Board of Trustees is a completely independent body answerable to the General Assembly, and enquiries and applications are dealt with in the strictest confidence.

Further information can be obtained from the Secretary, Miss Lin J. Macmillan MA, at the Church of Scotland Offices, 121 George Street, Edinburgh EH2 4YN (Tel: 0131-225 5722 ext. 310; Fax: 0131-240 2264; E-mail: lmacmillan@cofscotland.org.uk; Website: www.churchofscotland.org.uk).

---

(13) STEWARDSHIP AND FINANCE

MEMBERSHIP – BOARD OF STEWARDSHIP AND FINANCE
(72 members: 24 appointed by the Assembly, plus Convener and Vice Convener, and 44 Presbytery Representatives who attend three meetings of the Board, at which they have full rights as Board members. The General Treasurer and the Director of Stewardship are *ex officiis* members of the Board.)
Convener: Rev. J. Colin Caskie BA BD (2001)

Vice Convener: Mrs Vivienne A. Dickson CA (2004)

STAFF

General Treasurer: Mr Donald F. Ross MA CA
Director of Stewardship: Rev. Gordon D. Jamieson MA BD
Administrative Secretary: Mr Fred Marsh MCIBS

BOARD REMIT

1. To promote teaching and understanding of Christian Stewardship throughout the Church. To provide programmes and training to assist congregations in visiting members, making known the work of the Church, promoting Christian giving and administering congregational finances.

2. To be responsible with the Board of Ministry and Presbyteries for allocating among congregations the expenditure contained in the Co-ordinated Budget approved by the General Assembly, and for seeking to ensure that congregations meet their obligations by transmitting contributions towards their allocations regularly throughout the year.

3. To provide financial, administrative and accounting services and standards for Boards, Committees and Statutory Corporations.

STEWARDSHIP DEPARTMENT

The Stewardship Department is responsible for the promotion of Christian Stewardship through-out the Church (part 1 of the Board Remit). This involves the production of material to assist congregations in developing an understanding of Christian Stewardship and encouraging a higher level of giving of time, talents and money from members of the Church. The staff of the Stewardship Department are regularly involved in meetings with congregations and Presbyteries.

STAFF

Director of Stewardship: Rev. Gordon D. Jamieson MA BD
Deputy Director: Mr W. Crawford Conochie
Stewardship Consultants: Mrs Gillian M. Paterson
                             Mr W. John Gray
                             Mrs Edith Scott

GIFT AID

As a result of changes to the Gift Aid Scheme which were introduced in April 2000, the £250 minimum for Gift Aid donations has been abolished, so that the scheme now applies to all donations from taxpayers, whether large or small, regular or one-off.

The separate tax relief for payments made under Deed of Covenant has been withdrawn, and relief for such payments is now given under the Gift Aid Scheme.

Gift Aid Certificates have now been replaced by new, simpler and more flexible Gift Aid Declarations, which can be made in advance of the donation, at the time of the donation, or at any time after the donation (subject to the normal six-year limit), and can cover one or more donations.

Donors no longer must pay basic rate income tax – they simply have to pay an amount of income tax or capital gains tax, whether at the basic rate or some other rate, equal to the tax deducted from their donations.

Donors who pay tax at the higher rate will be able to claim further relief in their Self-Assessment tax return against either income tax or capital gains tax.

Companies will no longer be required to deduct tax from their donations to charities.

The new Gift Aid Scheme offers an opportunity for congregations to increase the tax recovered on both regular offerings and one-off donations from taxpayers. In order to meet Inland Revenue requirements, offerings must be received from the donor by cheque, Banker's Order, or cash through Offering Envelopes. Cash put into the Open Plate, which cannot be recorded against the name of the particular person, cannot be treated as Gift Aid donations.

Each congregation is responsible for maintaining proper records, for obtaining Gift Aid Declarations from the donors, and for making repayment claims to the Inland Revenue.

Claims should be submitted on Charity Repayment Claim Form R68 (2000), supported by Schedule R68 (New Gift Aid), to IR (Charities) Scotland, Meldrum House, 15 Drumsheugh Gardens, Edinburgh EH3 7UL (Tel: 0131-777 4040).

GIVING WITH A WILL
Making a will is a sensitive but wise decision. It is also an aspect of good stewardship. The provisions of a will can show our love and concern for our families and friends. They can also provide us with an opportunity to continue supporting the work of the Church of Scotland. The Church acknowledges with gratitude the many legacies it has received over the years and the kind and generous thoughts which have been their inspiration. Such giving is encouraged by the government: gifts of money to the Church are exempt from Inheritance Tax without limit.

The General Treasurer or the Solicitor of the Church of Scotland will always be ready to give information about the work of the Church to members (and their solicitors) interested in providing a legacy.

---

(14) THE CHURCH OF SCOTLAND PENSION TRUSTEES

Chairman:	Mr W.D.B. Cameron CA
Vice Chairman:	Mr W.J. McCafferty ACII ASFA CIP
Secretary:	Mrs S. Dennison BA

STAFF

Pensions Manager:	Mrs S. Dennison BA
Assistant Pensions Administrators:	Mrs M. Marshall
	Mr M. Hannam

REMIT

The body acts as Trustees for the Church of Scotland's three Pension Schemes:

1.   The Church of Scotland Pension Scheme for Ministers and Overseas Missionaries
2.   The Church of Scotland Pension Scheme for Staff
3.   The Church of Scotland Pension Scheme for Board of National Mission staff.

The Trustees have wide-ranging duties and powers detailed in the Trust Law, Pension Acts and other regulations, but in short the Trustees are responsible for the administration of the Pension Schemes and for the investment of the Scheme Funds. Six Trustees are appointed by the General Assembly, and members nominate up to three Trustees for each Scheme.

The investment of the Funds is delegated to external Investment Managers under the guidelines and investment principles set by the Trustees: Baillie Gifford & Co., Tilney Fund Management and SVM Asset Management.

The benefits provided by the three Pension Schemes differ in detail, but all provide a pension to the Scheme member and dependants on death of the member, and a lump sum death benefit on death in service. Scheme members also have the option to improve their benefits by paying additional voluntary contributions (AVCs) to arrangements set up by the Trustees with leading Insurance Companies.

Further information on any of the Church of Scotland Pension Schemes or on individual benefits can be obtained from the Pensions Manager, Mrs S. Dennison, at the Church of Scotland Offices, 121 George Street, Edinburgh EH2 4YN (Tel: 0131-225 5722 ext. 206; Fax: 0131-240 2220; E-mail: sdennison@cofscotland.org.uk).

---

(15) THE CHURCH OF SCOTLAND GUILD

NATIONAL OFFICE-BEARERS AND EXECUTIVE STAFF

Convener:	Mrs Elspeth Dale
Vice Convener:	Mrs Norah Summers MA
General Secretary:	Mrs Alison Twaddle MA JP
	(E-mail: atwaddle@cofscotland.org.uk)
Information Officer:	Mrs Fiona J. Lange MIPR
	(Tel: 0131-225 5722 ext. 317; 0131-240 2217;
	E-mail: flange@cofscotland.org.uk)

The Church of Scotland Guild is a movement within the Church of Scotland whose aim is **'to invite and encourage both women and men to commit their lives to Jesus Christ and to enable them to express their faith in worship, prayer and action'**. Membership of the Guild is open to all who subscribe to that aim.

Groups at congregational level are free to organise themselves under the authority of the Kirk Session, as best suits their own local needs and circumstances. Large groups with frequent meetings and activities continue to operate with a committee or leadership team, while other, smaller groups simply share whatever tasks need to be done among the membership as a whole. Similarly, at Presbyterial Council level, frequency and style of meetings vary according to local needs, as do leadership patterns. Each Council may nominate one person to serve at national level, where six committees take forward the work of the Guild in accordance with the stated Aim.

These Committees are:

- Executive
- Finance and General Purposes
- Projects and Topics
- Programmes and Resources
- Marketing and Publicity
- Matters Relating to Younger People

There has always been a close relationship between the Boards and Committees of the Church and the Guild, and members welcome the opportunity to contribute to the wider work of the Church through the Project Partnership Scheme.

This scheme affords groups at congregational level the opportunity to select a project, or projects, from a range of up to six, selected by the Projects and Topics Committee from submissions by a wide range of Church Departments and other Church-related bodies. A project partner in each group seeks ways of promoting the project locally, increasing awareness of the issues raised by it, and encouraging support of a financial and practical nature. Support is offered by the Project Co-ordinator at Council level and by the Information Officer based at the Guild Office.

The Guild is very aware of the importance of good communication in any large organisation, and regularly sends mailings to its groups to pass on information and resources to the members. In addition, the Newsletter, sent to members three times per session, is a useful communication tool, as is the website www.cos-guild.org.uk. These are means of sharing both local news and experiences, and of communicating something of the wider interest and influence of the Guild, which is represented on other national bodies such as the Network of Ecumenical Women in Scotland and the Scottish Women's Convention.

Each year, the Guild follows a Theme and produces a resources pack covering worship and study material. In recent years, there has also been a Discussion Topic with supporting material and background information. The theme, topic and projects all relate to a common three-year strategy which, for 2003–6, is **'Dare to Care'**. Each of the six current projects – from National Mission, World Mission, Social Responsibility, L'Arche, Tearfund and Prison Fellowship – reflects some aspect of daring to care. The 2004–5 theme is **'Dare to Care with Compassion'**, and Guilds are invited to explore this in a variety of ways. The related discussion topic is **'Include Me In'**, which addresses the issue of inclusion and how the church community can reach out to those at the margins of our society.

---

(16) PANEL ON REVIEW AND REFORM

MEMBERSHIP
(10 members appointed by the General Assembly)
Convener: Rev. Ian Y. Gilmour BD (2004)
Vice Convener: Rev. Marion E. Dodd MA BD LRAM (2004)
(The Ecumenical Officer attends but without the right to vote or make a motion.)

STAFF
Research and Development Officer: Eleanor M. Todd MA MPhil
                                           (Tel: 0131-225 5722 ext. 311;
                                           E-mail: etodd@cofscotland.org.uk)

Administrative Secretary: Valerie A. Smith MA
(Tel: 0131-225 5722 ext. 336;
E-mail: vsmith@cofscotland.org.uk)

REMIT
The remit of the Panel on Review and Reform, as determined by the General Assembly of 2004, is as follows:

* To listen to the voices of congregations, Presbyteries, Agencies, and those beyond the Church of Scotland.
* To present a vision of what a Church in need of continual renewal might become and to offer paths by which congregations, Presbyteries and Agencies might travel towards that vision.
* To consider the changing needs, challenges and responsibilities of the Church.
* To make recommendations to the Council of Assembly, and, through the report of that Council, to report to the General Assembly.
* To have particular regard to the Gospel imperative of priority for the poor, needy and marginalised.

(17) CHURCH AND NATION

MEMBERSHIP – CHURCH AND NATION COMMITTEE
(48 members: 32 appointed by the Assembly; 16 appointed by Presbyteries)
Convener: Rev. Alan D. McDonald LLB BD MTh (2000)
Vice Convener: Mrs Morag Mylne BA LLB (2001)
Secretary: Rev. David I. Sinclair BSc BD PhD DipSW
(E-mail: dsinclair@cofscotland.org.uk)

REMIT
The remit of the Church and Nation Committee as defined by the Assembly is:

'to watch over developments of the Nation's life in which moral and spiritual considerations specially arise, and to consider what action the Church from time to time may be advised to take to further the highest interests of the people'.

The committee's work is divided among four groups:

* Holyrood Group
* Westminster Group
* Europe Group
* International Group

(18) PANEL ON DOCTRINE

MEMBERSHIP
(20 members: 16 appointed by the Assembly, and four from the four University Faculties/
Departments of Divinity, with the Principal Clerk, the Procurator and the Convener of the Board
of Practice and Procedure *ex officiis*)
Convener: Rev. Peter H. Donald MA PhD BD (2004)
Vice Convener: Rev. Angus Morrison MA BD PhD (2004)

STAFF
Secretary: Rev. Douglas Galbraith MA BD BMus MPhil ARSCM
                                   (E-mail: dgalbraith@cofscotland.org.uk)

REMIT
The responsibilities of the Panel on Doctrine include: the fulfilling of remits from the General
Assembly on matters concerning doctrine; drawing the attention of the General Assembly to
matters inside the Church of Scotland or elsewhere which might have significant doctrinal
implications, with recommendations for action; being available for consultation by other
Committees of the General Assembly on any matter which might be of doctrinal significance;
communicating and consulting in an ecumenical context on matters involving doctrine.

---

(19) PANEL ON WORSHIP

MEMBERSHIP
(28 members: all appointed by the Assembly)
Convener: Rev. M. Leith Fisher MA BD (2003)
Vice Convener: Rev. Alan D. Birss MA BD (2004)

STAFF
Secretary: Rev. Douglas Galbraith MA BD BMus MPhil ARSCM
                                   (E-mail: dgalbraith@cofscotland.org.uk)

REMIT
The Panel on Worship exists to witness to the importance of worship as a primary function of
the Church. It has three major committees:

1. The Liturgical Committee is concerned with the provision of worship materials for public
   use and is responsible, among other things, for the production of *Common Order*.
2. The Prayer and Devotion Committee is responsible for *Pray Now* and for courses and
   retreats to promote spiritual growth.
3. The Music Committee encourages new developments in church music, the training of
   musicians and the publication of relevant materials.

The Panel is also engaged in providing materials for worship in Gaelic and is involved in the compilation of new hymn books and supplements. From time to time, it publishes occasional papers on aspects of the practice of public worship.

(20) COMMITTEE ON ARTISTIC MATTERS

MEMBERSHIP
(22 members (of whom no fewer than five shall have professional or practical skills and knowledge) appointed by the General Assembly, one appointed from the General Trustees and two appointed from the Committee on New Charge Development, plus up to five co-opted persons with special knowledge)

Convener: Prof. John Hume OBE BSc ARCST HonFRIAS FSA FSA(Scot) (2003)
Vice Convener: Rev. Richard E. Frazer BA BD DMin (2002)

STAFF
Administrative Secretary: Rev. Douglas Galbraith MA BD BMus MPhil ARSCM (E-mail: dgalbraith@cofscotland.org.uk)
Congregational Liaison: Mrs Alison Robertson MA BMus

REMIT
The Committee advises congregations and Presbyteries regarding the most appropriate way of carrying out renovations, alterations and reordering of interiors, having regard to the architectural quality of Church buildings. It also advises on the installation of stained glass, tapestries, memorials, furniture and furnishings, and keeps a list of accredited artists and craftsworkers.

Any alteration to the exterior or interior of a Church building which affects its appearance must be referred to the Committee for approval, which is given through the General Trustees. Congregations contemplating alterations are urged to consult the Committee at an early stage.

Members of the Committee are prepared, when necessary, to visit churches and meet office-bearers. The Committee's services are given free.

The Committee seeks the conservation of the nation's heritage as expressed in its Church buildings, while at the same time helping to ensure that these buildings continue to serve the worship and witness of the Church in the present day.

In recent years, the General Assembly has conferred these additional duties on the Committee:
1. preparation of reports on the architectural, historical and aesthetic merit of the buildings of congregations involved in questions of readjustment
2. verification of the propriety of repair and renovation work forming the basis of grant applications to public bodies
3. the offering of advice on the maintenance and installation of organs
4. facilitating the transfer of unwanted furnishings from one church to another through the quarterly *Exchange and Transfer*
5. the compilation of a Register of Churches
6. the processing of applications from congregations for permission to dispose of surplus communion plate, and the carrying out of an inventory of sacramental vessels held by congregations.

(21) DEPARTMENT OF MINISTRY
Tel: 0131-225 5722;   Fax: 0131-240 2201
E-mail: ministry@cofscotland.org.uk

BOARD OF MINISTRY
MEMBERSHIP
(88 members: 28 appointed by the Assembly, the Convener and four Vice Conveners, 45 Presbytery Representatives, the Chairperson and Secretary of the Housing and Loan Fund, the Convener and Vice Convener of the Committee on Chaplains to Her Majesty's Forces, the President and Vice President of the Diaconate Council and one member each from the Faculties of Divinity in the Universities of Aberdeen, Edinburgh, Glasgow and St Andrews)

Convener:	Rev. R. Douglas Cranston MA BD
Vice Conveners:	Rev. Alan F.M. Downie MA BD
	Rev. Barry W. Dunsmore MA BD
	Rev. E. Lorna Hood (Mrs) MA BD
	Rev. John W. Paterson BSc BD DipEd

REMIT
The Board of Ministry is responsible for all aspects of the recruitment, education, training, in-service training and support of ministers, auxiliary ministers and deacons as well as for making the financial provision for that work. To enable the Board to discharge these responsibilities and fulfil its Remit, the Board shall determine from time to time what Constituent Committees are required. The exceptions to this will be in respect of the Housing and Loan Fund for Retired Ministers and Widows and Widowers of Ministers and the Committee on Chaplains to Her Majesty's Forces, the Trustees and members respectively of which continue to be appointed as at present. They report separately to the General Assembly.

STAFF

Acting General Secretary and Senior Pastoral Adviser:	Rev. John P. Chalmers BD (Tel: ext. 309; E-mail: jchalmers@cofscotland.org.uk)
Director of Education and Training:	Rev. Nigel J. Robb FCP MA BD ThM MTh (Tel: ext. 347; E-mail: nrobb@cofscotland.org.uk)
Director of Vocational Guidance:	Rev. Martin Scott DipMusEd RSAM BD PhD (Tel: ext. 389; E-mail: mscott@cofscotland.org.uk)
Director of Finance and Resources:	Mrs Pauline Willder MA PgDipIS (Tel: ext. 269; E-mail: pwillder@cofscotland.org.uk)
Finance Officer:	Miss Elizabeth Dailly (Tel: ext. 361; E-mail: edailly@cofscotland.org.uk)
Ministry Officers:	Mrs Elizabeth Chalmers (Tel: ext. 348; E-mail: lchalmers@cofscotland.org.uk)
	Rev. Gavin Elliott MA BD (Tel: ext. 255; E-mail: gelliott@cofscotland.org.uk)
	Rev. Angus R. Mathieson MA BD (Tel: ext. 315; E-mail: amathieson@cofscotland.org.uk)
	Mrs Moira Whyte MA PGTQFE (Tel: ext. 266; E-mail: mwhyte@cofscotland.org.uk)

DEPARTMENT OF MINISTRY

Further information about the Board's work and services is obtainable through the Department of Ministry at the Church Offices. Information is available on a wide range of matters including the Consolidated Stipend Fund, Stipend Ministry requirements (National Stipend Fund), Endowment Grants, Travelling and other Expenses, Pulpit Supply, Study Leave, Ministry Development conferences, pastoral care services including occupational health, Enquiry and Assessment, Education and Training and so on.

COMMITTEES

The policy development and implementation of the work of the Board of Ministry is managed under the following committees:

1.   CO-ORDINATING COMMITTEE

Convener: Rev. R. Douglas Cranston MA BD

The Co-ordinating Committee is the Board's executive committee. Its function is to link the Board to the work of its Implementation Committees (listed below), to ensure the integrated implementation of the Board's strategy and, further, to ensure that the Board's work is contained within agreed budgets. The Co-ordinating Committee also serves as the Board's 'nomination committee'.

In addition, in light of the *Ministers of the Gospel* report, the Co-ordinating Committee is responsible for reviewing and developing policy on all financial, developmental and pastoral matters related to ministry. This includes such matters as Stipend Policy, manses and housing issues, listed expenses, hardship grants, travel expenses, Study Leave provision, Ministerial Review, Child Protection, Ministry Conferences, Manse Family Counselling, Occupational Health, Shetland Arrangements and so on. Furthermore, it is responsible for reviewing and developing policy on the promotion of vocations in the Church, the Enquiry and Assessment Process, the admission and readmission of ministers and the supervision and training of students and graduate candidates.

The following Implementation Committees work in conjunction with the Co-ordinating Committee:

1.1   Ministry Finance Implementation Committee

Convener: Rev. Jeffrey A. McCormick BD

The Ministry Finance Implementation Committee operates with powers to deal with the National Stipend Scheme, Vacancy Schedules, Maintenance Allowances, Hardship Grants and Bursaries, Stipend Advances, management of investments, writing-off shortfalls and the granting of further endowments.

1.2   Ministry Development Implementation Committee

Convener: Rev. Ian Dick MA MSc BD

The Ministry Development Implementation Committee is responsible for running and evaluating the current programme of conferences, the promotion of ministry development, processing Study Leave applications, continuing to deliver Child Protection training and developing the personal ministerial review process.

1.3   Pastoral Support Implementation Committee

Convener: Rev. Catherine E.E. Collins BA BD

The Pastoral Support Implementation Committee is responsible for the oversight of the

Board's concerns in all areas of pastoral care. This includes liaison with the Medical Panel, the integration of Occupational Health with other ministerial support services, the development of the Pastoral Colleague Scheme as well as the telephone and face-to-face counselling services and oversight of the working of Act XV 2002 anent Long-term Illness of Ministers in Charge (as amended by Act VIII 2003).

1.4   Interim Ministry Implementation Committee
Convener: Rev. E. Lorna Hood (Mrs) MA BD

The Interim Ministry Implementation Committee is responsible for maintaining current arrangements, reporting progress on current assignments and reviewing guidelines for the future deployment of interim ministries. It is responsible for the review and investigation of the future development of Interim Ministry within the Church, and, where appropriate, it works in consultation with the Board of National Mission.

1.5   Assessment Scheme Implementation Committee
Convener: Rev. James Dewar MA BD

The Assessment Scheme Implementation Committee is responsible for overseeing and reviewing the current Enquiry and Assessment Process for Ministers, Auxiliaries and Deacons together with the admission and readmission of ministers. The Committee has powers to make final recommendations on suitability for training, undertaking Committee reviews, recruiting and training Assessors, Director training and feedback, and liaison with presbyteries.

1.6   Candidate Supervision Implementation Committee
Convener: Rev. Donald MacLeod BD LRAM DRSAM

The Candidate Supervision Implementation Committee is responsible for the supervision of students and probationers (including deacons), the production of candidates' reports, operating with powers to sustain placements, university liaison, the recruitment and training of Supervisors, arranging placements, delivering the residential and conference programme, liaison with presbyteries, Bible exams and other Church requirements and Auxiliary Ministry training.

2.   CHAPLAINS TO HM FORCES (20 members)
Convener: Professor Herbert Kerrigan QC
Vice Convener: Rev. John Shedden CBE BD DipPSS
Secretary: Mr Douglas M. Hunter WS
                   Henderson Boyd Jackson
                   Exchange Tower
                   19 Canning Street
                   Edinburgh EH3 8EH.

Recruitment
The Chaplains' Committee is entrusted with the task of recruitment of Chaplains for the Regular, Reserve and Auxiliary Forces. Vacancies occur periodically, and the Committee is happy to receive enquiries from all interested ministers.

Forces Registers
The Committee maintains a Register of all those who have been baptised and/or admitted to Communicant Membership by Service Chaplains.

At the present time, registers are being meticulously prepared and maintained. Parish

Ministers are asked to take advantage of the facilities by applying for Certificates from the Secretary of the Committee.

Full information may be obtained from the Honorary Secretary, Mr Douglas M. Hunter, Henderson Boyd Jackson, Exchange Tower, 19 Canning Street, Edinburgh EH3 8EH (Tel: 0131-228 2400).

A list of Chaplains may be found in List B in Section 6.

(22) NATIONAL MISSION

MEMBERSHIP –
BOARD OF NATIONAL MISSION (34 members)
Convener: Rev. John C. Matthews MA BD
Vice Conveners: Rev. Stanley A. Brook BD MTh
                                          Mrs Myrtle A. Gillies MBE

PARISH APPRAISAL (52 members)
Convener: Rev. David W. Clark MA BD
Vice Convener: Mr Andrew M. Blake BSc FRSA

NEW CHARGE DEVELOPMENT (23 members)
Convener: Rev. Norman A. Smith MA BD
Vice Convener: Mr William Greenock

PARISH ASSISTANCE (16 members)
Convener: Rev. Charles J. Finnie LTh DPS
Vice Convener: Mrs Diane Ashton

MISSION AND EVANGELISM RESOURCES (30 members)
Convener: Rev. Rosemary Frew (Mrs) MA BD
Vice Convener: Rev. Kenneth D. Stott MA BD

CHAPLAINCIES (25 members)
Convener: Lady Elinor Arbuthnott
Vice Conveners:
  Church and Industry: Rev. Colin M. Anderson BA BD STM MPhil
  Hospitals, Healthcare and
    Universities: Rev. T. David Watson BSc BD
  Prisons: Rev. David C. Cameron BD CertMin

IONA COMMUNITY BOARD
Convener: Rev. Tom Gordon MA BD

JOINT FAITHS ADVISORY BOARD ON CRIMINAL JUSTICE
                                          Father Andrew Mann

SCOTTISH CHURCHES COMMUNITY TRUST
Church of Scotland representative: Rev. Ewan R. Aitken MA BD

STAFF
General Secretary:	Rev. Douglas A.O. Nicol MA BD
Secretary Depute:	Rev. Alex M. Millar MA BD MBA
Accountant:	Miss Elizabeth Orr BSc CA
Property and Safety Manager:	Mr Colin Wallace
Chaplaincies Administrator:	Mr John K. Thomson
Parish Staffing Administrator:	Mr John Jackson
New Developments Administrator:	Mr Garry B.J. Leach BD BSc
Communications Officer:	Mrs Laura Vermeulen

REMIT

1. THE BOARD OF NATIONAL MISSION

Established on 1 January 1990, the Board, with its Constituent Committees, has the responsibility for planning and co-ordinating the Church's strategy and provision for the fulfilment of its mission as the National Church.

The Board's policy is that the most effective missionary strategy for our time is 'the development of strong congregations, adequately resourced, with a missionary concern for the parishes they are called to serve – and all this work at congregational level backed by an interface with strategic areas of Scottish life'.

Subject to the General Assembly, the Board's remit is as follows:

1. **Development of Policy:**
   Aided by reflecting on regular consultations, the Board will develop its policy which will be communicated to, and pursued by, its five Constituent Committees.
2. **Finance:**
   The agreement of the annual budget and the monitoring of income and expenditure will be the responsibility of the Board.
3. **New Work:**
   Constituent Committees will refer to the Board new work and work which is likely to exceed the budget of the Committee. The Board will consider such referrals and grant permission if agreed.
4. **Property:**
   The Board will have responsibility for the acquisition and disposal of properties and for the proper maintenance of all its properties.
5. **Presbytery Representatives:**
   The Board will have the responsibility of resolving on which Constituent Committees Presbytery representatives would serve.
6. **General Assembly Report:**
   The Board will have the responsibility for the approval of the Report to the General Assembly on the work of the Board and the five Constituent Committees.

Reporting to the General Assembly in association with the Board of National Mission are:
The Iona Community Board
The Joint Faiths Advisory Board on Criminal Justice
The Scottish Churches Community Trust
The Committee on the Parish Development Fund.

In addition, the Board receives reports from the following groups:

1. **Glasgow Lodging House Mission:** This work is based in the Institute in East Campbell Street, Glasgow, and its object is to care for the thousands of homeless in Scotland's industrial capital. Oversight of the work is by a Management Committee appointed by the Presbytery of Glasgow (Tel: 0141-552 0285).

2. **Residential Centres' Executive:** On behalf of the Board, this group manages National Mission's residential centre, the Badenoch Christian Centre. Situated at Kincraig in Strathspey, this Centre offers individuals, families and groups opportunities for enjoying retreats, short breaks and the many outdoor pursuits of the area from a base of Christian fellowship. Opened in 1976, the Centre is mainly self-catering. Full information from the Manager (Tel: 01540 651373; E-mail: badenoch@uk.uumail.com).

3. **Support Group for Ministry among Deaf People:** The Board appoints three community ministers for ministry among deaf people. Currently, they are the Rev. John R. Osbeck in Aberdeen, the Rev. Alistair F. Kelly in Edinburgh and the Rev. Richard C. Durno in Glasgow.

4. **Statistics for Mission:** The Board has information available about parish statistics based on the 2001 census.

5. **World Exchange Scotland:** The Board operates a career gap programme: full information is available from the Board's office in Edinburgh.

2. COMMITTEE ON CHAPLAINCIES

In accordance with the overall policy of the Board, the Committee on Chaplaincies will be responsible, through its subcommittees on Hospitals, Healthcare and Universities, Church and Industry, and Prisons, for the encouragement, development, support and, where appropriate, review of chaplaincies in hospitals, healthcare, universities, industry and prisons.

Healthcare Chaplaincies: The Committee administers the scheme by which, under the 1947 National Health Act, ministers and others are appointed as chaplains in all hospitals in Scotland. There are currently well over thirty full-time and around 195 part-time chaplains. Appointments of chaplains are made by the General Secretary of the Board as the 'appointing authority' after consultation with, where appropriate, the Presbytery of the bounds and the relevant hospital authority. Presbyteries are responsible for the oversight of part-time chaplains' work. The Committee also employs some full-time and half-time chaplains' assistants.

A List of Hospital Chaplains will be found in List C in Section 6.

Church and Industry: The aim of industrial mission is threefold:

1. to provide pastoral care and witness to the gospel for men and women in all branches of industry in their place of work;

2. to assess in the interest of the gospel the nature of the influence which industry exerts both on individuals and on society;

3. to promote the desire for just relationships and understanding at all levels of our industrial society. The work, which is fully ecumenical in character, is now involved in most key industrial sectors. There are about eighty part-time industrial chaplains and six full-time industrial chaplains. The Co-ordinator of Scottish Churches Industrial Mission is the Rev. Erik M. Cramb (Tel: 01382 458764).

A list of Industrial Chaplains will be found in List D in Section 6.

Prison Chaplaincies: The Committee takes an interest in all matters relating to Church of Scotland chaplains appointed by the Scottish Prison Service.

A list of Church of Scotland Prison Chaplains will be found in List E in Section 6.

Universities: The Committee takes an interest in all matters relating to the appointment and support of chaplains to universities.

A list of University Chaplains will be found in List F in Section 6.

3.   COMMITTEE ON CONGREGATIONAL AND MISSION DEVELOPMENT

In accordance with the overall policy of the Board, the Committee on Congregational and Mission Development will be responsible for:
- encouraging mission and evangelism in parishes through congregations of the Church of Scotland by means of research, development and training;
- co-operating with other Boards and Committees in strengthening the life of congregations;
- ensuring that the personnel and centres under the Committee's direction are serving the missionary and evangelistic purposes of the Church to the best advantage;
- identifying, originating and supporting projects which are advancing mission and evangelism in key areas of life in Scotland.

The Committee will have responsibility for the work of the Advisers in Mission and Evangelism and Area Facilitators and will include the work of the Rural Committee, www.trustfunding.com, The Netherbow: Scottish Storytelling Centre (including John Knox House), 'The Well', Badenoch Christian Centre, Society, Religion and Technology Project, Projects in Evangelism (including 'Impact Teams'), World Exchange Scotland, Statistics for Mission and Apologetics.

A full list of Advisers will be found in List J in Section 6.

The Committee is also responsible for the work of a number of component Committees, projects and centres:

1.   **The Apologetics Committee** engages in the work of apologetics with key areas of Scottish thought and culture, and produces resources to equip churches in the task of giving a reason for the Christian faith.

2.   **The Netherbow: Scottish Storytelling Centre:** The integrated facilities of the **Netherbow Theatre** and the **John Knox House Museum**, together with the **Scottish Storytelling Centre**, are an important cultural and visitor centre on the Royal Mile and provide advice and assistance nationally in the use of the arts in mission, education and worship. 'Story Source', 'Script Aid' and other resources are available. Contact the Director, The Netherbow: Scottish Storytelling Centre, 43–45 High Street, Edinburgh EH1 1SR (Tel: 0131-556 9579/2647; Website: www.storytellingcentre.org.uk). (The Netherbow is undergoing development, but advice and assistance is still available.)

3. The **Projects in Evangelism Committee** oversees the work of **Mission Projects** and **'Impact' Teams**, whereby teams of volunteers are recruited and trained to assist parish-based and high-school missions. Youth mission is a priority. Details can be obtained from the Missions Co-ordinator's office at 59 Elmbank Street, Glasgow G2 4PQ (Tel: 0141-352 6946). In addition, the Committee's remit is to identify, originate and support projects in mission and evangelism of a short-term, trial or temporary nature and to liaise with and advise on local or national evangelistic campaigns. (Website: http://www.summermission.org.uk).

4. The **Rural Committee** maintains an awareness of developments in rural Scottish life on both regional and topical bases and seeks to share good practice in mission and evangelism in rural Scotland through its publication *The Rural Spirit*, local consultations and the Church of Scotland Stand at the Royal Highland Show. Contact the National Mission Kirkcaldy office (Tel: 01592 646406; E-mail: nmkirkcaldy@uk.uumail.com).

5. The **Society, Religion and Technology Project:** This unique project, initiated in 1970, studies the impact of new technologies on society and helps the Church to form its response in ways which are practical and prophetic. The project is a forum for all who wish to shape the Church's response to some of the most pressing issues of our time. A newsletter, the *SRT Bulletin*, is available. Contact the SRT Director at John Knox House, 45 High Street, Edinburgh EH1 1SR (Tel: 0131-556 2953; E-mail: srtp@srtp.org.uk; Website: http://www.srtp.org.uk).

6. The **Well Asian Information and Advice Centre:** The Committee provides support and funding for the Presbytery of Glasgow's innovative project that serves the south side of Glasgow by assisting with welfare, housing, immigration, asylum and personal problems. The Well has a strong mission basis on the clear principles that sharing the love of Christ has to include accepting people for who they are and respecting the beliefs of others. A regular prayer letter is available. Contact the Well, 48/50 Albert Road, Glasgow G42 8DN (Tel: 0141-424 4523; Fax: 0141-422 1722; E-mail: the.well@btinternet.co.uk).

7. **Church Pastoral Aid Society:** The Board has accredited the work of the Church Pastoral Aid Society; and the CPAS Scotland Consultant, the Rev. Richard Higginbottom, encourages local congregations in mission and evangelism through consultancy, preaching, training and resources. He can be contacted at: 2 Highfield Place, Bankfoot, Perth PH1 4AX (Tel: 01738 787429; E-mail: rhigginbottom@cpas.org.uk).

4. COMMITTEE ON NEW CHARGE DEVELOPMENT

In accordance with the overall policy of the Board of National Mission, the Committee on New Charge Development, without prejudice to any other body such as the General Assembly's Committee on Parish Appraisal which may have prior rights or jurisdiction, will be responsible for the following areas of work.

1. Following the instructions of the Committee on Parish Appraisal, and in accordance with the provisions of Act XIII 2000 anent New Charge Development (as amended by Acts V and VIII 2003 and Act VII 2004) and equivalent subsequent legislation, to facilitate the creation of new charges. The Committee, in co-operation with other bodies, including

Boards, Committees and Presbyteries, will enable the new charge to begin its mission in the new parish area or in a non-geographical setting, and will be responsible for:
(a) the development of the Charge
(b) the appointment of the Minister
(c) the provision of a suitable building as the place of worship which may be a new church funded and erected by the Committee, or an existing location within a community which would be suitable for the purpose of worship.

2. In the case of established charges where significant change is being experienced by the construction of new housing, the Committee on New Charge Development will, on the instruction of the Committee on Parish Appraisal, enter into discussion with Presbyteries and appropriate committees to determine the needs of the area with respect to the provision of a place of witness.

3. Facilitating and supporting the mission of new charges and those not yet in full status in co-operation with other Committees or Boards as deemed necessary.

4. Church Extension Charges.

5. (a) Advising on, and, within the limitations of its budget, assisting where there are major problems and expenditure associated with ongoing necessary maintenance of buildings, where there are building debts outstanding on the part of the congregations concerned, or where the congregation concerned is not yet in full status.

    (b) The purchase of land and the purchase or erection, maintenance and disposal of buildings pertaining to the work of the Committee on New Charge Development are the express responsibility of the Committee (until responsibility is passed to the charge).

6. Providing arbiters to make the choice of buildings to be retained in a readjustment situation.

The Committee has responsibility for twelve New Church Developments and nine Church Extension Charges, with a number of other projects at various stages of development.

5. COMMITTEE ON PARISH APPRAISAL

In accordance with the overall policy of the Board, the Committee on Parish Appraisal
• Will undertake full responsibilities and rights in connection with the implementation of Act IV 1984, Act VII 2003, Act VIII 2003 and equivalent subsequent legislation directly to the General Assembly
• Will be responsible for dealing with all matters coming from Presbyteries regarding planning and vacancies
• Will deal with proposals for the staffing needs of parishes
• Will, in consultation with the Presbyteries concerned, and following detailed discussion with the Committee on New Charge Development, determine where new charges shall be established, or where, as a result of significant change in an existing charge, an alternative location for the place of worship is deemed desirable
• Will be available, when requested, to assist and advise Presbyteries in regard to their own forward and readjustment planning.

6. COMMITTEE ON PARISH STAFFING

In accordance with the overall policy of the Board, and to meet the staffing needs of parishes in regard to National Mission appointments as determined by Presbyteries with the approval of the Committee on Parish Appraisal, the Committee will:

- Be responsible for investigating all applications for National Mission appointments
- Be responsible for Departmental matters relating to the selection, recruitment, training, personal development, employment, deployment and support of National Mission appointments
- Be responsible for sharing with others such as the Inter-Board Group on Team Ministry the development of team ministry
- Be responsible for the Departmental matters relating to existing 'New Forms of Parish Ministry' appointments
- Be responsible for summer student appointments.

The Committee has responsibility for over seventy Deacons, Parish Assistants and Project Workers, and also for ministers appointed through National Mission appointments. Posts are advertised, and people are recruited who have the relevant educational standards, expertise and skills and who are called to the work of mission and outreach. Many staff serve in the large housing areas of Scotland's towns and cities where the number of ordained ministers is low in relation to the population.

For more than thirty years, the Board has been providing financial support to **Bridgeton, St Francis-in-the-East Church House,** a centre providing club facilities for young and old who have little or no Church connection. A club leader and assistant are in charge of the work under a Committee of Management whose chair is the minister of the parish (Tel: 0141-554 8045).

7.   COMMITTEE ON PRIORITY AREAS

In accordance with the overall policy of the Board, the Committee on Priority Areas will:
- Develop, encourage, implement and oversee strategy within priority area parishes
- Develop resources to enable other congregations to make appropriate responses to the needs of people living in poverty in their parishes and to raise awareness of the effects of poverty on people's lives in Scotland
- Co-ordinate the strategy of the wider Church in its priority to Scotland's poorest parishes.

Contact the Support Worker's office: 59 Elmbank Street, Glasgow   G2 4PQ (Tel: 0141-333 1948).

8.   BOARDS AND COMMITTEES ASSOCIATED WITH THE BOARD OF NATIONAL MISSION

(a) The Iona Community Board: The Iona Community Board is the body through which the Iona Community reports to the General Assembly. It is made up of members of the Community and members of the Church appointed by the Assembly. It meets twice yearly, to hear reports of the Community's work both on Iona and Mull and on the mainland, and to assist and guide the Community in its task of seeking 'new ways to touch the hearts of all'.

(b) Joint Faiths Advisory Board on Criminal Justice: The General Assembly of 2000 set up this Board with representatives from the Church of Scotland, the Roman Catholic Church, the Scottish Episcopal Church, Action of Churches Together in Scotland (ACTS) and the Scottish Interfaith Council. Its principal remit is to contribute to the development of Criminal Justice philosophy, penal reform, and to the rights of offenders, untried persons and their families, and to stimulate the interest and participation of all faiths in ministry within the Criminal Justice System.

(c) The Scottish Churches Community Trust: The Scottish Churches Community Trust has been fully operational since January 2001. There are currently nine member churches: Baptist Union, Church of Scotland, Congregational Federation, Roman Catholic Church, Scottish

Episcopal Church, Methodist Church, Religious Society of Friends, United Free Church and United Reformed Church. Each member church has a nominated representative on the Board of Trustees. In 2003, twelve projects were awarded funding to a total of £154,992.00. Support so far has gone to children's and youth projects, transport and furniture initiatives, and work with families, ex-offenders, refugees, homeless and rehoused people. Grants are also supplemented by additional training allowances which can be requested for specific purposes.

Office-bearers: Rev. Ian Moir: Chair
Rev. Richard Toller: Vice Chair
Mr Gordon Armour: Treasurer
Ms Jennifer Stuart: Development Co-ordinator

Applications or offers of support should be made to: Scottish Churches Community Trust, 200 Balmore Road, Glasgow   G22 6LJ (Tel: 0141-336 3766; Fax: 0131-336 3771; E-mail: admin@scct.org.uk).

(23) PARISH DEVELOPMENT FUND COMMITTEE

MEMBERSHIP
(16 members: nine appointed by the General Assembly together with seven non-voting representatives from the General Trustees and the Boards of Ministry, National Mission, Social Responsibility, Stewardship and Finance, Parish Education and World Mission. In addition, the Committee has powers to co-opt up to three additional non-voting advisors, each for a period of three years, who represent public and voluntary agencies.)
Convener: The Very Rev. Dr Andrew McLellan (2002)
Vice Convener: Mrs Lorna Paterson (2002)

STAFF
Development Worker: Iain Johnston
(Tel: 0131-225 5722;
E-mail: parishdevelopment@uk.uumail.com)

REMIT
The aim of the Parish Development Fund is to encourage local churches to work for the benefit of the whole community – and to take risks in living and sharing the Gospel in relevant ways.
    Twice each year, the Committee considers applications which are in the spirit of the above aim and the following principles:

- making a positive difference in the lives of people in greatest need in the community
- encouraging partnership work
- helping local people develop their gifts
- encouraging imagination and creativity.

Further information on the types of projects supported by the Fund can be found in the Parish Development Fund section of the Church of Scotland website. Please contact the staff for informal discussion about grant application enquiries and general advice on funding and project development.

(24) THE COMMITTEE PLANNING THE CHURCH WITHOUT WALLS CELEBRATION 2005

This group was formerly known as the Stakeholders' Conference Planning Group. It was set up by the General Assembly of 2001 in accordance with the Report of the Special Commission anent Review and Reform. The following is a summary of the group's remit: 'Resolve to appoint a planning group of seven persons . . . to prepare a "Stakeholders Conference" in 2005 as a point of National Celebration and a milestone of progress'.

The group reports directly to the General Assembly and has done so for the past three Assemblies. The committee is now in the final stages of planning local, regional and national celebrations. For more details, see www.churchwithoutwalls.org.uk

(25) SOCIAL RESPONSIBILITY
Charis House, 47 Milton Road East, Edinburgh EH15 2SR
Tel: 0131-657 2000;   Fax: 0131-657 5000
E-mail: info@charis.org.uk

BOARD OF SOCIAL RESPONSIBILITY
The Board of Social Responsibility engages in social care as part of the Christian witness of the Church to the people of Scotland. In addition, the Board offers guidance to the Church and the media about social, moral and ethical issues.

REMIT
The Board of Social Responsibility is one of Scotland's largest social-work agencies in the voluntary sector, employing 1,500 full-time staff. The purpose of the Board can be broadly defined as follows:
1.   to offer care and help through the varied establishments and projects it operates, and to encourage and enable caring work at parish level
2.   to offer to the Church informed opinion on contemporary social, moral and ethical issues
3.   to encourage balanced judgements on these issues in the light of the Christian faith, and to put forward these judgements at all levels of influence.

MEMBERSHIP
(96 members: 44 appointed by the Assembly plus Convener and two Vice Conveners; 47 from Presbyteries; a representative of the Church of Scotland Guild; and a representative from the Committee on Church and Nation. They attend three meetings of the Board per year, in February, June and October, and may be asked to serve on one of the five committees.)

Convener: Rev. James M. Cowie (2001)
Vice Conveners: Rev. Graham T. Dickson (2004)
                                          Mrs Lyn Hair (2003)

STAFF

Director of Social Work:	Mr Ian G. Manson
	(E-mail: imanson@charis.org.uk)
Deputy Director:	Mr James Maguire
	(E-mail: jmaguire@charis.org.uk)

MANAGEMENT STRUCTURE

The Board's management structure changed in April 2004 to become service-based. There are six Heads of Service, each with specialist responsibilities. They are supported by Principal Officers who have lead roles for particular types of service and client groups.

Head of Service (Services to Older People):	Margaret Wilkinson
Principal Officers:	Netta Smith (North)
	Brenda Fraser (East)
	Marlene Smith (West)
	Donald Macaskill (Dementia)

Head of Service (Children & Families, Criminal Justice and Learning Disabilities):	Paul Robinson
Principal Officers:	David Clark
	George McNeilly

Head of Service (Addictions, Mental Health, Homelessness and Counselling):	Calum Murray
Principal Officers:	Flora Mackenzie
	Gerard Robson
	Dominic Gray (part-time)
	vacancy (part-time)

Head of Service (Planning & Development):	Jeannette Deacon
Principal Officers:	Greg Dougal
	Graham Lumb

Head of Service (Finance):	Robert Nelson
Principal Officers:	Alastair Purves
	vacancy

Head of Service (Human Resources):	Peter Bailey
Principal Officers:	Jane Allan
	Pat Sinclair
	Mari Rennie

IT Manager:	Yvonne Farrant
Estates Manager:	David Reid

Heads of Service and Managers can be contacted via Charis House on 0131-657 2000. (Until February 2005, Calum Murray will be based at Kandahar House in Dundee on 01382 305920.)

LIST OF SERVICES
Details of the Board's services can be obtained from Charis House on 0131-657 2000.

FUNDRAISING, MARKETING AND COMMUNICATIONS
Manager: Pam Taylor (E-mail: ptaylor@charis.org.uk)
Communications Officer (Media): Hugh Brown (E-mail: hbrown@charis.org.uk)
Communications Officer (Congregations): Maggie Hunt (E-mail: mhunt@charis.org.uk)

The Fundraising, Marketing and Communications department encompasses the functions of Fundraising, Media and Public Relations, Publicity, Congregational Liaison and Volunteer Development. Fundraising aims to increase income development for the Board's work to ensure the long-term sustainability of our valuable care services across Scotland. We want to inform people about our mission and work with the most needy people in our society. We invite people to donate money to support our work and to volunteer their time – either to fundraise or to help carry out essential tasks of all kinds. We also ask people to pray with us about our services; and, to help them do that, a free prayer letter is produced three times a year. You can also keep up to date with the latest news about Social Responsibility by receiving our free newspaper *Circle of Care*, which has a print run of 42,000 copies three times a year.

If you would like to know more about any of the above work, or be added to our mailing list, please contact us at Charis House on 0131-657 2000.

CONGREGATIONAL CONTACTS
Congregational Contacts are the link people between the Board and local churches. Each church should have an appointed Contact who receives mailings three times per year. There are currently over 1,000 Congregational Contacts. They undertake work in a variety of ways. They provide current, correct and appropriate information to their Church. They often act as distributors for the *Circle of Care* newspaper and they act as agents for our calendar, Christmas-card and merchandise sales.

Church members are the most important part of the 'Circle of Care' provided by the Church of Scotland. It is the caring work in the communities of Scotland which is our largest area of service provision. Congregational Contacts provide the vital link between the formal services provided by the Board and the community work and prayers of the local churches, and the Board greatly appreciates all the work done by these volunteer champions.

SOCIAL INTERESTS
Social Interests Officer: Kristine Gibbs (E-mail: kristine@charis.org.uk)
The remit of the Board of Social Responsibility instructs it 'to study and present essential Christian judgements on social and moral issues arising within the area of its concern'. It does this through Study Groups, which present their findings to the Board of Social Responsibility. The Board then reports to the General Assembly. Some of the recent issues reported upon have been: Euthanasia; Human Sexuality; Human Genetics; Human Fertilisation and Embryology; Decriminalisation of Drugs; Prostitution; Human Cloning; Begging.

SPEAKERS FOR GUILDS AND GROUPS
Members of staff and of the Board will gladly visit congregations and other Church organisations to speak about the work of the Board. To request a speaker, please write to the F, M and C Team at Charis House, 47 Milton Road East, Edinburgh EH15 2SR.

(26) WORLD MISSION
Tel: 0131-225 5722;   Fax: 0131-226 6121
Update: 0131-226 4121;   Answerphone: 0131-240 2231
E-mail: world@cofscotland.org.uk

MEMBERSHIP – BOARD OF WORLD MISSION
(27 members: 12 from Presbyteries, 12 nominated by the General Assembly, Convener and two Vice Conveners)

Convener:	Rev. Alan Greig BSc BD (2002)
Vice Conveners:	Dr Fiona Burnett BSc PhD (2003)
	Rev. Andrew F. Anderson MA BD (2002)

DEPARTMENTAL STAFF

General Secretary:	Rev. Prof. Kenneth R. Ross BA BD PhD
Partnership Team:	
Leader, Overseas Charges, Middle East:	Mr Walter T. Dunlop ARICS
Sub-Saharan Africa:	Mr Calum J. Strang
Europe, Middle East, Americas:	Rev. Ian W. Alexander BA BD STM
Asia:	Mr Sandy Sneddon
Local Involvement:	Carol Finlay RGN RMN OIPCNE MSc
Finance:	Mrs Anne Macintosh BA CA
	(General Treasurer's Department)
Personnel:	Miss Sheila Ballantyne MA PgDipPM

REMIT
- Give life to the Church of Scotland's understanding that it is part of the Universal Church committed to the advance of the Kingdom of God throughout the world.
- Discern priorities and form policies to guide the Church of Scotland's ongoing worldwide participation in God's transforming mission, through the gospel of Jesus Christ.
- Develop and maintain mutually enriching relationships with partner churches overseas through consultation and the two-way sharing of human and material resources.
- Equip and encourage Church of Scotland members at local, Presbytery and national levels to enjoy being involved in the life of the world church.
- Help the people of Scotland to appreciate the worldwide nature of the Christian faith.

The Board carries on its work through the following constituent committees and groups:

Europe:	Convener: Mrs Margaret Foggie
Overseas Charges:	Convener: Rev. Bruce Lawrie
Local Involvement:	Convener: Rev. Neil Urquhart
Asia:	Convener: Mr John Milne
Americas:	Convener: Rev. Bruce Lawrie
Budget and Finance:	Convener: Rev. Andrew Anderson (acting)
Middle East:	Convener: Dr Fiona Burnett (acting)
Personnel:	Convener: Mrs Jean Rutherford
Sub-Saharan Africa:	Convener: Mrs Elizabeth Paterson

STRATEGIC COMMITMENTS: 2001–10
* Working with partner churches on new initiatives in evangelism
* Working for justice, peace and reconciliation in situations of conflict or threat
* Resourcing the Church to set people free from the oppression of poverty
* Contributing meaningfully to the struggle against the HIV/AIDS epidemic
* Increasing the involvement of Scottish Christians in the world Church.

PARTNERSHIP PRIORITIES
Following a consultation with partner Churches held in St Andrews in September 1999, the Board has identified the following priority areas for partnership in mission:
1. **Theological Education:** developing ministerial and lay training at appropriate levels in all our churches.
2. **Evangelism:** helping one another to create new models and launch new initiatives to take the Gospel to all people.
3. **Holistic Mission:** enabling one another to respond with Christian compassion to human needs in our rapidly changing societies.
4. **Mission in Pluralistic Societies:** strengthening Christian identity in our multi-religious and multi-cultural societies by supporting one another and sharing our experiences.
5. **Prophetic Ministry:** inspiring one another to discern and speak God's Word in relation to critical issues which arise in our times.
6. **Human and Material Resources:** finding new and imaginative ways of sharing our resources at all levels of Church life.

WORLD MISSION AND WORLD RESOURCES
Sharing in the mission of God worldwide requires a continuing commitment to sharing the Church of Scotland's resources of people and money for mission in six continents as contemporary evidence that it is 'labouring for the advancement of the Kingdom of God throughout the world' (First Article Declaratory). Such resource-sharing remains an urgent matter because most of our overseas work is in the so-called 'Third World', or 'South', in nations where the effects of the widening gap between rich and poor is *the* major issue for the Church. Our partner Churches in Africa, most of Asia, in the Caribbean, South and Central America are desperately short of financial and technical resources, which we can to some extent meet with personnel and grants. However, they are more than willing to share the resources of their Christian Faith with us, including things which the Church in the West often lacks: enthusiasm in worship, hospitality and evangelism, and a readiness to suffer and struggle for righteousness, and in many areas a readiness to sink denominational differences. Mutual sharing in the World Church witnesses to its international nature, and has much to offer a divided world, not least in Scotland.

VACANCIES OVERSEAS. The Board welcomes enquiries from men and women interested in serving in the Church overseas. This is usually with indigenous denominations and related organisations with which we are in partnership overseas, in Church of Scotland congregations mostly in Europe, or within our work in Israel. Owing to financial constraints, the Board has reluctantly had to limit its recruitment in 2004–5, but hopes to be in a position to resume active recruitment in the near future. Those interested in more information are invited to write to the Assistant Secretary (Personnel) in the first instance.

HIV/AIDS PROJECT. The General Assembly of 2002 adopted an HIV/AIDS Project to be run by the Board of World Mission in 2002–7. The Project aims to raise awareness in congregations about the impact of HIV/AIDS and seeks to channel urgently needed support to partner churches. For further information, contact the Co-ordinator, HIV/AIDS Project, Board of World Mission, 121 George Street, Edinburgh EH2 4YN.

JUBILEE SCOTLAND. The Board plays an active role in the coalition which works within Scotland for the cancellation of unpayable international debt. For further information, contact the Co-ordinator, Jubilee Scotland, 41 George IV Bridge, Edinburgh EH1 1EL (Tel: 0131-225 4321; Fax: 0131-225 8861; E-mail: mail@jubileescotland.org.uk).

CHRISTIAN AID SCOTLAND. Christian Aid is an official relief development agency of churches in Britain and Ireland. Christian Aid's mandate is to challenge and enable us to fulfil our responsibilities to the poor of the world. Half a million volunteers and collectors and nearly 200 paid staff make this possible, with money given by millions of supporters. The Church of Scotland marks its commitment as a church to this vital part of its mission through an annual grant from the Mission and Aid Fund, transmitted through World Mission, which keeps in close touch with Christian Aid and its work.

Up-to-date information about projects and current emergency relief work can be obtained from the National Secretary, Rev. John Wylie, Christian Aid Scotland, 41 George IV Bridge, Edinburgh EH1 1EL (Tel: 0131-220 1254); the three area co-ordinators, Ms Eildon Dyer and Mrs Ailsa Henderson, Glasgow Office, 759a Argyle Street G3 8DS (Tel: 0141-221 7475), Miss Marjorie Clark, Perth Office, 28 Glasgow Road, Perth PH2 0NX (Tel: 01738 643982); or the Director, Dr Daleep Mukarji, Christian Aid Office, PO Box 100, London SE1 7RT (Tel: 020 7620 4444).

ACCOMMODATION IN ISRAEL. The Church of Scotland has two Christian Residential Centres in Israel which provide comfortable accommodation for pilgrims and visitors to the Holy Land. Further information is available from:
(a) St Andrew's Guest House, Jerusalem (PO Box 8619, Jerusalem)
    (Tel: 00 972 2 6737235; Fax: 00 972 2 6731711; E-mail: standjer@netvision.net.il)
(b) The Scots Hotel, St Andrew's, Galilee, Tiberias (PO Box 104, Tiberias)
    (Tel: 00 972 4 6710710; Fax: 00 972 4 6710711; E-mail: scottie@netvision.net.il)

A list of Overseas Appointments will be found in List K in Section 6.

A *World Mission Year Book* is available with more details of our partner churches and of people currently serving abroad, including those with ecumenical bodies and para-church bodies.

A list of Retired Missionaries will be found in List L in Section 6.

(27) ECUMENICAL RELATIONS

MEMBERSHIP – COMMITTEE ON ECUMENICAL RELATIONS
(27 members: 12 nominated by the General Assembly, 13 appointed by the main Boards and

Committees of the Church, plus five Corresponding Members – the General Secretary of ACTS, one from the Roman Catholic Church in Scotland and three on a rotating basis from the Scottish Episcopal Church, the Synod of the Methodist Church in Scotland, the Salvation Army, the Religious Society of Friends, the United Free Church of Scotland, the United Reformed Church and the Baptist Union of Scotland: Convener and Vice Convener)

Convener: Rev. Erik M. Cramb LTh (2002)
Secretary: Rev. Sheilagh M. Kesting BA BD

REMIT

The purpose of the Committee is to enable the Church of Scotland, at local, Presbytery and national levels, increasingly to maximise opportunities and resources for worship, witness and service together with other churches and related organisations in this country and overseas, working wherever possible through existing Boards and Committees of the Church.

In fulfilment of this remit, the Committee will

1. be the body within the Church of Scotland through which WCC, ACTS, CTBI and, as appropriate, the other Ecumenical Instruments in Britain and Ireland relate
2. call together for planning, briefing and the exchanging of information, the Church of Scotland's representatives on WCC, ACTS (Scottish Churches' Forum and Networks), CTBI (the Assembly and the Church Representatives Meetings) and the like
3. bring to the General Assembly for the approval of the General Assembly the names of those who might serve for the following year (or appropriate term) on ACTS, on CTBI and, as appropriate, on Committees, Commissions and the like of these bodies
4. following consultation with the Board of World Mission, bring to the General Assembly for the approval of the General Assembly the names of those who might serve for the following year (or appropriate term) on such bodies as the World Alliance of Reformed Churches, the Conference of European Churches and the World Council of Churches
5. bring to the General Assembly for the approval of the General Assembly the names of those who might be invited to represent the Church of Scotland at the Assemblies or Synods of other Churches in Britain and at Conferences and Gatherings organised on an ecumenical basis at which official Church of Scotland representation is appropriate
6. (a) call for and receive reports from representatives of the Church of Scotland attending the Assemblies or Synods of other Churches and those ecumenical conferences and gatherings which are from time to time held
    (b) ensure that appropriate parts of such reports are made available to relevant Boards and Committees
7. (a) be informed of, assist centrally where appropriate, and report to the General Assembly on the Local Ecumenical Partnerships which already exist in Scotland and which may in the future come to exist
    (b) in consultation with the Board of Practice and Procedure (where matters of Church Law and Practice are involved), advise congregations and Presbyteries seeking to establish new Ecumenical Partnerships or to amend existing Partnerships
8. be the Committee through which reports are submitted to the General Assembly from Groups appointed to take part on behalf of the Church of Scotland in formal conversations and doctrinal dialogues with other Church and ecumenical bodies.

INTER-CHURCH ORGANISATIONS

WORLD COUNCIL OF CHURCHES

The Church of Scotland is a founder member of the World Council of Churches, formed in 1948. As its basis declares, it is 'a fellowship of Churches which confess the Lord Jesus Christ as God and Saviour according to the Scriptures, and therefore seek to fulfil their common calling to the Glory of the one God, Father, Son and Holy Spirit'. Its member Churches, which number over 300, are drawn from all continents and include all the major traditions – Eastern and Oriental Orthodox, Reformed, Lutheran, Anglican, Baptist, Disciples, Methodist, Moravian, Friends, Pentecostalist and others. Although the Roman Catholic Church is not a member, there is very close co-operation with the departments in the Vatican.

The World Council holds its Assemblies every seven years. The last, held in Harare, Zimbabwe, in December 1998, had the theme 'Turn to God: Rejoice in Hope'. At that Assembly, the Rev. Norman Shanks was elected to the Central Committee of the Council. The next Assembly is due to be held in Brazil in 2006.

Presently, the World Council is co-ordinating a 'Decade to Overcome Violence' which the Church of Scotland has taken up as part of the context in which we do our work.

The World Council also continues to provide up-to-date information on what churches and the faith communities are saying and doing in the aftermath of 11 September 2001 and in the context of war on terrorism.

The General Secretary is Rev. Dr Sam Kobia, 150 route de Ferney, 1211 Geneva 2, Switzerland (Tel: 00 41 22 791 61 11; Fax: 00 41 22 791 03 61; E-mail: nan@wcc-coe.org).

WORLD ALLIANCE OF REFORMED CHURCHES

The Church of Scotland is a founder member of the World Alliance of Reformed Churches, which began in 1875 as 'The Alliance of the Reformed Churches Throughout the World Holding the Presbyterian System' and which now includes also Churches of the Congregational tradition. Today it is composed of more than 200 Churches in nearly 100 countries, with an increasing number in Asia. It brings together, for mutual help and common action, large Churches which enjoy majority status and small minority Churches. It engages in theological dialogue with other Christian traditions – Orthodox, Roman Catholic, Lutheran, Methodist, Baptist and so on. It is organised in three main departments – Co-operation with Witness, Theology, and Partnership. The twenty-fourth General Council was held in Accra, Ghana, from 30 July to 12 August 2004. The theme was 'That all may have life in fullness'.

The General Secretary is Rev. Dr Setri Nyomi, 150 route de Ferney, 1211 Geneva 2, Switzerland (Tel: 00 41 22 791 62 38; Fax: 00 41 22 791 65 05; E-mail: sn@warc.ch).

CONFERENCE OF EUROPEAN CHURCHES

The Church of Scotland is a founder member of the Conference of European Churches, formed in 1959 and until recently the only body which involved in common membership representatives of every European country (except Albania) from the Atlantic to the Urals. More than 100 Churches, Orthodox and Protestant, are members. Although the Roman Catholic Church is not a member, there is very close co-operation with the Council of European Catholic Bishops' Conferences. With the removal of the long-standing political barriers in Europe, the Conference has now opportunities and responsibilities to assist the Church throughout the continent to offer united witness and service.

Its General Secretary is Rev. Dr Keith Clements, 150 route de Ferney, 1211 Geneva 2, Switzerland (Tel: 00 41 22 791 61 11; Fax: 00 41 22 791 03 61; E-mail: cec@cec-kek.org).

CEC: CHURCH AND SOCIETY COMMISSION

The Church of Scotland was a founder member of the European Ecumenical Commission for Church and Society (EECCS). The Commission owed its origins to the Christian concern and vision of a group of ministers and European civil servants about the future of Europe. It was established in 1973 by Churches recognising the importance of this venture. Membership included Churches and ecumenical bodies from the European Union. The process of integration with CEC was completed in 2000, and the name, Church and Society Commission (CSC), established. In Brussels, CSC monitors Community activity, maintains contact with MEPs and promotes dialogue between the Churches and the institutions. It plays an educational role and encourages the Churches' social and ethical responsibility in European affairs. It has a General Secretary, a study secretary and an executive secretary in Brussels and a small office in Strasbourg and Geneva.

The General Secretary is Rev. Rudiger Noll, Ecumenical Centre, 174 rue Joseph II, B-1000 Brussels, Belgium (Tel: 00 32 2 230 17 32; Fax: 00 32 2 231 14 13; E-mail: mo@cec-kek.be).

CHURCHES TOGETHER IN BRITAIN AND IRELAND (CTBI)
and ACTION OF CHURCHES TOGETHER IN SCOTLAND (ACTS)

In September 1990, Churches throughout Britain and Ireland solemnly committed themselves to one another, promising to one another to do everything possible together. To provide frameworks for this commitment to joint action, the Churches established CTBI for the United Kingdom and Ireland, and for Scotland, ACTS, with sister organisations for Wales and for England.

CTBI has a large Assembly meeting once every three years, a Church Representatives Meeting held twice a year, and a Steering Committee meeting five times a year. It has commissions on Mission, Racial Justice and Interfaith Relations. It is staffed by a General Secretary and Co-ordinating Secretaries for Church Life, Church and Society, International Affairs and Communication.

The General Secretary of CTBI is Dr David R. Goodbourn, Third Floor, Bastille Court, 2 Paris Garden, London SE1 8ND (Tel: 020 7654 7254; Fax: 020 7654 7222). The General Secretariat can be contacted by telephoning 020 7654 7211 (E-mail: davidgoodbourn@ctbi.org.uk; Website: http://www.ctbi.org.uk).

ACTS was restructured at the beginning of 2003. The new structure comprises the Scottish Churches' Forum (replacing the Central Council) composed of church representatives from trustee member churches. There are four Networks: Church Life, Faith Studies, Mission, and Church and Society. Contributing to the life of the Networks will be associated ecumenical groups. Such groups are expressions of the churches' commitment to work together and to bring together key people in a defined field of interest or expertise. ACTS is an expression of the commitment of the churches to one another.

ACTS is staffed by a General Secretary, an Assistant General Secretary, two Network Officers, an Administration and Booking Officer and a Bursar. Scottish Churches House, in which their offices are based, is run by a Warden and a Deputy Warden. Scottish Churches House is based in Dunblane.

These structures facilitate regular consultation and intensive co-operation among those who frame the policies and deploy the resources of the churches in Scotland and throughout Britain and Ireland. At the same time, they afford greater opportunity for a wide range of members of different churches to meet in common prayer and study.

The General Secretary is Rev. Dr Kevin Franz, Scottish Churches House, Dunblane FK15 0AJ (Tel: 01786 823588; Fax: 01786 825844; E-mail: kevinfranz@acts-scotland.org).

The Scottish Churches Parliamentary Office: The Scottish Churches Parliamentary Office supports the churches in their relationships with the Scottish Parliament and Executive, providing briefings and updates on Parliamentary activity and advice on contacting MSPs and so on. The Parliamentary Officer is Rev. Dr Graham K. Blount, and the Office is at 14 Johnston Terrace, Edinburgh   EH1 2PW (Tel: 0131-622 2278; Fax: 0131-622 7226; E-mail: gkblount@dial.pipex.com; Website: www.actsparl.org).

(28) PARISH EDUCATION
21 Young Street, Edinburgh EH2 4HU
Tel: 0131-260 3110;   Fax: 0131-260 3120
E-mail: enquiries@parished.org.uk

MEMBERSHIP: BOARD OF PARISH EDUCATION
(Convener, Vice-Convener, 50 members appointed by the General Assembly, one representative from the Church of Scotland Guild)

Convener:	Rev John C. Christie (2001)
Vice-convener:	Mr Ron Lavalette (2003)
Director and General Secretary:	Mr Iain W. Whyte

STAFF

Section Head, Publications:	Ms Gillian Cloke / Ms Janet de Vigne
Section Head, Adult Education:	Rev. Jane Denniston
Section Head, Youth Ministry:	Mr Steve Mallon
Regional Development Worker (South-west):	Mr Calum Sabey
Secretary for the Readership:	Ms Mary Stobo
National Adviser in Elder Training:	Ms Sheilah Steven
Section Head, Children's Ministry and Regional Services:	Mr Doug Swanney
Cowal Education Field Officer:	Ms Jen Zielinski

Child Protection Unit

National Adviser in Child Protection:	Ms Jennifer McCreanor
Child Protection Trainer:	Ms Caroline McLoughlin
Associate National Adviser in Child Protection:	Ms Fiona Mackay

REMIT
Based at 21 Young Street, Edinburgh, the Board of Parish Education's remit is to oversee the development of an education and leadership training service for the Church of Scotland. The Board's provision covers a wide spectrum of courses and events catering for all ages and abilities. This involves training and resources for children's workers, youth workers, elders and the Readership. Resource material and publications to support this work are also produced through Scottish Christian Press (formerly Parish Education Publications).

COMMITTEES
The Board itself meets twice annually, in February and September, with its committees meeting four or five times per annum. The committees are organised to reflect the Board's commitment to learning for all, and to developing the concept of the Faith Community.
ADULT MINISTRIES

The remit of the Adult Ministries Section is to support and develop the vast range of adult learning that takes place in the church.

Adult Education

The development of a vibrant and growing congregation rests in two areas – worship and education. For many folk in the church, education has historically been a difficulty, but many congregations have at least some form of adult education programme – including discussion groups, Bible study, prayer groups and Lent groups – which they are keen to expand. The Adult Education Advisor's role is to assist in this development and to help congregations examine new areas of development. In particular, we have developed a congregational renewal programme based on the *Church Without Walls* report, with study material and an evaluation package to help congregations identify where they can develop and how they can go about taking the necessary steps to achieve their goals.

Eldership

Being an elder is a demanding but rewarding role – an important part of the Church of Scotland in its team ministry. The Eldership Working Party supports this crucial leadership role within the Church, working with a network of Elder Trainers – at present forty-five in twenty-five Presbyteries, with six more in training. Elder Trainers are regularly impressed by the commitment of time and talent to the Church shown by the elders with whom they come in contact, and the Eldership Working Party supports this by holding regular conferences and training days for elders and session clerks, and by providing a variety of study material on eldership, including books and videos. Interest in eldership is increasing as elders seek to rediscover their spiritual role. Workshops are available locally: topics include Exploring Eldership, Pastoral Care, Faith Sharing, and Leading Worship. Enquiries are always welcome.

Readership

The Board of Parish Education provides training opportunities and services to maintain this important component of the Church's team ministry. A Reader is a member of the Church set apart by his or her Presbytery for 'duties principally concerned with the Ministry of the Word and the conduct of public worship'. Recently the Reader's role has developed; while still associated primarily with worship and preaching, there are new opportunities for the fully trained Reader. Further information for those interested in Readership is available from the Board on request.

CHILDREN'S, YOUTH AND REGIONAL MINISTRY

Children's and Youth Ministry in the Board is based around the principles of education, empowerment and creating best practice for the whole Church. The Board is involved in training children's and youth leaders through its *Choices* programme – a series of sessions available to local churches in CD format. Both the children's and the youth programmes cover a wide range of subjects and provide a grounding for anyone working with children and youth. Both areas are served by websites offering updates and information for the whole Church. Youth ministry can be found at www.cosy.net.uk and Children's Ministry through www.chok.org.uk (launching in the autumn of 2003).

Children's Ministry

Chok, the Children's Ministry newsletter, continues to be available to children's workers across the country. Children's Forums also meet locally, with two regional gatherings a year, one focused on enabling the children of the Church to have an input into the General Assembly.

Youth Ministry

The Board is also responsible for both the National Youth Assembly and the Youth Representatives to the General Assembly. The Youth Assembly is an annual event attracting young adults from all over the UK, centring around debate, fellowship, worship and community. As well as events at home, the Board organises and participates in ecumenical events and trips abroad. It also resources youth groups by providing training for youth leaders and by supplying educational material. The Board is also a major contributor to the Crossover Festival, a weekend event of worship, speakers, debates, fun and reflection.

SCOTTISH CHRISTIAN PRESS
The Scottish Christian Press (formerly Parish Education Publications, or PEP) is the publishing and information unit of the Board of Parish Education. To support parish development, SCP produces a wide variety of resources which derive both from ongoing work in the field by the Board's own staff and from commissions within the Church.

The unit produces an annual catalogue listing SCP's own publications in the field of Christian education. It offers also resources available from other bodies within the Church, some of the best available parish resourcing material from other denominations and material from educational publishers world-wide. Details of SCP's current catalogue can be found through our website on www.scottishchristianpress.org.uk.

SCP also produces a regular online newsletter, *Online Parish Education News* (OPEN), with a circulation of around 7,000; for information, or to receive this, contact SCP through the Edinburgh office or the general enquiry line.

CHILD PROTECTION
It has long been the vision of the Board that integrating the principles of protection and safety with the nurture and education of our young people is essential in the Church. The Child Protection Unit puts this ideal into practice, regularly organising training throughout the country for children's and youth workers, ensuring the highest standards and best practice. This section also has responsibility for implementing the Church's policy on Child Protection through the network of Child Protection Co-ordinators. It has produced a handbook on good practice within this area which will be regularly updated, and a policy statement for the protection of children within the Church. In addition, this Unit has been given by the General Assembly responsibility for administration concerned with criminal-records checks enabled by recent legislation.

(29) EDUCATION COMMITTEE

MEMBERSHIP:
(20 members together with Convener and Vice Convener)
Convener: Mr David Alexander (2003)
Vice Convener: Rev. Professor Duncan B. Forrester

STAFF
Secretary: Ms Susan Leslie
Assistant: Mrs Agnes Mullen

REMIT

The Education Committee is the oldest continuing Committee of the General Assembly (formed in 1825) and has a long and historic connection with Scottish Education. The key aspects of the Committee's remit are:

1. to represent the Church on matters of state education at every level
2. to support the Church Representatives whom it appoints on behalf of the General Assembly to deal with education on each of Scotland's thirty-two Local Authorities and to monitor the development of Local Authority policies on religious observance following the issue of a circular by the Scottish Executive
3. to co-operate with Presbyteries and Local Authorities in undertaking the support and training of chaplains in schools and in Further Education Colleges
4. to promote good learning and teaching in the curriculum and ensure the place of Religious and Moral Education
5. to commission and produce resources to ensure that Scottish Christianity and the life and work of the Church of Scotland can be properly represented in the curriculum and to participate in development work arising from the Religious Observance Report published in May 2004
6. actively to support the work of the Scottish Commissioner for Children and Young People
7. to co-operate with other Churches and faith groups working to enhance Scottish Education.

The Committee responds to consultation documents from the Scottish Executive and seeks to develop and maintain links with Education Ministers, with Members of the Scottish Parliament and with the relevant Committees.

It is actively involved in the area of tertiary education and participates in training and accreditation in relation to the delivery of chaplaincy in schools and colleges.

It participates in the work of the Scottish Joint Committee on Religious and Moral Education and is represented on the Religious Education Movement (Scotland) and the Association for the Teaching of Religious Education in Scotland (ATRES).

It has established useful and practical links with the Roman Catholic Church through its Catholic Education Services, and it has a good record of liaison with the Scottish unions in the educational field. It nominates one person to represent the Church on the General Teaching Council (Scotland).

---

(30) COMMUNICATION

MEMBERSHIP
BOARD OF COMMUNICATION
(18 members, appointed by the Assembly)
Convener: Rev. W. Peter Graham (2003)
Vice Convener: Rev. Iain F. Paton (2002)
Secretary: Mr Brian McGlynn

STAFF
Secretary and Director: Mr Brian McGlynn
Finance Unit: Mr Steven Lane, Acting Head of Finance
Media Relations Unit: Mrs Pat Holdgate, Head of Media Relations

Design Services:	Mr Peter J.F. Forrest, Head of Design Services
Life & Work:	Ms Lynne Robertson, Editor
Saint Andrew Press:	Mrs Ann Crawford, Head of Publishing
Pathway Media:	Mr John Williams, Head of Audiovisual Services
Ministers' Forum:	Rev. John A. Ferguson, Editor
Year Book:	Rev. Ronald S. Blakey, Editor

REMIT
Under a revised constitution approved by the General Assembly in 1995, the Board is responsible for providing the Church with professional communication services as well as promoting effective communication within the Church and to the outside world. The Board's services are as follows:

DIRECTOR
Mr Brian McGlynn   direct line 0131-240 2236
                         (E-mail: bmcglynn@cofscotland.org.uk)

Marketing and Publicity Officer
Alison Fleming   0131-225 5722 ext. 239
                         (E-mail: afleming@cofscotland.org.uk)

1.   MEDIA RELATIONS UNIT

Head of Media Relations:	Pat Holdgate	0131-240 2243
Senior Media Relations Officer:	Brian McGuire	0131-240 2204
Senior Media Relations Officer:	Grant McLennan	0131-240 2202
Website Editor:	Lynsae Tulloch	0131-225 5722 ext. 244

(E-mail: mediarelations@cofscotland.org.uk)

The Media Relations Unit is the link between the media and the Church, and is the first point of contact for journalists seeking information on the work and views of the Church's Boards and Committees. The Unit issues regular press releases on matters of interest and provides an audio release service to independent local radio. The Unit develops and maintains the Church's website (www.churchofscotland.org.uk). Unit staff maintain close links with a large network of media contacts and are happy to facilitate interviews with key personnel within the Church. The Unit also supports parish ministers and Church members by promoting local news and events on their behalf and offering advice on local media work.

2.   DESIGN SERVICES
(Tel: 0131-225 5722/240 2224; Fax: 0131-220 5407; E-mail: design@churchofscotland.co.uk)
This part of the Board's work is concerned with the design and production of a wide range of promotional literature, display materials and exhibitions. Members of staff are pleased to advise congregations and Presbyteries on their particular communications needs.

A mailing list is maintained to provide parish magazine editors with suitable material and resources for their publications. Anyone wishing to be added to this list should provide their name and address to the Department.

3.   PATHWAY MEDIA – the Church's audio-visual production unit
(Tel: 0131-225 5722; Fax: 0131-240 2236; E-mail: pathway@cofscotland.org.uk)
From its premises at 123 George Street, Edinburgh EH2 4YN, the Unit produces and markets videos, tape-slide sets and audio cassettes. One of the Unit's key initiatives is developing webcasting as a new means of communication. Short training courses in television, radio and

video are also held here. The Unit has pioneered Church production and use of video as a means of Christian communication. It also produces occasional programmes for broadcast television. In conjunction with the Media Relations Unit, Pathway supports religious output on Independent Local Radio.

4.   LIFE & WORK
(Tel: 0131-225 5722; Fax: 0131-240 2207; E-mail: magazine@lifeandwork.org)
Life & Work is the Church of Scotland's monthly magazine. Its purpose is to keep the Church informed about events in church life at home and abroad and to provide a forum for Christian opinion and debate on a variety of topics. It has an independent editorial policy. Contributions which are relevant to any aspect of the Christian faith are welcome.
   The price of Life & Work this year is £1.20. With a circulation of around 46,000, it also offers advertisers a first-class opportunity to reach a discerning readership in all parts of Scotland.

5.   SAINT ANDREW PRESS
(Tel: 0131-240 2253; Fax: 0131-220 3113; E-mail: rallen@cofscotland.org.uk)
Saint Andrew Press is the Church of Scotland's publishing house. Since its creation in 1954, it has published many titles that have made a major contribution to Christian literature. The much-loved series of New Testament commentaries by the late Professor William Barclay is world-renowned. The series has been sensitively updated for a twenty-first-century readership and is published as the New Daily Study Bible series in seventeen volumes. Other best-sellers include the Glasgow Gospel by Jamie Stuart, and now Outside Verdict by Harry Reid, a headline-grabbing, Scottish top-ten book that probes the very heart of the Church of Scotland and makes a series of radical, inspiring proposals. Saint Andrew Press has also published on behalf of the Church of Scotland Panel on Worship the critically acclaimed Common Order and the ecumenical songbook Common Ground.
   Church of Scotland stationery is available from Saint Andrew Press.
   All proposals for new publications should be sent to the Head of Publishing in the form of a two-page description of the book and its readership together with one sample chapter. Saint Andrew Press staff are always willing to offer professional help and advice.
   Saint Andrew Press books are now distributed by STL Ltd, Carlisle.

LOCAL BROADCASTING
The Board of Communication encourages the work of a number of ecumenical groups assisting local radio stations with their religious broadcasting. Enquiries about local religious broadcasting should be made to the Media Relations Unit (see above).

THE CHURCHES' MEDIA COUNCIL
The Churches' Media Council – originally CACLB (the Churches' Advisory Council for Local Broadcasting) – has been established by the Churches to advance the Christian faith through the media. It brings together the churches, Christian broadcasters, the broadcasting authorities and trainers under its Chairman, Rt Rev. Dr Tom Butler. Peter Blackman is Director.
   The Council is responsible for influencing government policy-making, for undertaking work and research and for the provision of support services that would normally fall to one or more of the individual denominational churches – all as a way of providing consistent accurate information and services in a timely and cost-effective manner.
   The Council is an agency of Churches Together in Britain and Ireland and of Churches Together in England. It has close links with other ecumenical bodies in Britain and Ireland.

Present Officers
President: Prunella Scales CBE

Chairperson: Rt Rev. Dr Tom Butler, Church of England
Director: Peter Blackman, Churches' Media Council,
                 PO Box 6613, South Woodham Ferrers, Essex CM3 5DY
                 (Tel: 01245 322158; Fax: 01245 321957;
                 E-mail: office@churchesmediacouncil.org.uk)

ASSOCIATION OF CHRISTIANS IN THE MEDIA (ACM)

The ACM is a network of individuals and organisations involved in, or relating to, the media. It provides an information support network, a chance to meet like-minded people in similar media streams, access to information and advice, contact details and training information.

Christian influence and involvement are vital, and ACM exists to bring people together for mutual benefit, fellowship and prayer, and to encourage support for and promote the importance of Christians working in the media. The Association is operated via the Internet and directly between members using the members' contact database and a number of less formal links.

For further information about membership, contact Peter Blackman, Association of Christians in the Media (ACM), PO Box 6613, South Woodham Ferrers, Essex CM3 5DY (Tel: 01245 322158; Fax: 01245 321957; E-mail: acm@churchesmediacouncil.org.uk).

(31) CHURCH OF SCOTLAND TRUST

MEMBERSHIP
(Members are appointed by the General Assembly, on the nomination of the Trust)
Chairman: Mr Christopher N. Mackay WS
Vice Chairman: Mr Robert Brodie CB WS
Treasurer: Mr Donald F. Ross MA CA
Secretary and Clerk: Mrs Jennifer M. Hamilton BA

REMIT
The Church of Scotland Trust was established by Act of Parliament in 1932. The Trust's function since 1 January 1995 has been to hold properties outwith Scotland and to act as Trustee in a number of third-party trusts.

Further information can be obtained from the Secretary and Clerk of the Church of Scotland Trust, 121 George Street, Edinburgh EH2 4YN (Tel: 0131-240 2222; E-mail: jhamilton@ cofscotland.org.uk).

SECTION 2

General Information

(1) OTHER CHURCHES IN THE UNITED KINGDOM

ASSOCIATED PRESBYTERIAN CHURCHES
Clerk of Presbytery: Rev. A.N. McPhail, APC Manse, Polvimister Road, Oban PA34 5TN
(Tel: 01631 567076).

THE REFORMED PRESBYTERIAN CHURCH OF SCOTLAND
Stated Clerk: Rev. G.M. Milligan, RP Manse, 1 Albert Terrace, London Road, Stranraer DG9 8AB.

THE FREE CHURCH OF SCOTLAND
Principal Clerk: Rev. James MacIver, The Mound, Edinburgh EH1 2LS (Tel: 0131-226 4978/5286;
E-mail: freechurch@compuserve.com).

THE FREE PRESBYTERIAN CHURCH OF SCOTLAND
Clerk of Synod: Rev. John Macleod, 16 Matheson Road, Stornoway HS1 2LA (Tel: 01851
702755).

THE UNITED FREE CHURCH OF SCOTLAND
General Secretary: Rev. John Fulton BSc BD, United Free Church Offices, 11 Newton Place,
Glasgow G3 7PR (Tel: 0141-332 3435; E-mail: ufcos@charis.co.uk).

THE PRESBYTERIAN CHURCH IN IRELAND
Clerk of the General Assembly and General Secretary: Rev. Dr Donald J. Watts,
Church House, Fisherwick Place, Belfast BT1 6DW (Tel: 02890 322284; E-mail:
clerk@presbyterianireland.org).

THE PRESBYTERIAN CHURCHES OF WALES
General Secretary: Rev. Ifan R.H. Roberts, Tabernacle Chapel, 81 Merthyr Road, Whitchurch,
Cardiff CF14 1DD (Tel: 02920 494913; Fax: 02920 464293; E-mail: ebcpcw@aol.com).

THE UNITED REFORMED CHURCH
General Secretary: Rev. David Cormick, 86 Tavistock Place, London WC1H 9RT (Tel: 020 7916
2020; Fax: 020 7916 2021).

UNITED REFORMED CHURCH SCOTLAND SYNOD
Synod Clerk: Rev. Kenneth M. Forbes BA BD, Church House, PO Box 189, Glasgow G1 2BX
(Tel: 0141-332 7667; E-mail: scotland@urc.org.uk).

BAPTIST UNION OF SCOTLAND
General Director: Rev. William G. Slack, 14 Aytoun Road, Glasgow G41 5RT (Tel: 0141-423
6169; E-mail: admin@scottishbaptist.org.uk).

CONGREGATIONAL FEDERATION IN SCOTLAND
Rev. Alan Gibbon, 61 Fifth Avenue, Glasgow G12 0AR (Tel: 0141-334 1351).

RELIGIOUS SOCIETY OF FRIENDS (QUAKERS)
Clerk to the General Meeting of Scotland: Pamela McDougall, Havana, 3 Teapot Lane, Inverkeillor,
Arbroath DD1 5RP (E-mail: pamjames@totalserve.co.uk).

ROMAN CATHOLIC CHURCH
The Rt Rev. Mgr Henry Docherty, General Secretariat, Bishops' Conference for Scotland, 64 Aitken Street, Airdrie ML6 6LT (Tel: 01236 764061; Fax: 01236 762489; E-mail: gensec@bpsconfscot.com).

THE SALVATION ARMY
Scotland Secretary: Major Robert McIntyre, Scotland Secretariat, 12A Dryden Road, Loanhead EH20 9LZ (Tel: 0131-440 9101; E-mail: scotland@salvationarmy.org.uk).

SCOTTISH EPISCOPAL CHURCH
General Secretary: Mr John F. Stuart, 21 Grosvenor Crescent, Edinburgh EH12 5EL (Tel: 0131-225 6357; E-mail: secgen@scotland.anglican.org).

THE SYNOD OF THE METHODIST CHURCH IN SCOTLAND
Secretary: Mrs Janet Murray, Methodist Church Office, Scottish Churches House, Kirk Street, Dunblane FK15 0AJ (Tel/Fax: 01786 820295; E-mail: meth@scottishchurcheshouse.org).

GENERAL SYNOD OF THE CHURCH OF ENGLAND
Secretary General: Mr William Fitall, Church House, Great Smith Street, London SW1P 3NZ (Tel: 020 7898 1000).

(2) OVERSEAS CHURCHES

PRESBYTERIAN CHURCH IN AMERICA
Stated Clerk: 1700 North Brown Road, Suite 105, Lawrenceville, GA 30043, USA (E-mail: ac@pcanet.org; Website: http://www. pcanet.org).

PRESBYTERIAN CHURCH IN CANADA
Clerk of Assembly: 50 Wynford Drive, North York, Ontario M3C 1J7, Canada (E-mail: pccadmin@presbycan.ca; Website: http://www.presbycan.ca).

UNITED CHURCH OF CANADA
General Secretary: Suite 300, 3250 Bloor Street West, Toronto, Ontario M8X 2Y4, Canada (Website: http://www.united-church.ca).

PRESBYTERIAN CHURCH (USA)
Stated Clerk: 100 Witherspoon Street, Louisville, KY 40202-1396, USA (E-mail: presbytel@pcusa.org; Website: http://www.pcusa.org).

REFORMED PRESBYTERIAN CHURCH IN NORTH AMERICA
Stated Clerk: 7408 Penn Avenue, Pittsburgh, PA15208, USA (Website: http://www.reformedpresbyterian.org).

CUMBERLAND PRESBYTERIAN CHURCH
General Secretary: 1978 Union Avenue, Memphis, TN 38104, USA (E-mail: gac@cumberland.org; Website: http://www.cumberland.org).

REFORMED CHURCH IN AMERICA
General Secretary: 475 Riverside Drive, NY 10115, USA (E-mail: rcamail@rca.org).

UNITED CHURCH OF CHRIST
General Minister: 700 Prospect Avenue, Cleveland, Ohio 44115, USA
Website: (http://www.ucc.org).

UNITING CHURCH IN AUSTRALIA
General Secretary: PO Box A2266, Sydney South, New South Wales 1235, Australia (E-mail: enquiries@nat.uca.org.au).

PRESBYTERIAN CHURCH OF AUSTRALIA
Clerk of Assembly: PO Box 2196, Strawberry Hills, NSW 2012; 168 Chalmers Street, Surry Hills, NSW 2010, Australia (E-mail: general@pcnsw.org.au).

PRESBYTERIAN CHURCH OF AOTEAROA, NEW ZEALAND
Executive Secretary: PO Box 9049, 100 Tory Street, Wellington, New Zealand (E-mail: aes@pccnz.org.nz; Website: http://www.presbyterian.org.nz).

EVANGELICAL PRESBYTERIAN CHURCH, GHANA
Synod Clerk: PO Box 18, Ho, Volta Region, Ghana.

PRESBYTERIAN CHURCH OF GHANA
Director of Ecumenical and Social Relations: PO Box 1800, Accra, Ghana.

PRESBYTERIAN CHURCH OF EAST AFRICA
Secretary General: PO Box 27573, 00506 Nairobi, Kenya.

CHURCH OF CENTRAL AFRICA PRESBYTERIAN
Secretary General, General Synod: PO Box 30398, Lilongwe 3, Malawi.
General Secretary, Blantyre Synod: PO Box 413, Blantyre, Malawi.
General Secretary, Livingstonia Synod: PO Box 112, Mzuzu, Malawi.
General Secretary, Nkhoma Synod: PO Box 45, Nkhoma, Malawi.

IGREJA EVANGELICA DE CRISTO EM MOÇAMBIQUE (EVANGELICAL CHURCH OF CHRIST IN MOZAMBIQUE)
(Nampula) General Secretary: Cx. Postale 284, Nampula 70100, Mozambique.
(Zambezia) Superintendente: Cx. Postale 280, Zambezia, Quelimane, Mozambique.

PRESBYTERIAN CHURCH OF NIGERIA
Principal Clerk: 26–29 Ehere Road, Ogbor Hill, PO Box 2635, Aba, Abia State, Nigeria.

UNITING PRESBYTERIAN CHURCH IN SOUTHERN AFRICA (SOUTH AFRICA)
General Secretary: PO Box 96188, Brixton 2019, South Africa.

UNITING PRESBYTERIAN CHURCH IN SOUTHERN AFRICA (ZIMBABWE)
Presbytery Clerk: PO Box CY224, Causeway, Harare, Zimbabwe.

PRESBYTERIAN CHURCH OF SUDAN (A)
Executive Secretary: PO Box 66168, Nairobi, Kenya.

PRESBYTERIAN CHURCH OF SUDAN (M)
General Secretary: PO Box 3421, Khartoum, Sudan.

UNITED CHURCH OF ZAMBIA
General Secretary: Nationalist Road at Burma Road, PO Box 50122, 15101 Ridgeway, Lusaka, Zambia.

CHURCH OF BANGLADESH
Moderator: Synod Office, 54 Johnson Road, Dhaka 1100, Bangladesh.

CHURCH OF NORTH INDIA
General Secretary: Synod Office, 16 Pandit Pant Marg, New Delhi 110 001, India.

CHURCH OF SOUTH INDIA
General Secretary: Synod Office, 5 White's Road, Royapettah, Chennai 600 114, India.

PRESBYTERIAN CHURCH OF KOREA
General Secretary: CPO Box 1125, Seoul 110 611, Korea.

PRESBYTERIAN CHURCH IN THE REPUBLIC OF KOREA
General Secretary: 1501 The Korean Ecumenical Building, 136–156 Yunchi-Dong, Chongno-Ku, Seoul, Korea.

THE UNITED MISSION TO NEPAL
Executive Director: PO Box 126, Kathmandu, Nepal.

CHURCH OF PAKISTAN
General Secretary: Mission Compound, Daska, Distr Sialkot, Punjab, Pakistan.

PRESBYTERY OF LANKA
Moderator: 127/1 D S Senanayake Veedyan, Kandy, Sri Lanka.

PRESBYTERIAN CHURCH IN TAIWAN
General Secretary: 3 Lane 269 Roosevelt Road, Sec. 3, Taipei, Taiwan 10763, ROC.

CHURCH OF CHRIST IN THAILAND
General Secretary: 109 CCT (13th Floor), Surawong Road, Khet Bangrak, Bangkok 10500, Thailand.

PRESBYTERY OF GUYANA
Moderator: 81 Croal Street, PO Box 10151, Georgetown, Guyana.

NATIONAL PRESBYTERIAN CHURCH OF GUATEMALA
Executive Secretary: Av. Simeon Canas 7–13, Zona 2, Aptdo 655, Guatemala City, Guatemala (E-mail: ienpg@terra.com.gt).

UNITED CHURCH IN JAMAICA AND THE CAYMAN ISLANDS
General Secretary: 12 Carlton Crescent, PO Box 359, Kingston 10, Jamaica (E-mail: unitedchurch@colis.com).

PRESBYTERIAN CHURCH IN TRINIDAD AND TOBAGO
General Secretary: Box 92, Paradise Hill, San Fernando, Trinidad (E-mail: pctt@tstt.net.tt).

BELGIAN PROTESTANT CHURCH
Rue de Champ de Mars 5, B-1050 Bruxelles, Belgium (E-mail: epub@epub.be; Website: http://www.protestanet.be/epub).

REFORMED CHRISTIAN CHURCH IN CROATIA
Bishop's Office: Vladimira Nazora 31, HR-32100 Vinkovci, Croatia (E-mail: reformed.church.rcc@vk.tel.hr; Website: http://www.geocities.com/langh.geo/).

EVANGELICAL CHURCH OF THE CZECH BRETHREN
Moderator: Jungmannova 9, PO Box 466, CZ-11121 Praha 1, Czech Republic (E-mail: exumena@srcce.cz; Website: http://www.srcce.cz).

EGLISE REFORMEE DE FRANCE
General Secretary: 47 rue de Clichy, F-75311 Paris, France (E-mail: erf@unacerf.org; Website: http://www.eglise-reformee-fr.org).

HUNGARIAN REFORMED CHURCH
General Secretary: H-1440 Budapest, PO 5, Hungary (E-mail: zsinatko@axelero.hu; Website: http://www.reformatus.hu).

WALDENSIAN CHURCH
Moderator: Via Firenze 38, 00184, Rome, Italy (E-mail: moderatore@chiesavaldese.org.it; Website: http://www.chiesavaldese.org).

NETHERLANDS REFORMED CHURCH
Landelijk Dienstcentrum Samen op Weg-Kerken, Postbus 8504, NL-3503 RM Utrecht (E-mail: ccs@ngk.nl; Website: http://www.ngk.nl).

REFORMED CHURCH IN ROMANIA
Bishop's Office: Str. IC Bratianu No. 51, R-3400, Cluj-Napoca, Romania (E-mail: office@reformatus.ro).

REFORMED CHRISTIAN CHURCH IN YUGOSLAVIA
Bishop's Office: Bratstva 26, YU-24323 Feketic, Yugoslavia.

SYNOD OF THE NILE OF THE EVANGELICAL CHURCH
General Secretary: Synod of the Nile of the Evangelical Church, PO Box 1248, Cairo, Egypt (E-mail: pcegypt@link.net).

DIOCESE OF THE EPISCOPAL CHURCH IN JERUSALEM AND THE MIDDLE EAST
Bishop's Office: PO Box 19122, Jerusalem 91191, via Israel (E-mail: ediosces@netvision.net.il; Website: http://www.jerusalem.anglican.org).

NATIONAL EVANGELICAL SYNOD OF SYRIA AND LEBANON
General Secretary: PO Box 70890, Antelias, Lebanon (E-mail: nessl@minero.net).

[Full information on Churches overseas may be obtained from the Board of World Mission.]

(3) SCOTTISH DIVINITY FACULTIES

[*denotes a Minister of the Church of Scotland]

[(R) Reader   (SL) Senior Lecturer   (L) Lecturer]

ABERDEEN

(School of Divinity, History and Philosophy)
King's College, Old Aberdeen AB24 3UB
(Tel: 01224 272380;   Fax: 01224 273750;
E-mail: divinity@abdn.ac.uk)

Master of Christ's College:	Rev. Professor John Swinton BD PhD RNM RNMD
Acting Head of School:	S. Kunin BA MA PhD
Deputy Head of School:	A.D. Clarke BA MA PhD
Professors:	F.B. Watson BA DPhil (New Testament)
	Rev. J. Swinton* BD PhD RNM (Practical Theology and Pastoral Care)
	J. Webster MA PhD DD (Systematic Theology)

Lecturers:

K.T. Aitken BD PhD (Hebrew Bible)
A.D. Clarke BA MA PhD (SL) (New Testament)
Rev. J.W. Drane MA PhD (SL) (Practical Theology)
S. Gathercole BA MA PhD (New Testament)
S. Kunin BA PhD (SL) (Anthropology of Religion)
I.A. McFarland BA MDiv ThM MPhil PhD (Systematic Theology)
Gabriele Marranci BA MA PhD (Religious Studies)
M.A. Mills MA PhD (Religious Studies)
F.A. Murphy BA MA PhD (R) (Systematic Theology)
E. Stoddart BD PhD (Practical Theology)
N.J. Thompson BA MA MTh PhD (Church History)
P. Williams MA MPhil PhD (New Testament)
Rev. Karla Wubbenhorst BA MDiv (Doctrine and Ethics)

ST ANDREWS

(University College of St Mary)
St Mary's College, St Andrews, Fife KY16 9JU
(Tel: 01334 462850/1;   Fax: 01334 462852)

Principal:	T.A. Hart BA PhD
Dean of Faculty:	M.I. Aguilar BA MA STB PhD
Acting Head of School:	M.I. Aguilar BA MA STB PhD
Chairs:	R.J. Bauckham BA MA PhD FBA (New Testament Studies)
	P.F. Esler BA LLB LLM DPhil (Biblical Criticism)

T.A. Hart BA PhD (Divinity)
R.A. Piper BA BD PhD (Christian Origins)
C.R. Seitz AB MTS MA MPhil PhD
    (Old Testament and Theological Studies)
A.J. Torrance* MA BD DrTheol (Systematic Theology)

Readerships, Senior Lectureships, Lectureships:

M.I. Aguilar BA MA STB PhD (SL) (Religion and Contextual Theology)
I.C. Bradley* BA MA BD DPhil (SL) (Practical Theology)
J.R. Davila BA MA PhD (Early Jewish Studies)
M. Elliott BA BD PhD (Church History)
S.R. Holmes BA MA MTh PGDip PhD (Theology)
B.W. Longenecker BA MRel PhD (New Testament)
E.D. Reed BA PhD (Theology and Ethics)
N. MacDonald MA MPhil (Old Testament and Hebrew)

Teaching Fellows and Research Fellows:

S.R. Guthrie BMus BD PhD (RF) (Institute of Theology, Imagination and the Arts)

EDINBURGH
(School of Divinity and New College)
New College, Mound Place, Edinburgh EH1 2LX
(Tel: 0131-650 8900; Fax: 0131-650 1952; E-mail: divinity.faculty@ed.ac.uk)

Head of School: Rev. Professor David A.S. Fergusson* MA BD DPhil FRSE
Principal of New College: Rev. A. Graeme Auld* MA BD PhD DLitt FSAScot

Chairs: Rev. A. Graeme Auld* MA BD PhD DLitt FSAScot
                              (Hebrew Bible)
                              Stewart J. Brown BA MA PhD FRHistS
                              (Ecclesiastical History)
                              Rev. David A.S. Fergusson* MA BD DPhil FRSE (Divinity)
                              Larry W. Hurtado BA MA PhD
                              (New Testament Language, Literature and Theology)
                              David Kerr MA BA DPhil
                              (Christianity in the Non-Western World)
                              Rev. William F. Storrar* MA BD PhD
                              (Christian Ethics and Practical Theology)
                              Nicolas Wyatt BA BD MTh PhD
                              (Ancient Near Eastern Religions)

Readers, Senior Lecturers and Lecturers:

Biblical Studies:	A. Peter Hayman BA PhD (SL)
	Timothy Lim BA MPhil DPhil (R)
	David J. Reimer BTh BA MA MA (SL)
	Graham Paul Foster PhD MSt BD
	Helen K. Bond MTheol PhD (SL)

Theology and Ethics:
Marcella Althaus Reid BTh PhD (SL)
Jolyon Mitchell BA MA (SL)
Michael S. Northcott MA PhD (R)
Murray Chalmers* MA (Part-time) (L)
Ewan Kelly* MB ChB BD (L)
Nicholas S. Adams BA PhD (L)
John C. McDowell BD PhD (L)
Michael Purcell MA PhD PhL PhB (SL)

Ecclesiastical History:
Jane E.A. Dawson BA PhD DipEd (SL)
Jack Thompson BA PhD (SL)
Susan Hardman Moore MA PhD (L)

Religious Studies:
James L. Cox BA MDiv PhD (R)
Jeanne Openshaw BA MA PhD (L)
Elizabeth Kopping MA PhD DipSocSci MTh (L)

Fulton Lecturer in Speech and Communication:
Richard Ellis BSc MEd LGSM

GLASGOW
(School of Divinity and Trinity College)
4 The Square, University of Glasgow, Glasgow G12 8QQ
(Tel: 0141-330 6526; Fax: 0141-330 4943; E-mail: divinity@arts.gla.ac.uk)

Head of School:	Rev. Professor David Jasper
Head of Department:	Dr Mona Siddiqui
Principal of Trinity College:	Rev. Professor George M. Newlands*

Chairs:
Rev. David Jasper MA PhD BD DD (Literature and Theology)
W. Ian P. Hazlett BA BD Dr theol DLitt (Ecclesiastical History)
Rev. Donald Macleod MA (Visiting Hon. Professor)
Rev. George M. Newlands* MA BD PhD (Divinity)
Rev. John K. Riches MA (Hon. Professor)
Perry Schmidt-Leukel Dipl theol MA Dr theol Dr theol habil
(Systematic Theology and Religious Studies)

Senior Lecturers and Lecturers: Theology and Religious Studies:
Julie P. Clague BSc PGCE PGDip MTh (L)
Rev. Alastair G. Hunter* MSc BD PhD (SL)
Louise Lawrence BA MA PhD (L)
Sarah Nicholson MTheol PhD (L)
Lesley Orr MA BD PhD (L)
Lloyd V.J. Ridgeon BA MA PhD (L)
Yvonne M. Sherwood BA PhD DipJS (SL)
Mona Siddiqui MA MLL PhD DLitt (SL)
Kyoshi Tsuchiya MA PhD (L)
Heather E. Walton BA MA(Econ) PhD (L)

Centre for Study of Literature, Theology and the Arts:
Director: Dr Yvonne M. Sherwood
Assistant Director: Dr Kyoshi Tsuchiya

Centre for Study of Islam:
Director: Dr Mona Siddiqui

---

(4) SOCIETIES AND ASSOCIATIONS

The undernoted list shows the name of the Association, along with the name and address of the Secretary.

INTER-CHURCH ASSOCIATIONS

THE FELLOWSHIP OF ST ANDREW: The fellowship promotes dialogue between churches of the east and the west in Scotland. Further information available from Mr Peter Desmond, 4 Ballengeich Road, Stirling FK8 1TN (Tel: 01786 479875).

THE FELLOWSHIP OF ST THOMAS: An ecumenical association formed to promote informed interest in and learn from the experience of Churches in South Asia (India, Pakistan, Bangladesh, Nepal, Sri Lanka). Secretary: Dr R.L. Robinson, 43 Underwood Road, Burnside, Rutherglen, Glasgow G73 3TE (Tel: 0141-643 0612; E-mail: robinson.burnside @surefish.co.uk).

THE SCOTTISH ORDER OF CHRISTIAN UNITY: Secretary: Rev. William D. Brown MA, 121 Dalkeith Road, Edinburgh EH16 5AJ (Tel/Fax: 0131-667 1124; E-mail: wdbrown@woolsackbc.fsnet.co.uk; Website: www.socu.org.uk).

CHURCH PASTORAL AID SOCIETY (CPAS): Consultant for Scotland: Rev. Richard W. Higginbottom, 2 Highfield Place, Bankfoot, Perth PH1 4AX (Tel: 01738 787429). A home mission agency working cross-denominationally through consultancy training and resources to encourage churches in local evangelism: accredited officially to the Board of National Mission.

FRONTIER YOUTH TRUST: Encourages and resources those engaged in youth work, particularly with disadvantaged young people. Co-ordinator: Feri Salvesen, c/o Anderson/ Kelvingrove Church, 759b Argyle Street, Glasgow G3 8DS (Tel: 0141-204 4800).

IONA COMMUNITY: Leader: Rev. Kathy Galloway, Fourth Floor, Savoy House, 140 Sauchiehall Street, Glasgow G2 3DH (Tel: 0141-332 6343; Fax: 0141-332 1090); Warden: Ms Jan Sutch Pickard, Iona Abbey, Isle of Iona, Argyll PA76 6SN (Tel: 01681 700404; E-mail: ionacomm@gla.iona.org.uk; Website: http://www.iona.org.uk).

SCOTTISH CHRISTIAN YOUTH ASSEMBLY: Chairperson: Mr Eric Whitten, 41 Kingston Avenue, Glasgow G14 0EB.

SCOTTISH CHURCHES HOUSING AGENCY: Provides the Churches with information, education, advice and support concerning homelessness. Co-ordinator: Alastair Cameron, 28 Albany Street, Edinburgh EH1 3QH (Tel: 0131-477 4500; Fax: 0131-477 2710; E-mail: scotchho@ednet.co.uk; Website: www.churches-housing.org).

WORLD EXCHANGE: Volunteers can help turn the world upside down, in Scotland and in the developing world. When it comes to making the world a better place, there are no limits to what's possible. Teachers, ministers, managers, accountants, joiners, engineers, musicians, artists and others are all invited to explore the possibility of working with World Exchange.
• Consultancies and work camps (4–6 weeks)
• Six-month 'gap' projects
• One-year programme (in Scotland or overseas)
Church-based community projects in Scotland, Africa, South Asia, Europe and the Caribbean (Tel: 0131-315 4444; Website: www.worldexchange.org.uk). Your potential is boundless. Now may be the time to unleash it.

ST COLM'S INTERNATIONAL HOUSE: English-language and Capacity Building Courses for community leaders from the developing world. A place to meet in the heart of the Capital on the perimeter of the Royal Botanic Gardens (Tel: 0131-315 4444).

SCOTTISH JOINT COMMITTEE ON RELIGIOUS AND MORAL EDUCATION: Ms Susan Leslie, 121 George Street, Edinburgh EH2 4YN (Tel: 0131-225 5722), and Mr Lachlan Bradley, 6 Clairmont Gardens, Glasgow G3 7LW (Tel: 0141-353 3595).

SCOTTISH NATIONAL COUNCIL OF YMCAs: National General Secretary: Mr Peter Crory, 11 Rutland Street, Edinburgh EH1 2AE (Tel: 0131-228 1464; E-mail: info@ymcascotland.org; Website: www.ymcascotland.org).

INTERSERVE SCOTLAND: Interserve is an evangelical and interdenominational mission agency with roots stretching back over 150 years to India. Currently, the International Fellowship of Interserve is active in twenty-six countries in the Middle East and Asia, where nearly 600 missionary partners serve, twenty-four of whom are from Scotland. Director: Mr John M. Jackson, 12 Elm Avenue, Lenzie, Glasgow G66 4HJ (Tel: 0141-578 0207; Fax: 0141-578 0208; E-mail: info@isscott.org; Website: www.interservescotland.org.uk).

SCRIPTURE UNION SCOTLAND: 70 Milton Street, Glasgow G4 0HR (Tel: 0141-332 1162; Fax: 0141-352 7600; E-mail: info@suscotland.org.uk; Website: http://www.suscotland.org.uk).

STUDENT CHRISTIAN MOVEMENT: Co-ordinator: Mrs Elinor Mensingh, SCM Office,

University of Birmingham, Wesley Park Road, Selly Oak, Birmingham B29 6LL (Tel: 0121-471 2404; E-mail: scm@movement.org.uk; Website: http://www.movement.org.uk). See also Christian Action and Thought.

CHRISTIAN ACTION AND THOUGHT (Edinburgh SCM): Mr Robert Beattie, CAT, Chaplaincy Centre, 1 Bristo Square, Edinburgh EH8 9AL (E-mail: robert.beattie@ed.ac.uk; Website: http://www.eusa.ed.ac.uk/societies/euscm).

UNIVERSITIES AND COLLEGES CHRISTIAN FELLOWSHIP: Alan Hewerdine, 38 De Montfort Street, Leicester LE1 7GP (Tel: 0116-255 1700; E-mail: agh@uccf.org.uk).

WORLD DAY OF PRAYER: SCOTTISH COMMITTEE: Convener: Col. Ruth Flett; 25 South View, Wick KW1 4PL. Secretaries: Mrs M. Broster (Tel: 07811 659929; E-mail: sec@wdpscotland.org.uk), Mrs M. Hannah, 8 Dovecot View, Kirkintilloch, Glasgow G66 3HY (Tel: 0141-776 1337; Website: http://www.wdpscotland.org.uk).

CHURCH OF SCOTLAND SOCIETIES

ASSOCIATION OF GENERAL ASSEMBLY AND PRESBYTERY CLERKS: Rev. R.A. Baigrie MA, 32 Inchcolm Terrace, South Queensferry EH30 9NA (Tel: 0131-331 4311).

AROS (Association of Returned Overseas Staff of the Church of Scotland Board of World Mission): Hon. Secretary: Miss Mary S. Ritchie, 1 Afton Bridgend, New Cumnock KA18 4AX (Tel: 01290 338218).

SCOTTISH CHURCH SOCIETY: Secretary: Rev. W. Gerald Jones MA BD MTh, The Manse, Kirkmichael, Maybole KA19 7PJ (Tel: 01655 750286).

SCOTTISH CHURCH THEOLOGY SOCIETY: Rev. Gordon R. Mackenzie BSc(Agr) BD, The Manse of Dyke, Brodie, Forres IV36 2TD (Tel: 01309 641239; E-mail: rev.g.mackenzie@btopenworld.com). The Society encourages theological exploration and discussion of the main issues confronting the Church in the twenty-first century.

SOCIETY OF FRIENDS OF ST ANDREW'S JERUSALEM: Hon. Secretary: Major D.J. McMicking LVO, Board of World Mission, 121 George Street, Edinburgh EH2 4YN. Hon. Treasurer: Mr Donald Ross, General Treasurer, The Church of Scotland, 121 George Street, Edinburgh EH2 4YN (Tel: 0131-225 5722).

THE CHURCH OF SCOTLAND CHAPLAINS' ASSOCIATION: Hon. Secretary: Rev. Donald M. Stephen TD MA BD ThM, 10 Hawkhead Crescent, Edinburgh EH16 6LR (Tel: 0131-658 1216).

THE CHURCH OF SCOTLAND RETIRED MINISTERS' ASSOCIATION: Hon. Secretary: Rev. Elspeth G. Dougall MA BD, 60B Craigmillar Park, Edinburgh EH16 5PU (Tel: 0131-668 1342).

THE CHURCH SERVICE SOCIETY: Secretary: Rev. Neil N. Gardner MA BD, Cambridge Street, Alyth, Blairgowrie PH11 8AW (Tel: 01828 632104).

THE IRISH MINISTERS' FRATERNAL: Secretary: Rev. Colin R. Williamson LLB BD, Manse of Aberdalgie, Perth PH2 0QD (Tel: 01738 625854).

THE NATIONAL CHURCH ASSOCIATION: Secretary: Miss Margaret P. Milne, 10 Balfron Crescent, Hamilton ML3 9UH.

BIBLE SOCIETIES

THE SCOTTISH BIBLE SOCIETY: Executive Director: Rev. M. Douglas Campbell BA MDiv, 7 Hampton Terrace, Edinburgh EH12 5XU (Tel: 0131-337 9701).

WEST OF SCOTLAND BIBLE SOCIETY: Rev. Alexander Macdonald MA BD, Manse of Neilston, Glasgow G78 3NP (Tel: 0141-881 1958; E-mail: alexmacdonald42@aol.com).

GENERAL

THE BOYS' BRIGADE: Scottish Headquarters, Carronvale House, Carronvale Road, Larbert FK5 3LH (Tel: 01324 562008; Fax: 01324 552323; E-mail: carronvale@boys-brigade.org.uk).

THE GIRLS' BRIGADE SCOTLAND: 11A Woodside Crescent, Glasgow G3 7UL (Tel: 0141-332 1765; E-mail: hq@girls-brigade-scotland.org.uk; Website: http://www.girls-brigade-scotland.org.uk)

GIRLGUIDING SCOTLAND: 16 Coates Crescent, Edinburgh EH3 7AH (Tel: 0131-226 4511; Fax: 0131-220 4828; E-mail: administrator@girlguiding-scot.org.uk).

THE SCOUT ASSOCIATION: Scottish Headquarters, Fordell Firs, Hillend, Dunfermline KY11 7HQ (Tel: 01383 419073; E-mail: shq@scouts-scotland.org.uk).

BOYS' AND GIRLS' CLUBS OF SCOTLAND: 88 Giles Street, Edinburgh EH6 6BZ (Tel: 0131-555 1729; E-mail: bgcs@freezone.co.uk).

YOUTH SCOTLAND: Balfour House, 19 Bonnington Grove, Edinburgh EH6 4BL (Tel: 0131-554 2561; Fax: 0131-454 3438; E-mail: office@youthscotland.org.uk).

CHRISTIAN AID SCOTLAND: National Secretary: Rev. John Wylie, 41 George IV Bridge, Edinburgh EH1 1EL (Tel: 0131-220 1254; Fax: 0131-225 8861).

FEED THE MINDS: Scottish Secretary, Mr Stanley Bonthron, 41 George IV Bridge, Edinburgh EH1 1EL (Tel: 0131-226 5254; Fax: 0131-225 8861; Home Tel: 0131-663 1458; E-mail: stanleybonthron@aol.com).

LADIES' GAELIC SCHOOLS AND HIGHLAND BURSARY ASSOCIATION: Mr Donald J. Macdonald, 9 Hatton Place, Edinburgh EH9 1UD (Tel: 0131-667 1740).

COUPLE COUNSELLING SCOTLAND: Chief Executive: Mrs Hilary Campbell, 18 York Place, Edinburgh EH1 3EP (Tel: 0131-558 9669; Fax: 0131-556 6596; E-mail: enquiries@couplecounselling.org.uk; Website: www.couplecounselling.org).

RUTHERFORD HOUSE: Warden: Rev. Robert Fyall MA BD PhD, 17 Claremont Park, Edinburgh EH6 7PJ (Tel: 0131-554 1206; Fax: 0131-555 1002).

SCOTTISH CHURCH HISTORY SOCIETY: Rev. Peter H. Donald MA PhD BD, 39 Southside Road, Inverness IV2 4XA (Tel: 01463 231140; Fax: 01463 230537).

SCOTTISH EVANGELICAL THEOLOGY SOCIETY: Secretary: Rev. Canon Peter Cook, Bel Abri, Leadgate, Alston, Cumbria CA9 3EL (Tel: 01434 381873).

CHRISTIAN ENDEAVOUR IN SCOTLAND: Winning, Teaching and Training Youngsters for Christ and the Church: The Murray Library, 8 Shore Street, Anstruther, Fife KY10 3EA (Tel: 01333 310345).

TEARFUND: 100 Church Road, Teddington TW11 8QE (Tel: 020 8977 9144). Manager: Peter Chirnside, Tearfund Scotland, Challenge House, Canal Street, Glasgow G4 0AD (Tel: 0141-332 3621).

THE LEPROSY MISSION: 89 Barnton Street, Stirling FK8 1HJ (Tel: 01786 449266; Fax 01786 449766). Executive Director: Miss Linda Todd. Scottish Meetings Co-ordinator: Rev. J.G. McConnell, 7 Henderson Court, East Calder EH53 0RQ (Tel: 01506 881125).

THE LORD'S DAY OBSERVANCE SOCIETY: Rev. A. Hanna, 2 The Gallolee, Edinburgh EH13 9QJ (Tel: 0131-441 3116).

THE MONTHLY VISITOR TRACT SOCIETY: 122 Thirlestane Road, Edinburgh EH9 1AN.

THE SCOTTISH REFORMATION SOCIETY: The Society, The Magdalen Chapel, 41 Cowgate, Edinburgh EH1 1JR (Tel: 0131-220 1450; E-mail: ashbethany43@hotmail.com; Website: www.scottishreformation.co.uk).

THE SOCIETY IN SCOTLAND FOR PROPAGATING CHRISTIAN KNOWLEDGE: David McLetchie Esq., Tods Murray WS, 66 Queen Street, Edinburgh EH2 4NE (Tel: 0131-226 4771).

THE WALDENSIAN MISSIONS AID SOCIETY FOR WORK IN ITALY: David A. Lamb SSC, 36 Liberton Drive, Edinburgh EH16 6NN (Tel: 0131-664 3059; E-mail: dlamb@dial.pipex.com.uk).

YWCA SCOTLAND: Chief Executive: Elaine Samson, 7B Randolph Crescent, Edinburgh EH3 7TH (Tel: 0131-225 7592; E-mail: info@ywcascotland.org; Website: http://www.ywcascotland.org).

(5) TRUSTS AND FUNDS

THE SOCIETY FOR THE BENEFIT OF THE SONS AND DAUGHTERS OF THE CLERGY OF THE CHURCH OF SCOTLAND

Chairman: Dr Douglas Grant
Secretary and Treasurer: R. Graeme Thom FCA
                                                   17 Melville Street
                                                   Edinburgh EH3 7PH (Tel: 0131-473 3500)

Annual grants are made to assist in the education of the children (normally between the ages of 12 and 25 years) of ministers of the Church of Scotland. The Society also gives grants to aged and infirm daughters of ministers and ministers' unmarried daughters and sisters who are in need. Applications are to be lodged by 31 May in each year.

THE GLASGOW SOCIETY OF THE SONS AND DAUGHTERS OF MINISTERS OF THE CHURCH OF SCOTLAND

President: Rev. John P. Cubie
Secretary and Treasurer: R. Graeme Thom FCA
                                                   17 Melville Street
                                                   Edinburgh EH3 7PH (Tel: 0131-473 3500)

The Society's primary purpose is to grant financial assistance to children (no matter what age) of deceased ministers of the Church of Scotland. Applications are to be submitted by 1 February in each year. To the extent that funds are available, grants are also given for the children of ministers or retired ministers, although such grants are normally restricted to students. These latter grants are considered in conjunction with the Edinburgh-based Society. Limited funds are also available for individual application for special needs or projects. Applications are to be submitted by 31 May in each year. Emergency applications can be dealt with at any time when need arises. Application forms may be obtained from the Secretary.

HOLIDAYS FOR MINISTERS

The undernoted hotels provide special terms for ministers and their families. Fuller information may be obtained from the establishments:

CRIEFF HYDRO HOTEL and MURRAYPARK HOTEL: The William Meikle Trust Fund and Paton Fund make provision whereby active ministers and their spouses, members of the Diaconate and other full-time Church workers may enjoy the accommodation and leisure facilities. Facilities available are Lagoon Leisure Centre, Cinema and over thirty-five activities and sports both indoor and out. Self-catering Chalets are also available. There is a registered children's club which provides expert supervised care. Enquiries to the Accommodation Sales Team, Crieff Hydro Hotel, Crieff PH7 3LQ (Tel: 01764 651670; E-mail: enquiries@crieffhydro.com).

THE CINTRA BEQUEST: The Trust provides financial assistance towards the cost of accommodation in Scotland for missionaries on leave, or for ministers on temporary holiday, or on rest. Applications should be made to Mrs J.S. Wilson, Solicitor, 121 George Street, Edinburgh EH2 4YN.

THE LYALL BEQUEST: Makes available the following benefits to ministers of the Church of Scotland:

1. A payment towards the cost of holiday accommodation at any hotel or guest house or self-catering accommodation in St Andrews will be paid to any minister and to his or her spouse at the rate of £10 per day each for a minimum stay of three days and a maximum stay of one week. Due to the number of applications which the Trustees now receive, an applicant will not be considered to be eligible if he or she has received a grant from the Bequest during the three years prior to the holiday for which application is made. Applications should be made prior to the holiday to the Secretaries.

2. Grants towards costs of sickness and convalescence so far as not covered by the National Health Service or otherwise may be available to applicants, who should apply to the Secretaries giving relevant details.

All communications should be addressed to Pagan Osborne, Solicitors, Secretaries to the Lyall Bequest, 106 South Street, St Andrews KY16 9QD (Tel: 01334 475001; E-mail: elcalderwood@pagan.co.uk).

MARGARET AND JOHN ROSS TRAVELLING FUND: Offers grants to ministers and their spouses for travelling and other expenses for trips to the Holy Land where the purpose is recuperation or relaxation. Applications should be made to the Secretary and Clerk, Church of Scotland Trust, 121 George Street, Edinburgh EH2 4YN (Tel: 0131-240 2222; E-mail: jhamilton@cofscotland.org.uk).

The undernoted represents a list of the more important trusts available for ministers, students and congregations. A brief indication is given of the trust purposes, but application should be made in each case to the person named for full particulars and forms of application.

THE ABERNETHY TRUST: Offers residential accommodation and outdoor activities for Youth Fellowships, Church family weekends, Bible Classes and so on at four outdoor centres in Scotland. Further details from the Executive Director, Abernethy Trust, Nethybridge PH25 3ED (Tel/Fax: 01479 821279; Website: www.abernethytrust.org.uk).

THE ARROL TRUST: The object of the Trust is 'to promote the benefit and advance the education of young people between the ages of 16 and 25 years who are physically or mentally disadvantaged or are in necessitous circumstances by assisting such persons to gain experience through education and training for their future careers through travel within or without the United Kingdom'. Further details and forms of application can be obtained from C.S. Kennedy WS, Lindsays WS, 11 Atholl Crescent, Edinburgh EH3 8HE (Tel: 0131-229 1212).

THE BAIRD TRUST: Assists in the building and repair of churches and halls, endows Parishes and generally assists the work of the Church of Scotland. Apply to Ronald D. Oakes CA ACMA, 182 Bath Street, Glasgow G2 4HG (Tel: 0141-332 0476; Fax: 0141-331 0874).

THE REV. ALEXANDER BARCLAY BEQUEST: Assists mother, daughter, sister or niece of deceased minister of the Church of Scotland who at the time of his death was acting as his housekeeper and who is in needy circumstances. Apply to Robert Hugh Allan LLB DipLP NP, Pomphreys, 79 Quarry Street, Hamilton ML3 7AG (Tel: 01698 891616).

BELLAHOUSTON BEQUEST FUND: Gives grants to Protestant evangelical denominations in the City of Glasgow and certain areas within five miles of the city boundary for building and repairing churches and halls and the promotion of religion. Apply to Mr John A.M. Cuthbert, Mitchells Roberton, 36 North Hanover Street, Glasgow G1 2AD.

BEQUEST FUND FOR MINISTERS: Assists ministers in outlying districts with manse furnishings, pastoral efficiency aids, educational or medical costs. Apply to A. Linda Parkhill CA, 60 Wellington Street, Glasgow G2 6HJ (Tel: 0141-226 4994).

CARNEGIE TRUST FOR THE UNIVERSITIES OF SCOTLAND: In cases of hardship, the Carnegie Trust is prepared to consider applications by students of Scottish birth or extraction (at least one parent born in Scotland), or who have had at least two years' education at a secondary school in Scotland, for financial assistance with the payment of their fees for a first degree at a Scottish university. For further details, students should apply to the Secretary, Carnegie Trust for the Universities of Scotland, Cameron House, Abbey Park Place, Dunfermline, Fife KY12 7PZ (Tel: 01383 622148; E-mail: jgray@carnegie-trust.org; Website: www.carnegie-trust.org).

CHURCH OF SCOTLAND INSURANCE CO. LTD: Undertakes insurance of Church property and pays surplus profits to Church schemes. The company can also arrange household insurance for members and adherents of the Church of Scotland. At 67 George Street, Edinburgh EH2 2JG (Tel: 0131-220 4119; Fax: 0131-220 4120; E-mail: enquiries@cosic.co.uk).

CHURCH OF SCOTLAND MINISTRY BENEVOLENT FUND: Makes grants to retired men and women who have been ordained or commissioned for the ministry of the Church of Scotland and to widows, widowers, orphans, spouses or children of such, who are in need. Apply to the General Secretary, Board of Ministry, 121 George Street, Edinburgh EH2 4YN (Tel: 0131-225 5722).

CLARK BURSARY: Awarded to accepted candidate(s) for the ministry of the Church of Scotland whose studies for the ministry are pursued at the University of Aberdeen. Applications or recommendations for the Bursary to the Clerk to the Presbytery of Aberdeen, Mastrick Church, Greenfern Road, Aberdeen AB16 6TR by 16 October annually.

THE REV. JOHN CLARK FUND: Provides annuities (1) for blind persons and (2) for orphan or fatherless children of ministers or missionaries of the Church of Scotland. Apply to Fyfe Ireland WS, Orchard Brae House, 30 Queensferry Road, Edinburgh EH4 2HG.

CRAIGCROOK MORTIFICATION:
Preses: Michael J.R. Simpson
Clerk and Factor: R. Graeme Thom FCA
                                     17 Melville Street
                                     Edinburgh EH3 7PH (Tel: 0131-473 3500)

Pensions are paid to poor men and women over 60 years old, born in Scotland or who have resided in Scotland for not less than ten years. At present, pensions amount to £600 p.a.
    Ministers are invited to notify the Clerk and Factor of deserving persons and should be prepared to act as a referee on the application form.

THE ALASTAIR CRERAR TRUST FOR SINGLE POOR: Provides churches, Christian organisations and individual Christians with grants to help single adults and groups of single people, who live on low incomes and have little capital, to improve their quality of life. Apply to the Secretary, Michael I.D. Sturrock, Garden Flat, 34 Mayfield Terrace, Edinburgh EH9 1RZ (Tel: 0131-668 3524).

CROMBIE SCHOLARSHIP: Provides grants annually on the nomination of the Deans of Faculty of Divinity of the Universities of St Andrews, Glasgow, Aberdeen and Edinburgh, who each nominate one matriculated student who has taken a University course in Greek (Classical or Hellenistic) and Hebrew. Award by recommendation only.

THE DRUMMOND TRUST: Makes grants towards the cost of publication of books of 'sound Christian doctrine and outreach'. The Trustees are willing to receive grant requests towards the cost of audio-visual programme material, but not equipment. Requests for application forms should be made to the Secretaries, Hill and Robb, 3 Pitt Terrace, Stirling FK8 2EY (Tel: 01786 450985; E-mail: douglaswhyte@hillandrobb.co.uk). Manuscripts should *not* be sent.

THE DUNCAN TRUST: Makes grants annually to students for the ministry in the Faculties of Arts and Divinity. Preference is given to those born or educated within the bounds of the former Presbytery of Arbroath. Applications not later than 31 October to G.J.M. Dunlop, Brothockbank House, Arbroath DD11 1NE (Tel: 01241 872683).

ESDAILE TRUST:
Chairman: Dr Douglas Grant
Clerk and Treasurer: R. Graeme Thom FCA
                                 17 Melville Street
                                 Edinburgh EH3 7PH (Tel: 0131-473 3500)
Assists education and advancement of daughters of ministers, missionaries and widowed deaconesses of the Church of Scotland between 12 and 25 years of age. Applications are to be lodged by 31 May in each year.

FERGUSON BEQUEST FUND: For the maintenance and promotion of religious ordinances and education and missionary operations in the first instance in the Counties of Ayr, Kirkcudbright, Wigtown, Lanark, Renfrew and Dunbarton. Apply to Ronald D. Oakes CA ACMA, 182 Bath Street, Glasgow G2 4HG (Tel: 0141-332 0476; Fax: 0141-331 0874).

GEIKIE BEQUEST: Makes small grants to students for the ministry, including students studying for entry to the University, preference being given to those not eligible for SAAS awards. Apply to the Accountant, Board of Ministry, 121 George Street, Edinburgh EH2 4YN.

JAMES GILLAN'S BURSARY FUND: Bursaries are available for students for the ministry who were born or whose parents or parent have resided and had their home for not less than three years continually in the old counties (not Districts) of Moray or Nairn. Apply to R. and R. Urquhart, 121 High Street, Forres IV36 0AB.

HALDANE TRUST FUND: Provides grants to ministers of the Church of Scotland on their first induction, towards the purchase of theological books. Apply to Bennett and Robertson LLP Solicitors, 25 George IV Bridge, Edinburgh EH1 1EP (Tel: 0131-225 4001).

HAMILTON BURSARY TRUST: Awarded, subject to the intention to serve overseas under the Church of Scotland Board of World Mission or to serve with some other Overseas Mission Agency approved by the Committee, to a student at the University of Aberdeen. Preference given to a student born or residing in (1) Parish of Skene, (2) Parish of Echt, (3) the Presbytery of Aberdeen, Kincardine and Deeside, or Gordon; failing which to Accepted Candidate(s) for the Ministry of the Church of Scotland whose studies for the Minstry are pursued at Aberdeen

University. Applications or recommendations for the Bursary to the Clerk to the Presbytery of Aberdeen by 16 October annually.

MARTIN HARCUS BEQUEST: Makes annual grants to candidates for the ministry resident within the City of Edinburgh. Applications to the Clerk to the Presbytery of Edinburgh, 10 Palmerston Place, Edinburgh EH12 5AA by 15 October.

THE HOGARTH FUND: Provides annuities to orphan or fatherless children of ministers and missionaries of the Church of Scotland. Apply to Fyfe Ireland WS, Orchard Brae House, 30 Queensferry Road, Edinburgh EH4 2HG.

THE HOPE TRUST: Gives some support to organisations involved in combating drink and drugs, and has as its main purpose the promotion of the Reformed Faith throughout the world. There is also a Scholarship programme for Postgraduate Theology Study in Scotland. Apply to Robert P. Miller SSC LLB, 31 Moray Place, Edinburgh EH3 6BY (Tel: 0131-226 5151).

GILLIAN MACLAINE BURSARY FUND: Open to candidates for the ministry of the Church of Scotland of Scottish or Canadian nationality. Preference is given to Gaelic-speakers. Bursaries are awarded after an examination which is held annually in November. Information and application forms from Rev. Jeffrey A. McCormick BD, The Manse, Ardchattan, Connel, Argyll PA37 1QZ (Tel: 01631 710364; E-mail: akph64@uk.uumail.com).

THE E. McLAREN FUND: The persons intended to be benefited are widows and unmarried ladies, preference being given to ladies above 40 years of age in the following order:
(a) Widows and daughters of Officers in the Highland Regiment, and
(b) Widows and daughters of Scotsmen.
Further details from the Secretary, The E. McLaren Fund, Apsley House, 29 Wellington Street, Glasgow G2 6JA (Tel: 0141-221 8004; Fax: 0141-221 9762; E-mail: rrs@bmkwilson.co.uk).

THE MISSES ANN AND MARGARET McMILLAN'S BEQUEST: Makes grants to ministers of the Free and United Free Churches, and of the Church of Scotland, in charges within the Synod of Argyll, with income not exceeding the minimum stipend of the Church of Scotland. Apply by 30 June in each year to Business Manager, Royal Bank of Scotland, 37 Victoria Street, Rothesay, Isle of Bute PA20 0AP.

THE MANSE AUXILIARY: Convener: Mrs Jean Baigrie, 32 Inchcolm Terrace, South Queensferry EH30 9NA (Tel: 0131-331 4311). Assists with clothing and household linen to parish ministers, missionaries, ministers' widows and others, especially those in remote areas. Enquiries to the Convener.

MORGAN BURSARY FUND: Makes grants to students for the ministry in Arts and Divinity at the University of Glasgow. Apply to Rev. David W. Lunan MA BD, 260 Bath Street, Glasgow G2 4JP (Tel/Fax: 0141-332 6606).

NOVUM TRUST: Provides small short-term grants to initiate projects in Christian research and action which cannot readily be financed from other sources. Special consideration is given to proposals aimed at the welfare of young people, the training of lay people, and new ways of communicating the faith. The Trust cannot support large building projects, nor can it support individuals applying for maintenance during courses or training. Applications to Rev. Alex M. Millar, 121 George Street, Edinburgh EH2 4YN (E-mail: amillar@cofscotland.org.uk).

PARK MEMORIAL BURSARY FUND: Provides grants for the benefit of Divinity students from the Presbytery of Glasgow who are nominated candidates under full-time training for the Ministry of the Church of Scotland. Apply to Rev. David W. Lunan MA BD, Presbytery of Glasgow, 260 Bath Street, Glasgow G2 4JP (Tel: 0141-332 6606).

PATON TRUST: Assists ministers in ill health to have a recuperative holiday outwith, and free from the cares of, their parishes. Apply to Iain A.T. Mowat CA, Alexander Sloan, Chartered Accountants, 144 West George Street, Glasgow G2 2HG (Tel: 0141-354 0354; Fax: 0141-354 0355; E-mail iatm@alexandersloan.co.uk).

RENFIELD STREET TRUST: Assists in the building and repair of churches and halls. Apply to Ronald D. Oakes CA ACMA, 182 Bath Street, Glasgow G2 4HG (Tel: 0141-332 0476; Fax: 0141-331 0874).

SCOTTISH CHURCHES ARCHITECTURAL HERITAGE TRUST: Assists congregations of any denomination in the preservation of churches regularly used for public worship and of architectural value and historic interest. Apply to the Secretary, 15 North Bank Street, The Mound, Edinburgh EH1 2LP (Tel/Fax: 0131-225 8644).

SMIETON FUND: Makes small holiday grants to ministers on the minimum stipend. Applications to the General Secretary, Board of Ministry, 121 George Street, Edinburgh EH2 4YN.

MARY DAVIDSON SMITH CLERICAL AND EDUCATIONAL FUND FOR ABERDEENSHIRE: Assists ministers who have been ordained for five years or over and are in full charge of a congregation in Aberdeen, Aberdeenshire and the north, to purchase books, or to travel for educational purposes, and assists their children with scholarships for further education or vocational training. Apply to Alan J. Innes MA LLB, 100 Union Street, Aberdeen AB10 1QR.

THE NAN STEVENSON CHARITABLE TRUST FOR RETIRED MINISTERS: Provides houses, or loans to purchase houses, for retired ministers or missionaries on similar terms to the Housing and Loan Fund, with preference given to those with a North Ayrshire connection. Secretary: Rev. Johnston R. McKay, Upper Burnfoot, 27 Stanlane Place, Largs KA30 8DD.

SYNOD OF ARGYLL BURSARY FUND: Provides book grants for candidates for the ministry of the Church of Scotland who are native to or have strong connections within the bounds of the former Synod of Argyll (i.e. the Presbyteries of Dunoon, Lorn and Mull and South Argyll). Applications should be made by 31 October to Rev. Jeffrey A. McCormick BD, The Manse, Ardchattan, Connel, Argyll PA37 1QZ (Tel: 01631 710364; E-mail: akph64@uk.uumail.com).

SYNOD OF GRAMPIAN CHILDREN OF THE CLERGY FUND: Makes annual grants to children of deceased ministers. Apply to Rev. Iain U. Thomson, Clerk and Treasurer, The Manse, Skene, Westhill AB32 6LX.

SYNOD OF GRAMPIAN WIDOWS FUND: Makes annual grants (currently £225 p.a.) to widows or widowers of deceased ministers who have served in a charge in the former Synod. Apply to Rev. Iain U. Thomson, Clerk and Treasurer, The Manse, Skene, Westhill AB32 6LX.

YOUNG MINISTERS' FURNISHING LOAN FUND: Makes loans (of £1,000) to ministers in their first charge to assist with furnishing the manse. Apply to the Accountant, Board of Ministry, 121 George Street, Edinburgh EH2 4YN.

(6) RECENT LORD HIGH COMMISSIONERS
TO THE GENERAL ASSEMBLY

1965/66	The Hon. Lord Birsay CBE QC TD
1967/68	The Rt Hon. Lord Reith of Stonehaven GCVO GBE CB TD
1969	Her Majesty the Queen attended in person
1970	The Rt Hon. Margaret Herbison PC
1971/72	The Rt Hon. Lord Clydesmuir of Braidwood CB MBE TD
1973/74	The Rt Hon. Lord Ballantrae of Auchairne and the Bay of Islands GCMG GCVO DSO OBE
1975/76	Sir Hector MacLennan KT FRCPGLAS FRCOG
1977	Francis David Charteris, Earl of Wemyss and March KT LLD
1978/79	The Rt Hon. William Ross MBE LLD
1980/81	Andrew Douglas Alexander Thomas Bruce, Earl of Elgin and Kincardine KT DL JP
1982/83	Colonel Sir John Edward Gilmour BT DSO TD
1984/85	Charles Hector Fitzroy Maclean, Baron Maclean of Duart and Morvern KT GCVO KBE
1986/87	John Campbell Arbuthnott, Viscount of Arbuthnott CBE DSC FRSE FRSA
1988/89	Sir Iain Mark Tennant KT FRSA
1990/91	The Rt Hon. Donald MacArthur Ross FRSE
1992/93	The Rt Hon. Lord Macfarlane of Bearsden
1994/95	Lady Marion Fraser
1996	Her Royal Highness the Princess Royal LG GCVO
1997	The Rt Hon. Lord Macfarlane of Bearsden
1998/99	The Rt Hon. Lord Hogg of Cumbernauld
2000	His Royal Highness the Prince Charles, Duke of Rothesay
2001/02	The Rt Hon. Viscount Younger of Leckie
2003/04	The Rt Hon. Lord Steel of Aikwood

(7) RECENT MODERATORS
OF THE GENERAL ASSEMBLY

1965	Archibald Watt STM DD, Edzell and Lethnot
1966	R. Leonard Small OBE DD, Edinburgh St Cuthbert's
1967	W. Roy Sanderson DD, Stenton with Whittingehame
1968	J.B. Longmuir TD DD, Principal Clerk of Assembly
1969	T.M. Murchison MA DD, Glasgow St Columba Summertown
1970	Hugh O. Douglas CBE DD LLD, Dundee St Mary's

1971	Andrew Herron MA BD LLB, Clerk to the Presbytery of Glasgow
1972	R.W.V. Selby Wright JP CVO TD DD FRSE, Edinburgh Canongate
1973	George T.H. Reid MC MA BD DD, Aberdeen Langstane
1974	David Steel MA BD DD, Linlithgow St Michael's
1975	James G. Matheson MA BD DD, Portree
1976	Thomas F. Torrance MBE DLitt DD FRSE, University of Edinburgh
1977	John R. Gray VRD MA BD ThM, Dunblane Cathedral
1978	Peter P. Brodie MA BD LLB DD, Alloa St Mungo's
1979	Robert A.S. Barbour MA BD STM DD, University of Aberdeen
1980	William B. Johnston MA BD DD, Edinburgh Colinton
1981	Andrew B. Doig BD STM DD, National Bible Society of Scotland
1982	John McIntyre CVO DD DLitt FRSE, University of Edinburgh
1983	J. Fraser McLuskey MC DD, London St Columba's
1984	John M.K. Paterson MA ACII BD, Milngavie St Paul's
1985	David M.B.A. Smith MA BD DUniv, Logie
1986	Robert Craig CBE DLitt LLD DD, Emeritus of Jerusalem
1987	Duncan Shaw *Bundesverdienstkreuz* PhD ThDr JP, Edinburgh Craigentinny St Christopher's
1988	James A. Whyte MA LLD, University of St Andrews
1989	William J.G. McDonald MA BD DD, Edinburgh Mayfield
1990	Robert Davidson MA BD DD FRSE, University of Glasgow
1991	William B.R. Macmillan MA BD LLD DD, Dundee St Mary's
1992	Hugh R. Wyllie MA MCIBS DD, Hamilton Old Parish Church
1993	James L. Weatherhead CBE MA LLB DD, Principal Clerk of Assembly
1994	James A. Simpson BSc BD STM DD, Dornoch Cathedral
1995	James Harkness CB OBE MA DD, Chaplain General (Emeritus)
1996	John H. McIndoe MA BD STM DD, London: St Columba's linked with Newcastle: St Andrew's
1997	Alexander McDonald BA CMIWSc DUniv, General Secretary, Department of Ministry
1998	Alan Main TD MA BD STM PhD, Professor of Practical Theology at Christ's College, University of Aberdeen
1999	John B. Cairns LTh LLB LLD DD, Dumbarton Riverside
2000	Andrew R.C. McLellan MA BD STM DD, Edinburgh St Andrew's and St George's
2001	John D. Miller BA BD DD, Glasgow Castlemilk East
2002	Finlay A.J. Macdonald MA BD PhD DD, Principal Clerk of Assembly
2003	Iain R. Torrance TD MA BD DPhil, Professor of Patristics and Christian Ethics at the University of Aberdeen and Master of Christ's College
2004	Alison Elliot OBE MA MSc PhD LLD

MATTER OF PRECEDENCE

The Lord High Commissioner to the General Assembly of the Church of Scotland (while the Assembly is sitting) ranks next to the Sovereign and the Duke of Edinburgh and before the rest of the Royal Family.

The Moderator of the General Assembly of the Church of Scotland ranks next to the Lord Chancellor of Great Britain and before the Prime Minister and the Dukes.

(8) HER MAJESTY'S HOUSEHOLD IN SCOTLAND
ECCLESIASTICAL

Dean of the Chapel Royal: Very Rev. James Harkness CB OBE MA DD

Dean of the Order of the Thistle: Very Rev. Gilleasbuig Macmillan
CVO MA BD Drhc DD

Domestic Chaplain: Rev. Robert P. Sloan MA BD

Chaplains in Ordinary:

Very Rev. Gilleasbuig Macmillan
CVO MA BD Drhc DD
Rev. Charles Robertson MA JP
Rev. Norman W. Drummond MA BD
Rev. John L. Paterson MA BD STM
Rev. Alastair H. Symington MA BD
Very Rev. John B. Cairns LTh LLB LLD DD
Very Rev. Prof. Iain R. Torrance TD MA BD DPhil
Very Rev. Finlay A.J. Macdonald
MA BD PhD DD
Rev. James M. Gibson TD LTh LRAM

Extra Chaplains:

Very Rev. W. Roy Sanderson DD
Very Rev. Prof. John McIntyre
CVO DD DLitt Drhc FRSE
Rev. H.W.M. Cant MA BD STM
Rev. Kenneth MacVicar MBE DFC TD MA
Very Rev. Prof. Robert A.S. Barbour
KCVO MC BD STM DD
Rev. Alwyn Macfarlane MA
Very Rev. William B. Johnston
MA BD DD DLitt
Rev. Mary I. Levison BA BD DD
Very Rev. William J. Morris KCVO PhD LLD DD JP
Rev. John MacLeod MA
Rev. A. Stewart Todd MA BD DD
Very Rev. James L. Weatherhead CBE MA LLB DD
Rev. Maxwell D. Craig MA BD ThM
Very Rev. James A. Simpson BSc BD STM DD

(9) LONG SERVICE CERTIFICATES

Long Service Certificates, signed by the Moderator, are available for presentation to elders and others in respect of not less than thirty years of service. It should be noted that the period is years of *service*, not (for example) years of ordination in the case of an elder.

In the case of Sunday School teachers and Bible Class leaders, the qualifying period is twenty-one years of service.

Certificates are not issued posthumously, nor is it possible to make exceptions to the rules, for example by recognising quality of service in order to reduce the qualifying period, or by reducing the qualifying period on compassionate grounds, such as serious illness.

A Certificate will be issued only once to any particular individual.

Applications for Long Service Certificates should be made in writing to the Principal Clerk at 121 George Street, Edinburgh EH2 4YN by the parish minister, or by the session clerk on behalf of the Kirk Session. Certificates are not issued from this office to the individual recipients, nor should individuals make application themselves.

(10) LIBRARIES OF THE CHURCH

GENERAL ASSEMBLY LIBRARY AND RECORD ROOM
Most of the books contained in the General Assembly Library have been transferred to the New College Library. Records of the General Assembly, Synods, Presbyteries and Kirk Sessions are now in HM Register House, Edinburgh.

CHURCH MUSIC
The Library of New College contains a selection of works on Church music.

(11) RECORDS OF THE CHURCH OF SCOTLAND

Church records more than fifty years old, unless still in use, should be sent or delivered to the Principal Clerk for onward transmission to the Scottish Record Office. Where ministers or session clerks are approached by a local repository seeking a transfer of their records, they should inform the Principal Clerk, who will take the matter up with the National Archives of Scotland.

Where a temporary retransmission of records is sought, it is extremely helpful if notice can be given three months in advance so that appropriate procedures can be carried out satisfactorily.

SECTION 3

Church Procedure

(1) THE MINISTER AND BAPTISM

The administration of Baptism to infants is governed by Act V 2000 as amended by Act IX 2003. A Statement and Exposition of the Doctrine of Baptism may be found at page 13/8 in the published volume of Reports to the General Assembly of 2003.

The Act itself is as follows:

3. Baptism signifies the action and love of God in Christ, through the Holy Spirit, and is a seal upon the gift of grace and the response of faith.
   (a) Baptism shall be administered in the name of the Father and of the Son and of the Holy Spirit, with water, by sprinkling, pouring, or immersion.
   (b) Baptism shall be administered to a person only once.
4. Baptism may be administered to a person upon profession of faith.
   (a) The minister and Kirk Session shall judge whether the person is of sufficient maturity to make personal profession of faith, where necessary in consultation with the parent(s) or legal guardian(s).
   (b) Baptism may be administered only after the person has received such instruction in its meaning as the minister and Kirk Session consider necessary, according to such basis of instruction as may be authorised by the General Assembly.
   (c) In cases of uncertainty as to whether a person has been baptised or validly baptised, baptism shall be administered conditionally.
5. Baptism may be administered to a person with learning difficulties who makes an appropriate profession of faith, where the minister and Kirk Session are satisfied that the person shall be nurtured within the life and worship of the Church.
6. Baptism may be administered to a child:
   (a) where at least one parent, or other family member (with parental consent), having been baptised and being on the communion roll of the congregation, will undertake the Christian upbringing of the child;
   (b) where at least one parent, or other family member (with parental consent), having been baptised but not on the communion roll of the congregation, satisfies the minister and Kirk Session that he or she is an adherent of the congregation and will undertake the Christian upbringing of the child;
   (c) where at least one parent, or other family member (with parental consent), having been baptised, professes the Christian faith, undertakes to ensure that the child grows up in the life and worship of the Church and expresses the desire to seek admission to the communion roll of the congregation;
   (d) where the child is under legal guardianship, and the minister and Kirk Session are satisfied that the child shall be nurtured within the life and worship of the congregation;
   and, in each of the above cases, only after the parent(s), or other family member, has received such instruction in its meaning as the minister and Kirk Session consider necessary, according to such basis of instruction as may be authorised by the General Assembly.
7. Baptism shall normally be administered during the public worship of the congregation in which the person makes profession of faith, or of which the parent or other family member is on the communion roll, or is an adherent. In exceptional circumstances, baptism may be administered elsewhere (e.g. at home or in hospital). Further, a minister may administer baptism to a person resident outwith the minister's parish, and who is not otherwise connected with the congregation, only with the consent of the minister of the parish in

which the person would normally reside, or of the Presbytery.

8. In all cases, an entry shall be made in the Kirk Session's Baptismal Register and a Certificate of Baptism given by the minister. Where baptism is administered in a chaplaincy context, it shall be recorded in the Baptismal Register there, and, where possible, reported to the minister of the parish in which the person resides.

9. Baptism shall normally be administered by an ordained minister. In situations of emergency,
    (a) a minister may, exceptionally, notwithstanding the preceding provisions of the Act, respond to a request for baptism in accordance with his or her pastoral judgement, and
    (b) baptism may be validly administered by a person who is not ordained, always providing that it is administered in the name of the Father and of the Son and of the Holy Spirit, with water.
    In every occurrence of the latter case, of which a minister or chaplain becomes aware, an entry shall be made in the appropriate Baptismal Register and where possible reported to the Clerk of the Presbytery within which the baptism was administered.

10. Each Presbytery shall form, or designate, a committee to which reference may be made in cases where there is a dispute as to the interpretation of this Act. Without the consent of the Presbytery, no minister may administer baptism in a case where to his or her knowledge another minister has declined to do so.

11. The Church of Scotland, as part of the Universal Church, affirms the validity of the sacrament of baptism administered in the name of the Father and of the Son and of the Holy Spirit, with water, in accordance with the discipline of other members of the Universal Church.

---

(2) THE MINISTER AND MARRIAGE

1. BACKGROUND

Prior to 1939, every marriage in Scotland fell into one or other of two classes: regular or irregular. The former was marriage by a minister of religion after due notice of intention had been given; the latter could be effected in one of three ways: (1) declaration *de presenti*, (2) by promise *subsequente copula*, or (3) by habit and repute.

The Marriage (Scotland) Act of 1939 put an end to (1) and (2) and provided for a new classification of marriage as either religious or civil.

The law of marriage as it was thus established in 1939 had two important limitations to the celebration of marriage: (1) certain preliminaries had to be observed; and (2) in respect of religious marriage, the service had to be conducted according to the forms of either the Christian or the Jewish faith.

2. THE MARRIAGE (SCOTLAND) ACT 1977

These two conditions were radically altered by the Marriage (Scotland) Act 1977.

Since 1 January 1978, in conformity with the demands of a multi-racial society, the benefits of religious marriage have been extended to adherents of other faiths, the only requirements being the observance of monogamy and the satisfaction of the authorities with the forms of the vows imposed.

Since 1978, the calling of banns has also been discontinued. The couple themselves must each complete a Marriage Notice form and return this to the District Registrar for the area in which they are to be married, irrespective of where they live, at least fifteen days before the ceremony is due to take place. The form details the documents which require to be produced with it.

If everything is in order, the District Registrar will issue, not more than seven days before the date of the ceremony, a Marriage Schedule. This must be in the hands of the minister officiating at the marriage ceremony before the service begins. Under no circumstances must the minister deviate from this rule. To do so is an offence under the Act.

Ministers should note the advice given by the Procurator of the Church in 1962, that they should not officiate at any marriage until at least one day after the 16th birthday of the younger party.

3. THE MARRIAGE (SCOTLAND) ACT 2002

Although there have never been any limitations as to the place where a religious marriage can be celebrated, civil marriage can take place only in the Office of a Registrar. The Marriage (Scotland) Act 2002, when it comes into effect, will, however, permit the solemnisation of civil marriages at places approved by Local Authorities. Regulations are to be made to specify the kinds of place which may be 'approved' with a view to ensuring that the places approved will not compromise the solemnity and dignity of civil marriage and will have no recent or continuing connection with any religion so as to undermine the distinction between religious and civil ceremonies.

4. PROCLAMATION OF BANNS

Proclamation of banns is no longer required in Scotland; but, in the Church of England, marriage is governed by the provisions of the Marriage Act 1949, which requires that the parties' intention to marry has to have been proclaimed and which provides that in the case of a party residing in Scotland a Certificate of Proclamation given according to the law or custom prevailing in Scotland shall be sufficient for the purpose. In the event that a minister is asked to call banns for a person resident within the registration district where his or her church is situated, the proclamation needs only to be made on one Sunday if the parties are known to the minister. If they are not, it should be made on two Sundays. In all cases, the Minister should, of course, have no reason to believe that there is any impediment to the marriage.

Proclamation should be made at the principal service of worship in this form:

There is a purpose of marriage between AB (Bachelor/Widower/Divorced), residing at .... in this Registration District, and CD (Spinster/Widow/Divorced), residing at .... in the Registration District of ...., of which proclamation is hereby made for the first and only (second and last) time.

Immediately after the second reading, or not less than forty-eight hours after the first and only reading, a Certificate of Proclamation signed by either the minister or the Session Clerk should be issued in the following terms:

At .... the ...... day of ...... 20 ....
It is hereby certified that AB, residing at ...., and CD, residing at ...., have been duly proclaimed in order to marriage in the Church of .... according to the custom of the Church of Scotland, and that no objections have been offered.
Signed .... minister or
Signed .... Session Clerk

5. MARRIAGE OF FOREIGNERS

Marriages in Scotland of foreigners, or of foreigners with British subjects, are, if they satisfy the requirements of Scots Law, valid within the United Kingdom and the various British overseas territories; but they will not necessarily be valid in the country to which the foreigner belongs. This will be so only if the requirements of the law of his or her country have also been complied with. It is therefore most important that, before the marriage, steps should be taken to obtain from the Consul, or other diplomatic representative of the country concerned, a satisfactory assurance that the marriage will be accepted as valid in the country concerned.

6. REMARRIAGE OF DIVORCED PERSONS

By virtue of Act XXVI 1959, a minister of the Church of Scotland may lawfully solemnise the marriage of a person whose former marriage has been dissolved by divorce and whose former spouse is still alive. The minister, however, must carefully adhere to the requirements of the Act which, as slightly altered in 1985, are briefly as follows:

1. The minister should not accede as a matter of routine to a request to solemnise such a marriage. To enable a decision to be made, he or she should take all reasonable steps to obtain relevant information, which should normally include the following:
   (a) Adequate information concerning the life and character of the parties. The Act enjoins the greatest caution in cases where no pastoral relationship exists between the minister and either or both of the parties concerned.
   (b) The grounds and circumstances of the divorce case.
   (c) Facts bearing upon the future well-being of any children concerned.
   (d) Whether any other minister has declined to solemnise the proposed marriage.
   (e) The denomination to which the parties belong. The Act enjoins that special care should be taken where one or more parties belong to a denomination whose discipline in this matter may differ from that of the Church of Scotland.
2. The minister should consider whether there is danger of scandal arising if he or she should solemnise the remarriage, at the same time taking into careful consideration before refusing to do so the moral and spiritual effect of a refusal on the parties concerned.
3. As a determinative factor, the minister should do all he or she can to be assured that there has been sincere repentance where guilt has existed on the part of any divorced person seeking remarriage. He or she should also give instruction, where needed, in the nature and requirements of a Christian marriage.
4. A minister is not required to solemnise a remarriage against his or her conscience. Every Presbytery is required to appoint certain individuals with one of whom ministers in doubt as to the correct course of action may consult if they so desire. The final decision, however, rests with the minister who has been asked to officiate.

---

(3) CONDUCT OF MARRIAGE SERVICES
(CODE OF GOOD PRACTICE)

The code which follows was submitted to the General Assembly in 1997. It appears, on page 1/10, in the Volume of Assembly Reports for that year within the Report of the Board of Practice and Procedure.

1. *Marriage in the Church of Scotland is solemnised by an ordained minister in a religious ceremony wherein, before God, and in the presence of the minister and at least two competent witnesses, the parties covenant together to take each other as husband and wife as long as they both shall live, and the minister declares the parties to be husband and wife. Before solemnising a marriage, a minister must be assured that the necessary legal requirements are being complied with and that the parties know of no legal impediment to their marriage, and he or she must afterwards ensure that the Marriage Schedule is duly completed.* (Act I 1977)

2. Any ordained minister of the Church of Scotland who is a member of Presbytery or who holds a current Ministerial Certificate may officiate at a marriage service (see Act II 1987).

3. While the marriage service should normally take place in church, a minister may, at his or her discretion, officiate at a marriage service outwith church premises. Wherever conducted, the ceremony will be such as to reflect appropriately both the joy and the solemnity of the occasion. In particular, a minister shall ensure that nothing is done which would bring the Church and its teaching into disrepute.

4. A minister agreeing to conduct a wedding should endeavour to establish a pastoral relationship with the couple within which adequate pre-marriage preparation and subsequent pastoral care may be given.

5. 'A minister should not refuse to perform ministerial functions for a person who is resident in his or her parish without sufficient reason' (Cox, *Practice and Procedure in the Church of Scotland*, sixth edition, page 55). Where either party to the proposed marriage has been divorced and the former spouse is still alive, the minister invited to officiate may solemnise such a marriage, having regard to the guidelines in the Act anent the Remarriage of Divorced Persons (Act XXVI 1959 as amended by Act II 1985).

6. A minister is acting as an agent of the National Church which is committed to bringing the ordinances of religion to the people of Scotland through a territorial ministry. As such, he or she shall not be entitled to charge a fee or allow a fee to be charged for conducting a marriage service. When a gift is spontaneously offered to a minister as a token of appreciation, the above consideration should not be taken to mean that he or she should not accept such an unsolicited gift. The Financial Board of a congregation is at liberty to set fees to cover such costs as heat and light, and in addition Organists and Church Officers are entitled to a fee in respect of their services at weddings.

7. A minister should not allow his or her name to be associated with any commercial enterprise that provides facilities for weddings.

8. A minister is not at liberty to enter the bounds of another minister's parish to perform ministerial functions without the previous consent of the minister of that parish. In terms of Act VIII 1933, a minister may 'officiate at a marriage or funeral by private invitation', but, for the avoidance of doubt, an invitation conveyed through a commercial enterprise shall not be regarded as a 'private invitation' within the meaning of that Act.

9. A minister invited to officiate at a Marriage Service where neither party is a member of his or her congregation or is resident within his or her own parish or has any connection with the parish within which the service is to take place should observe the following courtesies:
   (a) he or she should ascertain from the parties whether either of them has a Church of Scotland connection or has approached the appropriate parish minister(s);
   (b) if it transpires that a ministerial colleague has declined to officiate, then he or she (the invited minister) should ascertain the reasons therefor and shall take these and all other relevant factors into account in deciding whether or not to officiate.

(4) THE MINISTER AND WILLS

The Requirements of Writing (Scotland) Act 1995, which came into force on 1 August 1995, has removed the power of a minister to execute wills notarially. Further clarification, if required, may be obtained from the Solicitor of the Church.

(5) PROCEDURE IN A VACANCY

Procedure in a vacancy is regulated by Acts VII and VIII 2003. The text of the most immediately relevant sections is given here for general information. Schedules of Intimation referred to are also included. The full text of both Acts can be obtained from the Principal Clerk.

1. Vacancy Procedure Committee
(1)   Each Presbytery shall appoint a number of its members to be available to serve on Vacancy Procedure Committees and shall provide information and training as required for those so appointed.
(2)   As soon as the Presbytery Clerk is aware that a vacancy has arisen or is anticipated, he or she shall consult the Moderator of the Presbytery and they shall appoint a Vacancy Procedure Committee of five persons from among those appointed in terms of subsection (1), which Committee shall (a) include at least one minister and at least one elder and (b) exclude any communicant member or former minister of the vacant charge or of any constituent congregation thereof. The Vacancy Procedure Committee shall include a Convener and Clerk, the latter of whom need not be a member of the Committee but may be the Presbytery Clerk. The same Vacancy Procedure Committee may serve for more than one vacancy at a time.
(3)   The Vacancy Procedure Committee shall have a quorum of three for its meetings.
(4)   The Convener of the Vacancy Procedure Committee may, where he or she reasonably believes a matter to be non-contentious, consult members individually, provided that reasonable efforts are made to consult all members of the Committee. A meeting shall be held at the request of any member of the Committee.
(5)   Every decision made by the Vacancy Procedure Committee shall be reported to the next meeting of Presbytery, but may not be recalled by Presbytery where the decision was subject to the provisions of section 2 below.

2. Request for Consideration by Presbytery
Where in this Act any decision by the Vacancy Procedure Committee is subject to the provisions of this section, the following rules shall apply:
(1)   The Presbytery Clerk shall intimate to all members of the Presbytery by mailing or at a Presbytery meeting the course of action or permission proposed, and shall arrange for one Sunday's pulpit intimation of the same to be made to the congregation or congregations concerned, in terms of Schedule A. The intimation having been made, it shall be displayed as prominently as possible at the church building for seven days.
(2)   Any four individuals, being communicant members of the congregation or full members of

the Presbytery, may give written notice requesting that action be taken in terms of subsection (3) below, giving reasons for the request, within seven days after the pulpit intimation.

(3)   Upon receiving notice in terms of subsection (2), the Presbytery Clerk shall sist the process or permission referred to in subsection (1), which shall then require the approval of the Presbytery.

(4)   The Moderator of the Presbytery shall in such circumstances consider whether a meeting *pro re nata* of the Presbytery should be called in order to avoid prejudicial delay in the vacancy process.

(5)   The Presbytery Clerk shall cause to have served upon the congregation or congregations an edict in terms of Schedule B citing them to attend the meeting of Presbytery for their interest.

(6)   The consideration by Presbytery of any matter under this section shall not constitute an appeal or a Petition, and the decision of Presbytery shall be deemed to be a decision at first instance subject to the normal rights of appeal or dissent-and-complaint.

3. Causes of Vacancy

The causes of vacancy shall normally include:

(a)   the death of the minister of the charge;

(b)   the removal of status of the minister of the charge or the suspension of the minister in terms of section 20(2) of Act III 2001;

(c)   the dissolution of the pastoral tie in terms of Act I 1988 or Act XV 2002;

(d)   the demission of the charge and/or status of the minister of the charge;

(e)   the translation of the minister of the charge to another charge;

(f)   the termination of the tenure of the minister of the charge in terms of Act VI 1984.

4. Release of Departing Minister

The Presbytery Clerk shall be informed as soon as circumstances have occurred that cause a vacancy to arise or make it likely that a vacancy shall arise. Where the circumstances pertain to section 3(d) or (e) above, the Vacancy Procedure Committee shall

(1)   except in cases governed by subsection (2) below, decide whether to release the minister from his or her charge and, in any case involving translation to another charge or introduction to an appointment, instruct him or her to await the instructions of the Presbytery or another Presbytery;

(2)   in the case of a minister in the first five years of his or her first charge, decide whether there are exceptional circumstances to justify releasing him or her from his or her charge and proceeding in terms of subsection (1) above;

(3)   determine whether a vacancy has arisen or is anticipated and, as soon as possible, determine the date upon which the charge becomes actually vacant, and

(4)   inform the congregation or congregations by one Sunday's pulpit intimation as soon as convenient;

(5)   The provisions of section 2 above shall apply to the decisions of the Vacancy Procedure Committee in terms of subsections (1) and (2) above.

5. Demission of Charge

(1)   Subject to the provisions of subsection (2) below, when a vacancy has occurred in terms of section 3(c), (d) or (f) above, the Presbytery shall determine whether the minister is, in the circumstances, entitled to a seat in the Presbytery in terms of section 16 of Act III 2000 (as amended).

(2)   In the case where it is a condition of any basis of adjustment that a minister shall demit his

or her charge to facilitate union or linking, and the minister has agreed in writing in terms of the appropriate regulations governing adjustments, formal application shall not be made to the Presbytery for permission to demit. The minister concerned shall be regarded as retiring in the interest of adjustment, and he or she shall retain a seat in Presbytery unless in terms of Act III 2000 (as amended) he or she elects to resign it.

(3)   A minister who demits his or her charge without retaining a seat in the Presbytery shall, if he or she retains status as a minister, be subject to the provisions of sections 5 to 15 of Act II 2000 (as amended).

6. Appointment of Interim Moderator
At the same time as the Vacancy Procedure Committee makes a decision in terms of section 4 above, or where circumstances pertain to section 3(a), (b), (c) or (f) above, the Vacancy Procedure Committee shall appoint an Interim Moderator for the charge and make intimation thereof to the congregation subject to the provisions of section 2 above. The Interim Moderator shall be either a ministerial member of the Presbytery in terms of Act III 2000 or Act V 2001 or a member of the Presbytery selected from a list of those who have received such preparation for the task as the Board of Ministry shall from time to time recommend or provide, and he or she shall not be a member in the vacant charge nor a member of the Vacancy Procedure Committee. The name of the Interim Moderator shall be forwarded to the Board of Ministry.

7. Duties of Interim Moderator
(1)   It shall be the duty of the Interim Moderator to preside at all meetings of the Kirk Session (or of the Kirk Sessions in the case of a linked charge) and to preside at all congregational meetings in connection with the vacancy, or at which the minister would have presided had the charge been full. In the case of a congregational meeting called by the Presbytery in connection with adjustment, the Interim Moderator, having constituted the meeting, shall relinquish the chair in favour of the representative of the Presbytery, but he or she shall be at liberty to speak at such a meeting. In consultation with the Kirk Session and the Financial Court, he or she shall make arrangements for the supply of the vacant pulpit.

(2)   The Interim Moderator appointed in a prospective vacancy may call and preside at meetings of the Kirk Session and of the congregation for the transaction of business relating to the said prospective vacancy. He or she shall be associated with the minister until the date of the actual vacancy; after that date, he or she shall take full charge.

(3)   The Interim Moderator shall act as an assessor to the Nominating Committee, being available to offer guidance and advice. If the Committee so desire, he or she may act as their Convener, but in no case shall he or she have a vote.

(4)   In the event of the absence of the Interim Moderator, the Vacancy Procedure Committee shall appoint a member of the Presbytery who is not a member of the vacant congregation to fulfil any of the rights and duties of the Interim Moderator in terms of this section.

(5)   The Interim Moderator shall have the same duties and responsibilities towards all members of ministry teams referred to in section 16 of Act VII 2003 anent Appraisal and Adjustment as if he or she were the parish minister, both in terms of this Act and in respect of the terms and conditions of such individuals.

8. Permission to Call
When the decision to release the minister from the charge has been made and the Interim Moderator appointed, the Vacancy Procedure Committee shall consider whether it may give permission to call a minister in terms of Act VII 2003, and may proceed subject to the provisions of section 2 above. The Vacancy Procedure Committee must refer the question of permission to call to the Presbytery if:

(a)   shortfalls exist which in the opinion of the Committee require consideration in terms of section 9 hereunder;

(b)   the Committee has reason to believe that the vacancy schedule referred to in section 10 below will not be approved;

(c)   the Committee has reason to believe that the Presbytery will, in terms of section 11 below, instruct work to be carried out on the manse before a call can be sustained, and judges that the likely extent of such work warrants a delay in the granting of permission to call, or

(d)   the Committee has reason to believe that the Presbytery may wish to delay or refuse the granting of permission for any reason.

Any decision by Presbytery to refuse permission to call shall be subject to appeal or dissent-and-complaint.

9. Shortfalls

(1)   As soon as possible after intimation of a vacancy or anticipated vacancy reaches the Presbytery Clerk, the Presbytery shall ascertain whether the charge has current or accumulated shortfalls in contributions to central funds, and shall determine whether and to what extent any shortfalls that exist are justified.

(2)   If the vacancy is in a charge in which the Presbytery has determined that shortfalls are to any extent unjustified, it shall not resolve to allow a call of any kind until:

(a)   the shortfalls have been met to the extent to which the Presbytery determined that they were unjustified, or

(b)   a scheme for the payment of the unjustified shortfall has been agreed between the congregation and the Presbytery and receives the concurrence of the Board of Ministry and/or the Board of Stewardship and Finance for their respective interests, or

(c)   a fresh appraisal of the charge in terms of Act VII 2003 has been carried out, regardless of the status of the charge in the current Presbytery plan:

   (i)   During such appraisal, no further steps may be taken in respect of filling the vacancy, and the Presbytery shall make final determination of what constitutes such steps.

   (ii)   Following such appraisal and any consequent adjustment or deferred adjustment, the shortfalls shall be met or declared justifiable or a scheme shall be agreed in terms of subsection (b) above; the Presbytery shall inform the Board of Ministry and the Board of Stewardship and Finance of its decisions in terms of this section; and the Presbytery shall remove the suspension-of-vacancy process referred to in sub-paragraph (i).

10. Vacancy Schedule

(1)   When in terms of sections 4 and 6 above the decision to release the minister from the charge has been made and the Interim Moderator appointed, there shall be issued by the Board of Ministry a Schedule or Schedules for completion by the responsible Financial Board(s) of the vacant congregation(s) in consultation with representatives of the Presbytery, setting forth the proposed arrangements for stipend and payment of ministerial expenses and for provision of a manse, and showing the amount of aid, if any, to be given to, or to be received from, the Minimum Stipend Fund, with details of any endowment income. The Schedule, along with an extract minute from each relevant Kirk Session containing a commitment fully and adequately to support a new ministry, shall be forwarded to the Presbytery Clerk.

(2)   The Schedule shall be considered by the Vacancy Procedure Committee and, if approved, transmitted to the Board of Ministry by the Presbytery Clerk. The Vacancy Procedure Committee or Presbytery must not sustain an appointment and call until the Schedule has been approved by them and by the Board of Ministry, which shall intimate its decision within six weeks of receiving the schedule from the Presbytery.

(3)   The accuracy of the Vacancy Schedule shall be kept under review by the Vacancy Procedure Committee.

(4)   The provisions of section 2 above shall apply to the decisions of the Vacancy Procedure Committee.

11. Manse

As soon as possible after the Manse becomes vacant, the Presbytery Property Committee shall inspect the Manse and come to a view on what work, if any, must be carried out to render it suitable for a new incumbent. The views of the Property Committee should then be communicated to the Presbytery which should, subject to any modifications which might be agreed by that Court, instruct the Financial Board of the congregation to have the work carried out. No induction date shall be fixed until the Presbytery Property Committee has again inspected the Manse and confirmed that the work has been undertaken satisfactorily.

12. Advisory Committee

(1)   As soon as possible after intimation of a vacancy or anticipated vacancy reaches the Presbytery Clerk, the Vacancy Procedure Committee shall appoint an Advisory Committee of three, subject to the following conditions:

(a)   at least one member shall be an elder and at least one shall be a minister;

(b)   the Advisory Committee shall contain no more than two members of the Vacancy Procedure Committee;

(c)   the Advisory Committee may contain individuals who are not members of the Presbytery;

(d)   the appointment shall be subject to section 2 above.

(2)   The Advisory Committee shall meet:

(a)   before the election of the Nominating Committee, with the Kirk Session, or Kirk Sessions both separately and together, of the vacant charge to consider together in the light of the whole circumstances of the parish or parishes, what kind of ministry would be best suited to their needs;

(b)   with the Nominating Committee before it has taken any steps to fill the vacancy, to consider how it should proceed;

(c)   with the Nominating Committee before it reports to the Kirk Session and Presbytery the identity of the nominee, to review the process followed and give any further advice it deems necessary;

(d)   with the Nominating Committee at any other time by request of either the Nominating Committee or the Advisory Committee.

In the case of charges which are in the opinion of the Presbytery remote, it will be adequate if the Interim Moderator (accompanied if possible by a member of the Nominating Committee) meets with the Advisory Committee for the purposes listed in paragraphs (a) to (c) above.

13. Electoral Register

(1) It shall be the duty of the Kirk Session of a vacant congregation to proceed to make up the Electoral Register of the congregation. This shall contain (1) as communicants the names of those persons (a) whose names are on the communion roll of the congregation as at the date on which it is made up and who are not under Church discipline, (b) whose names have been added or restored to the communion roll on revision by the Kirk Session subsequently to the occurrence of the vacancy, and (c) who have given in valid Certificates of Transference by the date specified in terms of Schedule C hereto; and (2) as adherents the names of those persons who, being parishioners or regular worshippers in the congregation at the date when the vacancy occurred, being at least 18 years of age, and not being members of any other congregation, have claimed (in writing in the form prescribed in Schedule D and within the time specified in Schedule C) to be placed on the Electoral Register, the Kirk Session being satisfied that they desire to be permanently connected with the congregation and knowing of no adequate reasons why they should not be admitted as communicants should they so apply.

(2) At a meeting to be held not later than fourteen days after intimation has been made in terms of Schedule C hereto, the Kirk Session shall decide on the claims of persons to be placed on the Electoral Register, such claims to be sent to the Session Clerk before the meeting. At this meeting, the Kirk Session may hear parties claiming to have an interest. The Kirk Session shall thereupon prepare the lists of names and addresses of communicants and of adherents which it is proposed shall be the Electoral Register of the congregation, the names being arranged in alphabetical order and numbered consecutively throughout. The decision of the Kirk Session in respect of any matter affecting the preparation of the Electoral Register shall be final.

(3) The proposed Electoral Register having been prepared, the Interim Moderator shall cause intimation to be made on the first convenient Sunday in terms of Schedule E hereto that on that day an opportunity will be given for inspecting the Register after service, and that it will lie for inspection at such times and such places as the Kirk Session shall have determined; and further shall specify a day when the Kirk Session will meet to hear parties claiming an interest and will finally revise and adjust the Register. At this meeting, the list, having been revised, numbered and adjusted, shall on the authority of the court be attested by the Interim Moderator and the Clerk as the Electoral Register of the congregation.

(4) This Register, along with a duplicate copy, shall without delay be transmitted to the Presbytery Clerk, who, in name of the Presbytery, shall attest and return the principal copy, retaining the duplicate copy in his or her own possession. For all purposes connected with this Act, the congregation shall be deemed to be those persons whose names are on the Electoral Register, and no other.

(5) If after the attestation of the Register any communicant is given a Certificate of Transference, the Session Clerk shall delete that person's name from the Register and initial the deletion. Such a Certificate shall be granted only when application for it has been made in writing, and the said written application shall be retained until the vacancy is ended.

(6) When a period of more than six months has elapsed between the Electoral Register being attested and the congregation being given permission to call, the Kirk Session shall have power, if it so desires, to revise and update the Electoral Register. Intimation of this intention shall be given in terms of Schedule F hereto. Additional names shall be added to the Register in the form of an Addendum which shall also contain authority for the deletions which have been made; two copies of this Addendum, duly attested, shall be lodged with the Presbytery Clerk who, in name of the Presbytery, shall attest and return the principal copy, retaining the duplicate copy in his or her own possession.

14. Appointment of Nominating Committee

(1) When permission to call has been given and the Electoral Register has been attested, intimation in terms of Schedule G shall be made that a meeting of the congregation is to be held to appoint a Committee of its own number for the purpose of nominating one person to the congregation with a view to the appointment of a minister.

(2) (a) The Interim Moderator shall preside at this meeting, and the Session Clerk, or in his or her absence a person appointed by the meeting, shall act as Clerk.

   (b) The Interim Moderator shall remind the congregation of the number of members it is required to appoint in terms of this section and shall call for Nominations. To constitute a valid Nomination, the name of a person on the Electoral Register has to be proposed and seconded, and assurance given by the proposer that the person is prepared to act on the Committee. The Clerk shall take a note of all Nominations in the order in which they are made.

   (c) When it appears to the Interim Moderator that the Nominations are complete, they shall be read to the congregation and an opportunity given for any withdrawals. If the number of persons nominated does not exceed the maximum fixed in terms of subsection (4) below, there is no need for a vote, and the Interim Moderator shall declare that these persons constitute a Nominating Committee. If the number exceeds the maximum, the Interim Moderator shall submit the names one by one as they appear on the list to the vote of the congregation, each member having the right to vote for up to the maximum number fixed for the Committee, and voting being by standing up. In the event of a tie for the last place, a vote shall be taken between those tying.

   (d) The Interim Moderator shall announce the names of those thus elected to serve on the Nominating Committee, and intimate to them the time and place of their first meeting, which may be immediately after the congregational meeting provided that has been intimated along with the intimation of the congregational meeting.

(3) Where there is an agreement between the Presbytery and the congregation or congregations that the minister to be inducted shall serve either in a team ministry involving another congregation or congregations, or in a designated post such as a chaplaincy, it shall be competent for the agreement to specify that the Presbytery shall appoint up to two representatives to serve on the Nominating Committee.

(4) The Vacancy Procedure Committee shall, subject to the provisions of section 2 above, determine the number who will act on the Nominating Committee, being an odd number up to a maximum of thirteen.

(5) When the vacancy is in a linked charge, or when a union or linking of congregations has been agreed but not yet effected, or when there is agreement to a deferred union or a deferred linking, or where the appointment is to more than one post, the Vacancy Procedure Committee shall, subject to the provisions of section 2 above, determine how the number who will act on the Nominating Committee will be allocated among the congregations involved, unless provision for this has already been made in the Basis of Union or Basis of Linking as the case may be.

(6) The Nominating Committee shall not have power to co-opt additional members, but the relevant Kirk Session shall have power when necessary to appoint a replacement for any of its appointees who ceases, by death or resignation, to be a member of the Nominating Committee, or who, by falling ill or by moving away from the area, is unable to serve as a member of it.

15. Constitution of the Nominating Committee
It shall be the duty of the Interim Moderator to summon and preside at the first meeting of the Nominating Committee, which may be held at the close of the congregational meeting at which it is appointed and at which the Committee shall appoint a Convener and a Clerk. The Clerk, who need not be a member of the Committee, shall keep regular minutes of all proceedings. The Convener shall have a deliberative vote (if he or she is not the Interim Moderator) but shall in no case have a casting vote. If the Clerk is not a member of the Committee, he or she shall have no vote. At all meetings of the Committee, only those present shall be entitled to vote.

16. Task of the Nominating Committee
(1)   The Nominating Committee shall have the duty of nominating one person to the congregation with a view to the election and appointment of a minister. It shall proceed by a process of announcement in a monthly vacancy list, application and interview, and may also advertise, receive recommendations and pursue enquiries in other ways.
(2)   The Committee shall give due weight to any guidelines which may from time to time be issued by the Board of Ministry or the General Assembly.
(3)   The Committee shall make themselves aware of the roles of the other members of any ministry team as described in section 16 of Act VII 2003 anent Appraisal and Adjustment and may meet with them for this purpose, but shall not acquire responsibility or authority for the negotiation or alteration of their terms and conditions.

17. Eligibility for Election
The following categories of persons, and no others, are eligible to be nominated, elected and called as ministers of parishes in the Church of Scotland, but always subject, where appropriate, to the provisions of Act IX 2002 anent Admission and Readmission of Ministers and Others:
(1)   A minister of a parish of the Church, a minister holding some other appointment that entitles him or her to a seat in Presbytery or a minister holding a current Practising Certificate in terms of section 5 of Act II 2000.
(2)   A minister of the Church of Scotland who has retired from a parish or appointment as above, provided he or she has not reached his or her 65th birthday.
(3)   (a)   A licentiate of the Church of Scotland who has satisfactorily completed, or has been granted exemption from, his or her period of probationary service.
        (b)   A graduate candidate in terms of sections 26 and 27 of Act V 1998 (as amended).
(4)   A minister, licentiate or graduate candidate of the Church of Scotland who with the approval of the Board of World Mission, has entered the courts of an overseas Church as a full member, provided he or she has ceased to be such a member.
(5)   A minister, licentiate or graduate candidate of the Church of Scotland, who has neither relinquished nor been judicially deprived of the status he or she possessed and who has served, or is serving, furth of Scotland in any Church which is a member of the World Alliance of Reformed Churches.
(6)   The holder of a Certificate of Eligibility in terms of Act IX 2002 anent Admission and Readmission of Ministers and Others.

18. Ministers of a Team
Ministers occupying positions within a team ministry in the charge, or larger area including the charge, and former holders of such positions, shall be eligible to apply and shall not by virtue of office be deemed to have exercised undue influence in securing the call. A *locum tenens* in the vacant charge shall not by virtue of office be deemed to have exercised undue influence in securing the call. Any Interim Moderator in the current vacancy shall not be eligible to apply.

19. Ministers of Other Churches

(1) Where a minister of a church furth of Scotland, who holds a certificate of eligibility in terms of Act IX 2002 anent Admission and Readmission of Ministers and Others, is nominated, the nominee, Kirk Session and Presbytery may agree that he or she shall be inducted for a period of three years only and shall retain status as a minister of his or her denomination of origin.

(2) Upon induction, such a minister shall be accountable to the Presbytery for the exercise of his or her ministry and to his or her own church for matters of life and doctrine. He or she shall be awarded corresponding membership of the Presbytery.

(3) With the concurrence of the Presbytery and the Board of Ministry, and at the request of the congregation, the period may be extended for one further period of not more than three years.

20. Nomination

(1) Before the candidate is asked to accept Nomination, the Interim Moderator shall ensure that the candidate is given an adequate opportunity to see the whole ecclesiastical buildings (including the manse) pertaining to the congregation, and to meet privately with all members of staff of the charge or of any wider ministry team, and shall be provided with a copy of the constitution of the congregation, a copy of the current Presbytery Plan and of any current Basis of Adjustment or Basis of Reviewable Tenure, and the most recent audited accounts and statement of funds, and the candidate shall acknowledge receipt in writing to the Interim Moderator.

(2) Before any Nomination is intimated to the Kirk Session and Presbytery Clerk, the Clerk to the Nominating Committee shall secure the written consent thereto of the nominee.

(3) Before reporting the Nomination to the Vacancy Procedure Committee, the Presbytery Clerk shall obtain from the nominee or Interim Moderator evidence of the eligibility of the nominee to be appointed to the charge.

   (a) In the case of a minister not being a member of any Presbytery of the Church of Scotland, this shall normally constitute an Exit Certificate in terms of Act V 1998 as amended, or evidence of status from the Board of Ministry, or a current practising certificate, or certification from the Board of Ministry of eligibility in terms of Act IX 2002.

   (b) In the case of a minister in the first five years of his or her first charge, this shall consist of an extract minute either from the Vacancy Procedure Committee of his or her current Presbytery, or from that Presbytery, exceptionally releasing the minister.

21. Preaching by Nominee

(1) The Interim Moderator, on receiving notice of the Committee's Nomination, shall arrange that the nominee conduct public worship in the vacant church or churches, normally within four Sundays, and that the ballot take place immediately after each such service.

(2) The Interim Moderator shall thereupon cause intimation to be made on two Sundays regarding the arrangements made in connection with the preaching by the nominee and the ballot thereafter – all in terms of Schedule H hereto.

22. Election of Minister

(1) The Interim Moderator shall normally preside at all congregational meetings connected with the election, which shall be in all cases by ballot. The Interim Moderator shall be in charge of the ballot.

(2) The Interim Moderator may invite one or more persons (not being persons whose names are on the Electoral Register of the vacant congregation) to assist him or her in the conduct of a ballot vote when he or she judges this desirable.

(3) When a linking or a deferred union or deferred linking is involved, the Interim Moderator shall consult and reach agreement with the minister or Interim Moderator of the other congregation regarding the arrangements for the conduct of public worship in these congregations by the nominee as in section 21(1) above. The Interim Moderator shall in writing appoint a member of Presbytery to take full charge of the ballot vote for the other congregation. In the case of a deferred union or deferred linking, the minister already inducted shall not be so appointed, nor shall he or she be in any way involved in the conduct of the election.

23. Ballot Procedure

(1) The Kirk Session shall arrange to have available at the time of election a sufficient supply of voting-papers printed in the form of Schedule I hereto, and these shall be put into the custody of the Interim Moderator who shall preside at the election, assisted as in section 22 above. He or she shall issue on request to any person whose name is on the Electoral Register a voting-paper, noting on the Register that this has been done. Facilities shall be provided whereby the voter may mark the paper in secrecy, and a ballot-box shall be available wherein the paper is to be deposited when marked. The Interim Moderator may assist any person who asks for help in respect of completing the voting-paper, but no other person whatever shall communicate with the voter at this stage. The Interim Moderator, or the deputy appointed by him or her, shall be responsible for the safe custody of ballot-box, papers and Electoral Register.

(2) As soon as practicable, and at latest within twenty-four hours after the close of the voting, the Interim Moderator shall constitute the Kirk Session, or the joint Kirk Sessions when more than one congregation is involved, and in presence of the Kirk Session shall proceed with the counting of the votes, in which he or she may be assisted as provided in section 22 above. When more than one ballot-box has been used and when the votes of more than one congregation are involved, all ballot-boxes shall be emptied and the voting-papers shall be mixed together before counting begins so that the preponderance of votes in one area or in one congregation shall not be disclosed.

(3) If the number voting For exceeds the number voting Against, the nominee shall be declared elected and the Nominating Committee shall be deemed to be discharged.

(4) If the number voting For is equal to or less than the number voting Against, the Interim Moderator shall declare that there has been failure to elect and that the Nominating Committee is deemed to have been discharged. He or she shall proceed in terms of section 26(b) without further reference to the Presbytery.

(5) After the counting has been completed, the Interim Moderator shall sign a declaration in one of the forms of Schedule J hereto, and this shall be recorded in the minute of the Kirk Session or of the Kirk Sessions. An extract shall be affixed to the notice-board of the church, or of each of the churches, concerned. In the presence of the Kirk Session, the Interim Moderator shall then seal up the voting-papers along with the marked copy of the Electoral Register, and these shall be transmitted to the Presbytery Clerk in due course along with the other documents specified in section 27 below.

24. Withdrawal of Nominee

(1) Should a nominee intimate withdrawal before he or she has preached as nominee, the Nominating Committee shall continue its task and seek to nominate another nominee.

(2) Should a nominee intimate withdrawal after he or she has been elected, the Interim Moderator shall proceed in terms of sections 23(4) above and 26(b) below without further reference to the Presbytery.

25. The Call

(1)   The Interim Moderator shall, along with the intimation regarding the result of the voting, intimate the arrangements made for members of the congregation over a period of not less than eight days to subscribe the Call (Schedule K). Intimation shall be in the form of Schedule L hereto.

(2)   The Call may be subscribed on behalf of a member not present to sign in person, provided a mandate authorising such subscription is produced as in Schedule M. All such entries shall be initialled by the Interim Moderator or by the member of the Kirk Session appending them.

(3)   Those eligible to sign the call shall be all those whose names appear on the Electoral Roll. A paper of concurrence in the Call may be signed by regular worshippers in the congregation over 14 years of age and by adherents whose names have not been entered on the Electoral Register.

26. Failure to Nominate

The exercise by a congregation of its right to call a minister shall be subject to a time-limit of one year; this period shall be calculated from the date when intimation is given of the agreement to grant leave to call. If it appears that an appointment is not to be made within the allotted time (allowing one further calendar month for intimation to the Presbytery), the congregation may make application to the Presbytery for an extension, which will normally be for a further three months. In exceptional circumstances, and for clear cause shown, a further extension of three months may be granted. If no election has been made and intimated to the Presbytery by the expiry of that time, the permission to call shall be regarded as having lapsed. The Presbytery may thereupon look afresh at the question of adjustment. If the Presbytery is still satisfied that a minister should be appointed, it shall itself take steps to make such an appointment, proceeding in one of the following ways:

(1)   (a)   The Presbytery may discharge the Nominating Committee, strengthen the Advisory Committee which had been involved in the case by the appointment of an additional minister and elder, instruct that Committee to bring forward to a subsequent meeting the name of an eligible individual for appointment to the charge and intimate this instruction to the congregation. If satisfied with the recommendation brought by the Advisory Committee, the Presbytery shall thereupon make the appointment.

(b)   The Presbytery Clerk shall thereupon intimate to the person concerned the fact of his or her appointment, shall request him or her to forward a letter of acceptance along with appropriate Certificates if these are required in terms of section 27 below, and shall arrange with him or her to conduct public worship in the vacant church or churches on an early Sunday.

(c)   The Presbytery Clerk shall cause intimation to be made in the form of Schedule N that the person appointed will conduct public worship on the day specified and that a Call in the usual form will lie with the Session Clerk or other suitable person for not less than eight free days to receive the signatures of the congregation. The conditions governing the signing of the Call shall be as in section 25 above.

(d)   At the expiry of the time allowed, the Call shall be transmitted by the Session Clerk to the Presbytery Clerk, who shall lay it, along with the documents referred to in sub-paragraph (b) above, before the Presbytery at its first ordinary meeting or at a meeting *in hunc effectum*.

(2)   Otherwise, the Presbytery shall instruct that a fresh Nominating Committee be elected in terms of section 14 above. The process shall then be followed in terms of this Act from the point of the election of the Nominating Committee.

27. Transmission of Documents

(1)   After an election has been made, the Interim Moderator shall secure from the person appointed a letter of acceptance of the appointment.

(2)   The Interim Moderator shall then without delay transmit the relevant documents to the Presbytery Clerk. These are: the minute of Nomination by the Nominating Committee, all intimations made to the congregation thereafter, the declaration of the election and appointment, the voting-papers, the marked copy of the Register and the letter of acceptance. He or she shall also inform the Clerk of the steps taken in connection with the signing of the Call, and shall arrange that, at the expiry of the period allowed for subscription, the Call shall be transmitted by the Session Clerk to the Presbytery Clerk.

(3)   After the person elected has been inducted to the charge, the Presbytery Clerk shall:

(a)   deliver to him or her the approved copy of the Vacancy Schedule referred to in section 10(2) above, and

(b)   destroy the intimations and voting-papers lodged with him or her in terms of subsection (2) above and ensure that confidential documents and correspondence held locally are destroyed.

28. Sustaining the Call

(1)   All of the documents listed in section 27 above shall be laid before the Vacancy Procedure Committee, which may resolve to sustain the call and determine arrangements for the induction of the new minister, subject to (a) a request for the release, if appropriate, of the minister from his or her current charge in terms of this Act and (b) the provisions of section 2 above. The Moderator of the Presbytery shall, if no ordinary meeting of the Presbytery falls before the proposed induction date, call a meeting *pro re nata* for the induction.

(2)   In the event that the matter comes before the Presbytery in terms of section 2 above, the procedure shall be as follows:

(a)   The Call and other relevant documents having been laid on the table, the Presbytery shall hear any person whom it considers to have an interest. In particular, the Advisory Committee shall be entitled to be heard if it so desires, or the Presbytery may ask for a report from it. The Presbytery shall then decide whether to sustain the appointment in terms of subsection (1) above, and in doing so shall give consideration to the number of signatures on the Call. It may delay reaching a decision and return the Call to the Kirk Session to give further opportunity for it to be subscribed.

(b)   If the Presbytery sustain an appointment and Call to a Graduate Candidate, and there be no appeal tendered in due form against its judgement, it shall appoint the day and hour and place at which the ordination and induction will take place.

(c)   If the Presbytery sustain an appointment and Call to a minister of the Church of Scotland not being a minister of a parish, or to a minister of another denomination, and there be no ecclesiastical impediment, the Presbytery shall appoint the day and hour and place at which the induction will take place.

(3)   In the event that the Call is not sustained, the Presbytery shall determine either (1) to give more time for it to be signed in terms of section 25 above or (2) to proceed in terms of subsection (a) or (b) of section 26 above.

29. Admission to a Charge

(1)   When the Presbytery has appointed a day for the ordination and induction of a Graduate Candidate, or for the induction of a minister already ordained, the Clerk shall arrange for an edict in the form of Schedule O to be read to the congregation on the two Sundays preceding the day appointed.

(2)   At the time and place named in the edict, the Presbytery having been constituted, the Moderator shall call for the return of the edict attested as having been duly served. If the minister is being translated from another Presbytery, the relevant minute of that Presbytery or of its Vacancy Procedure Committee agreeing to translation shall also be laid on the table. Any objection, to be valid at this stage, must have been intimated to the Presbytery Clerk at the objector's earliest opportunity, must be strictly directed to life or doctrine and must be substantiated immediately to the satisfaction of the Presbytery, in which case procedure shall be sisted and the Presbytery shall take appropriate steps to deal with the situation that has arisen. Otherwise the Presbytery shall proceed with the ordination and induction, or with the induction, as hereunder.

(3)   The Presbytery shall proceed to the church where public worship shall be conducted by those appointed for the purpose. The Clerk shall read a brief narrative of the cause of the vacancy and of the steps taken for the settlement. The Moderator, having read the Preamble, shall, addressing him or her by name, put to the person to be inducted the questions prescribed (*see the Ordinal of the Church as authorised from time to time by the General Assembly*). Satisfactory answers having been given, the person to be inducted shall sign the Formula. If he or she has not already been ordained, the person to be inducted shall then kneel, and the Moderator by prayer and the imposition of hands, in which members of the Presbytery, appointed by the Presbytery for the purpose, and other ordained persons associated with it, if invited to share in such imposition of hands, shall join, shall ordain him or her to the office of the Holy Ministry. Prayer being ended, the Moderator shall say: 'I now declare you to have been ordained to the office of the Holy Ministry, and in the name of the Lord Jesus Christ, the King and Head of the Church, and by authority of this Presbytery, I induct you to this charge, and in token thereof we give you the right hand of fellowship'. The Moderator with all other members of Presbytery present and those associated with it shall then give the right hand of fellowship. The Moderator shall then put the prescribed question to the members of the congregation. Suitable charges to the new minister and to the congregation shall then be given by the Moderator or by a minister appointed for the purpose.

(4)   When an ordained minister is being inducted to a charge, the act of ordination shall not be repeated and the relevant words shall be omitted from the declaration. In other respects, the procedure shall be as in subsection (3) above.

(5)   When the appointment is for a limited or potentially limited period (including Reviewable Tenure, or an appointment in terms of section 19 above), the service shall proceed as in subsections (3) or (4) above, except that in the declaration the Moderator shall say: 'I induct you to this charge on the Basis of [specific Act and Section] and in terms of Minute of Presbytery of date …'.

(6)   After the service, the Presbytery shall resume its session, when the name of the new minister shall be added to the Roll of Presbytery, and the Clerk shall be instructed to send certified intimation of the induction to the Session Clerk to be engrossed in the minutes of the first meeting of Kirk Session thereafter, and, in the case of a translation from another Presbytery or where the minister was prior to the induction subject to the supervision of another Presbytery, to the Clerk of that Presbytery.

30. Service of Introduction

(1)   When a minister has been appointed to a linked charge, the Presbytery shall determine in which of the churches of the linking the induction is to take place. This shall be a service of induction to the charge, in consequence of which the person inducted shall become minister of each of the congregations embraced in the linking. The edict regarding the induction, which shall be in terms of Schedule P, shall be read in all of the churches

concerned. There shall be no other service of induction; but, if the churches are far distant from one another, or for other good reason, the Presbytery may appoint a service of introduction to be held in the other church or churches. Intimation shall be given of such service, but not in edictal form.

(2)   In any case of deferred union or deferred linking, the minister elected and appointed shall be inducted 'to the vacant congregation of A in deferred union (or linking) with the congregation of B' and there shall be no need for any further act to establish his or her position as minister of the united congregation or of the linked congregation as the case may be. The Presbytery, however, shall in such a case arrange a service of introduction to the newly united congregation of AB or the newly linked congregation of B. Intimation shall be given of such service, but not in edictal form.

(3)   When an appointment has been made to an extra-parochial office wholly or mainly under control of the Church (community ministry, full-time chaplaincy in hospital, industry, prison or university, full-time clerkship and so on), the Presbytery may deem it appropriate to arrange a service of introduction to take place in a church or chapel suitable to the occasion.

(4)   When an appointment has been made to a parochial appointment other than that of an inducted minister, the Presbytery may arrange a service of introduction to take place within the parish. If ordination is involved, suitable arrangements shall be made and edictal intimation shall be given in terms of Schedule P.

(5)   A service of introduction not involving ordination shall follow the lines of an induction except that instead of putting the normal questions to the minister the Moderator shall ask him or her to affirm the vows taken at his or her ordination. Where the service, in terms of subsection (3) or (4) above, includes the ordination of the minister, the vows shall be put in full. In either case, in the declaration, the Moderator in place of 'I induct you to ...' shall say: 'I welcome you as ...'.

31. Demission of Status

If a minister seeks to demit his or her status as a minister of the Church of Scotland, any accompanying demission of a charge will be dealt with by the Vacancy Procedure Committee in terms of section 4 of this Act without further delay, but the question of demission of status shall be considered by the Presbytery itself. The Moderator of Presbytery, or a deputy appointed by him or her, shall first confer with the minister regarding his or her reasons and shall report to the Presbytery if there appears to be any reason not to grant permission to demit status. Any decision to grant permission to demit status shall be immediately reported to the Board of Ministry.

32. Miscellaneous

For the purposes of this Act, intimations to congregations may be made (a) verbally during every act of worship or (b) in written intimations distributed to the whole congregation provided that the congregation's attention is specifically drawn to the presence of an intimation there in terms of this Act.

For the purposes of this Act, attestation of all intimations to congregations shall consist of certification thereof by the Session Clerk as follows:

(1)   Certification that all intimations received have been duly made on the correct number of Sundays shall be sent to the Presbytery Clerk before the service of induction or introduction.

(2)   Certification that any particular intimation received has been duly made on the correct number of Sundays shall be furnished on demand to the Vacancy Procedure Committee or the Presbytery Clerk.

(3)   Intimation shall be made immediately to the Presbytery Clerk in the event that intimation has not been duly made on the appropriate Sunday.

SCHEDULES

A INTIMATION OF ACTION OR DECISION OF VACANCY PROCEDURE COMMITTEE – Section 2(1)

To be read on one Sunday

The Vacancy Procedure Committee of the Presbytery of .... proposes [here insert action or permission proposed] .... Any communicant member of the congregation(s) of A [and B] may submit to the Presbytery Clerk a request for this proposal to be considered at the next meeting of the Presbytery: where such requests are received from four individuals, being communicant members of the congregation(s) or full members of the Presbytery, the request shall be met. Such request should be submitted in writing to [name and postal address of Presbytery Clerk] by [date seven days after intimation].

A .... B ....   Presbytery Clerk

B EDICT CITING A CONGREGATION TO ATTEND – Section 2(5)

To be read on one Sunday

Intimation is hereby given that in connection with the [anticipated] vacancy in this congregation a valid request has been made for the matter of [here insert action or permission which had been proposed] to be considered by the Presbytery. [The proposed course of action] is in the mean time sisted.

Intimation is hereby further given that the Presbytery will meet to consider this matter at .... on .... the .... day of .... at .... o'clock and that the congregation are hereby cited to attend for their interests.

A .... B ....   Presbytery Clerk

C PREPARATION OF ELECTORAL REGISTER – Section 13(1) and (2)

To be read on two Sundays

Intimation is hereby given that in view of the [1]anticipated vacancy, the Kirk Session is about to make up an Electoral Register of this congregation. Any communicant whose name is not already on the Communion Roll as a member should hand in to the Session Clerk a Certificate of Transference, and anyone wishing his or her name added to the Register as an adherent should obtain from the Session Clerk, and complete and return to him or her, a Form of Adherent's Claim. All such papers should be in the hands of the Session Clerk not later than .... The Kirk Session will meet in .... on .... at .... to make up the Electoral Register when anyone wishing to support his or her claim in person should attend.

C .... D ....   Interim Moderator

[1] This word to be included where appropriate – otherwise to be deleted

D FORM OF ADHERENT'S CLAIM – Section 13(1)

I, [1]......... of [2]........., being not under 18 years of age, being a parishioner or regular worshipper in the Church of .... and not being a member of any other congregation in Scotland, claim to have my name put on the Electoral Register of the parish of .... as an adherent.

Date ....   (Signed) ....

[1] Here enter full name in block capitals
[2] Here enter address in full

E INSPECTION OF ELECTORAL REGISTER – Section 13(3)

To be read on one Sunday

Intimation is hereby given that the proposed Electoral Register of this congregation has now been prepared and that an opportunity of inspecting it will be given today in .... at the close of this service, and that it will be open for inspection at .... on .... between the hours of .... and .... each day. Any questions regarding entries in the Register should be brought to the notice of the Kirk Session which is to meet in .... on .... at .... o'clock when it will finally make up the Electoral Register.

C .... D ....   Interim Moderator

F REVISION OF ELECTORAL REGISTER – Section 13(6)

To be read on two Sundays

Intimation is hereby given that more than six months having elapsed since the Electoral Register of this congregation was finally made up, it is now proposed that it should be revised. An opportunity of inspecting the Register will be given in .... at the close of this service, and also at .... on .... between the hours of .... and .... each day. Anyone wishing his or her name added to the Electoral Register as a member should give in a Transference Certificate, or as an adherent should give in a Form of Adherent's Claim (copies of which may be had from the Session Clerk) not later than .... The Kirk Session will meet in .... on .... at .... o'clock when it will finally make up the Revised Register.

C .... D ....   Interim Moderator

G INTIMATION OF ELECTION OF NOMINATING COMMITTEE – Section 14(1)

To be read on two Sundays

Intimation is hereby given that a meeting of this congregation will be held in the Church [or other arrangement may be given here] on Sunday .... at the close of morning worship for the purpose of appointing a Nominating Committee which will nominate one person to the congregation with a view to the appointment of a minister.

C .... D ....   Interim Moderator

H MINUTE OF NOMINATION BY NOMINATING COMMITTEE – Section 21

To be read on two Sundays

(1) The Committee chosen by this congregation to nominate a person with a view to the election and appointment of a minister, at a meeting held at .... on .... resolved to name and propose [1] .... and they accordingly do name and propose the said ....

Date ....

E .... F ....   Convener of Committee

[1] The name and designation of the person should at this point be entered in full

(2) Intimation is therefore hereby given that the Nominating Committee having, as by minute now read, named and proposed [Name], arrangements have been made whereby public worship will be conducted in this Church by him or her on Sunday the .... day of .... at .... o'clock; and that a vote will be taken by voting-papers immediately thereafter; and that electors may vote For or Against electing and appointing the said [Name] as minister of this vacant charge.

C .... D ....   Interim Moderator

I VOTING-PAPER – Section 23

FOR Electing [Name]
AGAINST Electing [Name]

Directions to Voters: If you are in favour of electing [Name], put a cross (x) on the upper space. If you are not in favour of electing [Name], put a cross (x) in the lower space. Do not put a tick or any other mark upon the paper; if you do, it will be regarded as spoilt and will not be counted.

Note: The Directions to Voters must be printed prominently on the face of the voting-paper

J DECLARATION OF ELECTION RESULT – Section 23(5)

First Form (Successful Election)

I hereby declare that the following are the results of the voting for the election and appointment of a minister to the vacant charge of [1] .... and that the said [Name] has accordingly been elected and appointed subject to the judgement of the courts of the Church.

Date ....   C .... D ....   Interim Moderator

[1] Here enter details

FOR Electing [Name]
AGAINST Electing [Name]

Second Form (Failure to Elect)

I hereby declare that the following are the results of the voting for the election and appointment of a minister to the vacant charge of [1]......... and that in consequence of this vote there has been a failure to elect, and the Nominating Committee is deemed to have been discharged. [Continue in terms of Schedule G if appropriate.]

Date ....   C .... D ....   Interim Moderator

[1] Here enter details

FOR Electing [Name]
AGAINST Electing [Name]

K THE CALL – Section 25(1)

Form of Call

We, members of the Church of Scotland and of the congregation known as .... , being without a minister, address this Call to be our minister to you, ..., of whose gifts and qualities we have been assured, and we warmly invite you to accept this Call, promising that we shall devote ourselves with you to worship, witness, mission and service in this parish, and also to the furtherance of these in the world, to the glory of God and for the advancement of His Kingdom.

Paper of Concurrence

We, regular worshippers in the congregation of the Church of Scotland known as ......, concur in the Call addressed by that congregation to .... to be their minister.
N.B. The Call and Paper of Concurrence should be dated and attested by the Interim Moderator before they are transmitted to the Clerk of the Presbytery

L SUBSCRIBING THE CALL – Section 25(1)

To be read on at least one Sunday

Intimation is hereby given that this congregation, having elected [Name] to be their minister, a Call to the said [Name] has been prepared and will lie in .... on .... the .... day of .... between the hours of .... and .... when those whose names are on the Communion Roll of the congregation may sign in person or by means of mandates. Forms of mandate may be obtained from the Session Clerk.

A paper of Concurrence will also be available for signature by persons of 14 years of age or over who are connected with the congregation but whose names are not on the Communion Roll of the congregation.

C .... D ....   Interim Moderator

M MANDATE TO SIGN CALL – Section 25(2)

I, ... of ...., being a person whose name is on the Electoral Register of the congregation, hereby authorise the Session Clerk, or other member of Session, to add my name to the Call addressed to [Name] to be our minister.

(Signed) ....

N CITATION IN CASE OF NOMINATION BY PRESBYTERY – Section 26(a)(iii)

To be read on one Sunday

Intimation is hereby given that [Name] whom the Presbytery has appointed to be minister of this congregation will conduct public worship in the Church on Sunday the .... day of .... at .... o'clock.

Intimation is hereby further given that a Call addressed to the said [Name] will lie in .... on .... the .... day of .... between the hours of .... and .... during the day and between the hours of .... and .... in the evening, when members may sign in person or by means of mandates, forms of which may be had from the Session Clerk.

Intimation is hereby further given that the Presbytery will meet to deal with the appointment and Call at .... on .... the .... day of .... at .... o'clock and that the congregation are hereby cited to attend for their interests.

A .... B ....   Presbytery Clerk

O EDICTAL INTIMATION OF ADMISSION – Section 29(1)

To be read on two Sundays

Whereas the Presbytery of .... has received a Call from this congregation addressed to [Name] to be their minister, and the said Call has been sustained as a regular Call, and has been accepted by him/her[1]:
And whereas the said Presbytery, having judged the said [Name] qualified[2] for the ministry of the Gospel and for this charge, has resolved to proceed to his or her[3] ordination and induction on .... the .... day of .... at .... o'clock unless something occurs which may reasonably impede it:
Notice is hereby given to all concerned that if they, or any of them, have anything to object to in the life or doctrine of the said [Name] they may appear at the Presbytery which is to meet at .... on .... the .... day of .... at .... o'clock; with certification that if no relevant objection be then made and immediately substantiated, the Presbytery will proceed without further delay.

By order of the Presbytery

A .... B ....   Presbytery Clerk

---

[1] add, where appropriate, 'and his or her translation has been agreed to by the Presbytery of ....'
[2] omit 'for the ministry of the Gospel and' if the minister to be inducted has been ordained previously
[3] omit, where appropriate, 'ordination and'

P EDICTAL INTIMATION OF ORDINATION IN CASE OF INTRODUCTION –
Section 30(1)

To be read on two Sundays

Whereas [narrate circumstances requiring service of introduction]

And whereas the Presbytery, having found the said [Name] to have been regularly appointed and to be qualified for the ministry of the Gospel and for the said appointment, has resolved to proceed to his or her ordination to the Holy Ministry and to his or her introduction as [specify appointment] on .... the .... day of .... at .... o'clock unless something occur which may reasonably impede it;

Notice is hereby given to all concerned that if they, or any of them, have anything to object to in the life or doctrine of the said [Name] they may appear at the Presbytery which is to meet at .... on .... the .... day of .... at .... o'clock; with certification that if no relevant objection be then made and immediately substantiated, the Presbytery will proceed without further delay.

By order of the Presbytery

A .... B ....   Presbytery Clerk

SECTION 4

The General Assembly of 2004

(1) OFFICIALS OF THE GENERAL ASSEMBLY

The Lord High Commissioner:	The Rt Hon. Lord Steel of Aikwood
Moderator:	Alison Elliot OBE MA MSc PhD LLD
Chaplains to the Moderator:	Rev. Sheilagh M. Kesting BA BD Rev. Johnston R. McKay MA BA
Principal Clerk:	Very Rev. Finlay A.J. Macdonald MA BD PhD DD
Depute Clerk:	Rev. Marjory A. MacLean LLB BD PhD
Procurator:	Mr Patrick S. Hodge QC
Law Agent:	Mrs Janette S. Wilson LLB NP
Convener of the Business Committee:	Rev. David W. Lacy BA BD
Vice-Convener of the Business Committee:	Rev. William C. Hewitt BD DipPS
Precentor:	Rev. Douglas Galbraith MA BD BMus MPhil ARSCM
Assembly Officer:	Mr David McColl
Assistant Assembly Officer:	Mr Craig Marshall

(2) THE MODERATOR

Dr Alison Elliot OBE

Dr Elliot was born in Edinburgh in 1948 and brought up in West Lothian, where her father was Physician Superintendent at Bangour Village Hospital. She was educated at Bathgate Academy, Edinburgh University and Sussex University, gaining an MA in Mathematics with General Linguistics (Edinburgh 1970), an MSc in Experimental Psychology (Sussex 1971) and a PhD in Children's Language Development (Edinburgh 1976). She lectured in the Psychology Departments of Edinburgh and Lancaster Universities from 1974–85.

Associate Director of Edinburgh University's Centre for Theology and Public Issues (CTPI) since 2001, Dr Elliot is an Honorary Fellow of New College. CTPI promotes research into public issues to which theology can make a vital contribution.

Alison Elliot was ordained an elder in 1984 in Greyfriars, Tolbooth and Highland Kirk in Edinburgh, of which she is now Session Clerk. In 1988, she was appointed both a member of the Church and Nation Committee and a Church of Scotland representative to the First European Ecumenical Assembly in Basel. These two commitments, to the social and political outreach of the Church and to its ecumenical engagement, have characterised her work as a Church representative.

She was Convener of the Church and Nation Committee from 1996–2000, an exciting period which covered the start of the Scottish Parliament and which opened up opportunities for working alongside many Scottish civic organisations. She is currently Convener of the Scottish Churches Forum, the principal representative body for the nine mainstream Scottish churches that are members of ACTS (Action of Churches Together in Scotland). Members of the Forum are chosen from the senior people in each church. Between 1999 and 2002, she was Convener of the ACTS Commission on Justice, Peace, Social and Moral Issues.

Dr Elliot is a member of the Central Committee of the Conference of European Churches and has served on the Executive of its Church and Society Commission. This Commission is based principally in Brussels and is a channel for communication between the churches and the main European political institutions. She is also a member of the Churches Commission on International Affairs of the World Council of Churches, a stimulating body that contributes to the churches' thinking on international issues, like sanctions or humanitarian intervention, and monitors significant political developments round the world.

Dr Elliot holds several civic appointments – member of Council of the Scottish Civic Forum since 2000; chairwoman of the Lay Advisory Group of the Royal College of Physicians, Edinburgh; member of the Scottish Executive Department of Health's National Advisory Group for Improving Mental Health and Wellbeing; and, from 1999–2001, chair of the Scottish Land Reform Convention.

Broadcasting is part of her work that she particularly enjoys. She frequently writes journal articles, and expects that her short book about chaplaincy, *Frontier Spirit*, published by Scottish Christian Press, will be ready before the General Assembly. She was awarded the OBE in 2003 for services to the Church of Scotland and ecumenical relations.

Alison Elliot and her husband, Jo, have a daughter and a son, both students.

(From information supplied through the Media Relations Unit, May 2004)

One commissioner to the 2004 General Assembly, reporting diligence to his Presbytery, said that many of those who had commented on how refreshingly different and relaxed the Assembly was had attributed it to the fact that the Moderator was a woman. 'That's nonsense', said the commissioner; 'it was because the Moderator was Alison Elliot.'

No one who has watched Alison Elliot quietly questioning groups of church people at a meeting, or been close to her as she listened on the Mull of Kintyre to the sad ten-year-old girl who mourned the grandfather she had never known, or who has seen her emerging visibly moved from the Holocaust Museum in Jerusalem, will have been surprised at the gentle courtesy of her chairing of the General Assembly. Her style has always been to listen very patiently and then to ask the penetrating question.

No one who served with Alison Elliot in the four years she was Convener of the Church and Nation Committee, or who observed her in the four years before that as Vice Convener, will have been surprised at her complete mastery of the Assembly's business. As always, she had done her homework so thoroughly that there were times when it seemed as if her grasp of the reports to the Assembly was at least as thorough as that of the Conveners who were proposing them. Her agile and probing mind made sure that before every day's proceedings began she had a grasp of all the issues being discussed, even those which some of us assured her would never see the light of debate.

And no-one who knows how much the ecumenical expression of Christian faith matters to her, or how committed she is to her work with Action of Churches Together in Scotland, will have been surprised that, in the year that stretches ahead of her after the Assembly, she has asked that wherever possible her engagements should have an ecumenical dimension. And no one who knows how much she is respected, admired and loved in the other churches and faith communities in Scotland will be surprised at the welcome she has received among them.

All of that is public knowledge. Only Alison's friends know that what she has achieved in public has been possible because of what she is given by Jo, Christina and Johnny, and what she shares with them.

Johnston McKay

(3) DIGEST OF ASSEMBLY DECISIONS

What has traditionally been included in this section of the *Year Book* has been the Editor's personal selection of those decisions of the most recent Assembly which, in his view at the time of writing, seemed likely to be of most interest not only to the committed Church member but also to the more casual observer of the Assembly.

On occasion over recent years, it may have seemed as if the real 'excitement' of the most recent Assembly lay not in what had actually been decided but in what had been tentatively spoken of for the future. Talk of radical change had been in the air, but 'in due course' and 'not yet' rather than 'now' had been the always cautious timetable. The Assembly of 2004, however, took a number of decisions which, at least to the eye of this Editor, cannot but have far-reaching implications for the life, work and structures of our Church. The full text of the Reports, Acts and Deliverances of the Assembly can, as always, be obtained from the Principal Clerk. It will be a surprise, and possibly a disappointment, if he does not receive this year more requests than normal for such material. The brief summary that follows cannot begin to do justice to all that is and will be involved.

Specific reference will be made to important decisions on the Reports of some of the individual Boards and Committees, but note is first taken of four decisions which will have implications across a number of these individual Agencies. (The writer is somehow reminded of an occasion some years ago when, as a visiting consultant, he was present at an important meeting of a sister denomination furth of Scotland. Plans to unleash a Council with far-reaching powers were at an advanced stage. A number of worthy committees were as a result to be thanked and discharged with warm hopes expressed for increased efficiency, streamlined administration and significant financial savings. There was but one voice of hesitation: 'We may find we need one new committee,' said the speaker, 'a committee on bruised feelings and trampled toes'.)

(a) The major decisions of the Assembly included the following:

- The newly established Council of Assembly was given an impressive remit, with powers not just to talk and to consult but also to act across key areas of the Church's life.
- Boards, Committees and Panels which fall within the definition of Agencies of the General Assembly are to be organised and reconstituted within six new Councils.
- The newly established Panel on Review and Reform will continue the remit of the former Assembly Council in respect of that Council's listening, monitoring and research roles. It will take forward the Church without Walls agenda and offer reflection on the functioning and development of the new structure outlined above which is being introduced under the auspices of the Council of Assembly.
- The Assembly approved the principle of flexible tenure whereby ministers of word and sacrament could be inducted to a Presbytery or to a group of Presbyteries which would in

turn appoint and introduce these ministers to particular parishes or parish groupings. The appropriate Report and its Appendix were sent to Presbyteries for comment. The Board of Practice and Procedure will consider what legislation would be required to implement this new form of tenure.

(b) The following decisions were taken on the Reports of Boards and Committees:

ASSEMBLY COUNCIL

The Assembly affirmed that the primary purpose of the Church's 'central' administration is to equip, resource and support the local communities of faith in their worship, witness and service and beyond that to enable the Church nationally to act, to care and to speak in ways that cannot effectively be done by congregations or Presbyteries alone, and to provide the support services required to sustain the necessary organisational structure of a large denomination.

BOARD OF COMMUNICATION

The Assembly endorsed the principle of establishing a Communication Forum and strongly urged the Council of Assembly to implement this in collaboration with the Board.

The Assembly noted the action being taken to generate income for the Church through advertising on the Church's website and instructed the Board, in consultation with other Boards and central agencies of the Church, to bring to the Assembly of 2005 proposals for the Assembly to determine.

BOARD OF MINISTRY

In respect of manses:
* the Assembly reaffirmed the customary practice of the Church to provide a manse for the use of the parish minister and reminded ministers that it was their duty to occupy the manse so provided;
* the Assembly noted that procedures involving the Board of Ministry and the General Trustees were in place for examining exceptional circumstances whereby a minister might have his or her own house recognised as the manse of the charge;
* in the light of escalating house prices, the Assembly instructed the Board, in full consultation with the Housing and Loan Fund, to examine in detail the financial implications for occupants of a tied manse, both during their ministry and at retirement, and to report to the Assembly of 2005.

The Assembly noted that the Board would meet the costs of carrying out Scottish Criminal Record Checks on all ministers and deacons, and instructed all ministers and deacons to respond promptly to the application process for Enhanced Disclosure Certificates.

BOARD OF NATIONAL MISSION

The Assembly approved the Principles and Basis of Calculation of a National Plan, and instructed the Board to publish the proposed Plan in full by 1 September 2004 and to issue copies to every Presbytery. Presbyteries were instructed to consider the proposed Plan and to submit written comments thereon to the Board not later than 31 December 2004. In consultation with the Boards of Practice and Procedure and of Ministry, the Board was instructed to study these comments and to report to the Assembly of 2005 with an analysis of Presbyteries' responses and with further proposals.

The Committee on Parish Appraisal was instructed to investigate the particular needs of rural priority-area parishes and to report to the Assembly of 2005.

BOARD OF PARISH EDUCATION

The Board was instructed to work with other relevant Boards and Committees to review the theology and practice of Church membership.

Presbyteries were urged to encourage those involved in the planning and organisation of team ministries to include Readers in this, recognising the skills that they could offer to the team. Presbyteries were further encouraged to give Readers the status of corresponding members of Presbytery.

BOARD OF PRACTICE AND PROCEDURE

The Assembly agreed that, following the necessary amendment to the Marriage (Scotland) Act 1977 and on a date to be determined by the Principal Clerk, 'the functions of a deacon shall include the solemnisation of marriage, subject to the permission and supervision of the minister or Interim Moderator of the parish in which the marriage takes place'.

BOARD OF SOCIAL RESPONSIBILITY

The Assembly affirmed the revised vision statement of the Board in the following terms:
* to provide Christ-centred social care, of the highest quality, to those in most need throughout Scotland;
* to be active in the local church and in local communities, both in the provision of Christ-centred care and in the facilitating and enabling of others to provide such care;
* to work in partnership with others, while at all times ensuring that our faith is distinctive and recognised as the motivation for all our activities;
* that its staff and the wider Church own this vision of Christ-centred social care in Scotland;
* to continue to be a Christian voice on key social, moral and ethical issues in Scotland.

BOARD OF STEWARDSHIP AND FINANCE

The Assembly welcomed the Board's report on Christian Giving, with its New Testament emphasis on sacrificial giving, and instructed the Board to arrange area meetings throughout Scotland to promote the teaching and practising of sacrificial giving.

The Assembly noted the indicative Rolling Budget for 2005–9 and expressed grave concern at the scale of budgetary cuts being projected in Mission and Renewal work.

BOARD OF WORLD MISSION

The Assembly gave thanks for, and affirmed the continuing importance of, the work of the Church of Scotland in continental Europe, notably the ministry and mission of the Presbytery of Europe and the congregations thereof and the Church's participation in international ecumenical agencies.

CHURCH OF SCOTLAND GUILD

The Assembly welcomed the Scottish Executive's initiative in setting up the Scottish Women's Convention and encouraged the Guild in its involvement in the Convention and in its membership of the Steering Group.

COMMITTEE ON ARTISTIC MATTERS

The Assembly welcomed the opportunity of sharing with the Scottish Episcopal Church in a common approach to the care of church buildings.

COMMITTEE ON CHAPLAINS TO HM FORCES

The Assembly commended to eligible Ministers of the Church the thought that they might offer for Chaplaincy in the Royal Navy, Naval Reserve, Regular Army, Territorial Army or Army Cadet Force, Royal Air Force or Air Cadets.

COMMITTEE ON CHURCH AND NATION

Remembering with thanksgiving the overcoming of apartheid in South Africa, the Assembly recommitted the Church to its opposition to racism wherever it may be found.

In condemning violence in any form, the Assembly affirmed the right of both Palestinians and Israelis to live in peace and security.

The Assembly called on Her Majesty's Government always to act within international law and in accordance with the will of the United Nations in issues of peace and security.

COMMITTEE ON ECUMENICAL RELATIONS

The Assembly welcomed the informal talks with the Free Church and the decision to continue them at six-monthly intervals. Ministers and congregations were encouraged to be open to finding appropriate ways of relating to any Free Church minister and congregation in their parish.

COMMITTEE ON EDUCATION

The Assembly encouraged the Committee to continue to take an interest in the setting up, and use by pupils and staff, of contemplation areas in non-denominational schools.

The Assembly instructed the Committee to take an active interest in the work of the Scottish Children's Commissioner.

COMMITTEE TO REVISE THE HYMNARY

The Assembly welcomed the fact that it was anticipated that the new Hymnary would be launched on or around St Andrew's Day 2004.

GENERAL TRUSTEES

The Assembly instructed congregations to take all reasonable steps to make their buildings equally welcoming to those with disabilities.

HIV/AIDS PROJECT

The Assembly agreed to commend and support all agencies working to eliminate stigma and discrimination for people living with HIV/AIDS both overseas and in Scotland.

IONA COMMUNITY BOARD

The Assembly welcomed the continued ecumenical emphasis of the Iona Community expressed through the new members joining the Community, through the commitment to continuing ecumenical lay training and education, and through the direct engagement of Community members with the worldwide Church at every level.

JOINT BOARDS GROUP ON THE PROTECTION OF CHILDREN AND YOUNG PEOPLE IN THE CHURCH

The Assembly instructed all Kirk Sessions to ensure that recruitment procedures were adhered to and that Child Protection Co-ordinators were appropriately trained to allow them to be accredited as authorised signatories for criminal-record checks.

JOINT REPORT ON LOCALLY RECOGNISED NON-STIPENDIARY MINISTRY

The Assembly agreed to encourage a more vigorous recruitment of auxiliary ministers and Readers in the Church of Scotland. The Assembly instructed the Board of Ministry, in collaboration with the Board of Parish Education and the Panel on Doctrine, to form a Review Group to examine and consider the interface between the auxiliary ministry and the Readership and to report to the Assembly of 2005 or as soon thereafter as possible.

JOINT REPORT ON TIBERIAS

The Assembly instructed the Board of World Mission to continue to consult with partner churches and institutions within Israel and Palestine about how best St Andrew's Jerusalem Church and Guest House, Tabeetha School and St Andrew's Galilee can support the Christian presence in the land of the Holy One and to report to the General Assembly of 2005.

PANEL ON DOCTRINE

The Assembly invited the National Youth Assembly to consider how well current procedures for becoming Church members suited the culture of today's younger people and to transmit their findings to the Principal Clerk.

The Assembly instructed the Board of Practice and Procedure to examine the present method of keeping a roll of members of the Church, to compare it with other models, both proposed and in practice, in other churches and to bring a report with proposals to a future Assembly.

PANEL ON WORSHIP

The Assembly commended as a guide to Kirk Sessions the Recommended Salary Scales for Organists.

SOCIETY, RELIGION AND TECHNOLOGY PROJECT

The Assembly commended the SRT Project for gaining Scottish Executive funding to support the Eco-Congregation Programme and urged congregations to join the Programme. The eight Eco-Congregation Award-winning churches were congratulated, with special commendation for Westray Church, which had achieved complete self-sufficiency in renewable energy.

TASK FORCE FOR CHANGE

The Assembly instructed Presbyteries, with the support of the Board of Practice and Procedure, to revisit the matter of the size and number of Presbyteries with a view to enabling them to fulfil their missionary responsibilities more effectively.

TRUSTEES OF THE CHURCH OF SCOTLAND HOUSING AND LOAN FUND

The Assembly approved the concept of extending eligibility for benefit from the Church of Scotland Housing and Loan Fund for Retired Ministers and Widows and Widowers of Ministers to separated or divorced spouses of ministers.

SECTION 5

Presbytery Lists

SECTION 5 – PRESBYTERY LISTS

In each Presbytery list, the congregations are listed in alphabetical order. In a linked charge, the names appear under the first named congregation. Under the name of the congregation will be found the name of the minister and, where applicable, that of an associate minister, auxiliary minister and member of the Diaconate. The years indicated after a minister's name in the congregational section of each Presbytery list are the year of ordination (column 1) and the year of current appointment (column 2). Where only one date is given, it is both the year of ordination and the year of appointment.

In the second part of each Presbytery list, those named are listed alphabetically. The first date is the year of ordination, and the following date is the year of appointment or retirement. If the person concerned is retired, then the appointment last held will be shown in brackets.

KEY TO ABBREVIATIONS

(E)   Indicates a Church Extension charge. New Charge Developments are separately indicated.
(GD)   Indicates a charge where it is desirable that the minister should have a knowledge of Gaelic.
(GE)   Indicates a charge where public worship must be regularly conducted in Gaelic.
(H)   Indicates that a Hearing Aid Loop system has been installed. In Linked charges, the (H) is placed beside the appropriate building as far as possible.
(L)   Indicates that a Chair Lift has been installed.
(T)   Indicates that the minister has been appointed on the basis of Terminable Tenure.

PRESBYTERY NUMBERS

1	Edinburgh	18	Dumbarton
2	West Lothian	19	Argyll
3	Lothian	20	
4	Melrose and Peebles	21	
5	Duns	22	Falkirk
6	Jedburgh	23	Stirling
7	Annandale and Eskdale	24	Dunfermline
8	Dumfries and Kirkcudbright	25	Kirkcaldy
9	Wigtown and Stranraer	26	St Andrews
10	Ayr	27	Dunkeld and Meigle
11	Irvine and Kilmarnock	28	Perth
12	Ardrossan	29	Dundee
13	Lanark	30	Angus
14	Greenock and Paisley	31	Aberdeen
15		32	Kincardine and Deeside
16	Glasgow	33	Gordon
17	Hamilton	34	Buchan
35	Moray		
36	Abernethy		
37	Inverness		
38	Lochaber		
39	Ross		
40	Sutherland		
41	Caithness		
42	Lochcarron–Skye		
43	Uist		
44	Lewis		
45	Orkney		
46	Shetland		
47	England		
48	Europe		
49	Jerusalem		

(1) EDINBURGH

Meets at Palmerston Place Church, Edinburgh, on the first Tuesday of October, November, December, February, March, April and May and on the second Tuesday in September and on the last Tuesday of June. When the first Tuesday of April falls in Holy Week, the meeting is on the second Tuesday.

Clerk:	REV. W. PETER GRAHAM MA BD	10 Palmerston Place, Edinburgh EH12 5AA [E-mail: akph50@uk.uumail.com]	0131-225 9137

1 Edinburgh: Albany Deaf Church of Edinburgh (H)
Alistair F. Kelly BL (Locum) 1961 19 Avon Place, Edinburgh EH4 6RE 0131-317 9877

2 Edinburgh: Balerno (H)
Jared W. Hay BA MTh DipMin DMin 1987 2001 3 Johnsburn Road, Balerno EH14 7DN 0131-449 3830
[E-mail: jared.hay@blueyonder.co.uk]
Charles W.H. Barrington MA BD (Assoc) 1997 502 Lanark Road, Edinburgh EH14 5DH 0131-453 4826
[E-mail: charles.barrington@classicfm.net]

3 Edinburgh: Barclay (0131-229 6810) (E-mail: admin@barclaychurch.org.uk)
Vacant 38 Cluny Gardens, Edinburgh EH10 6BN 0131-447 8702

4 Edinburgh: Blackhall St Columba (0131-332 4431) (E-mail: secretary@blackhallstcolumba.org.uk)
Alexander B. Douglas BD 1979 1991 5 Blinkbonny Crescent, Edinburgh EH4 3NB 0131-343 3708
[E-mail: alexandjill@btopenworld.com]

5 Edinburgh: Bristo Memorial Craigmillar
Angus L. Bayne LTh BEd MTh 1969 1994 72 Blackchapel Close, Edinburgh EH15 3SL 0131-657 3266
[E-mail: angus@mccookies.com]
Agnes M. Rennie (Miss) DCS 3/1 Craigmillar Court, Edinburgh EH16 4AD 0131-661 8475

6 Edinburgh: Broughton St Mary's (H) (0131-556 4786)
Joanne C. Hood (Miss) MA BD 2003 103 East Claremont Street, Edinburgh EH7 4JA 0131-556 7313
[E-mail: joanneclairehood@jch9.freeserve.co.uk]

7 Edinburgh: Canongate (H)
Charles Robertson MA 1965 1978 Manse of Canongate, Edinburgh EH8 8BR 0131-556 3515
[E-mail: canongate1@aol.com]

8 Edinburgh: Carrick Knowe (H) (0131-334 1505) (E-mail: carrickknowechurch@btinternet.com)
Fiona M. Mathieson (Mrs) BEd BD 1988 2001 21 Traquair Park West, Edinburgh EH12 7AN 0131-334 9774
[E-mail: fiona.mathieson@ukgateway.net]

9 Edinburgh: Colinton (H) (0131-441 2232)
George J. Whyte BSc BD DMin 1981 1992 The Manse, Colinton, Edinburgh EH13 0JR 0131-441 2315
[E-mail: georgewhyte@vestry.fsnet.co.uk]
Mark Evans DCS 13 East Drylaw Drive, Edinburgh EH4 2QA 0131-343 3089

10   **Edinburgh: Colinton Mains (H)**   1993
     Ian A. McQuarrie BD
     17 Swanston Green, Edinburgh EH10 7EW
     [E-mail: ian.mcquarrie1@btinternet.com]
     0131-445 3451

11   **Edinburgh: Corstorphine Craigsbank (H) (0131-334 6365)**
     Stewart M. McPherson BD CertMin   1991   2003
     17 Craigs Bank, Edinburgh EH12 8HD
     [E-mail: smcpherson@blueyonder.co.uk]
     0131-467 6826
     07814 901429 (Mbl)

12   **Edinburgh: Corstorphine Old (H) (0131-334 7864)**
     James Bain BD DipMin   1996   2002
     23 Manse Road, Edinburgh EH12 7SW
     [E-mail: jimbain@blueyonder.co.uk]
     0131-334 5425

13   **Edinburgh: Corstorphine St Anne's (0131-316 4740)**
     MaryAnn R. Rennie (Mrs) BD MTh   1998   2002
     23 Belgrave Road, Edinburgh EH12 6NG
     [E-mail: maryann.rennie@blueyonder.co.uk]
     0131-334 3188

14   **Edinburgh: Corstorphine St Ninian's (H) (E-mail: st-ninians@corstorphine144.freeserve.co.uk)**
     Alexander T. Stewart MA BD FSAScot   1975   1995
     17 Templeland Road, Edinburgh EH12 8RZ
     [E-mail: alextstewart@blueyonder.co.uk]
     0131-334 2978

     Margaret Gordon (Mrs) DCS
     92 Lanark Road West, Currie EH14 5LA
     0131-449 2554

15   **Edinburgh: Craigentinny St Christopher's**
     Lilly C. Easton (Mrs)   1999
     61 Milton Crescent, Edinburgh EH15 3PQ
     0131-669 2429

16   **Edinburgh: Craiglockhart (H) (E-mail: craiglockhart_church@fsmail.net)**
     Andrew Ritchie BD DipMin DMin   1984   1991
     202 Colinton Road, Edinburgh EH14 1BP
     [E-mail: andrewritchie@talk21.com]
     0131-443 2020

17   **Edinburgh: Craigmillar Park (T) (H) (0131-667 5862)**
     Sarah E.C. Nicol (Mrs) BSc BD   1985   1994
     14 Hallhead Road, Edinburgh EH16 5QJ
     [E-mail: sneditions@easynet.co.uk]
     0131-667 1623

18   **Edinburgh: Cramond (H) (E-mail: cramond.kirk@blueyonder.co.uk)**
     G. Russell Barr BA BD MTh DMin   1979   1993
     Manse of Cramond, Edinburgh EH4 6NS
     [E-mail: rev.r.barr@blueyonder.co.uk]
     0131-336 2036

19   **Edinburgh: Currie (H) (0131-451 5141) (E-mail: currie.kirk@btinternet.com)**
     Keith W. Ross MA BD   1984   2000
     43 Lanark Road West, Currie EH14 5JX
     [E-mail: kirk.ross@btopenworld.com]
     0131-449 4719

20   **Edinburgh: Dalmeny**
     To be linked with Kirkliston

21 **Edinburgh: Davidson's Mains (H) (0131-312 6282) (E-mail: life@dmainschurch.plus.com)**
Jeremy R.H. Middleton LLB BD   1981   1988   1 Hillpark Terrace, Edinburgh EH4 7SX   0131-336 3078

22 **Edinburgh: Dean (H)**
Mark M. Foster BSc BD   1998   1 Ravelston Terrace, Edinburgh EH4 3EF   0131-332 5736
[E-mail: markmfoster@mac.com]

23 **Edinburgh: Drylaw (0131-343 6643)**
Vacant

24 **Edinburgh: Duddingston**
James A.P. Jack DMin BSc BArch BD   1989   2001   Manse of Duddingston, Old Church Lane, Edinburgh EH15 3PX   0131-661 4240
[E-mail: jamesapjack@aol.com]

25 **Edinburgh: Fairmilehead (H) (0131-445 2374) (E-mail: fairmilehead.p.c@btconnect.com)**
John R. Munro BD   1976   1992   6 Braid Crescent, Edinburgh EH10 6AU   0131-446 9363
[E-mail: revjohnmunro@hotmail.com]

26 **Edinburgh: Gilmerton (New Charge Development)**
Paul H. Beautyman MA BD   1993   2002   43 Ravenscroft Street, Edinburgh EH17 8QJ   0131-664 7538
[E-mail: ncdgilmerton@uk.uumail.com]

27 **Edinburgh: Gorgie (H) (0131-337 7936)**
Peter I. Barber MA BD   1984   1995   90 Myreside Road, Edinburgh EH10 5BZ   0131-337 2284
[E-mail: pibarber@supanet.com]

28 **Edinburgh: Granton (H) (0131-552 3033)**
Vacant   8 Wardie Crescent, Edinburgh EH5 1AG   0131-551 2159
Marilynn Steele (Mrs) DCS   2 Northfield Gardens, Prestonpans EH32 9LQ   01875 811497

29 **Edinburgh: Greenbank (H) (0131-447 9969) (E-mail: greenbankchurch@btconnect.com)**
Ian G. Scott BSc BD STM   1965   1983   112 Greenbank Crescent, Edinburgh EH10 5SZ   0131-447 4032
[E-mail: igscott@blueyonder.co.uk]

30 **Edinburgh: Greenside (H) (0131-556 5588)**
Andrew F. Anderson MA BD   1981   80 Pilrig Street, Edinburgh EH6 5AS   0131-554 3277 (Tel/Fax)
[E-mail: andrew@pilrig.fsnet.co.uk]

31 **Edinburgh: Greyfriars Tolbooth and Highland Kirk (GE) (H) (0131-225 1900) (E-mail: greyfriarskirk@compuserve.com)**
Richard E. Frazer BA BD DMin   1986   2003   12 Tantallon Place, Edinburgh EH9 1NZ   0131-667 6610

32 **Edinburgh: High (St Giles') (0131-225 4363) (E-mail: stgilescathedral@btconnect.com)**
Gilleasbuig Macmillan   1969   1973   St Giles' Cathedral, Edinburgh EH1 1RE   0131-225 4363
CVO MA BD Drhc DD   [E-mail: minister.stgiles@btconnect.com]
Hilary W. Smith (Miss)   1999   2003   11 South Lauder Road, Edinburgh EH9 2NB   0131-667 6539
BD DipMin MTh PhD (Assistant)

33	**Edinburgh: Holyrood Abbey (H) (0131-661 4883)**			
	Philip R. Hair BD	1980	100 Willowbrae Avenue, Edinburgh EH8 7HU [E-mail: hairmail@compuserve.com]	0131-652 0640
34	**Edinburgh: Holy Trinity (H) (0131-442 3304)**			
	Vacant		16 Thorburn Road, Edinburgh EH13 0BQ	0131-441 7167
	Michael S. Dawson BTech BD (Assoc)	1979	12 Sighthill Crescent, Edinburgh EH11 4QE	0131-453 6279
	Joyce Mitchell (Mrs) DCS		16/4 Murrayburn Place, Edinburgh EH14 2RR	0131-453 6548
	Oliver M. Clegg BD (Youth Minister)	2003	1/5 Quarry View, Edinburgh EH14 2TL	0131-478 9938
35	**Edinburgh: Inverleith (H)**			
	D. Hugh Davidson MA	1965	43 Inverleith Gardens, Edinburgh EH3 5PR [E-mail: hdavidson@freeuk.com]	0131-552 3874
36	**Edinburgh: Juniper Green (H)**			
	James S. Dewar MA BD	1983	476 Lanark Road, Juniper Green, Edinburgh EH14 5BQ [E-mail: jsdewar@supanet.com]	0131-453 3494
37	**Edinburgh: Kaimes Lockhart Memorial**			
	Iain D. Penman BD	1977	76 Lasswade Road, Edinburgh EH16 6SF [E-mail: iainpenmanklm@aol.com]	0131-664 2287
38	**Edinburgh: Kirkliston**			
	Glenda J. Keating (Mrs) MTh	1996	43 Main Street, Kirkliston EH29 9AF [E-mail: kirkglen@aol.com]	0131-333 3298
39	**Edinburgh: Kirk o' Field (T) (H)**			
	Ian D. Maxwell MA BD PhD	1977	31 Hatton Place, Edinburgh EH9 1UA [E-mail: i.d.maxwell@quista.net]	0131-667 7954
40	**Edinburgh: Leith North (H) (0131-553 7378)**			
	Kenneth S. Baird MSc PhD BD CEng MIMarE	1998	6 Craighall Gardens, Edinburgh EH6 4RJ	0131-552 4411
41	**Edinburgh: Leith St Andrew's (H)**			
	John Cook MA BD	1967	13 Claremont Park, Edinburgh EH6 7PJ	0131-554 7695
42	**Edinburgh: Leith St Serf's (T) (H)**			
	Sara R. Embleton (Mrs) BA BD	1977	20 Wilton Road, Edinburgh EH16 5NX [E-mail: sara.embleton@which.net]	0131-478 1624
43	**Edinburgh: Leith St Thomas' Junction Road (T)**			
	George C. Shand MA BD	1981	107 Easter Warriston, Edinburgh EH7 4QZ [E-mail: georgeshand@blueyonder.co.uk]	0131-467 7789

44 Edinburgh: Leith South (H) (0131-554 2578) (E-mail: slpc@dial.pipex.com)
Ian Y. Gilmour BD   1985   1995   37 Claremont Road, Edinburgh EH6 7NN   0131-554 3062
[E-mail: ianyg@aol.com]
Jennifer Booth (Mrs) BD (Assoc)   1996   39 Lilyhill Terrace, Edinburgh EH8 7DR   0131-661 3813

45 Edinburgh: Leith Wardie (H) (0131-551 3847) (E-mail: admin@wardiechurch.freeserve.co.uk)
Brian C. Hilsley LLB BD   1990   35 Lomond Road, Edinburgh EH5 3JN   0131-552 3328
[E-mail: brian@wardie10.freeserve.co.uk]

46 Edinburgh: Liberton (H)
John N. Young MA BD PhD   1996   7 Kirk Park, Edinburgh EH16 6HZ   0131-664 3067
[E-mail: john@nicolyoung.freeserve.co.uk]

47 Edinburgh: Liberton Northfield (H) (0131-551 3847)
John M. McPake LTh   2000   9 Claverhouse Drive, Edinburgh EH16 6BR   0131-658 1754
[E-mail: john-mcpake@euphony.net]

48 Edinburgh: London Road (H) (0131-661 1149)
William L. Armitage BSc BD   1976   1991   26 Inchview Terrace, Edinburgh EH7 6TQ   0131-669 5311
[E-mail: billarm@blueyonder.co.uk]

49 Edinburgh: Marchmont St Giles' (H) (0131-447 4359)
Karen K. Watson BD MTh   1997   2002   19 Hope Terrace, Edinburgh EH9 2AP   0131-447 2834
[E-mail: karen@marchmontstgiles.org.uk]

50 Edinburgh: Mayfield Salisbury (0131-667 1522)
Scott S. McKenna BA BD   1994   2000   26 Seton Place, Edinburgh EH9 2JT   0131-667 1286
[E-mail: scottsmckenna@aol.com]
John R. Wells BD DipMin (Assoc)   1991   2003   18 West Mayfield, Edinburgh EH9 1TQ   0131-662 0367

51 Edinburgh: Morningside (H) (0131-447 6745) (E-mail: office@morningsideparishchurch.net)
Derek Browning MA BD DMin   1987   2003   20 Braidburn Crescent, Edinburgh EH10 6EN   0131-447 1617 (Tel/Fax)
[E-mail: derek.browning@btinternet.com]   07050 133876 (Mbl)

52 Edinburgh: Morningside United (H) (0131-447 3152)
John R. Smith MA BD   1973   1998   1 Midmar Avenue, Edinburgh EH10 6BS   0131-447 8724
[E-mail: ministermuc@blueyonder.co.uk]

53 Edinburgh: Muirhouse St Andrew's (E)
Frederick D.F. Shewan MA BD   1970   1980   35 Silverknowes Road, Edinburgh EH4 5LL   0131-336 4546

54 Edinburgh: Murrayfield (H) (0131-337 1091) (E-mail: murrayfield@parish-church.fsnet.co.uk)
William D. Brown BD CQSW   1987   2001   45 Murrayfield Gardens, Edinburgh EH12 6DH   0131-337 5431
[E-mail: wdb@fish.co.uk]

55 Edinburgh: Newhaven (H)
Grant MacLaughlan BA BD   1998   158 Granton Road, Edinburgh EH5 3RF   0131-552 8906

No.	Charge / Minister	Year	Address	Phone
56	**Edinburgh: New Restalrig (H) (0131-661 5676)** David L. Court BSc BD	1989	19 Abercorn Road, Edinburgh EH8 7DP [E-mail: david@lamont-court.freeserve.co.uk]	0131-661 4045
57	**Edinburgh: Old Kirk (H)** Vacant		24 Pennywell Road, Edinburgh EH4 4HD	0131-332 4354
58	**Edinburgh: Palmerston Place (H) (0131-220 1690) (E-mail: palmerston.admin@euphony.net)** Colin A.M. Sinclair BA BD	1981 1996	30B Cluny Gardens, Edinburgh EH10 6BJ [E-mail: colins.ppc@virgin.net]	0131-447 9598 0131-225 3312 (Fax)
59	**Edinburgh: Pilrig St Paul's (0131-553 1876)** John M. Tait BSc BD	1985 1999	78 Pilrig Street, Edinburgh EH6 5AS [E-mail: john.m.tait@btinternet.com]	0131-554 1842
60	**Edinburgh: Polwarth (H) (0131-346 2711)** Vacant		6 Trotter Haugh, Edinburgh EH9 2GZ	0131-667 4055
61	**Edinburgh: Portobello Old (H)** Neil Buchanan BD	1991	6 Hamilton Terrace, Edinburgh EH15 1NB [E-mail: neil.buchanan@talk21.com]	0131-669 5312
62	**Edinburgh: Portobello St James' (H)** Peter Webster BD	1977 2002	34 Brighton Place, Edinburgh EH15 1LT [E-mail: peterwebster101@hotmail.com]	0131-669 1767
63	**Edinburgh: Portobello St Philip's Joppa (H) (0131-669 3641)** Stewart G. Weaver BA BD PhD	2003	6 St Mary's Place, Edinburgh EH15 2QF [E-mail: stewartweaver@beeb.net]	0131-669 2410
64	**Edinburgh: Priestfield (H) (0131-667 5644)** Thomas N. Johnston LTh	1972 1990	13 Lady Road, Edinburgh EH16 5PA [E-mail: tomjohnston@blueyonder.co.uk]	0131-668 1620
65	**Edinburgh: Queensferry (H)** John G. Carrie BSc BD	1971	1 Station Road, South Queensferry EH30 9HY [E-mail: john.carrie@virgin.net]	0131-331 1100
66	**Edinburgh: Ratho** Ian J. Wells BD	1999	Ratho, Newbridge EH28 8NP [E-mail: ian@rathomanse.fsnet.co.uk]	0131-333 1346

67 Edinburgh: Reid Memorial (H) (0131-662 1203) (E-mail: reid.memorial@u-genie.co.uk)
Brian M. Embleton BD   1976   1985   20 Wilton Road, Edinburgh EH16 5NX   0131-667 3981
[E-mail: brian.embleton@which.net]

68 Edinburgh: Richmond Craigmillar (H) (0131-661 6561)
Elizabeth M. Henderson (Miss)   1985   1997   13 Wisp Green, Edinburgh EH15 3QX   0131-669 1133
MA BD MTh   [E-mail: lizhende@aol.com]

69 Edinburgh: St Andrew's and St George's (H) (0131-225 3847) (E-mail: standrewsandstgeorges@eh.quik.co.uk)
Roderick D.M. Campbell TD BD FSAScot   1975   2003   25 Comely Bank, Edinburgh EH4 1AJ   0131-332 5324
[E-mail: rdmcampbell@aol.com]

70 Edinburgh: St Andrew's Clermiston
Alistair H. Keil BD DipMin   1989   87 Drum Brae South, Edinburgh EH12 8TD   0131-339 4149
[E-mail: alistair.h.keil@talk21.com]

71 Edinburgh: St Catherine's Argyle (H) (0131-667 7220)
Victor W.N. Laidlaw BD   1975   5 Palmerston Road, Edinburgh EH9 1TL   0131-667 9344
[E-mail: viclaid@aol.com]

72 Edinburgh: St Colm's (T) (H)
Vacant   1 Merchiston Gardens, Edinburgh EH10 5DD   0131-337 1107

73 Edinburgh: St Cuthbert's (H) (0131-229 1142) (E-mail: office@stcuthberts.net)
Tom C. Cuthell MA BD MTh   1965   1976   34A Murrayfield Road, Edinburgh EH12 6ER   0131-337 6637
[E-mail: cuthell@tccuthell.fsnet.co.uk]
Fiona E.T. Hutchinson (Mrs) BD (Assoc)   2004   6 Abercorn Avenue, Edinburgh EH8 7HP   0131-661 3877

74 Edinburgh: St David's Broomhouse (H) (0131-443 9851)
Vacant   33 Traquair Park West, Edinburgh EH12 7AN   0131-334 1730
Liz Crocker (Mrs) DipComEd DCS   77C Craigcrook Road, Edinburgh EH4 3PH   0131-332 0227

75 Edinburgh: St George's West (H) (0131-225 7001) (E-mail: gwest@dircon.co.uk)
Peter J. Macdonald BD DipMin   1986   1998   6 Wardie Avenue, Edinburgh EH5 2AB   0131-552 4333
[E-mail: petermacdonald@blueyonder.co.uk]

76 Edinburgh: St John's Oxgangs
Gillean P. Maclean (Mrs) BD   1994   2003   2 Caiystane Terrace, Edinburgh EH10 6SR   0131-445 1688
[E-mail: gmaclean@fish.co.uk]

77 Edinburgh: St Margaret's (H) (0131-554 7400) (E-mail: stm.parish@virgin.net)
Carol H.M. Ford DSD RSAMD BD   2003   43 Moira Terrace, Edinburgh EH7 6TD   0131-669 7329
[E-mail: fordcaro@fish.co.uk]
Marion Buchanan (Mrs) MA DCS   6 Hamilton Terrace, Edinburgh EH15 1NB   0131-669 5312

78 Edinburgh: St Martin's
Elizabeth J.B. Youngson BD 1996 1999 5 Duddingston Crescent, Edinburgh EH15 3AS 0131-657 9894
[E-mail: e,youngson@btinternet.com]

79 Edinburgh: St Michael's (H) (E-mail: office@stmichael-kirk.co.uk)
Vacant

80 Edinburgh: St Nicholas' Sighthill
Kenneth J. Mackay MA BD 1971 1976 122 Sighthill Loan, Edinburgh EH11 4NT 0131-453 6921

81 Edinburgh: St Stephen's Comely Bank (0131-315 4416)
Graham T. Dickson MA BD 1985 1996 8 Blinkbonny Crescent, Edinburgh EH4 3NB 0131-332 3364 (Tel/Fax)
[E-mail: graham@dickson22.fsnet.co.uk]

82 Edinburgh: Slateford Longstone
Vacant
Mary Gargrave (Mrs) DCS 50 Kingsknowe Road South, Edinburgh EH14 2JW 0131-443 2960
229/3 Calder Road, Edinburgh EH11 4RG 0131-476 3493

83 Edinburgh: Stenhouse St Aidan's
Colin A. Strong BSc BD 1989 2001 65 Balgreen Road, Edinburgh EH12 5UA 0131-337 7711
[E-mail: colinastrong@aol.com]
Mary Gargrave (Mrs) DCS 229/3 Calder Road, Edinburgh EH11 4RG 0131-476 3493

84 Edinburgh: Stockbridge (H) (0131-332 0122)
Anne T. Logan (Mrs) MA BD MTh DMin 1981 1993 19 Eildon Street, Edinburgh EH3 5JU 0131-557 6052
[E-mail: anne@logan68.freeserve.co.uk]

85 Edinburgh: Tron Moredun
Vacant 467 Gilmerton Road, Edinburgh EH17 7JG 0131-666 2584

86 Edinburgh: Viewforth (T) (H) (0131-229 1917)
Anthony P. Thornthwaite MTh 1995 91 Morningside Drive, Edinburgh EH10 5NN 0131-447 6684
[E-mail: tony.thornthwaite@blueyonder.co.uk]

Aitken, Alexander R. MA	1965 1997	(Newhaven)	36 King's Meadow, Edinburgh EH16 5JW	0131-667 1404
Alexander, Ian W. BA BD STM	1990 1995	Board of World Mission	c/o 121 George Street, Edinburgh EH2 4YN	0131-225 5722
Anderson, Robert S. BD	1988 1997	Scottish Churches World Exchange	St Colm's International House, 23 Inverleith Terrace, Edinburgh EH3 5NS	0131-315 4444
Auld, A. Graeme MA BD PhD DLitt FSAScot	1973 1973	University of Edinburgh	Nether Swanshiel, Hobkirk, Bonchester Bridge, Hawick TD9 8JU	
Baigrie, R.A. MA	1945 1985	(Kirkurd with Newlands)	32 Inchcolm Terrace, South Queensferry EH30 9NA	0131-331 4311
Baxter, Richard F. OBE MA BD	1954 1990	(Assistant at St Andrew's and St George's)	138 Braid Road, Edinburgh EH10 6JB	0131-447 7735

Name			Charge / Role	Address	Telephone
Beckett, David M. BA BD	1964	2002	(Greyfriars, Tolbooth and Highland Kirk)	1F1, 31 Sciennes Road, Edinburgh EH9 1NT [E-mail: davidbeckett3@aol.com]	0131-667 2672
Blakey, Ronald S. MA BD MTh	1962	2000	Editor: *The Year Book*	5 Moss Side Road, Biggar ML12 6GF	01899 229226 (Mbl) 07752 450642
Brady, Ian D. BSc ARCST BD	1967	2001	(Edinburgh: Corstorphine Old)	28 Frankfield Crescent, Dalgety Bay, Dunfermline KY11 9LW [E-mail: pidb@dbay28.fsnet.co.uk]	01383 825104
Brown, William D. MA	1963	1989	(Wishaw Thornlie)	121 Dalkeith Road, Edinburgh EH16 5AJ	0131-667 1124
Bruce, Lilian M. (Miss) BD MTh	1971	2001	(Daviot and Dunlichity with Moy, Dalarossie and Tomatin)	33 Falcon Court, Edinburgh EH10 4AF	
Cameron, G. Gordon MA BD STM	1957	1997	(Juniper Green)	4 Ladywell Grove, Clackmannan FK10 4JQ	01259 723769
Cameron, John W.M. MA BD	1957	1996	(Liberton)	10 Plewlands Gardens, Edinburgh EH10 5JP	0131-447 1277
Chalmers, John P. BD	1979	1995	Department of Ministry	10 Liggars Place, Dunfermline KY12 7XZ	01383 739130
Chalmers, Murray MA	1965	1991	Hospital Chaplain	52 Eyre Place, Edinburgh EH3 5EJ	0131-556 8053
Cheyne, Alexander C. MA BD BLitt DLitt	1958	1986	(University of Edinburgh)	12 Crossland Crescent, Peebles EH45 8LF	01721 722288
Clinkenbeard, William W. BSc BD STM	1966	2000	(Edinburgh: Carrick Knowe)	4 Aline Court, Dalgety Bay, Dunfermline KY11 5GP [E-mail: bjclinks@compuserve.com]	01383 824011
Cobain, Alan R. BD	2000		Army Chaplain	26 St Michael's Road, Colchester CO2 9NZ	01206 572361
Cook, John Weir MA BD	1962	2002	(Edinburgh: Portobello St Philip's Joppa)	74 Pinkie Road, Musselburgh EH21 7QT [E-mail: jwc@freeuk.com]	0131-653 0992
Crichton, Thomas JP ChStJ MA	1965	2004	(Hospital Chaplain)	18 Carlton Terrace, Edinburgh EH7 5DD	0131-557 0009
Cross, Brian F. MA	1961	1998	(Coalburn)	1474 High Road, Whetstone, London N20 9QD	
Currie, David E.P. BSc BD	1983	2000	Adviser in Evangelism	21 Rosa Burn Avenue, Lindsayfield, East Kilbride G75 9DE	01355 248510
Davidson, Ian M.P. MBE MA BD	1957	1994	(Stirling: Allan Park South with Church of the Holy Rude)	13/8 Craigend Park, Edinburgh EH16 5XX	0131-664 0074
Dilbey, Mary L. (Miss) BD	1997	2002	(West Kirk of Calder)	41 Bonaly Rise, Edinburgh EH13 0QU	0131-441 9092
Dougall, Elspeth G. (Mrs) MA BD	1989	2001	(Edinburgh: Marchmont St Giles')	60B Craigmillar Park, Edinburgh EH16 5PU	0131-668 1342
Doyle, Ian B. MA BD PhD	1946	1991	(Department of National Mission)	21 Lygon Road, Edinburgh EH16 5QD	0131-667 2697
Drummond, Rhoda (Miss) DCS			(Deaconess)	Flat K, 23 Grange Loan, Edinburgh EH9 2ER	0131-668 3631
Dunn, W. Iain C. DA LTh	1983	1998	(Pilrig and Dalmeny Street)	10 Fox Covert Avenue, Edinburgh EH12 6UQ	0131-334 1665
Elliott, Gavin J. MA BD	1976	2004	Department of Ministry	c/o 121 George Street, Edinburgh EH2 4YN	0131-225 5722
Faulds, Norman L. MA BD FSAScot	1968	2000	(Aberlady with Gullane)	Wellwood, 8 Juniper Place, Juniper Green, Edinburgh EH14 5TX	0131-453 4984
Fergusson, David A.S. MA BD DPhil FRSE	1984	2000	University of Edinburgh	23 Riselaw Crescent, Edinburgh EH10 6HN	0131-447 4022
Finlayson, J. Clarence MA	1930	1972	(Grange)	52 Falcon Avenue, Edinburgh EH10 4AW	0131-447 6550
Forrester, Duncan B. MA BD DPhil DD	1962	1978	(University of Edinburgh)	25 Kingsburgh Road, Edinburgh EH12 6DZ	0131-337 5646
Forrester, Margaret R. (Mrs) MA BD	1974	2003	(Edinburgh: St Michael's)	25 Kingsburgh Road, Edinburgh EH12 6DZ [E-mail: margaret@theforresters.fsnet.co.uk]	0131-337 5646
Fraser, Shirley A. (Miss) MA BD	1992	2001	Edinburgh Team Leader: Friends International Office for Worship	30 Parkhead Avenue, Edinburgh EH11 4SG	0131-443 7268
Galbraith, Douglas MA BD BMus MPhil ARSCM	1965	1995	Doctrine and Artistic Matters (Glamis, Inverarity and Kinnettles)	c/o 121 George Street, Edinburgh EH2 4YN [E-mail: dgalbraith@cofscotland.org.uk]	0131-240 2233
Gardner, John V.	1997	2003		104 Comiston Drive, Edinburgh EH10 5QU [E-mail: jvg66@hotmail.com]	0131-447 6859
Gibson, John C.L. MA BD DPhil	1959	1994	(University of Edinburgh)	Cairnbank, Morton Street South, Edinburgh EH15 2NB	0131-669 3635

Name			Position	Address	Tel.
Gillon, J. Blair MA	1935	1980	(Borthwick with Heriot)	12A Craigmillar Park, Edinburgh EH16 5PS	0131-667 0004
Gordon, Tom MA BD	1974	1994	(Chaplain: Fairmile Marie Curie Centre)	22 Gosford Road, Port Seton, Prestonpans EH32 0HF	01875 812262
Graham, W. Peter MA BD	1967	1993	Presbytery Clerk	23/6 East Comiston, Edinburgh EH10 6RZ [E-mail: akph50@uk.uumail.com]	0131-445 5763
Harkness, James CB OBE QHC MA DD	1961	1995	(Chaplain General: Army)	13 Saxe Coburg Place, Edinburgh EH3 5BR	0131-343 1297
Hill, J. William BA BD	1967	2001	(Corstorphine St Anne's)	33/9 Murrayfield Road, Edinburgh EH12 6EP	0131-332 8020
Hutchison, Maureen (Mrs) DCS	1974	2000	(Deaconess)	23 Drylaw Crescent, Edinburgh EH4 2AU	01506 412020
Jamieson, Gordon D. MA BD	1954	1994	Director of Stewardship	41 Goldpark Place, Livingston EH54 6LW	
Jeffrey, Eric W.S. JP MA			(Edinburgh Bristo Memorial)	18 Gillespie Crescent, Edinburgh EH10 4HT	0131-229 7815
Johnston, William B. MA BD DD DLitt	1945	1991	(Colinton)	15 Elliot Road, Edinburgh EH14 1DU	0131-441 3387
Kant, Everard FVCM MTh	1953	1988	(Kinghorn)	10/1 Maxwell Street, Edinburgh EH10 5GZ	0131-466 2607
Kelly, Ewan R. MB ChB BD	1994	1998	Edinburgh University	2 Highfield Avenue, Linlithgow EH49 7BE	01506 847883
Lamont, A. Donald BSc BD	1941	1975	(Nakuru)	36 St Clair Terrace, Edinburgh EH10 5PS	0131-447 4267
Lawson, Kenneth C. MA BD	1963	1999	(Adviser in Adult Education)	56 Easter Drylaw View, Edinburgh EH4 2QP	0131-539 3311
Lyall, David BSc BD STM PhD	1965	2002	(University of Edinburgh)	1 North Megetland, Edinburgh EH14 1XG	0131-443 7640
Lyon, D.H.S. MA BD STM	1952	1986	(Board of World Mission and Unity)	30 Mansfield Road, Balerno EH14 7JZ	0131-449 5031
Macdonald, Finlay A.J. MA BD PhD	1971	1996	Principal Clerk	c/o 121 George Street, Edinburgh EH2 4YN	0131-225 5722
Macdonald, William J. BD	1976	1999	(Board of National Mission: New Charge Development)	1/13 North Werber Park, Edinburgh EH4 1SY	0131-332 0254
McDonald, William J.G. DD	1953	1992	(Mayfield)	7 Blacket Place, Edinburgh EH9 1RN	0131-667 2100
McDowell, Brian		1999	(Chaplain: Fettes College)	6 West Woods, Fettes College, Edinburgh EH4 1RA	0131-332 9510
McGillivray, A. Gordon MA BD STM	1951	1993	(Presbytery Clerk)	7 Greenfield Crescent, Balerno EH14 7HD	0131-449 4747
MacGregor, Margaret S. (Miss) MA BD DipEd	1985	1994	(Calcutta)	16 Learmonth Court, Edinburgh EH4 1PB	0131-332 1089
McGregor, Alistair G.C. QC BD	1987	2002	(Edinburgh: Leith North)	22 Primrose Bank Road, Edinburgh EH5 3JG	0131-551 2802
McGregor, T. Stewart MBE MA BD	1957	1998	(Chaplain: Edinburgh Royal Infirmary)	19 Lonsdale Terrace, Edinburgh EH3 9HL [E-mail: cetsm@dircon.uk]	0131-229 5332
McIntyre, John CVO DLitt DD Drhc FRSE	1941	1986	(University of Edinburgh)	27/317 West Savile Terrace, Edinburgh EH9 3DT	0131-667 1203
Maclagan, David W. MA ThD	1965	1991	(Largs: St John's)	Flat 19, 14 Maxwell Street, Edinburgh EH10 5HU	0131-447 9729
Maclean, Ailsa G. (Mrs) BD DipCE	1979	1988	(Chaplain: George Heriot's School)	28 Swan Spring Avenue, Edinburgh EH10 6NJ	0131-445 1320
MacLean, Marjory A. (Miss) LLB BD PhD	1991	1998	(Board of Practice and Procedure)	c/o 121 George Street, Edinburgh EH2 4YN	0131-225 5722
McLeod, Roderick MA BD	1951	1990	(Lochwinnoch)	2 East Savile Road, Edinburgh EH16 5ND	0131-667 1475
MacMurchie, F. Lynne LLB BD	1998	2003	Health Care Chaplain	Edinburgh Community Mental Health Chaplaincy, 41 George IV Bridge, Edinburgh EH1 1EL	0131-220 5150
McPheat, Elspeth DCS			(Deaconess: Social Responsibility)	11/5 New Orchardfield, Edinburgh EH6 5ET	0131-554 4143
McPhee, Duncan C. MA BD	1953	1993	(Department of National Mission)	8 Belvedere Park, Edinburgh EH6 4LR	0131-552 6784
Macpherson, Allan S. MA	1967	1993	(Chaplain: Merchiston Castle School)	36 Craigmillar Castle Road, Edinburgh EH16 4AR	0131-667 1456
Macpherson, Colin C.R. MA BD	1958	1996	(Dunfermline St Margaret's)	7 Eva Place, Edinburgh EH9 3ET	0131-334 9774
Mathieson, Angus R. MA BD	1988	1998	Department of Ministry	21 Traquair Park West, Edinburgh EH12 7AN	0131-332 2748
Moir, Ian A MA BD	1962	2000	(Adviser for Urban Priority Areas)	28/6 Comely Bank Avenue, Edinburgh EH4 1EL	

Name	Years	Office	Address	Telephone
Morrice, William G. MA BD STM PhD	1957 1991	(St John's College Durham)	Flat 37, The Cedars, 2 Manse Road, Edinburgh EH12 7SN [E-mail: w.g.morrice@btinternet.com]	0131-316 4845
Morrison, Mary B. (Mrs) MA BD DipEd	1978 2000	(Edinburgh: Stenhouse St Aidan's)	14 Eildon Terrace, Edinburgh EH3 5LU	0131-556 1962
Morton, Andrew R. MA BD DD	1956 1994	(Board of World Mission and Unity)	11 Oxford Terrace, Edinburgh EH4 1PX	0131-332 6592
Morton, R. Colin BA BD	1960 1998	(Jerusalem)	313 Lanark Road West, Currie EH14 5RS	0131-449 7359
Moyes, Sheila A. (Miss) DCS		(Deaconess)	158 Pilton Avenue, Edinburgh EH5 2JZ	0131-551 1731
Mulligan, Anne (Miss) DCS	1968 2000	Deaconess: Hospital Chaplain	27A Craigour Avenue, Edinburgh EH17 1NH	0131-664 3426
Munro, George A.M.	1951 1990	(Edinburgh: Cluny)	108 Caiyside, Edinburgh EH10 7HR	0131-445 5829
Murison, William G.	1953 1996	(Department of World Mission and Unity)	21 Hailes Gardens, Edinburgh EH13 0JL	0131-441 2460
Murrie, John BD		(Kirkliston)	31 Nicol Road, The Whins, Broxburn EH52 6JJ	01506 852464
Neilson, Peter MA BD MTh	1975 2003	Board of National Mission: Mission Developments Facilitator	12 Strathalmond Court, Edinburgh EH4 8AE	0131-339 4536
Nicol, Douglas A.O. MA BD	1974 1991	National Mission Secretary	24 Corbiehill Avenue, Edinburgh EH4 5DR	0131-336 1965
Page, Ruth MA BD DPhil	1976 2000	(University of Edinburgh)	22/5 West Mill Bank, West Mill Road, Edinburgh EH13 0QT	0131-441 3740
Paterson, Ian M. MA	1947 1985	(Eccles with Greenlaw)	45/15 Maidencraig Crescent, Edinburgh EH4 2UU	0131-332 9735
Paterson, J.M.K. MA ACII BD DD	1964 1987	(Milngavie St Paul's)	58 Orchard Drive, Edinburgh EH4 2DZ	0131-332 5876
Paterson, John M.	1976 1987	(Blackbraes and Shieldhill)	28/21 Roseburn Place, Edinburgh EH12 5NX	0131-337 0095
Philip, James MA	1948 1997	(Holyrood Abbey)	3 Ferguson Gardens, Musselburgh EH21 6XF	0131-653 2310
Philp, Connie (Miss) BD	1980 1995	(Arbuthnott with Bervie)	22/5 South Elixa Place, Baronscourt View, Edinburgh EH8 7PG	0131-661 3124
Plate, Maria A.G. (Miss) LTh BA	1983 2000	(South Ronaldsay and Burray)	Flat 29, 77 Barnton Park View, Edinburgh EH4 6EL	0131-339 8539
Potts, Jean (Miss) DCS		(Deaconess)	28B East Claremont Street, Edinburgh EH7 4JP	0131-557 2144
Rae, David L.	1955 1990	(Kolhapur)	29 Falcon Avenue, Edinburgh EH10 4AL	0131-447 3158
Reid, W. Scott BD MA DipPS PhD	1950 1990	(London Road)	14/37 Ethel Terrace, Edinburgh EH10 5NA	0131-447 7642
Renton, Ian P.	1958 1990	(St Colm's)	98 Homeross House, Strathearn Road, Edinburgh EH9 2QY	0131-447 0601
Ridland, Alistair K. MA BD	1982 2000	Chaplain: Western General Hospital	13 Stewart Place, Kirkliston EH29 0BQ	0131-333 2711
Ronald, Norma A. (Miss) MBE DCS		(Deaconess)	43/26 Gillespie Crescent, Edinburgh EH10 4HY	0131-228 1008
Ross, Andrew C. MA BD STM PhD	1958 1998	(University of Edinburgh)	27 Colinton Road, Edinburgh EH10 5DR	0131-447 5987
Ross, Kenneth R. BA BD PhD	1982 1999	General Secretary, Board of World Mission	c/o 121 George Street, Edinburgh EH2 4YN	0131-225 5722
Schofield, Melville F. MA	1960 2000	(Chaplain: Western General Hospitals)	25 Rowantree Grove, Currie EH14 5AT	0131-449 4745
Scott, Martin DipMus RSAM BD PhD	1986 2000	Department of Ministry	18 Covenanters Rise, Dunfermline KY11 8QS	01383 722328
Sim, John G. MA	1946 1987	(Kirkcaldy Old)	7 Grosvenor Crescent, Edinburgh EH12 5EP	0131-226 3190
Skinner, Donald M. MBE JP FIES	1962 2000	(Edinburgh: Gilmerton)	12 Straid a Choc, Clynder, Helensburgh G84 0QX	
Slorach, Alexander CA BD	1970 2002	(Kirk of Lammermuir with Langton and Polwarth)	61 Inverleith Row, Edinburgh EH3 5PX	
Stephen, Donald M. TD MA BD ThM	1962 2001	(Edinburgh: Marchmont St Giles')	10 Hawkhead Crescent, Edinburgh EH16 6LR	0131-658 1216
Stevenson, John MA BD	1963 2001	(Department of Education)	12 Swanston Gardens, Edinburgh EH10 7DL	0131-445 3960
Stirling, A. Douglas BSc	1956 1994	(Rhu and Shandon)	162 Avontoun Park, Linlithgow EH49 6QH	01506 845021
Stiven, Iain K. MA BD	1960 1997	(Strachur and Strathlachlan)	3 Gloucester Place, Edinburgh EH3 6EE	0131-225 8177
Storrar, William F. MA BD PhD	1984 2000	University of Edinburgh	35 Strathalmond Park, Edinburgh EH4 8AH	
Taylor, Howard G. BSc BD MTh	1971 1998	Chaplain: Heriot Watt University	The Chaplaincy, Heriot Watt University, Riccarton, Currie EH14 4AS	0131-449 5111 (ext 4508)
Taylor, William R. MA BD	1983 2003	Chaplaincy Co-ordinator: Scottish Prison Service	33 Kingsknowe Drive, Edinburgh EH14 2JY	
Teague, Yvonne (Mrs) DCS		(Board of Ministry)	46 Craigcrook Avenue, Edinburgh EH4 3PX	0131-336 3113

Name				Phone
Telfer, Iain J. BD DPS	1978 2001	Chaplain: Royal Infirmary	32 Alnwickhill Park, Edinburgh EH16 6UH	0131-536 3084
Thom, Helen (Miss) DCS		(Deaconess)	84 Great King Street, Edinburgh EH3 6QU	0131-556 5687
Torrance, Thomas F. MBE DLitt DD DSc DrTheol DrTeol FBA FRSE				
Walker, R.W. MB ChB	1940 1979	(University of Edinburgh)	37 Braid Farm Road, Edinburgh EH10 6LE	0131-667 0578
Whyte, Iain A. BA BD STM	1941 1981	(Lesmahagow Abbeygreen)	39/22 Blackford Avenue, Edinburgh EH9 3HN	0131-220 5150
Wigglesworth, J. Christopher MBE BSc PhD BD	1968 2001	Community Mental Health Chaplain	41 George IV Bridge, Edinburgh EH1 1EL	
Wilkie, James L. MA BD	1968 1999	(St Andrew's College, Selly Oak)	12 Leven Terrace, Edinburgh EH3 9LW	0131-228 6335
	1959 1998	(Board of World Mission)	7 Comely Bank Avenue, Edinburgh EH4 1EW [E-mail: jl.wilkie@btinternet.com]	0131-343 1552
Wilkinson, John BD MD FRCP DTM&H	1946 1975	(Kikuyu)	70 Craigleith Hill Gardens, Edinburgh EH4 2JH	0131-332 2994
Williams, Jenny M. (Miss) BSc CQSW BD	1996 1997	Christian Fellowship of Healing	16 Blantyre Terrace, Edinburgh EH10 5AE	0131-447 0050
Wilson, John M. MA	1964 1995	(Adviser in Religious Education)	27 Bellfield Street, Edinburgh EH15 2BR	0131-669 5257
Young, Alexander W. BD DipMin	1988 1999	Chaplain: Western General Hospitals	Rosebank Villa, 68 Main Street, Newtongrange, Dalkeith EH22 4ND	

EDINBURGH ADDRESSES

Albany	At Greenside
Balerno	Johnsburn Road, Balerno
Barclay	Barclay Place
Blackhall St Columba	Queensferry Road
Bristo Memorial	Peffermill Road, Craigmillar
Broughton St Mary's	Bellevue Crescent
Canongate	Canongate
Carrick Knowe	North Saughton Road
Colinton	Dell Road
Colinton Mains	Oxgangs Road North
Corstorphine	
Craigsbank	Craig's Crescent
Old	Kirk Loan
St Anne's	Kaimes Road
St Ninian's	St John's Road
Craigentinny	
St Christopher's	Craigentinny Road
Craiglockhart	Craiglockhart Avenue
Craigmillar Park	Craigmillar Park
Cramond	Cramond Glebe Road
Currie	Kirkgate, Currie
Davidson's Mains	Quality Street
Dean	Dean Path
Drylaw	Groathill Road North
Duddingston	Old Church Lane, Duddingston
Fairmilehead	Frogston Road West, Fairmilehead
Gilmerton	Ravenscroft Street
Gorgie	Gorgie Road
Granton	Boswall Parkway
Greenbank	Braidburn Terrace
Greenside	Royal Terrace
Greyfriars Tolbooth and Highland Kirk	Greyfriars Place
High (St Giles')	High Street
Holyrood Abbey	Dalziel Place x London Road
Holy Trinity	Hailesland Place, Wester Hailes
Inverleith	Inverleith Gardens
Juniper Green	Lanark Road, Juniper Green
Kaimes Lockhart Memorial	Gracemount Drive
Kirkliston	The Square, Kirkliston
Kirk o' Field	Pleasance
Leith	
North	Madeira Street off Ferry Road
St Andrew's	Easter Road
St Serf's	Ferry Road
St Thomas' Junction Road	Great Junction Street
South	Kirkgate, Leith
Wardie	Primrosebank Road
Liberton	Kirkgate, Liberton
Northfield	Gilmerton Road, Liberton
London Road	Kilgraston Road
Marchmont St Giles'	Mayfield Road x West Mayfield
Mayfield Salisbury	Cluny Gardens
Morningside	Bruntsfield Place x Chamberlain Road
Morningside United	
Muirhouse St Andrew's	Pennywell Gardens
Murrayfield	Abinger Gardens
Newhaven	Craighall Road
New Restalrig	Willowbrae Road
Old Kirk	Pennywell Road
Palmerston Place	Palmerston Place
Pilrig St Paul's	Pilrig Street
Polwarth	Polwarth Terrace x Harrison Road
Portobello	
Old	Bellfield Street
St James'	Rosefield Place
St Philip's, Joppa	Abercorn Terrace
Priestfield	Dalkeith Road x Marchhall Place
Queensferry	The Loan, South Queensferry
Ratho	Baird Road, Ratho
Reid Memorial	West Savile Terrace
Richmond Craigmillar	Niddrie Mains Road
St Andrew's and St George's	George Street
St Andrew's Clermiston	Clermiston View
St Catherine's Argyle	Grange Road x Chalmers Crescent
St Colm's	Dalry Road x Cathcart Place
St Cuthbert's	Lothian Road
St David's Broomhouse	Broomhouse Crescent
St George's West	Shandwick Place
St John's Oxgangs	Oxgangs Road
St Margaret's	Restalrig Road South
St Martin's	Magdalene Drive
St Michael's	Slateford Road
St Nicholas' Sighthill	Calder Road
St Stephen's Comely Bank	Comely Bank

(2) WEST LOTHIAN

Meets in the church of the incoming Moderator on the first Tuesday of September and in St John's Church Hall, Bathgate, on the first Tuesday of every other month, except December, when the meeting is on the second Tuesday, and January, July and August, when there is no meeting.

Clerk: REV. DUNCAN SHAW BD MTh   St John's Manse, Mid Street, Bathgate EH48 1QD [E-mail: akph78@uk.uumail.com]   **01506 653146**

Abercorn linked with Pardovan, Kingscavil and Winchburgh
A. Scott Marshall DipComm BD   1984   1998   The Manse, Winchburgh, Broxburn EH52 6TT [E-mail: pkwla@aol.com]   01506 890919

Armadale (H)
J. Edward Andrews MA BD DipCG   1985   2003   70 Mount Pleasant, Armadale, Bathgate EH48 3HB [E-mail: edward.andrews@btinternet.com]   01501 730358

Avonbridge linked with Torphichen
Clifford R. Acklam BD MTh   1997   2000   Manse Road, Torphichen, Bathgate EH48 4LT [E-mail: cliff@torphichen.org]   01506 652794

Bathgate: Boghall (H)
Vacant   1 Manse Place, Ash Grove, Bathgate EH48 1NJ   01506 652940

Bathgate: High (H)
Ronald G. Greig MA BD   1987   1998   19 Hunter Grove, Bathgate EH48 1NN [E-mail: ron.greig@care4free.net]   01506 652654

Bathgate: St David's
Elliot G.S. Wardlaw BA BD DipMin   1984   70 Marjoribanks Street, Bathgate EH48 1AH [E-mail: elliot@gswardlaw.freeserve.co.uk]   01506 653177

Bathgate: St John's (H)
Duncan Shaw BD MTh   1975   1978   St John's Manse, Mid Street, Bathgate EH48 1QD [E-mail: duncanshaw@uk.uumail.com]   01506 653146

Blackburn and Seafield
Robert A. Anderson MA BD DPhil   1980   1998   Blackburn, Bathgate EH47 7QR [E-mail: robertaland@supanet.com]   01506 652825

Blackridge linked with **Harthill: St Andrew's**
H. Warner Hardie BD   1979   East Main Street, Harthill, Shotts ML7 5QW   01501 751239
[E-mail: warner@hardies55.freeserve.co.uk]

Breich Valley
Thomas Preston BD   1978   2001   Stoneyburn, Bathgate EH47 8AU   01501 762018

Broxburn (H)
Richard T. Corbett BSc MSc PhD BD   1992   2 Church Street, Broxburn EH52 5EL   01506 852825
[E-mail: revcorbett@pgen.net]

Fauldhouse: St Andrew's
Elizabeth Smith (Mrs) BD   1996   2000   7 Glebe Court, Fauldhouse, Bathgate EH47 9DX   01501 771190
[E-mail: smithrevb@btinternet.com]

Harthill: St Andrew's See Blackridge

Kirknewton and East Calder
Ann M. Ballentine (Miss) MA BD   1981   1993   8 Manse Court, East Calder, Livingston EH53 0HF   01506 880802
[E-mail: annballentine@hotmail.com]

Kirk of Calder (H)
John M. Povey MA BD   1981   19 Maryfield Park, Mid Calder, Livingston EH53 0SB   01506 882495
[E-mail: revjpovey@aol.com]
Phyllis Thomson (Miss) DCS   2003   63 Caroline Park, Mid Calder, Livingston EH53 0SJ   01506 883207

Linlithgow: St Michael's (H) (E-mail: info@stmichaels-parish.org.uk)
D. Stewart Gillan BSc MDiv PhD   2004   St Michael's Manse, Kirkgate, Linlithgow EH49 7AL   01506 842195
                                            Cross House, Linlithgow EH49 7AL
James Francis BD PhD (Assoc)   2002   [E-mail: jim.francis@tiscali.co.uk]   01506 842665
Thomas S. Riddell BSc (Aux)   1993   1994   4 The Maltings, Linlithgow EH49 6DS   01506 843251
[E-mail: tsriddell@blueyonder.co.uk]

Linlithgow: St Ninian's Craigmailen (H)
W. Richard Houston BSc BD   1998   2004   29 Philip Avenue, Linlithgow EH49 7BH   01506 845535
[E-mail: wrhouston@blueyonder.co.uk]

Livingston Ecumenical Parish
Incorporating the Worship Centres at:
Carmondean and Knightsridge
Suzanna Bates BTh   13 Eastcroft Court, Livingston EH54 7ET
(The Methodist Church)
Craigshill (St Columba's) and Ladywell (St Paul's)
Colin R. Douglas MA BD STM   1969   1987   27 Heatherbank, Ladywell, Livingston EH54 6EE   01506 432326
[E-mail: colin-douglas@tiscali.co.uk]

Dedridge (The Lanthorn)
Eileen Thompson BD MTh
(Scottish Episcopal Church)
[E-mail: eileenet@fish.co.uk]

Livingston: Old (H)
Graham W. Smith BA BD FSAScot — 1995 — Manse of Livingston, Charlesfield Lane, Livingston EH54 7AJ — 01506 420227
[E-mail: gws@livoldpar.org.uk]

Pardovan, Kingscavil and Winchburgh See Abercorn

Polbeth Harwood linked with West Kirk of Calder (H)
David A. Albon BA MCS — 2004 — 27 Learmonth Crescent, West Calder EH55 8AF — 01506 870460
Kay McIntosh (Mrs) DCS — 2003 — 4 Jacklin Green, Livingston EH54 8PZ — 01506 495472

Strathbrock
David W. Black BSc BD — 1968 1984 — 1 Manse Park, Uphall, Broxburn EH52 6NX — 01506 852550

Torphichen See Avonbridge

Uphall South (H)
Margaret Steele (Miss) BSc BD — 2000 — 8 Fernlea, Uphall, Broxburn EH52 6DF — 01506 852788
[E-mail: msteele@beeb.net]

West Kirk of Calder (H) See Polbeth Harwood

Whitburn: Brucefield (H)
Richard J.G Darroch BD MTh — 1993 2003 — Brucefield Drive, Whitburn, Bathgate EH47 8NU — 01501 740263
[E-mail: richdarr@aol.com]

Whitburn: South (H)
Christine Houghton (Mrs) BD — 1997 2004 — 5 Mansewood Crescent, Whitburn, Bathgate EH47 8HA — 01501 740333
[E-mail: christine@houghton1027.fsnet.co.uk]

Name				
Cameron, Ian MA BD	1953	1981	(Kilbrandon and Kilchattan)	37 Burghmuir Court, Linlithgow EH49 7LJ	01506 847987
Dickson, A. Stuart	1963	1995	(Glasgow: Govan Old – Assoc)	74 Netherwood Park, Deans, Livingston EH54 8RW	01506 420167
Dundas, Thomas B.S. LTh	1969	1996	(West Kirk of Calder)	35 Coolkill, Sandyford, Dublin 18, Republic of Ireland	00353 12953061
McMahon, John K.S. MA BD	1998	2004	Hospital Chaplain	28/2 Saughton Road, Edinburgh EH11 3PT	
MacRae, Norman I. LTh	1966	2003	(Inverness: Trinity)	144 Hope Park Gardens, Bathgate EH48 2QX	01506 633254
Manson, Robert L. MA DPS	1956	1991	(Chaplain: Royal Edinburgh Hospital)	4 Murieston Drive, Livingston EH54 9AU	01506 434746
Moore, J.W. MA	1950	1983	(Daviot with Rayne)	31 Lennox Gardens, Linlithgow EH49 7PZ	01506 842534
Morrice, Charles S. MA BD PhD	1959	1997	(Kenya)	104 Baron's Hill Avenue, Linlithgow EH49 7JG	01506 847167

[E-mail: cs.morrice@btopenworld.com]

| Morrison, Iain C. BA BD | 1990 | 2003 | (Linlithgow: St Ninian's Craigmailen) | Whaligoe, 53 Eastcroft Drive, Polmont, Falkirk FK2 0SU | 01324 713249 |

[E-mail: iain@kirkweb.org]

Murray, Ronald N.G. MA	1946 1986	(Pardovan and Kingscavil with Winchburgh)	42 Lennox Gardens, Linlithgow EH49 7QA	01506 845680
Nelson, Georgina (Mrs) MA BD PhD DipEd	1990 1995	Hospital Chaplain	6 Pentland Park, Craigshill, Livingston EH54 5NR	01506 434874
Robertson, Emmanuel ThM ThD	1953 1993	(Armadale)	39 Drumcross Road, Bathgate EH48 4HF	01506 654766
Russell, Archibald MA	1949 1991	(Duror with Glencoe)	4 Bonnytoun Avenue, Linlithgow EH49 7JS	01506 842530
Smith, W. Ewing BSc	1962 1994	(Livingston: Old)	8 Hardy Gardens, Bathgate EH48 1NH [E-mail: wesmith@hardygdns.freeserve.co.uk]	01506 652028
Trimble, Robert DCS	1959 1999	(Deacon)	5 Templar Rise, Dedridge, Livingston EH54 6PJ	01506 412504
Whitson, William S. MA		(Cumbernauld: St Mungo's)	2 Chapman's Brae, Bathgate EH48 4LH [E-mail: williambarbara@amserve.net]	01506 650027
Wilson, Glenda (Mrs) DCS		Deacon	88 Seafield Rows, Seafield, Bathgate EH47 7AW	01506 655298

(3) LOTHIAN

Meets at Musselburgh: St Andrew's High Parish Church on the last Thursday of January and June and the first Thursday of March, April, May, September, October, November and December. (Alternative arrangements are made to avoid meeting on Maundy Thursday.)

Clerk:	MR JOHN D. McCULLOCH DL		Auchindinny House, Penicuik EH26 8PE [E-mail: akph65@uk.uumail.com]	01968 676300 (Tel/Fax)
Aberlady (H) linked with Gullane (H)				
John B. Cairns LTh LLB LLD DD	1974	2001	The Manse, Hummel Road, Gullane EH31 2BG [E-mail: john@cairns3018.freeserve.co.uk]	01620 843192
Athelstaneford linked with Whitekirk and Tyninghame				
Kenneth D.F. Walker MA BD PhD		1976	The Manse, Athelstaneford, North Berwick EH39 5BE [E-mail: kandv-walker@connectfree.co.uk]	01620 880378
Belhaven (H) linked with Spott				
Laurence H. Twaddle MA BD MTh	1977	1978	The Manse, Belhaven Road, Dunbar EH42 1NH [E-mail: revtwaddle@aol.com]	01368 863098
Bolton and Saltoun linked with Humbie linked with Yester (H)				
Donald Pirie LTh	1975	1999	The Manse, Tweeddale Avenue, Gifford, Haddington EH41 4QN	01620 810515
Bonnyrigg (H)				
John Mitchell LTh CMin		1991	9 Viewbank View, Bonnyrigg EH19 2HU [E-mail: rev.jmitchell@tiscali.co.uk]	0131-663 8287 (Tel/Fax)

Borthwick (H) linked with Cranstoun, Crichton and Ford (H) linked with Fala and Soutra (H)
D. Graham Leitch MA BD   1974   2003   Cranstoun Cottage, Ford, Pathhead EH37 5RE   01875 320314
[E-mail: leitch@cranscott.fsnet.co.uk]

Cockenzie and Port Seton: Chalmers Memorial (H)
Robert L. Glover BMus BD MTh ARCO   1971   1997   Braemar Villa, 2 Links Road, Port Seton, Prestonpans EH32 0HA   01875 812481
[E-mail: rlglover@btinternet.com]

Cockenzie and Port Seton: Old (H)
Continued Vacancy   1 Links Road, Port Seton, Prestonpans EH32 0HA   01875 812310

Cockpen and Carrington (H) linked with Lasswade (H) linked with Rosewell (H)
Wendy F. Drake (Mrs) BD   1978   1992   11 Pendreich Terrace, Bonnyrigg EH19 2DT   0131-663 6884
[E-mail: drake@pendreich.fsnet.co.uk]

Cranstoun, Crichton and Ford (H) See Borthwick

Dalkeith: St John's and King's Park (H)
Keith L. Mack BD MTh DPS   2002   13 Weir Crescent, Dalkeith EH22 3JN   0131-454 0206
[E-mail: kthmacker@aol.com]

Dalkeith: St Nicholas' Buccleuch (H)
Alexander G. Horsburgh MA BD   1996   2004   116 Bonnyrigg Road, Dalkeith EH22 3HZ   0131-663 3036
[E-mail: alexanderhorsburgh@compuserve.com]

Dirleton (H) linked with North Berwick: Abbey (H) (01620 890110)
David J. Graham BSc BD PhD   1982   1998   20 Westgate, North Berwick EH39 4AF   01620 892410
[E-mail: davidjohn@grahams.fsbusiness.co.uk]

Dunbar (H)
Eric W. Foggitt MA BSc BD   1991   2000   The Manse, Bayswell Road, Dunbar EH42 1AB   01368 863749 (Tel/Fax)
[E-mail: ericleric3@btopenworld.com]

Dunglass
Anne R. Lithgow (Mrs) MA BD   1992   1994   The Manse, Cockburnspath TD13 5XZ   01368 830713
[E-mail: anne.lithgow@btinternet.com]

Fala and Soutra See Borthwick

Garvald and Morham linked with Haddington: West (H)
Cameron Mackenzie BD   1997   15 West Road, Haddington EH41 3RD   01620 822213
[E-mail: cdpl.mackenzie@quista.net]

Gladsmuir linked with Longniddry (H)
Robin E. Hill LLB PhD BD — 2004 — The Manse, Elcho Road, Longniddry EH32 0LB — 01875 853195
[E-mail: robinailsa@ntlworld.com]
Florence A. Underwood (Mrs) BD (Assistant) — 1992 — 2003 — The Shieling, Main Street, Stenton, Dunbar EH42 1TE — 01368 850629

Glencorse (H) linked with Roslin (H)
Vacant — 1981 — 38 Penicuik Road, Roslin EH25 9LH — 0131-440 2012

Gorebridge (H)
Mark S. Nicholas MA BD — 1999 — 100 Hunterfield Road, Gorebridge EH23 4TT — 01875 820387
[E-mail: mark.nicholas@fish.co.uk]

Gullane See Aberlady

Haddington: St Mary's (H)
James M. Cowie BD — 1977 — 2002 — 21 Sidegate, Haddington EH41 4BZ — 01620 823109
[E-mail: jcowie@home.bosr.org.uk]

Haddington: West See Garvald and Morham

Howgate (H) linked with Penicuik: South (H)
Frank Ribbons MA BD DipEd — 1985 — 18 Broomhill Avenue, Penicuik EH26 9EG — 01968 674692
[E-mail: frank@ribbonsfamily.co.uk]

Humbie See Bolton and Saltoun
Lasswade See Cockpen and Carrington

Loanhead
Graham L. Duffin BSc BD DipEd — 1989 — 2001 — 120 The Loan, Loanhead EH20 9AJ — 0131-448 2459
[E-mail: gduffin@fish.co.uk]

Longniddry See Gladsmuir

Musselburgh: Northesk (H)
Alison P. Matheson MA BD — 1991 — 1998 — 16 New Street, Musselburgh EH21 6JP — 0131-665 2128
[E-mail: alison.matheson@tiscali.co.uk]

Musselburgh: St Andrew's High (H) (0131-665 7239)
Vacant — 8 Ferguson Drive, Musselburgh EH21 6XA — 0131-665 5583

Musselburgh: St Clement's and St Ninian's
Moira McDonald MA BD — 1997 — The Manse, Wallyford Loan Road, Wallyford, Musselburgh EH21 8BU — 0131-653 6588
[E-mail: moira.mc@tesco.net]
John Buchanan DCS — 2004 — 19 Gillespie Crescent, Edinburgh EH10 4HU — 0131-229 0794

Musselburgh: St Michael's Inveresk
Andrew B. Dick BD DipMin   1986   1999   8 Hope Place, Musselburgh EH21 7QE [E-mail: dixbit@aol.com]   0131-665 0545

Newbattle (H) (http://freespace.virgin.net/newbattle.focus)
Monika R. Walker BA BD   2003   70 Newbattle Abbey Crescent, Dalkeith EH22 3LW [E-mail: monika.walker@ukgateway.net]   0131-663 3245
Gordon R. Steven BD DCS   2004   51 Nantwich Drive, Edinburgh EH7 6RB [E-mail: grsteven@btinternet.com]   0131-669 2054 07904 385256 (Mbl)

Newton
Jan E. Gillies (Mrs) BD   1998   2001   The Manse, Newton, Dalkeith EH22 1SR [E-mail: jgillies@fish.co.uk]   0131-663 3845

North Berwick: Abbey See Dirleton

North Berwick: St Andrew Blackadder (H) (E-mail: admin@standrewblackadder.org.uk) (Website: www.standrewblackadder.org.uk)
Neil J. Dougall BD   1991   2003   7 Marine Parade, North Berwick EH39 4LD [E-mail: neil@standrewblackadder.org.uk]   01620 892132

Ormiston linked with Pencaitland
Mark Malcolm MA BD   1999   The Manse, Pencaitland, Tranent EH34 5DL [E-mail: mark.minister@virgin.net]   01875 340208

Pencaitland See Ormiston

Penicuik: North (H)
John W. Fraser MA BD   1974   1982   93 John Street, Penicuik EH26 8AG [E-mail: john1946@fish.co.uk]   01968 672213

Penicuik: St Mungo's (H)
Vacant   31a Kirkhill Road, Penicuik EH26 8JB   01968 672916

Penicuik: South See Howgate

Prestonpans: Prestongrange
Robert R. Simpson BA BD   1994   The Manse, East Loan, Prestonpans EH32 9ED [E-mail: robert@pansmanse.co.uk]   01875 810308
Christine A.Y. Ritchie (Mrs) BD DipMin (Aux) 2002   Through-Gate, 78 High Street, Dunbar EH42 1JH [E-mail: critchie@fish.co.uk]   01368 863141

Rosewell See Cockpen and Carrington
Roslin See Glencorse
Spott See Belhaven

Tranent

Thomas M. Hogg BD		1986		244 Church Street, Tranent EH33 1BW	01875 610210
				[E-mail: tom@hoggtran.freeserve.co.uk]	

Traprain

Howard J. Haslett BA BD	1972	2000		The Manse, Preston Road, East Linton EH40 3DS	01620 860227 (Tel/Fax)
				[E-mail: howard.haslett@btopenworld.com]	

Whitekirk and Tyninghame See Athelstaneford

Yester See Bolton and Saltoun

Name			Charge	Address	Telephone
Black, A. Graham MA	1964	2003	(Gladsmuir with Longniddry)	26 Hamilton Crescent, Gullane EH31 2HR [E-mail: grablack@aol.com]	01620 843899
Brown, Ronald H.	1974	1998	(Musselburgh: Northesk)	6 Monktonhall Farm Cottages, Musselburgh EH21 6RZ	0131-653 2531
Brown, William BD	1972	1997	(Edinburgh: Polwarth)	13 Thornyhall, Dalkeith EH22 2ND [E-mail: william@brown1826.fsnet.co.uk]	(Tel/Fax) 0131-654 0929
Chalmers, William R. MA BD STM	1953	1992	(Dunbar)	18 Forest Road, Burghead, Elgin IV30 5XL	01343 835674
Donaldson, Colin V.	1982	1998	(Ormiston with Pencaitland)	3A Playfair Terrace, St Andrews KY16 9HX	01334 472889
Fraser, John W. BEM MA BD PhD	1950	1983	(Farnell)	12 Quarryfoot Green, Bonnyrigg EH19 2EJ	0131-663 8037
Gilfillan, James LTh	1968	1997	(East Kilbride: Old)	15 Long Cram, Haddington EH41 4NS	01620 824843
Hill, Arthur T.	1940	1981	(Ormiston with Prestonpans: Grange)	8A Hamilton Road, North Berwick EH39 4NA	01620 893961
Hutchison, Alan E.W.			(Deacon)	132 Lochbridge Road, North Berwick EH39 4DR	01620 894077
Jones, Anne M. (Mrs) BD	1998	2002	Hospital Chaplain	7 North Elphinstone Farm, Tranent EH33 2ND [E-mail: revamjones@aol.com]	01875 614442
Levison, L. David MA BD	1943	1982	(Ormiston with Pencaitland)	Westdene Conservatory Flat, 506 Perth Road, Dundee DD2 1LS	01382 630460
Macdonell, Alasdair W. MA BD	1955	1992	(Haddington: St Mary's)	St Andrews Cottage, Duns Road, Gifford, Haddington EH41 4QW	01620 810341
Macrae, Norman C. MA DipEd	1942	1985	(Loanhead)	49 Lixmount Avenue, Edinburgh EH5 3EW [E-mail: nandcmacrae@onetel.com]	0131-552 2428
Manson, James A. LTh	1981	2003	(Glencorse with Roslin)	31 Nursery Gardens, Kilmarnock KA1 3JA [E-mail: jamanson@supanet.com]	01563 535430
Maule-Brown, Robert MA	1949	1985	(Strathy and Halladale)	5 Acredales Walk, Haddington EH41 4RR	01620 824959
Ritchie, James McL. MA BD MPhil	1950	1985	(Coalsnaughton)	46 St James's Gardens, Penicuik EH26 9DU [E-mail: jasritch_77@hotmail.com]	01968 676123
Robertson, James LTh	1970	2000	(Newton)	11 Southfield Square, Edinburgh EH15 1QS	
Sanderson, W. Roy DD	1933	1973	(Stenton with Whittingehame)	20 Craigleith View, Station Road, North Berwick EH39 4BF	01620 892780
Sawers, E.A.H. VRD	1950	1989	(Cranstoun Crichton and Ford with Fala and Soutra)		
Swan, Andrew F. BD	1983	2000	(Loanhead)	18 Lydgait Gardens, Haddington EH41 3DB	01620 825830
Thomson, William H.	1964	1999	(Edinburgh: Liberton Northfield)	3 Mackenzie Gardens, Dolphinton, West Linton EH46 7HS 3 Baird's Way, Bonnyrigg EH19 3NS [E-mail: w.h.thomson@tesco.net]	01968 682247 0131-654 9799
Torrance, David W. MA BD	1955	1991	(Earlston)	38 Forth Street, North Berwick EH39 4IQ [E-mail: dwtmet@connectfree.co.uk]	(Tel/Fax) 01620 895109

| Underwood, Geoffrey H. BD DipTh FPhS | 1964 | 1992 | (Cockenzie and Port Seton: Chalmers Memorial) | The Shieling, Main Street, Stenton, Dunbar EH42 1TE [E-mail: geoff629@fish.co.uk] | 01368 850629 |
| Whiteford, David H. CBE MA BD PhD | 1943 | 1985 | (Gullane) | 3 Old Dean Road, Longniddry EH32 0QY | 01875 852980 |

(4) MELROSE AND PEEBLES

Meets at Innerleithen on the first Tuesday of February, March, May, October, November and December; and on the fourth Tuesday of June, and in places to be appointed on the first Tuesday of September.

| Clerk: | MR JACK STEWART | | | 3 St Cuthbert's Drive, St Boswells, Melrose TD6 0DF [E-mail: akph66@uk.uumail.com] | 01835 822600 |

Ashkirk linked with Selkirk (H)
| James W. Campbell BD | 1995 | | 1 Loanside, Selkirk TD7 4DJ [E-mail: revjimashkirk@aol.com] | 01750 22833 |

Bowden (H) linked with Newtown
| Joseph F. Crawford BA | 1970 | 2000 | The Manse, Newtown St Boswells, Melrose TD6 0PL [E-mail: joe@crawforda86.fsnet.co.uk] | 01835 822106 |

Broughton, Glenholm and Kilbucho (H) linked with Skirling linked with Stobo and Drumelzier linked with Tweedsmuir (H)
| Rachel J.W. Dobie (Mrs) LTh | 1991 | 1996 | The Manse, Broughton, Biggar ML12 6HQ [E-mail: revracheldobie@aol.com] | 01899 830331 |

Caddonfoot (H) linked with Galashiels: St Ninian's (H)
| Vacant | | | Mossilee Road, Galashiels TD1 1NF | 01896 752058 |

Carlops linked with Kirkurd and Newlands (H) linked with West Linton: St Andrew's (H)
| Thomas W. Burt BD | 1982 | 1985 | The Manse, West Linton EH46 7EN [E-mail: tomburt@westlinton.com] | 01968 660221 |

Channelkirk linked with Lauder: Old
| John M. Shields MBE LTh | 1972 | 1997 | Brownsmuir Park, Lauder TD2 6QD | 01578 722320 |

Earlston
| Michael D. Scculer MBE BSc BD | 1988 | 1992 | The Manse, High Street, Earlston TD4 6DE | 01896 849236 |

Eddleston (H) linked with Peebles: Old (H)
| Malcolm M. Macdougall BD | 1981 | 2001 | The Old Manse, Innerleithen Road, Peebles EH45 8BD [E-mail: calum.macdougall@btopenworld.com] | 01721 720568 |

Ettrick and Yarrow
Samuel Siroky BA MTh   2003   Yarrow Cottage, Yarrow, Selkirk TD7 5NE   01750 82336
[E-mail: sesiroky@onetel.net.uk]

Galashiels: Old and St Paul's (H) (http://www.oldparishandstpauls.org.uk)
Leslie M. Steele MA BD   1973   1988   Barr Road, Galashiels TD1 3HX   01896 752320
[E-mail: leslie@oldparishandstpauls.org.uk]

Galashiels: St Aidan's (H)
Morag A. Dawson BD   1999   2003   The Manse, High Road, Galashiels TD1 2BD   01896 752420
[E-mail: mdawson@fsmail.net]

Galashiels: St John's (H)
Stephen F. Clipston MA BD   1982   Hawthorn Road, Galashiels TD1 2JZ   01896 752573 (Tel)
[E-mail: steve.clipston@btinternet.com]   01896 758561 (Fax)

Galashiels: St Ninian's See Caddonfoot

Innerleithen (H), Traquair and Walkerburn
Janice M. Faris (Mrs) BSc BD   1991   2001   The Manse, 1 Millwell Park, Innerleithen, Peebles EH44 6JF   01896 830309
[E-mail: revjfaris@hotmail.com]

Kirkurd and Newlands See Carlops
Lauder: Old See Channelkirk

Lyne and Manor
Nancy M. Norman (Miss) BA MDiv MTh   1988   25 March Street, Peebles EH45 8EP   01721 721699
[E-mail: nancy.norman@btopenworld.com]

Maxton and Mertoun linked with St Boswells
Bruce F. Neill MA BD   1966   1996   St Modans Manse, Main Street, St Boswells, Melrose TD6 0BB   01835 822255
[E-mail: bneill@fish.co.uk]

Melrose (H)
Alistair G. Bennett BSc BD   1978   1984   Tweedmount Road, Melrose TD6 9ST   01896 822217
[E-mail: agbennettmelrose@aol.com]

Newtown See Bowden
Peebles: Old See Eddleston

Peebles: St Andrew's Leckie (H) (01721 723121)
James H. Wallace MA BD   1973   1983   Mansefield, Innerleithen Road, Peebles EH45 8BE   01721 721749 (Tel/Fax)
[E-mail: jimwallace10@freeuk.com]

St Boswells See Maxton and Mertoun

Selkirk See Ashkirk
Skirling See Broughton, Glenholm and Kilbucho
Stobo and Drumelzier See Broughton, Glenholm and Kilbucho

Stow: St Mary of Wedale and Heriot

Catherine A. Buchan (Mrs) MA MDiv	2002	The Manse, 209 Galashiels Road, Stow, Galashiels TD1 2RE [E-mail: buchan@alan-cath.freeserve.co.uk]	01578 730237

Tweedsmuir See Broughton, Glenholm and Kilbucho
West Linton: St Andrew's See Carlops

Brown, Rober: BSc	1962	1997	(Kilbrandon and Kilchattan)	11 Thornfield Terrace, Selkirk TD7 4DU [E-mail: thornfield@ukgateway.net]	01750 20311
Cashman, P. Hamilton BSc	1985	1998	(Dirleton with North Berwick: Abbey)	38 Abbotsford Road, Galashiels TD1 3HR [E-mail: mcashman@tiscali.co.uk]	01896 752711
Devenny, Robert P.	2002		(Borders Health Board)	Blakeburn Cottage, Wester Housebyres, Melrose TD6 9BW	01896 822350
Dick, J. Ronald BD	1973	1996	(Hospital Chaplain)	5 Georgefield Farm Cottages, Earlston TD4 6BH	01896 848956
Donald, Thomas W. LTh CA	1977	1987	(Bowden with Lilliesleaf)	The Quest, Huntly Road, Melrose TD6 9SB	01896 822345
Duncan, Charles A. MA	1956	1992	(Heriot with Stow: St Mary of Wedale)	10 Elm Grove, Galashiels TD1 3JA	01896 753261
Kellet, John M. MA	1962	1995	(Leith: South)	4 High Cottages, Walkerburn EH43 6AZ	01896 870351
Kennon, Stanley BA BD	1992	2000	(Chaplain: Navy)	1 Anson Way, Helston, Cornwall TR13 8BS	
Laing, William F. DSC VRD MA	1952	1986	(Selkirk: St Mary's West)	10 The Glebe, Selkirk TD7 5AB	01750 21210
McCann, George McD. BSc ATI	1994		(Auxiliary Minister)	Rosbeg, Parsonage Road, Galashiels TD1 3HS	01896 752055
MacFarlane, David C. MA	1957	1997	(Eddleston with Peebles: Old)	11 Station Bank, Peebles EH45 8EJ	01721 720639
Moore, W. Haisley MA	1966	1996	(Secretary: The Boys' Brigade)	26 Tweedbank Avenue, Tweedbank, Galashiels TD1 3SP	01896 668577
Rae, Andrew W.	1951	1987	(Annan: St Andrew's Greenknowe Erskine)	Roseneuk, Tweedside Road, Newtown St Boswells TD6 0PQ	01835 823783
Taverner, Glyn R. MA BD	1957	1995	(Maxton and Mertoun with St Boswells)	Woodcot Cottage, Waverley Road, Innerleithen EH44 6QW	01896 830156
Thomson, George F.M. MA	1956	1988	(Dollar Associate)	6 Abbotsford Terrace, Darnick, Melrose TD6 9AD	01896 823112

(5) DUNS

Meets at Duns, in the Old Parish Church Hall, normally on the first Tuesday of February, March, April, May, October, November, December, on the last Tuesday in June, and in places to be appointed on the first Tuesday of September.

Clerk:	MR JAMES B. WATSON BSc	49 Lennel Mount, Coldstream TD12 4NS [E-mail: akph49@uk.uumail.com] [E-mail: jamesbwatson@btopenworld.com]	01890 883149

Ayton (H) and Burnmouth linked with Grantshouse and Houndwood and Reston

Vacant	The Manse, Beanburn, Ayton, Eyemouth TD14 5QY	01890 781333

Berwick-upon-Tweed: St Andrew's Wallace Green (H) and Lowick
Paul M.N. Sewell MA BD   1970   2003   3 Meadow Grange, Berwick-upon-Tweed TD15 1NW   01289 303304

Bonkyl and Preston linked with Chirnside (H) linked with Edrom: Allanton (H)
Vacant   Parish Church Manse, Chirnside, Duns TD11 3XL   01890 818911

Chirnside See Bonkyl and Preston

Coldingham and St Abb's linked with Eyemouth
Daniel G. Lindsay BD   1978   1979   Victoria Road, Eyemouth TD14 5JD   01890 750327

Coldstream (H) linked with Eccles
Vacant   Duns Road, Coldstream TD12 4DP   01890 882537

Duns (H)
Andrew A. Morrice MA BD   1999   The Manse, Duns TD11 3DP   01361 883755
                                                           [E-mail: andrew.morrice@ntlworld.com]

Eccles See Coldstream
Edrom: Allanton See Bonkyl and Preston
Eyemouth See Coldingham and St Abb's

Fogo and Swinton linked with Ladykirk linked with Leitholm linked with Whitsome (H)
Alan C.D. Cartwright BSc BD   1976   Swinton, Duns TD11 3JJ   01890 860228

Foulden and Mordington linked with Hutton and Fishwick and Paxton
Geraldine H. Hope (Mrs) MA BD   1986   Hutton, Berwick-upon-Tweed TD15 1TS   01289 386396
                                                           [E-mail: geraldine.hope@virgin.net]

Gordon: St Michael's linked with Greenlaw (H) linked with Legerwood linked with Westruther
Thomas S. Nicholson BD DPS   1982   1995   The Manse, Todholes, Greenlaw, Duns TD10 6XD   01361 810316

Grantshouse and Houndwood and Reston See Ayton and Burnmouth
Greenlaw See Gordon: St Michael's
Hutton and Fishwick and Paxton See Foulden and Mordington

Kirk of Lammermuir linked with Langton and Polwarth
Ann Inglis (Mrs) LLB BD   1986   2003   The Manse, Cranshaws, Duns TD11 3SJ   01361 890289

Ladykirk See Fogo and Swinton
Langton and Polwarth See Kirk of Lammermuir
Legerwood See Gordon: St Michael's
Leitholm See Fogo and Swinton
Westruther See Gordon: St Michael's
Whitsome See Fogo and Swinton

Gaddes, Donald R.	1961	1994	(Kelso North and Ednam)	35 Winterfield Gardens, Duns TD11 3EZ [E-mail: doruga@winterfield.fslife.co.uk]	01361 883172
Gale, Ronald A.A. LTh	1982	1995	(Dunoon Old and St Cuthbert's)	55 Lennel Mount, Coldstream TD12 4NS	01890 883699
Hay, Bruce J.L.	1957	1997	(Makerstoun and Smailholm with Stichill, Hume and Nenthorn)		
Higham, Robert D. BD	1985	2002	(Tiree)	Tweed House, Tweed Street, Berwick-upon-Tweed TD15 1NG	01289 303171
Jackson, John MA	1958	1990	(Bonnybridge)	36 Low Greens, Berwick-upon-Tweed TD15 1LZ	01289 302392
Kerr, Andrew MA BLitt	1948	1991	(Kilbarchan West)	2 Milne Graden West, Coldstream TD12 4HE	01890 883435
Ledgard, J. Christopher BA	1969	2004	(Ayton and Burnmouth with Grantshouse and Houndwood and Reston)	Meikle Harelaw, Westruther, Gordon TD10 6XT	01578 740263
Macleod, Allan M. MA	1945	1985	(Gordon St Michael's with Legerwood with Westruther)	2 Farm Cottages, Northfield, St Abbs, Eyemouth TD14 5QF Silverlea, Machrihanish, Argyll PA28 6PZ	
Paterson, William BD	1977	2001	(Bonkyl and Preston with Chirnside with Edrom Allanton)	Benachie, Gavinton, Duns TD11 3QT	01361 882727

(6) JEDBURGH

Meets at Jedburgh on the first Wednesday of February, March, May, October, November and December and on the last Wednesday of June. Meets in the Moderator's church on the first Wednesday of September.

Clerk   REV. W. FRANK CAMPBELL BA BD   22 The Glebe, Ancrum, Jedburgh TD8 6UX   01835 830318
[E-mail: akph56@uk.uumail.com]
[E-mail: jedburghpresbytery@uk.uumail.com]

Ancrum linked with Crailing and Eckford linked with Lilliesleaf (T)
W. Frank Campbell BA BD   1989 1991   22 The Glebe, Ancrum, Jedburgh TD8 6UX   01835 830318

Cavers and Kirkton linked with Hawick: St Mary's and Old
Vacant   Braid Road, Hawick TD9 9LZ   01450 377865

Crailing and Eckford See Ancrum

Hawick: Burnfoot
Charles J. Finrie LTh DPS   1991 1997   29 Wilton Hill, Hawick TD9 8BA   01450 373181
[E-mail: charles@finnierev.freeserve.co.uk]

Hawick: St Mary's and Old (H) See Cavers and Kirkton

Hawick: Teviot (H) and Roberton
Neil R. Combe BSc MSc BD   1984   Teviot Manse, Buccleuch Road, Hawick TD9 0EL   01450 372150

Hawick: Trinity (H)
[E-mail: neil.combe@btinternet.com]
E.P. Lindsay Thomson MA   1964 1972   Fenwick Park, Hawick TD9 9PA   01450 372705

Hawick: Wilton linked with Teviothead
Lisa-Jane Rankin BD CPS   2003   4 Wilton Hill Terrace, Hawick TD9 8BE   01450 370744

Hobkirk and Southdean linked with Ruberslaw
Anthony M. Jones BD DPS DipTheol CertMin FRSA 2003   The Manse, Denholm, Hawick TD9 8NB   01450 870268 (Tel/Fax)
[E-mail: revanthonymjones@amserve.com]

Jedburgh: Old and Edgerston
Bruce McNicol JP BL BD   1967 1992   Honeyfield Drive, Jedburgh TD8 6LQ   01835 863417

Jedburgh: Trinity
John A. Riddell MA BD   1967   42 High Street, Jedburgh TD8 6DQ   01835 863223

Kelso: North (H) and Ednam (H) (01573 224154)
Tom McDonald BD   1994   20 Forestfield, Kelso TD5 7BX   01573 224677
[E-mail: revtom@20thepearlygates.fsnet.co.uk]

Kelso: Old (H) and Sprouston
Marion E. Dodd MA BD LRAM   1988 1989   Glebe Lane, Kelso TD5 7AU   01573 226254
[E-mail: mariondodd@macunlimited.net]

Lilliesleaf See Ancrum

Linton linked with Morebattle and Hownam linked with Yetholm (H)
Robin D. McHaffie BD   1979 1991   The Manse, Main Street, Kirk Yetholm, Kelso TD5 8PF   01573 420308
[E-mail: robin.mchaffie@virgin.net]

Makerstoun and Smailholm linked with Roxburgh linked with Stichill, Hume and Nenthorn
Valerie G.C. Watson (Ms) MA BD STM   1987 2001   The Manse, 1 The Meadow, Stichill, Kelso TD5 7TG   01573 470607
[E-mail: vwatson@tiscali.co.uk]

Morebattle and Hownam See Linton

Oxnam
Continued Vacancy

Roxburgh See Makerstoun and Smailholm
Ruberslaw See Hobkirk and Southdean
Stichill, Hume and Nenthorn See Makerstoun and Smailholm
Teviothead See Hawick: Wilton
Yetholm See Linton

Bowie, Adam McC.	1976	1996	(Cavers and Kirkton with Hobkirk and Southdean)	Glenbield, Redpath, Earlston TD4 6AD	01896 848173
Brown, Joseph MA	1954	1991	(Linton with Hownam and Morebattle with Yetholm)	The Orchard, Hermitage Lane, Shedden Park Road, Kelso TD5 7AN	01573 223481
Fox, G. Dudley A.	1972	1988	(Kelso Old)	14 Pinnacle Hill Farm, Kelso TD5 8HD	01573 223335
Hamilton, Robert MA BD	1938	1979	(Kelso Old)	Ridge Cottage, 391 Totnes Road, Collaton St Mary, Paignton TQ4 7PW	01803 526440
Longmuir, William LTh	1984	2001	(Bedrule with Denholm with Minto)	Viewfield, South Street, Gavinton, Duns TD11 3QT	01361 882728
McConnell, Robert	1959	1983	(Hawick: St Margaret's and Wilton: South with Roberton)		
Ritchie, Garden W.M.	1961	1995	(Ardersier with Petty)	Flat 31, Strathclyde House, 31–33 Shore Road, Skelmorlie PA17 5AN	01475 522532
Thompson, W.M.D. MA	1950	1997	(Crailing and Eckford with Oxnam with Roxburgh)	23 Croft Road, Kelso TD5 7EP	01573 224419
				Beech House, Etal, Cornhill-on-Tweed TD12 4TL	01890 820621

HAWICK ADDRESSES

Burnfoot	Fraser Avenue	St Mary's and Old	Kirk Wynd
		Teviot	off Buccleuch Road
		Trinity	Central Square
		Wilton	Princes Street

(7) ANNANDALE AND ESKDALE

Meets on the first Tuesday of February, May, September and December, and the third Tuesday of March, June and October, in a venue to be determined by Presbytery.

Clerk: REV. C. BRYAN HASTON LTh   The Manse, Gretna Green, Gretna DG16 5DU   **01461 338313 (Tel)**
[E-mail: cbhaston@cofs.demon.co.uk]   **08701 640119 (Fax)**
[E-mail: cbhaston@uk.uumail.com]

Annan: Old (H)
Hugh D. Steele LTh DipMin   1994   2004   12 Plumdon Park Avenue, Annan DG12 6EY   01461 201405
[E-mail: hugh.steele@btinternet.com]

Annan: St Andrew's (H) linked with Brydekirk
George K. Lind BD MCIBS   1998   1 Annerley Road, Annan DG12 6HE   01461 202626
[E-mail: gklind@bosinternet.com]

Applegarth and Sibbaldbie (H) linked with Johnstone linked with Lochmaben (H)
Jack M. Brown BSc BD   1977   2002   The Manse, Barrashead, Lochmaben, Lockerbie DG11 1QF   01387 810066
[E-mail: jackmbrown@tiscali.co.uk]

Brydekirk See Annan: St Andrew's

Canonbie United (H) linked with Liddesdale (H)
Alan D. Reid MA BD   1989   23 Langholm Street, Newcastleton TD9 0QX   01387 375242
[E-mail: canonbie.liddesdale@btopenworld.com]

Dalton linked with Hightae linked with St Mungo
Alexander C. Stoddart BD   2001   Hightae and Dalton Manse, Hightae, Lockerbie DG11 1JL   01387 811499
[E-mail: sandystoddart@supanet.com]

Dornock
Ronald S. Seaman MA   1967   Dornock, Annan DG12 6NR   01461 40268

Eskdalemuir linked with Hutton and Corrie linked with Tundergarth
Alan C. Ross CA BD   1988   2003   Yarra, Ettrickbridge, Selkirk TD7 5JN   01750 52324 (Tel/Fax)
[E-mail: alkaross@aol.com]

Gretna: Old (H), Gretna: St Andrew's and Half Morton and Kirkpatrick Fleming
C. Bryan Haston LTh   1975   The Manse, Gretna Green, Gretna DG16 5DU   01461 338313 (Tel)
[E-mail: cbhaston@cofs.demon.co.uk]   08701 640119 (Fax)

Hightae See Dalton

Hoddam linked with Kirtle-Eaglesfield linked with Middlebie linked with Waterbeck
Trevor C. Williams LTh   1990   1999   Kirtle Manse, Kirtlebridge, Lockerbie DG11 3LY   01461 500378
[E-mail: revwill@btopenworld.com]

Hutton and Corrie See Eskdalemuir
Johnstone See Applegarth and Sibbaldbie

Kirkpatrick Juxta linked with Moffat: St Andrew's (H) linked with Wamphray
David M. McKay MA BD   1979   2001   The Manse, 1 Meadowbank, Moffat DG10 9LR   01683 220128
[E-mail: demacmin@ukgateway.net]

Kirtle-Eaglesfield See Hoddam

Langholm, Ewes and Westerkirk
Robert B. Milne BTh   1999   1999   The Manse, Thomas Telford Road, Langholm DG13 0BL   01387 380252 (Tel)
[E-mail: rbmilne@aol.com]   01387 381399 (Fax)

Liddesdale (H) See Canonbie United

Lochmaben See Applegarth and Sibbaldbie

Lockerbie: Dryfesdale

David M. Almond BD	1996	The Manse, 5 Carlisle Road, Lockerbie DG11 2DW [E-mail: rev.almond@btinternet.com]	01576 202361

Middlebie See Hoddam
Moffat: St Andrew's (H) See Kirkpatrick Juxta
St Mungo See Dalton

The Border Kirk

David J. Thom BD	2000	2002	30 Dunmail Drive, Carlisle CA2 6DF [E-mail: david@kirkscotland.org.uk]	01228 819832

(Charge formed by the union of Carlisle: Chapel Street and Longtown: St Andrew's)

Tundergarth See Eskdalemuir
Wamphray See Kirkpatrick Juxta
Waterbeck See Hoddam

Annand, James M. MA BD	1955	1995	(Lockerbie Dryfesdale)	48 Main Street, Newstead, Melrose TD6 9DX	0131-225 3393
Beveridge, S. Edwin P. BA	1959	2004	(Brydekirk with Hoddam)	19 Rothesay Terrace, Edinburgh EH3 7RY	01461 206512
Byers, Alan J.	1959	1992	(Gamrie with King Edward)	Meadowbank, Plumdon Road, Annan DG12 6SJ	01461 206512
Byers, Mairi (Mrs) BTh CPS	1992	1998	(Jura)	Meadowbank, Plumdon Road, Annan DG12 6SJ	
Fisher, D. Ncel MA BD	1939	1979	(Glasgow: Sherbrooke St Gilbert's)	Sheraig Cottage, Killochries Fold, Kilmacolm PA13 4TE	01576 204653
Kirk, W. Logan MA BD MTh	1988	2000	(Dalton with Hightae with St Mungo)	2 Firpark Cottages, Lockerbie DG11 1BL	
MacMillan, William M. LTh	1980	1998	(Kilmory with Lamlash)	Balskia, 61 Queen Street, Lochmaben DG11 1PP	01387 811528
Macpherson, Duncan J. BSc BD	1993	2002	Chaplain: Army	1Bn The Black Watch, BFPO 38	
Rennie, John D. MA	1962	1996	(Broughton, Glenholm and Kilbucho with Skirling with Stobo and Drumelzier with Tweedsmuir)	Dundoran, Ballplay Road, Moffat DG10 9JX [E-mail: rennies@dundoran96.freeserve.co.uk]	01683 220223
Swinburne, Norman BA	1960	1993	(Sauchie)	Damerosehay, Birch Hill Lane, Kirkbride, Wigton CA7 5HZ	01697 351497

(8) DUMFRIES AND KIRKCUDBRIGHT

Meets at Dumfries, on the first Wednesday of February, March, April, May, September, October, November and December, and the fourth Wednesday of June.

Clerk:	REV. GORDON M.A. SAVAGE MA BD	11 Laurieknowe, Dumfries DG2 7AH [E-mail: akph44@uk.uumail.com]	01387 252929
Depute Clerk:	REV. WILLIAM T. HOGG MA BD	The Manse, Glasgow Road, Sanquhar DG4 6BS [E-mail: tervit@btopenworld.com]	01659 50247

Anwoth and Girthon linked with Borgue
Valerie J. Ott (Mrs) BA BD   2002   The Manse, Planetree Park, Gatehouse of Fleet, Castle Douglas DG7 2EQ
[E-mail: dandvott@aol.com]   01557 814233

Auchencairn and Rerrick linked with Buittle and Kelton
Vacant   Auchencairn, Castle Douglas DG7 1QS   01556 640288

Balmaclellan and Kells (H) linked with Carsphairn (H) linked with Dalry (H)
David S. Bartholomew BSc MSc PhD BD   1994   The Manse, Dalry, Castle Douglas DG7 3PJ
[E-mail: dhbart@care4free.net]   01644 430380

Balmaghie linked with Tarff and Twynholm (H)
Christopher Wallace BD DipMin   1988   Manse Road, Twynholm, Kirkcudbright DG6 4NY
[E-mail: minister@twynholm.org.uk]   01557 860381

Borgue   See Anwoth and Girthon
Buittle and Kelton   See Auchencairn and Rerrick

Caerlaverock linked with Dumfries: St Mary's-Greyfriars
Vacant   4 Georgetown Crescent, Dumfries DG1 4EQ   01387 257045
Elizabeth A. Mack (Miss) Dip PEd (Aux)   1994   2003   24 Roberts Crescent, Dumfries DG2 7RS   01387 264847

Carsphairn   See Balmaclellan and Kells

Castle Douglas (H)
Robert J. Malloch BD   1987   1 Castle View, Castle Douglas DG7 1BG
[E-mail: robert@scotnish.freeserve.co.uk]   01556 502171

Closeburn linked with Durisdeer
James W. Scott MA CDA   1952   1953   The Manse, Durisdeer, Thornhill DG3 5BJ   01848 500231

Colvend, Southwick and Kirkbean
James F. Gatherer BD   1984   2003   The Manse, Colvend, Dalbeattie DG5 4QN   01556 630255

Corsock and Kirkpatrick Durham linked with Crossmichael and Parton
James A. Guthrie   1969   1999   Knockdrocket, Clarebrand, Castle Douglas DG7 3AH   01556 503645

Crossmichael and Parton   See Corsock and Kirkpatrick Durham

Cummertrees linked with Mouswald linked with Ruthwell (H)
James Williamson BA BD   1986   1991   The Manse, Ruthwell, Dumfries DG1 4NP
[E-mail: jimwill@rcmkirk.freeserve.co.uk]   01387 870217

Dalbeattie (H) linked with Urr (H) Norman M. Hutcheson MA BD	1973	1988	36 Mill Street, Dalbeattie DG5 4HE [E-mail: norman.hutcheson@virgin.net]	01556 610029
Dalry See Balmaclellan and Kells				
Dumfries: Lincluden linked with Holywood Vacant			96 Glasgow Road, Dumfries DG2 9DE	01387 264298
Dumfries: Lochside Vacant			27 St Anne's Road, Dumfries DG2 9HZ	01387 252912
Dumfries: Maxwelltown West (H) Gordon M.A. Savage MA BD	1977	1984	Maxwelltown West Manse, 11 Laurieknowe, Dumfries DG2 7AH [E-mail: gordonsavage@uk.uumail.com]	01387 252929
Dumfries: St George's (H) Donald Campbell BD	1997		9 Nunholm Park, Dumfries DG1 1JP [E-mail: donald@campbell3.freeserve.co.uk]	01387 252965
Dumfries: St Mary's-Greyfriars (H) See Caerlaverock				
Dumfries: St Michael's and South Maurice S. Bond MTh BA DipEd PhD	1981	1999	39 Cardoness Street, Dumfries DG1 3AL	01387 253849
Dumfries: Troqueer (H) William W. Kelly BSc BD	1994		Troqueer Manse, Troqueer Road, Dumfries DG2 7DF [E-mail: wwkelly@dsl.pipex.com]	01387 253043
Dunscore linked with Glencairn and Moniaive Christine Sime (Miss) BSc BD	1994		Wallaceton, Auldgirth, Dumfries DG2 0TJ [E-mail: revsime@aol.com]	01387 820245
Durisdeer See Closeburn **Glencairn and Moniaive** See Dunscore **Holywood** See Dumfries: Lincluden				
Irongray, Lochrutton and Terregles David J. Taylor MA BD	1982	2002	Shawhead Road, Dumfries DG2 9SJ [E-mail: david@bunessan.f9.co.uk]	01387 730287
Kirkconnel (H) David Deas Melville BD	1989	1999	The Manse, 31 Kingsway, Kirkconnel, Sanquhar DG4 6PN [E-mail: ddm@kirkconn.freeserve.co.uk]	01659 67241
Kirkcudbright (H) Douglas R. Irving LLB BD WS	1984	1998	6 Bourtree Avenue, Kirkcudbright DG6 4AU [E-mail: douglasirving@kirkcudbright99.freeserve.co.uk]	01557 330489

Kirkgunzeon
Continued Vacancy

Kirkmahoe
Dennis S. Rose LTh   1996   Kirkmahoe, Dumfries DG1 1ST   01387 710572
[E-mail: dsrosekirk@aol.com]

Kirkmichael, Tinwald and Torthorwald
Louis C. Bezuidenhout MA DD   1978   2000   Manse of Tinwald, Tinwald, Dumfries DG1 3PL   01387 710246
[E-mail: macbez@btinternet.com]

Lochend linked with New Abbey
William Holland MA   1967   1971   The Manse, 28 Main Street, New Abbey, Dumfries DG2 8BY   01387 850232
[E-mail: bilholland@aol.com]

Mouswald See Cummertrees
New Abbey See Lochend

Penpont, Keir and Tynron linked with Thornhill (H)
Donald Keith MA BD   1971   2002   Beechhill, Manse Park, Thornhill DG3 5ER   01848 331191

Ruthwell (H) See Cummertrees

Sanquhar: St Bride's (H)
William T. Hogg MA BD   1979   2000   St Bride's Manse, Glasgow Road, Sanquhar DG6 6BZ   01659 50247
[E-mail: tervit@btopenworld.com]

Tarff and Twynholm See Balmaghie
Thornhill (H) See Penpont, Keir and Tynron
Urr See Dalbeattie

Name			Previous charge	Address	Tel
Baillie, David R.	1979	1990	(Crawford with Lowther)	4 Southwick Drive, Dalbeattie DG5 4HW	01556 610871
Bennett, David K.P. BA	1974	2000	(Kirkpatrick Irongray with Lochrutton with Terregles)	53 Anne Arundel Court, Heathhall, Dumfries DG1 3SL	01387 257755
Calderwood, Walter M. MA BD	1934	1974	(Leven Forman)	Flat 10, Daar Lodge, 6 St Mary Street, Kirkcudbright DG6 4AQ	01557 330330
Craig, N. Douglas MA BD	1947	1987	(Dalbeattie: Craignair with Urr)	33 Albert Road, Dumfries DG2 9DN	01387 252187
Elder, Albert B. MA	1960	1998	(Dumfries: St Michael's and South)	87 Glasgow Street, Dumfries DG2 9AG	01387 249778
Geddes, Alexander J. MA BD	1960	1998	(Stewarton: St Columba's)	166 Georgetown Road, Dumfries DG1 4DT	01387 252287
Gillespie, Ann M. (Miss) DCS			(Deaconess)	Barlochan House, Palnackie, Castle Douglas DG7 1PF	01556 600378
Greer, A. David C. LLB DMin DipAdultEd	1956	1996	(Barra)	10 Watling Street, Dumfries DG1 1HF	01387 256113
Hamill, Robert BA	1956	1989	(Castle Douglas: St Ringan's)	11 St Andrew Drive, Castle Douglas DG7 1EW	01556 502962
Hutchison, Mary L. (Mrs) BD	1982	1995	(Dumfries: Lincluden with Holywood)	7 Wellside Court, Wellside Place, Falkirk FK1 5RG	01324 611990
Leishman, James S. LTh BD MA(Div)	1969	1999	(Kirkmichael with Tinwald with Torthorwald)	11 Hunter Avenue, Heathhall, Dumfries DG1 3UX	01387 249241

Name			Charge	Address	Phone
Mackay, Donald MBE FCP FSAScot	1951	1986	(Ardrossan: St John's)	8 Urquhart Crescent, Dumfries DG1 8XF	01387 259132
McKenzie, William M. DA	1958	1993	(Dumfries: Troqueer)	41 Kingholm Road, Dumfries DG1 4SR [E-mail: mckenzie.dumfries@virgin.net]	01387 253688
Miller, John R. MA BD	1958	1992	(Carsphairn with Dalry)	4 Fairgreen Court, Rhonehouse, Castle Douglas DG7 1SA	01556 680428
Morrison, James G. MBE MA	1942	1980	(Rotterdam)	Auchenshiel, Rhonehouse, Castle Douglas DG7 1SA	01556 680526
Owen, John J.C. LTh	1967	2001	(Applegarth and Sibbaldbie with Lochmaben)	5 Galla Avenue, Dalbeattie DG5 4JZ [E-mail: jjowen@macunlimited.net]	01556 612125
Robertson, Ian W. MA BD	1956	1995	(Colvend, Southwick and Kirkbean)	10 Marjoriebanks, Lochmaben, Lockerbie DG11 1QH	01387 810541
Robertson, Thomas R. MA BD	1934	1976	(Broughton, Glenholm and Kilbucho with Skirling)	1 Church Row, Kirkcudbright DG6 4AP	01557 330795
Smith, Richmond OBE MA BD	1952	1983	(World Alliance of Reformed Churches)	Aignish, Merse Way, Kippford, Dalbeattie DG5 4LH	01556 620624
Strachan, Alexander E. MA BD	1974	1999	Dumfries Health Care Chaplain	2 Leafield Road, Dumfries DG1 2DS [E-mail: aestrachan@aol.com]	01387 279460
Vincent, C. Raymond MA FSAScot	1952	1992	(Stonehouse)	Rosebank, Newton Stewart Road, New Galloway, Castle Douglas DG7 3RT	01644 420451
Wilkie, James R. MA MTh	1957	1993	(Penpont, Keir and Tynron)	31 West Morton Street, Thornhill DG3 5NF	01848 331028
Wotherspoon, Robert C. LTh	1976	1998	(Corsock and Kirkpatrick Durham with Crossmichael and Parton)	7 Hillowton Drive, Castle Douglas DG7 1LL [E-mail: robert.wotherspoon1@btinternet.com]	01556 502267
Young, John MTh DipMin	1963	1999	(Airdrie: Broomknoll)	Craigview, North Street, Moniaive, Thornhill DG3 4HR	01848 200318

DUMFRIES ADDRESSES

Lincluden	Stewartry Road	
Lochside	Lochside Road	
Maxwelltown West	Laurieknowe	
St George's	George Street	
St Mary's-Greyfriars	St Mary's Street	
St Michael's and South	St Michael's Street	
Troqueer	Troqueer Road	

(9) WIGTOWN AND STRANRAER

Meets at Glenluce, in the church hall, on the first Tuesday of March, October and December for ordinary business; on the first Tuesday of September for formal business followed by meetings of committees; on the first Tuesday of November, February and May for worship followed by meetings of committees; and at a church designated by the Moderator on the first Tuesday of June for Holy Communion followed by ordinary business.

Clerk: REV. DAVID W. DUTTON BA   High Kirk Manse, Leswalt High Road, Stranraer DG9 0AA [E-mail: akph79@uk.uumail.com]   **01776 703268**

Ervie Kirkcolm linked with Leswalt

Michael J. Sheppard BD	1997		Ervie Manse, Stranraer DG9 0QZ [E-mail: mjs@kirkcolm-leswalt.fsnet.co.uk]	01776 854225
Mary Munro (Mrs) BA (Aux)	1993	2003	High Barbeth, Leswalt, Stranraer DG9 0QS	01776 870250

Glasserton and Isle of Whithorn linked with Whithorn: St Ninian's Priory
Alexander I. Currie BD CPS — 1990 — Bruce Street, Whithorn, Newton Stewart DG8 8PY — 01988 500267

Inch linked with Stranraer: Town Kirk (H)
John H. Burns BSc BD — 1985 — 1988 — Bayview Road, Stranraer DG9 8BE — 01776 702383

Kirkcowan (H) linked with Wigtown (H)
Martin Thomson BSc DipEd BD — 1988 — The Manse, Harbour Road, Wigtown, Newton Stewart DG8 9EL [E-mail: martin@thomsonm40.freeserve.co.uk] — 01988 402242

Kirkinner linked with Sorbie (H)
Jeffrey M. Mead BD — 1978 — 1986 — The Manse, Kirkinner, Newton Stewart DG8 9AL — 01988 840643

Kirkmabreck linked with Monigaff (H)
Vacant — Creebridge, Newton Stewart DG8 6NR — 01671 403361

Kirkmaiden (H) linked with Stoneykirk
Ian McIlroy BSS BD — 1996 — Church Street, Sandhead, Stranraer DG9 9JJ — 01776 830337

Leswalt See Ervie Kirkcolm

Mochrum (H)
Vacant — Manse of Mochrum, Port William, Newton Stewart DG8 9QP — 01988 700257

Monigaff (H) See Kirkmabreck

New Luce (H) linked with Old Luce (H)
Thomas M. McWhirter MA MSc BD — 1992 — 1997 — Glenluce, Newton Stewart DG8 0PU — 01581 300319

Old Luce See New Luce

Penninghame (H)
Neil G. Campbell BA BD — 1988 — 1989 — The Manse, Newton Stewart DG8 6HH [E-mail: neilcampbell@yahoo.com] — 01671 402259

Portpatrick linked with Stranraer: St Ninian's (H)
Gordon Kennedy BSc BD — 1993 — 2000 — London Road, Stranraer DG9 9AB [E-mail: gordon.kennedy1@btinternet.com] — 01776 702443

Sorbie See Kirkinner
Stoneykirk See Kirkmaiden

Stranraer: High Kirk (H)
David W. Dutton BA — 1973 — 1986 — High Kirk Manse, Leswalt High Road, Stranraer DG9 0AA [E-mail: akph79@uk.uumail.com] — 01776 703268

Stranraer: St Ninian's See Portpatrick
Stranraer: Town Kirk See Inch
Whithorn: St Ninian's Priory See Glasserton and Isle of Whithorn
Wigtown See Kirkcowan

Cairns, Alexander B. MA	1957 1997	(Ervie Kirkcolm with Leswalt)	Beechwood, Main Street, Sandhead, Stranraer DG9 9JG	01776 830389
Cordiner, John	1950 1986	(Portpatrick)	Tara, Fellview Road, Stranraer DG9 8BH	01776 704720
Dean, Roger A.F. LTh	1983 2004	(Mochrum)	Albion Cottage, 59 Main Street, Newton Stewart DG8 9AN	
Harkes, George	1962 1988	(Cumbernauld: Old)	11 Main Street, Sorbie, Newton Stewart DG8 8EG	01988 850255
McCreadie, David W.	1961 1995	(Kirkmabreck)	77 St John Street, Creetown, Newton Stewart DG8 7JB	01671 820390
McGill, Thomas W.	1972 1990	(Portpatrick with Stranraer: St Ninian's)	Ravenstone Moor, Dramrae, Whithorn, Newton Stewart DG8 8DS	01988 700449
Munro, Mary (Mrs) BA	1993 2004	(Auxiliary Minister)	High Barbeth, Leswalt, Stranraer DG9 0QS	01776 870250
Ogilvy, Oliver M.	1959 1985	(Leswalt)	8 Dale Crescent, Stranraer DG9 0HG	01776 706285

(10) AYR

Meets on the first Tuesday of every month from September to May, excluding January, and on the fourth Tuesday of June. The June meeting will be held in the Moderator's Church. One meeting will be held in a venue to be determined by the Business Committee. Other meetings will be held in Alloway Church Hall.

Clerk:	**REV. JAMES CRICHTON MA BD MTh**		30 Garden Street, Dalrymple KA6 6DG	01292 560263 (Fax)
			[E-mail: akph39@uk.uumail.com]	01292 560574 (Fax)
	Presbytery Office		[E-mail: akph40@uk.uumail.com]	01292 262184 (Tel/Fax)

Alloway (H)
Neil A. McNaught BD MA	1987	1999	1A Parkview, Alloway, Ayr KA7 4QG	01292 441252
			[E-mail: neilmcnaught3427.freeserve.co.uk]	

Annbank (H) linked with Tarbolton
Alexander Shuttleworth MA BD		2004	1 Kirkport, Tarbolton, Mauchline KA5 5QJ	01292 541236
			[E-mail: alec@ashuttle.freeserve.co.uk]	

Arnsheen Barrhill linked with Colmonell
John S. Lochrie BSc BD MTh PhD	1967	1999	Manse Road, Colmonell, Girvan KA26 0SA	01465 881224

Auchinleck (H) linked with Catrine
James Sloan BA MD	1987	2002	28 Mauchline Road, Auchinleck KA18 2BN	01290 421108

Ayr: Auld Kirk of Ayr (St John the Baptist) (H)
David R. Gemmell MA BD	1991	1999	58 Monument Road, Ayr KA7 2UB	01292 262580 (Tel/Fax)
			[E-mail: drgemmell@aol.com]	

Ayr: Castlehill (H) Peter B. Park BD MCIBS	1997	2003	3 Old Hillfoot Road, Ayr KA7 3LF [E-mail: peter.park1@virgin.net]	01292 267332
Ayr: Newton on Ayr (H) G. Stewart Birse CA BD BSc	1980	1989	9 Nursery Grove, Ayr KA7 3PH [E-mail: gstewart@birse21.freeserve.co.uk]	01292 264251
Ayr: St Andrew's (H) Harry B. Mealyea BArch BD	1984	2000	31 Bellevue Crescent, Ayr KA7 2DP [E-mail: mealyea@tiscali.co.uk]	01292 261126
Ayr: St Columba (H) Fraser R. Aitken MA BD	1978	1991	2 Hazelwood Road, Ayr KA7 2PY [E-mail: fraser.aitken@columba92.fsnet.co.uk]	01292 284177
Ayr: St James' Gillian Weighton (Mrs) BD STM	1992		1 Prestwick Road, Ayr KA8 8LD [E-mail: gillweighton@aol.com]	01292 262420
Ayr: St Leonard's (H) Robert Lynn MA BD	1984	1989	7 Shawfield Avenue, Ayr KA7 4RE [E-mail: robert@shawfield200.fsnet.co.uk]	01292 442109
Ayr: St Quivox (H) David T. Ness LTh	1972	1988	11 Springfield Avenue, Prestwick KA9 2HA [E-mail: dness@fish.co.uk]	01292 478306
Ayr: Wallacetown (H) Mary C. McLauchlan (Mrs) LTh	1997	2003	87 Forehill Road, Ayr KA7 3JR [E-mail: mcmclauchlan@ntlworld.com]	01292 263878
Ballantrae (H) Robert P. Bell BSc	1968	1998	Ballantrae, Girvan KA26 0NH [E-mail: revbobbell@aol.com]	01465 831252 (Tel) 01465 831260 (Fax)
Barr linked with Dailly linked with Girvan South Ian K. McLachlan MA BD		1999	30 Henrietta Street, Girvan KA26 9AL [E-mail: iankmclachlan@yetiville.freeserve.co.uk]	01465 713370

Catrine See Auchinleck
Colmonell See Arnsheen Barrhill

Coylton linked with Drongan: The Schaw Kirk
Paul R. Russell MA BD — 1984 — 1991 — 4 Hamilton Place, Coylton, Ayr KA6 6JQ
[E-mail: russellpr@btinternet.com] — 01292 570272

Craigie linked with Symington
Alastair M. Sanderson BA LTh — 1971 — 2000 — 16 Kerrix Road, Symington, Kilmarnock KA1 5QD
[E-mail: alel@sanderson29.fsnet.co.uk] — 01563 830205

Crosshill linked with Dalrymple
James Crichton MA BD MTh — 1969 — 30 Garden Street, Dalrymple KA6 6DG
[E-mail: akph39@uk.uumail.com] — 01292 560263 (Tel) / 01292 560574 (Fax)

Dailly See Barr

Dalmellington linked with Patna: Waterside
Kenneth B. Yorke BD DipEd — 1982 — 1999 — 4 Carsphairn Road, Dalmellington, Ayr KA6 7RE
[E-mail: k.yorke@zoom.co.uk] — 01292 550353

Muriel Wilson (Ms) DCS — 23 Jellieston Terrace, Patna, Ayr KA6 7JZ
[E-mail: murielw@fish.co.uk] — 01292 532492

Dalrymple See Crosshill
Drongan: The Schaw Kirk See Coylton

Dundonald (H)
Robert Mayes BD — 1982 — 1988 — 64 Main Street, Dundonald, Kilmarnock KA2 9HG — 01563 850243

Fisherton (H) linked with Kirkoswald
Arrick D. Wilkinson BSc BD — 2000 — 2003 — The Manse, Kirkoswald, Maybole KA19 8HZ
[E-mail: arrick@clergy.net] — 01655 760210

Girvan: North (Old and St Andrew's) (H)
Douglas G. McNab BA BD — 1999 — 38 The Avenue, Girvan KA26 9DS
[E-mail: dougmcnab@aol.com] — 01465 713203

Girvan: South See Barr linked with Dailly

Kirkmichael linked with Straiton: St Cuthbert's
W. Gerald Jones MA BD MTh — 1984 — 1985 — Patna Road, Kirkmichael, Maybole KA19 7PJ
[E-mail: revgerald@jonesg99.freeserve.co.uk] — 01655 750286

Kirkoswald (H) See Fisherton

Lugar linked with Old Cumnock: Old (H)
John W. Paterson BSc BD DipEd — 1994 — 33 Barrhill Road, Cumnock KA18 1PJ
[E-mail: ocochurchwow@hotmail.com] — 01290 420769

Mauchline (H)
Alan B. Telfer BA BD   1983   1991   4 Westside Gardens, Mauchline KA5 5DJ   01290 550386
[E-mail: abtelfer@btinternet.com]

Maybole
David Whiteman BD   1998   64 Culzean Road, Maybole KA19 8AH   01655 889456
[E-mail: soohsw@aol.com]
Douglas T. Moore (Aux)   2003   9 Midton Road, Prestwick KA9 1PU   01292 671352

Monkton and Prestwick: North (H)
Arthur A. Christie BD   1997   2000   40 Monkton Road, Prestwick KA9 1AR   01292 477499
[E-mail: revaac@btopenworld.com]

Muirkirk (H) linked with Sorn
Alex M. Welsh BD   1979   2003   2 Smallburn Road, Muirkirk, Cumnock KA18 3RF   01290 661157

New Cumnock (H)
Rona M. Young (Mrs) BD DipEd   1991   2001   37 Castle, New Cumnock, Cumnock KA18 4AG   01290 338296
[E-mail: revronyoung@hotmail.com]

Ochiltree linked with Stair
Carolyn M. Baker (Mrs) BD   1997   10 Mauchline Road, Ochiltree, Cumnock KA18 2PZ   01290 700365
[E-mail: carolynmbaker2001@yahoo.co.uk]

Old Cumnock: Old See Lugar

Old Cumnock: Trinity
John C. Christie BSc BD   1990   2004   46 Ayr Road, Cumnock KA18 1DW   01290 422145
[E-mail: jcc_larchview@btinternet.com]
(Trinity is the new name for Crichton West and St Ninian's)

Patna: Waterside See Dalmellington

Prestwick: Kingcase (H) (E-mail: office@kingcase.freeserve.co.uk)
T. David Watson BSc BD   1988   1997   15 Bellrock Avenue, Prestwick KA9 1SQ   01292 479571
[E-mail: tdwatson@tesco.net]

Prestwick: St Nicholas' (H)
George R. Fiddes BD   1979   1985   3 Bellevue Road, Prestwick KA9 1NW   01292 477613
[E-mail: george@gfiddes.freeserve.co.uk]

Prestwick: South (H)
Kenneth C. Elliott BD CertMin   1989   68 St Quivox Road, Prestwick KA9 1JF   01292 478788
[E-mail: kenneth@revelliott.freeserve.co.uk]

Sorn See Muirkirk

Straiton: St Cuthbert's See Kirkmichael
Symington See Craigie
Tarbolton See Annbank

Troon: Old (H)
Alastair H. Symington MA BD   1972   1998   85 Bentinck Drive, Troon KA10 6HZ   01292 313644
[E-mail: revahs@care4free.net]

Troon: Portland (H)
Ronald M.H. Boyd BD DipTh   1995   1999   89 South Beach, Troon KA10 6EQ   01292 313285
[E-mail: rmhboyd@btopenworld.com]

Troon: St Meddan's (H) (E-mail: st.meddan@virgin.net)
David L. Harper BSc BD   1972   1979   27 Bentinck Drive, Troon KA10 6HX   01292 311784
[E-mail: d.l.harper@btinternet.com]

Name			Position	Address	Phone
Andrew, R.J.M. MA	1955	1994	(Uddingston: Old)	6A Ronaldshaw Park, Ayr KA7 2TS	01292 263430
Banks, John BD	1968	2001	(Hospital Chaplain)	19 Victoria Drive, Troon KA10 6JF	01292 317758
Barr, John BSc PhD BD	1958	1979	(Kilmarnock: Old)	7 Kilbrandon Way, Doonfoot, Ayr KA7 4JY	01292 445631
Blyth, James G.S. BSc BD	1963	1986	(Glenmuick)	40 Robsland Avenue, Ayr KA7 2RW	01292 261276
Bogle, Thomas C. BD	1983	2003	(Fisherton with Maybole: West)	38 McEwan Crescent, Mossblown, Ayr KA6 5DR	01292 521215
Campbell, Effie C. (Mrs) BD	1981	1991	(Old Cumnock: Crichton West with St Ninian's)		
Cranston, George BD	1976	2001	(Rutherglen: Wardlawhill)	7 Lansdowne Road, Ayr KA8 8LS	01292 264282
Dickie, Michael M. BSc	1955	1994	(Ayr: Castlehill)	20 Capperview, Prestwick KA9 1BH	01292 476627
Garrity, T. Alan W. BSc BD MTh	1969	1999	Christ Church, Warwick, Bermuda	8 Nolmire Road, Ayr KA8 9ES PO Box PG88, Paget PG BX, Bermuda [E-mail: revtawg@logic.bm]	
Glencross, William M. LTh	1968	1999	(Bellshill: Macdonald Memorial)	1 Lochay Place, Troon KA10 7HH	01292 317097
Grant, J. Gordon MA BD	1957	1997	(Edinburgh: Dean)	33 Fullarton Drive, Troon KA10 6LE	01292 311852
Hannah, William BD MCAM MIPR	1987	2001	(Muirkirk)	8 Dovecot View, Kirkintilloch, Glasgow G66 3HY	0141-776 1337
Helon, George G. BA BD	1984	2000	(Barr linked with Dailly)	9 Park Road, Maxwelltown, Dumfries DG2 7PW	01387 259255
Johnston, Kenneth L. BA LTh	1969	2001	(Annbank)	2 Rylands, Prestwick KA9 2DX	01292 471980
Kent, Arthur F.S.	1966	1999	(Monkton and Prestwick: North)	17 St David's Drive, Evesham, Worcs WR11 6AS	01386 421562
Macdonald, Ian U.	1960	1997	(Tarbolton)	18 Belmont Road, Ayr KA7 2PF	01292 283085
McNidder, Roderick H. BD	1987	1997	Chaplain, South Ayrshire Hospitals Trust	6 Hollow Park, Alloway, Ayr KA7 4SR	01292 442554
McPhail, Andrew M. BA	1968	2002	(Ayr: Wallacetown)	25 Maybole Road, Ayr KA7 2QA	01292 282108
Mitchell, Sheila M. (Miss) BD MTh	1995	2002	Chaplain: Ayrshire and Arran Primary Care Trust		
Morrison, Alistair H. BTh DipYCS	1985	2004	(Paisley: St Mark's Oldhall)	Ailsa Hospital, Ayr KA6 6BQ 92 St Leonard's Road, Ayr KA7 2PU [E-mail: alistairmorrison@supanet.com]	01292 610556 01292 266021
Robertson, Daniel M. MA	1960	2000	(Auchinleck)	14 Corrie Place, Drongan, Ayr KA6 7DU	01292 590150
Saunders, Campbell M. MA BD	1952	1989	(Ayr: St Leonard's)	42 Marle Park, Ayr KA7 4RN	01292 441673
Stirling, Ian R. BSc BD	1990	2002	Chaplain: The Ayrshire Hospice	Ayrshire Hospice, 35–37 Racecourse Road, Ayr KA7 2TG	01292 269200

AYR ADDRESSES

Ayr

Auld Kirk	Kirkport (116 High Street)
Castlehill	Castlehill Road x Hillfoot Road
Lochside	Lochside Road x Murray Street
Newton-on-Ayr	Main Street
St Andrew's	Park Circus
St Columba	Midton Road x Carrick Park
St James'	Prestwick Road x
	Falkland Park Road
St Leonard's	St Leonard's Road x
	Monument Road
Wallacetown	John Street x Church Street

Girvan

North	Montgomerie Street
South	Stair Park

Maybole (both buildings still in use)

Old	Centre of Cassillis Road
West	Foot of Coral Glen

Prestwick

Kingcase	Waterloo Road
Monkton and	Monkton Road
Prestwick North	
St Nicholas	Main Street
South	Main Street

Troon

Old	Ayr Street
Portland	St Meddan's Street
St Meddan's	St Meddan's Street

(11) IRVINE AND KILMARNOCK

The Presbytery meets ordinarily at 6:30 pm in the Hall of Howard St Andrew's Church, Kilmarnock, on the first Tuesday of each month from September to May, (except January when it meets on the second Tuesday for the celebration of Holy Communion and in conference or socially) and on the fourth Tuesday in June.

Clerk: REV. COLIN G.F. BROCKIE BSc(Eng) BD	1992	2002	51 Portland Road, Kilmarnock KA1 2EQ [E-mail: akph57@uk.uumail.com]	01563 525311
Depute Clerk: I. STEUART DEY LLB NP			72 Dundonald Road, Kilmarnock KA1 1RZ [E-mail: steuart.dey@btinternet.com]	01563 521686
Treasurer: JAMES McINTOSH BA CA			15 Dundonald Road, Kilmarnock KA1 1RU	01563 523552
Crosshouse S. Ian Dennis BD			27 Kilmarnock Road, Crosshouse, Kilmarnock KA2 0EZ [E-mail: sid.dennis@virgin.net]	01563 521035
Darvel Charles M. Cameron BA BD PhD	1980	2001	46 West Main Street, Darvel KA17 0AQ	01560 322924
Dreghorn and Springside Gary E. Horsburgh BA	1976	1983	96A Townfoot, Dreghorn, Irvine KA11 4EZ	01294 217770
Dunlop Maureen M. Duncan (Mrs) BD	1996		4 Dampark, Dunlop, Kilmarnock KA3 4BZ	01560 484083

Fenwick (H)
Geoffrey Redmayne BSc BD MPhil — 2000 — 2 Kirkton Place, Fenwick, Kilmarnock KA3 6DW [E-mail: geoffmayne.fsnet.co.uk] — 01560 600217

Galston (H)
T.J. Loudon Blair MA BD — 1965 — 1980 — 60 Brewland Street, Galston KA4 8DX [E-mail: loudon.blair@virgin.net] — 01563 820246
John H.B. Taylor MA BD DipEd FEIS (Assoc) — 1952 — 1990 — 62 Woodlands Grove, Kilmarnock KA3 1TZ — 01563 526698

Hurlford (H)
James D. McCulloch BD MIOP — 1996 — 12 Main Road, Crookedholm, Kilmarnock KA3 6JT — 01563 535673

Irvine: Fullarton (H)
Neil Urquhart BD DipMin — 1989 — 48 Waterside, Irvine KA12 8QJ [E-mail: neilurquhart@beeb.net] — 01294 279909

Irvine: Girdle Toll (E) (H)
Clare B. Sutcliffe BSc BD — 2000 — 2 Littlestane Rise, Irvine KA11 2BJ [E-mail: revclare@tesco.net] — 01294 213565

Irvine: Mure (H)
Hugh M. Adamson BD — 1976 — West Road, Irvine KA12 8RE — 01294 279916

Irvine: Old (H) (01294 273503)
Robert Travers BA BD — 1993 — 1999 — 22 Kirk Vennel, Irvine KA12 0DQ [E-mail: robert@travers46.freeserve.co.uk] — 01294 279265

Irvine: Relief Bourtreehill (H)
Andrew R. Black BD — 1987 — 2003 — 4 Kames Court, Irvine KA11 1RT [E-mail: andrewblack@tiscali.co.uk] — 01294 216939

Irvine: St Andrew's (H) (01294 276051)
Vacant — 206 Bank Street, Irvine KA12 0YD — 01294 211403

Kilmarnock: Grange (H) (01563 534490)
Colin G.F. Bro-kie BSc(Eng) BD — 1967 — 1978 — 51 Portland Road, Kilmarnock KA1 2EQ [E-mail: revcol@revcol.demon.co.uk] — 01563 525311

Kilmarnock: Henderson (H) (01563 541302)
David W. Lacy BA BD — 1976 — 1989 — 52 London Road, Kilmarnock KA3 7AJ [E-mail: thelacys@tinyworld.co.uk] — 01563 523113 (Tel/Fax)

Kilmarnock: Howard St Andrew's (H)
Malcolm MacLeod BA BD — 1979 — 1989 — 1 Evelyn Villas, Holehouse Road, Kilmarnock KA3 7AX [E-mail: cal.macleod@ntlworld.com] — 01563 522278

Kilmarnock: Laigh West High (H) David S. Cameron BD	2001		1 Holmes Farm Road, Kilmarnock KA1 1TP [E-mail: david@cmron05.freeserve.co.uk]	01563 525416
Kilmarnock: Old High Kirk (H) William M. Hall BD	1972	1979	107 Dundonald Road, Kilmarnock KA1 1UP [E-mail: revwillie@tiscali.co.uk]	01563 525608
Kilmarnock: Riccarton (H) Thomas W. Jarvie BD	1953	1968	2 Jasmine Road, Kilmarnock KA1 2HD	01563 525694
Kilmarnock: St John's Onthank (H) Susan M. Anderson (Mrs)	1997		84 Wardneuk Drive, Kilmarnock KA3 2EX [E-mail: stjohnthank@yahoo.co.uk]	01563 521815
Catherine A.M. Shaw MA (Aux)	1998		40 Merrygreen Place, Stewarton, Kilmarnock KA3 5EP [E-mail: catherine.shaw@tesco.net]	01560 483352
Kilmarnock: St Kentigern's S. Grant Barclay LLB BD	1995		1 Thirdpart Place, Kilmarnock KA1 1UL [E-mail: grant.barclay@bigfoot.com]	01563 571280
Kilmarnock: St Marnock's (H) (01563 541337) James McNaughtan BD DipMin	1983	1989	35 South Gargieston Drive, Kilmarnock KA1 1TB [E-mail: jim@mcnaughtan.demon.co.uk]	01563 521665
Kilmarnock: St Ninian's Bellfield (01563 524705) linked with Kilmarnock: Shortlees H. Taylor Brown BD CertMin	1997	2002	14 McLelland Drive, Kilmarnock KA1 1SF [E-mail: htaylorbrown@hotmail.com]	01563 529920
Kilmarnock: Shortlees See Kilmarnock: St Ninian's Bellfield				
Kilmaurs: St Maur's Glencairn (H) John A. Urquhart BD	1993		9 Standalane, Kilmaurs, Kilmarnock KA3 2NB	01563 538289
Newmilns: Loudoun (H) John Macleod MA BD	2000		116A Loudoun Road, Newmilns KA16 9HH	01560 320174
Stewarton: John Knox Samuel Hosain BD MTh PhD	1979	1993	27 Avenue Street, Stewarton, Kilmarnock KA3 5AP [E-mail: samuel.h2@ukonline.co.uk]	01560 482418
Stewarton: St Columba's (H) Elizabeth A. Waddell (Mrs) BD	1999		1 Kirk Glebe, Stewarton, Kilmarnock KA3 5BJ	01560 482453

Ayrshire Mission to the Deaf

| S. Grant Barclay LLB BD (Chaplain) | 1991 | 1998 | 89 Mure Avenue, Kilmarnock KA3 1TT [E-mail: grant.barclay@bigfoot.com] | 01563 571280 |

Name			Charge / Address	Phone
Campbell, George H.	1957	1992	(Stewarton: John Knox) — 20 Woodlands Grove, Kilmarnock KA3 1TZ	01563 536365
Campbell, John A. JP FIEM	1984	1998	(Irvine: St Andrew's) — Flowerdale, Balmoral Lane, Blairgowrie PH10 7AF	01250 872795
Christie, Robert S. MA BD ThM	1964	2001	(Kilmarnock: West High) — 69 Dundonald Road, Kilmarnock KA1 1TJ	01563 525302
Davidson, James BD DipAFH	1989	2002	(Wishaw: Old) — 13 Redburn Place, Irvine KA12 9BQ	01294 312515
Downie, Andrew A. BD BSc DipEd DipMin ThB	1994	1999	Prison Chaplain — HMP Bowhouse, Mauchline Road, Kilmarnock KA1 5AA	01563 548928
Hare, Malcolm M.W. BA BD	1956	1994	(Kilmarnock: St Kentigern's) — 21 Raith Road, Fenwick, Kilmarnock KA3 6DB	01560 600388
Hay, W.J.R. MA BD	1959	1995	(Buchanan with Drymen) — 18 Jamieson Place, Stewarton, Kilmarnock KA3 3AY	01560 482799
Huggett, Judith A. (Miss) BA BD	1990	1998	Hospital Chaplain — 4 Westmoor Crescent, Kilmarnock KA1 1TX	
Kelly, Thomas A. Davidson MA BD FSAScot	1975	2002	(Glasgow: Govan Old) — 2 Springhill Stables, Portland Road, Kilmarnock KA1 2EJ	01563 573994
McAlpine, Richard H.M. BA FSAScot	1968	2000	(Lochgoilhead and Kilmorich) — 7 Kingsford Place, Kilmarnock KA3 6FG	01563 572075
MacDonald, James M.	1964	1987	(Kilmarnock: St John's Onthank) — 29 Carmel Place, Kilmaurs, Kilmarnock KA3 2QU	01563 525254
McGarva, Sarah (Miss) DCS			(Deaconess) — 87 Hunter Drive, Irvine KA12 9BS	01294 271257
Roy, James BA	1967	1982	(Irvine: Girdle Toll) — 23 Bowes Rigg, Stewarton, Kilmarnock KA3 5EL [E-mail: jroy@dougyr.globalnet.co.uk]	01560 482185
Scott, Thomas T.	1968	1989	(Kilmarnock: St Marnock's) — 6 North Hamilton Place, Kilmarnock KA1 2QN [E-mail: 101725.216@compuserve.com]	01563 531415
Urquhart, Barbara (Mrs) DCS			Deaconess, Part-time Hospital Chaplain and Presbytery S.S. Adviser — 9 Standalane, Kilmaurs, Kilmarnock KA3 2NB	01563 538289

IRVINE and KILMARNOCK ADDRESSES

Irvine

Dreghorn and Springside	Townfoot x Station Brae
Fullarton	Marress Road x Church Street
Girdle Toll	Bryce Knox Court
Mure	West Road
Old Parish	Kirkgate
Relief	Crofthead, Bourtreehill
St Andrew's	Caldon Road x Oaklands Ave

Kilmarnock

Ayrshire Mission to the Deaf	10 Clark Street
Grange	Woodstock Street
Henderson	London Road
Howard	5 Portland Road
Laigh	John Dickie Street
Old High	Church Street x Soulis Street
Riccarton	Old Street
St Andrew's	St Andrew's Street
Glencairn	84 Wardneuk Street
St John's Onthank	St Marnock's Street
St Marnock's	Whatriggs Road
St Ninian's Bellfield	Central Avenue
Shortlees	Portland Street
West High	

(12) ARDROSSAN

Meets at Saltcoats, New Trinity, on the first Tuesday of February, March, April, May, September, October, November and December, and on the second Tuesday of June.

Clerk:	REV. JOHNSTON R. McKAY MA BA		Upper Burnfoot, 27 Stanlane Place, Largs KA30 8DD [E-mail: akph38@uk.uumail.com]	01475 672960 01475 674380 (Fax) 07885 876021 (Mbl)

Ardrossan: Barony St John's (H) (01294 465009)

Vacant		10 Seafield Drive, Ardrossan KA22 8NU	01294 463868

Ardrossan: Park (01294 463711)

William R. Johnston BD	1998	35 Ardneil Court, Ardrossan KA22 7NQ	01294 471808
Marion L.K. Howie (Mrs) MA ACRS (Aux)	1992	51 High Road, Stevenston KA20 3DY [E-mail: marion.howie@ndirect.co.uk]	01294 466571

Beith: High (H) (01505 502686) linked with Beith: Trinity (H)

Vacant		2 Glebe Court, Beith KA15 1ET	01505 503858
Fiona C. Ross (Miss) BD DipMin (Assoc)	1996	16 Spiers Avenue, Beith KA15 1JD [E-mail: fionaross@calvin78.freeserve.co.uk]	01505 502131

Beith: Trinity (H) See Beith: High

Brodick linked with Corrie

Ian MacLeod LTh BA MTh PhD	1969	1974	4 Manse Crescent, Brodick, Isle of Arran KA27 8AS	01770 302334

Corrie See Brodick

Cumbrae

Marjory H. Mackay (Mrs) BD DipEd CCE	1998	Marine Parade, Millport, Isle of Cumbrae KA28 0ED	01475 530416

Dalry: St Margaret's

James A.S. Boag BD	1992	2002	Bridgend, Dalry KA24 4DA [E-mail: james@boag4458.fsnet.co.uk]	01294 832234

Dalry: Trinity (H)

Vacant		West Kilbride Road, Dalry KA24 5DX	01294 832363

Fairlie (H)

Vacant		14 Fairlieburne Gardens, Fairlie, Largs KA29 0ER	01475 568342

Charge / Minister	Ordained	Inducted	Address	Telephone
Fergushill linked with Kilwinning: Erskine Vacant			14 McLuckie Drive, Kilwinning KA13 6DL	01294 551565
Kilbirnie: Auld Kirk (H) Ian W. Benzie BD	1999		49 Holmhead, Kilbirnie KA25 6BS [E-mail: revian@btopenworld.com]	01505 682348
Kilbirnie: St Columba's (H) (01505 685239) Vacant			Manse of St Columba's, Kilbirnie KA25 7JU	01505 683342
Kilmory Vacant				
Kilwinning: Abbey (H) Gordon A. McCracken BD CertMin DMin	1988	2002	54 Dalry Road, Kilwinning KA13 7HE [E-mail: gordonangus@btinternet.com]	01294 552606
Kilwinning: Erskine (01294 552188) See Fergushill				
Kilwinning: Mansefield Trinity (E) (01294 550746) Douglas S. Paterson MA BD	1976	1999	27 Treesbank, Kilwinning KA13 6LY [E-mail: akph98@uk.uumail.com]	01294 552453
Lamlash linked with Lochranza and Pirnmill linked with Shiskine (H) Barry Knight BD	1991	2002	Shiskine, Brodick, Isle of Arran KA27 8EP [E-mail: pakurdnga@aol.com]	01770 860380
Largs: Clark Memorial (H) (01475 675186) Stephen J. Smith BSc BD	1993	1998	31 Douglas Street, Largs KA30 8PT [E-mail: stephenrevsteve@aol.com]	01475 672370
Largs: St Columba's (01475 686212) Roderick J. Grahame BD CPS	1991	2002	17 Beachway, Largs KA30 8QH [E-mail: rjgrahame@supanet.com]	01475 673107
Largs: St John's (H) (01475 674468) Andrew F. McGurk BD	1983	1993	1 Newhaven Grove, Largs KA30 8NS [E-mail: afmcg.largs@talk21.com]	01475 676123
Lochranza and Pirnmill See Lamlash				
Saltcoats: New Trinity (H) (01294 472001) Alexander D. McCallum BD	1987	1994	1 Montgomerie Crescent, Saltcoats KA21 5BX [E-mail: sandy@newtrinity.co.uk]	01294 461143

Saltcoats: North (01294 464679)
Alexander B. Noble MA BD ThM   1982 2003   25 Longfield Avenue, Saltcoats KA21 6DR   01294 604923
[E-mail: alexbnoble@themanse38.freeserve.co.uk]

Saltcoats: St Cuthbert's (H)
Brian H. Oxburgh BSc BD   1980 1988   10 Kennedy Road, Saltcoats KA21 5SF   01294 602674
[E-mail: boxburgh@aol.com]

Shiskine See Lamlash

Stevenston: Ardeer linked with Stevenston: Livingstone (H)
John M.M. Lafferty BD   1999   32 High Road, Stevenston KA20 3DR   01294 464180

Stevenston: High (H)
M. Scott Cameron MA BD   2002   Glencairn Street, Stevenston KA20 3DL   01294 463356
[E-mail: scottie_cameron@btinternet.com]

Stevenston: Livingstone (H) See Stevenston: Ardeer

West Kilbride: Overton (H)
Norman Cruickshank BA BD   1983   Goldenberry Avenue, West Kilbride KA23 9LJ   01294 823186

West Kilbride: St Andrew's (H) (01294 829902)
D. Ross Mitchell BA BD   1972 1980   7 Overton Drive, West Kilbride KA23 9LQ   01294 823142
[E-mail: ross.mitchell@virgin.net]

Whiting Bay and Kildonan
Elizabeth R.L. Watson (Miss) BA BD   1981 1982   Whiting Bay, Brodick, Isle of Arran KA27 8RE   01770 700289
[E-mail: revewatson@surefish.co.uk]

Dailly, J.R. BD DipPS	1979	1979	Staff Chaplain: Army	DACG, HQ 42 (NW) Bde, Fulwood Barracks, Preston PR2 8AA	
Downie, Alexander S.	1975	1997	(Ardrossan: Park)	14 Korsankel Wynd, Saltcoats KA21 6HY	01294 464097
Ewing, James MA BD	1948	1987	(Ardrossan: Barony)	8 Semple Crescent, Fairlie, Largs KA29 0EN	01475 568115
Fisher, Kenneth H.	1969	1994	(Stronsay with Eday)	33 Halfway Street, West Kilbride KA23 9EQ	01294 829973
Gordon, Kenneth C.	1953	1988	(Gigha and Cara)	16 Braeside Avenue, Largs KA30 8HD	
Grant, David I.M. MA BD	1969	2003	(Dalry: Trinity)	8 Mossbank Drive, Glasgow G33 1LS	
Harbison, David J.H.	1958	1998	(Beith: High with Beith: Trinity)	42 Mill Park, Dalry KA24 5BB	01294 834092
				[E-mail: djh@harbi.fsnet.co.uk]	
Hebenton, David J. MA BD	1958	2002	(Ayton and Burnmouth linked with Grantshouse and Houndwood and Reston)	22B Faulds Wynd, Seamill, West Kilbride KA23 9FA	

McCance, Andrew M. BSc	1986 1995	(Coatbridge: Middle)	15 The Crescent, Skelmorlie PA17 5DX	01475 672960
McKay, Johnston R. MA BA	1969 1987	(Religious Broadcasting: BBC)	Upper Burnfoot, 27 Stanlane Place, Largs KA30 8DD [E-mail: johnston.mckay@btopenworld.com]	0131-447 9729
Maclagan, David W. MA ThD	1965 1991	(Largs: St John's)	Flat 19, Morningside View, 14 Maxwell Street, Edinburgh EH10 5HU	01770 700569
Paterson, John H. BD	1977 2000	(Kirkintilloch: St David's Memorial Park)	Creag Bhan, Golf Course Road, Whiting Bay, Arran KA27 8QT	01560 483072
Roy, Iain M. MA BD	1960 1997	(Stevenston: Livingstone)	2 The Fieldings, Dunlop, Kilmarnock KA3 4AU	01475 529514
Selfridge, John BTh BREd	1969 1991	(Eddrachillis)	Strathclyde House, Apt 1, Shore Road, Skelmorlie PA17 5AN	01475 674709
Taylor, Andrew S. BTh FPhS	1959 1992	(Greenock Union)	9 Raillies Avenue, Largs KA30 8QY	01294 468685
Thomson, Margaret (Mrs)	1988 1993	(Saltcoats: Erskine)	72 Knockrivoch Place, Ardrossan KA22 7PZ	01294 823061
Walker, David S. MA	1939 1978	(Markerstoun with Smailholm with Stichill, Hume and Nenthorn)	6 Stairtie Crescent, West Kilbride KA23 9BT	

(13) LANARK

Meets at Lanark on the first Tuesday of February, March, April, May, September, October, November and December, and on the third Tuesday of June.

Clerk: REV. MICHAEL W. FREW BSc BD   18 Old Bridgend, Carluke ML8 4HN   01555 772259 (Tel/Fax)
[E-mail: akph60@uk.uumail.com]
[E-mail: lanarkpresbytery@uk.uumail.com]

Biggar (H)
Vacant   61 High Street, Biggar ML12 6DA   01899 220227

Black Mount linked with Culter linked with Libberton and Quothquan
James S.H. Cutler BD CEng MIStructE   1986   2004   17 Mercat Loan, Biggar ML12 6DG   01899 220625
[E-mail: jimcutler@virgin.net]

Cairngryffe linked with Symington
Graham R. Houston BSc BD MTh PhD   1978   2001   16 Abington Road, Symington, Biggar ML12 6JX   01899 308838
[E-mail: gandihouston@aol.com]

Carluke: Kirkton (H) (01555 750778)
Iain D. Cunningham MA BD   1979   1987   9 Station Road, Carluke ML8 5AA   01555 771262 (Tel/Fax)
[E-mail: iaindc@fish.co.uk]

Carluke: St Andrew's (H)
Helen E. Jamieson (Mrs) BD DipED   1989   120 Clyde Street, Carluke ML8 5BG   01555 771218
[E-mail: revhelenj@aol.com]

Carluke: St John's (H)
Michael W. Frew BSc BD   1978   1991   18 Old Bridgend, Carluke ML8 4HN   01555 772259 (Tel/Fax)
[E-mail: mwfrew@aol.com]

Carnwath (H)
Beverly G.D.D. Gauld MA BD — 1972 1978 — The Manse, Carnwath, Lanark ML11 8JY — 01555 840259

Carstairs linked with Carstairs Junction
J. Melvyn Coogan LTh — 1992 1996 — 80 Lanark Road, Carstairs, Lanark ML11 8QH — 01555 870250

Carstairs Junction See Carstairs

Coalburn linked with Lesmahagow: Old
Aileen Robson BD — 2003 — 9 Elm Bank, Lesmahagow, Lanark ML11 0EA
[E-mail: amrob65@aol.com] — 01555 895325

Crossford linked with Kirkfieldbank
Steven Reid BAcc CA BD — 1989 1997 — 74 Lanark Road, Crossford, Carluke ML8 5RE
[E-mail: stevenreid@v21mail.co.uk] — 01555 860415

Culter See Black Mount

Forth: St Paul's (H)
Vacant — 22 Lea-Rig, Forth, Lanark ML11 8EA — 01555 811748

Glencaple linked with Lowther
Margaret A. Muir (Miss) MA LLB BD — 1989 2001 — 66 Carlisle Road, Crawford, Biggar ML12 6TW — 01864 502625

Kirkfieldbank See Crossford

Kirkmuirhill (H)
Ian M. Watson LLB DipLP BD — 1998 2003 — The Manse, 2 Lanark Road, Kirkmuirhill, Lanark ML11 9RB
[E-mail: ian.watson21@btopenworld.com] — 01555 892409 (Tel/Fax)

Lanark: Greyfriars
Catherine E.E. Collins (Mrs) MA BD — 1993 — 2 Friarsdene, Lanark ML11 9EJ
[E-mail: greyfriars@webartz.com] — 01555 663363
David A. Collins BSc BD — 1993

Lanark: St Nicholas'
Alison A. Meikle (Mrs) BD — 1999 2002 — 2 Kaimhill Court, Lanark ML11 9HU
[E-mail: lanarkstnichs@fsnet.co.uk] — 01555 662600 (Tel)
01555 665905 (Fax)

Law
Anne McIvor (Miss) SRD BD — 1996 2003 — The Manse, 53 Lawhill Road, Law, Carluke ML8 5EZ — 01698 373180

Lesmahagow: Abbeygreen
David S. Carmichael — 1982 — Abbeygreen Manse, Lesmahagow, Lanark ML11 0DB
[E-mail: david@6abbeygreen.freeserve.co.uk] — 01555 893384

Lesmahagow: Old (H) See Coalburn
Libberton and Quothquan See Black Mount
Lowther See Glencaple
Symington See Cairngryffe

The Douglas Valley Church (www.douglasvalleychurch.org)

Bryan Kerr BA BD	2002	The Manse, Douglas, Lanark ML11 0RB	01555 851213 (Tel/Fax)

[E-mail: bryan@douglasvalleychurch.org]

(Charge formed by the union of Douglas: St Bride's and Douglas Water and Rigside)

Cowell, Susan G. (Miss) BA BD	1986 1998	(Budapest)	39 Main Street, Symington, Biggar ML12 6LL	01899 308257
Craig, William BA LTh	1974 1997	(Cambusbarron: The Bruce Memorial)	31 Heathfield Drive, Blackwood, Lanark ML11 9SR	01555 893710
Fox, George H.	1959 1977	(Coalsnaughton)	Brachead House, Crossford, Carluke ML8 5NQ	01555 860716
Jones, Philip H.	1968 1987	(Bishopbriggs: Kenmure)	39 Bankhouse, 62 Abbeygreen, Lesmahagow, Lanark ML11 0JS	
McCormick, W. Cadzow MA BD	1943 1983	(Glasgow: Maryhill Old)	82 Main Street, Symington, Biggar ML12 6LJ	01899 308221
McMahon, Robert J. BD	1959 1997	(Crossford with Kirkfieldbank)	7 Ridgepark Drive, Lanark ML11 9PG	01555 663844
Pacitti, Stephen A. MA	1963 2003	(Black Mount with Culter with Libberton and Quothquan)	157 Nithsdale Road, Glasgow G41 5RD	0141-423 5792
Seath, Thomas J.G.	1980 1992	(Motherwell: Manse Road)	1 Allan Avenue, Carluke ML8 5UA	01555 771644
Stewart, John M. MA BD	1964 2001	(Johnstone with Kirkpatrick Juxta)	5 Rathmor Road, Biggar ML12 6QG	01899 220398
Young, David A.	1972 2003	(Kirkmuirhill)	15 Mannachie Rise, Forres IV36 2US	01309 672849

[E-mail: youngdavid@aol.com]

(14) GREENOCK AND PAISLEY

Meets on the second Tuesday of September, December, February and May, on the fourth Tuesday of October and March, and on the third Tuesday of June.

Clerk:	REV. DAVID KAY BA BD MTh	6 Southfield Avenue, Paisley PA2 8BY	0141-884 3600 (Tel/Fax)
		[E-mail: akph69@uk.uumail.com]	
Associate Clerk:	REV. DAVID MILL KJSJ MA BD	105 Newark Street, Greenock PA16 7TW	01475 639602
		[E-mail: minister@finnart-stpauls-church.org]	
Presbytery Office:		Cottage 10, Quarrier's Village, Bridge of Weir PA11 3SX	01505 615033

Barrhead: Arthurlie (H) (0141-881 8442)

James S.A. Cowan BD DipMin	1986	1998	10 Arthurlie Avenue, Barrhead, Glasgow G78 2BU	0141-881 3457

[E-mail: jim_cowan@ntlworld.com]

Barrhead: Bourock (H) (0141-881 9813)
Maureen Leitch (Mrs) BA BD   1995
14 Maxton Avenue, Barrhead, Glasgow G78 1DY
[E-mail: maureen.leitch@ntlworld.com]
0141-881 1462

Barrhead: South and Levern (H) (0141-881 7825)
Morris M. Dutch BD BA   1998   2002
3 Colinbar Circle, Barrhead, Glasgow G78 2BE
[E-mail: mmdutch@yahoo.co.uk]
0141-571 4059

Bishopton (H)
Gayle J.A. Taylor (Mrs) MA BD   1999
The Manse, Newton Road, Bishopton PA7 5JP
[E-mail: gayletaylor@tiscali.co.uk]
01505 862161

Bridge of Weir: Freeland (H) (01505 612610)
Kenneth N. Gray BA BD   1988
15 Lawmarnock Crescent, Bridge of Weir PA11 3AS
[E-mail: aandkgray@btinternet.com]
01505 690918

Bridge of Weir: St Machar's Ranfurly (01505 614364)
Suzanne Dunleavy (Miss) BD DipEd   1990   1992
9 Glen Brae, Bridge of Weir PA11 3BH
01505 612975

Caldwell
John Campbell MA BA BSc   1973   2000
The Manse of Caldwell, Uplawmoor, Glasgow G78 4AL
[E-mail: johncampbell@minister.com]
01505 850215

Elderslie Kirk (H) (01505 323348)
Vacant
282 Main Road, Elderslie, Johnstone PA5 9EF
01505 321767

Erskine (0141-812 4620)
Ian W. Bell LTh   1990   1998
The Manse, 7 Leven Place, Linburn, Erskine PA8 6AS
[E-mail: rviwbepc@ntlworld.com]
0141-581 0955

Morag Erskine (Miss) DCS
111 Main Drive, Erskine PA8 7JJ
[E-mail: morag.erskine@ntlworld.com]
0141-812 6096

Gourock: Old Gourock and Ashton (H)
Frank J. Gardner MA   1966   1979
90 Albert Road, Gourock PA19 1NN
[E-mail: frankgardner@oldgourockashton.freeserve.co.uk]
01475 631516

Gourock: St John's (H)
P. Jill Clancy (Mrs) BD   2000
6 Barrhill Road, Gourock PA19 1JX
[E-mail: jgibson@totalise.co.uk]
01475 632143

Greenock: Ardgowan
Alan H. Ward MA BD   1978   2002
72 Forsyth Street, Greenock PA16 8SX
[E-mail: alanhward@ntlworld.com]
01475 790849

Greenock: Eastend David J. McCarthy BSc BD	1985	2003	29 Denholm Street, Greenock PA16 8RH [E-mail: ncdgreenockeast@uk.uumail.com]	01475 722111
Greenock: Finnart St Paul's (H) David Mill KJSJ MA BD	1978	1979	105 Newark Street, Greenock PA16 7TW [E-mail: minister@finnart-stpauls-church.org]	01475 639602
Greenock: Mount Kirk James H. Simpson BD LLB	1964	1965	76 Finnart Street, Greenock PA16 8HJ [E-mail: jameshsimpson@ntlworld.com]	01475 790775
Greenock: Old West Kirk C. Ian W. Johnson MA BD	1997		39 Fox Street, Greenock PA16 8PD [E-mail: ian_ciw_johnson@tesco.net]	01475 888277
Eileen Manson (Mrs) DipCE (Aux)	1994		1 Cambridge Avenue, Gourock PA19 1XT [E-mail: jrmanson@ntlworld.com]	01475 632401
Greenock: St George's North W. Douglas Hamilton BD	1975	1986	67 Forsyth Street, Greenock PA16 8SX [E-mail: revwdhamilton@lycos.co.uk]	01475 724003
Greenock: St Luke's (H) William C. Hewitt BD DipPS	1977	1994	50 Ardgowan Street, Greenock PA16 8EP [E-mail: william.hewitt@ntlworld.com]	01475 721048
Greenock: St Margaret's (01475 781953) Isobel J.M. Kelly (Miss) MA BD DipEd	1974	1998	105 Finnart Street, Greenock PA16 8HN	01475 786590
Greenock: St Ninian's Allan G. McIntyre BD	1985	1985	5 Auchmead Road, Greenock PA16 0PY [E-mail: agmcintyre@lineone.net]	01475 631878
Greenock: Wellpark Mid Kirk Alan K. Sorensen BD MTh DipMin FSAScot	1983	2000	101 Brisbane Street, Greenock PA16 8PA [E-mail: alansorensen@beeb.net]	01475 721741
Houston and Killellan (H) Georgina M. Baxendale (Mrs) BD	1981	1989	The Manse of Houston, Main Street, Houston, Johnstone PA6 7EL	01505 612569
Howwood David Stewart MA DipEd BD MTh	1977	2001	The Manse, Beith Road, Howwood, Johnstone PA9 1AS [E-mail: revdavidst@aol.com]	01505 703678
Inchinnan (H) (0141-812 1263) Marilyn MacLaine (Mrs) LTh	1995		The Manse, Inchinnan, Renfrew PA4 9PH	0141-812 1688

Inverkip (H) Elizabeth A. Crumlish (Mrs) BD	1995	2002	The Manse, Longhouse Road, Inverkip, Greenock PA16 0BJ [E-mail: lizcrumlish@aol.com]	01475 521207
Johnstone: High (H) (01505 336303) Ann C. McCool (Mrs) BD DSD IPA ALCM	1989	2001	76 North Road, Johnstone PA5 8NF [E-mail: ann.mccool@ntlworld.com]	01505 320006
Johnstone: St Andrew's Trinity May Bell (Mrs) LTh	1998	2002	The Manse, 7 Leven Place, Linburn, Erskine PA8 6AS [E-mail: may.bell@ntlbusiness.com]	0141-581 7352
Johnstone: St Paul's (H) (01505 321632) Alistair N. Shaw MA BD	1982	2003	9 Stanley Drive, Brookfield, Johnstone PA5 8UF [E-mail: alistairn@shaw98.freeserve.co.uk]	01505 320060
Kilbarchan: East John Owain Jones MA BD FSAScot	1981	2002	Church Street, Kilbarchan, Johnstone PA10 2JQ [E-mail: johnowainjones@hotmail.com]	01505 702621
Kilbarchan: West Arthur Sherratt BD	1994		West Manse, Shuttle Street, Kilbarchan, Johnstone PA10 2JR [E-mail: arthur.sherratt@ntlworld.com]	01505 342930
Kilmacolm: Old (H) Gordon D. Irving BD	1994	1998	Glencairn Road, Kilmacolm PA13 4NJ [E-mail: gordon@irving516.fslife.co.uk]	01505 873174
Kilmacolm: St Columba (H) R. Douglas Cranston MA BD	1986	1992	6 Churchill Road, Kilmacolm PA13 4LH [E-mail: robert.cranston@tiscali.co.uk]	01505 873271
Langbank (T) Andrew M. Smillie LTh	1990	2004	The Manse, Main Road, Langbank, Port Glasgow PA14 6XP [E-mail: andrewsmillie@fish.co.uk]	01475 540252
Linwood (H) (01505 328802) T. Edward Marshall BD	1987		The Manse, Bridge Street, Linwood, Paisley PA3 3DL [E-mail: marshall1654@hotmail.com]	01505 325131
Lochwinnoch (T) Robin N. Allison BD DipMin	1994	1999	1 Station Rise, Lochwinnoch PA12 4NA [E-mail: robin@mansemob.org]	01505 843484

Neilston (0141-881 9445)
Alexander Macdonald MA BD   1966   1984   The Manse, Neilston Road, Neilston, Glasgow   G78 3NP   0141-881 1958
[E-mail: alexmacdonald42@aol.com]

Paisley: Abbey (H) (Tel: 0141-889 7654; Fax: 0141-887 3929)
Alan D. Birss MA BD   1979   1988   15 Main Road, Castlehead, Paisley PA2 6AJ   0141-889 3587
[E-mail: alan.birss@paisleyabbey.com]

Paisley: Castlehead
Esther J. Ninian MA BD   1993   1998   28 Fulbar Crescent, Paisley PA2 9AS   01505 812304

Paisley: Glenburn (0141-884 2602)
Vacant   10 Hawick Avenue, Paisley PA2 9LD   0141-884 4903

Paisley: Laigh Kirk (H) (0141-889 7700)
Vacant   18 Oldhall Road, Paisley PA1 3HL   0141-882 2277

Paisley: Lylesland (H) (0141-561 7139)
Andrew W. Bradley BD   1975   1998   36 Potterhill Avenue, Paisley PA2 8BA   0141-884 2882
Greta Gray (Miss) DCS   67 Crags Avenue, Paisley PA3 6SG   0141-884 6178

Paisley: Martyrs' (0141-889 6603)
Alison Davidge (Mrs) MA BD   1990   1997   12 Low Road, Paisley PA2 6AG   0141-889 2182

Paisley: Oakshaw Trinity (H) (Tel: 0141-887 4647; Fax: 0141-848 5139; E-mail: iancurrie@ntlworld.com)
Ian S. Currie MBE BD   1975   1980   9 Hawkhead Road, Paisley PA1 3ND   0141-887 0884
Janette M.K. Black (Mrs) BD (Assist)   1993   2003   5 Craigiehall Avenue, Erskine PA8 7DB   0141-812 0794

Paisley: St Columba Foxbar (H) (01505 812377)
Vacant   13 Corsebar Drive, Paisley PA2 9QD   0141-889 9988

Paisley: St James' (0141-889 2422)
Eleanor J. McMahon (Miss) BEd BD   1994   38 Woodland Avenue, Paisley PA2 8BH   0141-884 3246
[E-mail: eleanor.mcmahon@ntlworld.com]

Paisley: St Luke's (H)
D. Ritchie M. Gillon BD DipMin   1994   31 Southfield Avenue, Paisley PA2 8BX   0141-884 6215
[E-mail: revgillon@surefish.co.uk]

Paisley: St Mark's Oldhall (H) (0141-882 2755)
Vacant   36 Newtyle Road, Paisley PA1 3JX   0141-889 4279

Paisley: St Ninian's Ferguslie (E) (0141-887 9436) (New Charge Development)
Vacant   10 Stanely Drive, Paisley PA2 6HE   0141-884 4177
William Wishart DCS   17 Swift Bank, Hamilton ML3 8PX   01698 429371
[E-mail: bill@hillhousechurch.co.uk]

Paisley: Sandyford (Thread Street) (0141-889 5078)
David Kay BA BD MTh — 1974 — 6 Southfield Avenue, Paisley PA2 8BY [E-mail: davidkay@ntlworld.com] — 0141-884 3600

Paisley: Sherwood Greenlaw (H) (0141-889 7060)
Alasdair F. Cameron BD CA — 1986 — 5 Greenlaw Drive, Paisley PA1 3RX [E-mail: alcamron@lineone.net] — 0141-889 3057

Paisley: Wallneuk North (Tel: 0141-889 9265; Fax: 0141-887 6670)
Thomas Macintyre MA BD — 1972 1988 — 27 Mansionhouse Road, Paisley PA1 3RG [E-mail: tom.mac@ntlworld.com] — 0141-581 1505

Port Glasgow: Hamilton Bardrainney
James A. Munro BD DMS — 1979 2002 — 80 Bardrainney Avenue, Port Glasgow PA14 6HD [E-mail: james.munro7@btopenworld.com] — 01475 701213

Port Glasgow: St Andrew's (H)
Andrew T. MacLean BA BD — 1980 1993 — St Andrew's Manse, Barr's Brae, Port Glasgow PA14 5QA [E-mail: standrews-pg@mac.com] — 01475 741486

Port Glasgow: St Martin's
John G. Miller BEd BD MTh — 1983 1998 — Clunebraehead, Clune Brae, Port Glasgow PA14 5SL — 01475 704115

Renfrew: North (0141-885 2154)
E. Lorna Hood (Mrs) MA BD — 1978 1979 — 1 Alexandra Drive, Renfrew PA4 8UB [E-mail: ssren@tiscali.co.uk] — 0141-886 2074

Renfrew: Old
Alexander C. Wark MA BD STM — 1982 1998 — 31 Gibson Road, Renfrew PA4 0RH [E-mail: alecwark@yahoo.co.uk] — 0141-886 2005

Renfrew: Trinity (H) (0141-885 2129)
Stuart C. Steell BD CertMin — 1992 — 25 Paisley Road, Renfrew PA4 8JH [E-mail: ssren@tinyonline.co.uk] — 0141-886 2131

Skelmorlie and Wemyss Bay
William R. Armstrong BD — 1979 — 3A Montgomerie Terrace, Skelmorlie PA17 5TD [E-mail: william@warmst.freeserve.co.uk] — 01475 520703

Abeledo, Benjamin J.A. BTh DipTh PTh	1991	2000	Army Chaplain	12 St Catherine's Close, Colchester, Essex CO2 9PP — 01206 364100
Alexander, Douglas N. MA BD	1961	1999	(Bishopton)	West Morningside, Main Road, Langbank, Port Glasgow PA4 6XP — 01475 540249
Bruce, A. William MA	1942	1981	(Fortingall and Glenlyon)	75 Union Street, Greenock PA16 8BG — 01475 787534

Name	Charge			Address	Tel
Cameron, Margaret (Miss) DCS	(Deaconess)			2 Rowans Gate, Paisley PA2 6RD [E-mail: margaret.cameron1@ntlworld.com]	0141-840 2479
Cant, Thomas M. MA BD	(Paisley: Leigh Kirk)	1964	2004	3 Meikle Cutstraw Cottages, Stewarton, Kilmarnock KA3 5HU	01560 480566
Chestnut, Alexander MBE BA	(Greenock: St Mark's Greenbank)	1948	1987	5 Douglas Street, Largs KA30 8PS	01475 674168
Copland, Agnes M. (Mrs) MBE DCS	(Deacon)			3 Craigmuschat Road, Gourock PA19 1SE	01475 631870
Cubie, John P. MA BD	(Caldwell)	1961	1999	36 Winram Place, St Andrews KY16 8XH	01334 474708
Hetherington, Robert M. MA BD	(Barrhead South and Levern)	1966	2002	31 Brodie Park Crescent, Paisley PA2 6EU [E-mail: rhetheri@fish.co.uk]	0141-848 6560
Johnston, Mary (Miss) DCS	(Deaconess)			19 Lounsdale Drive, Paisley PA2 9ED	0141-849 1615
Lowe, Edwin MA BD	(Caldwell)	1950	1988	45 Duncarnock Crescent, Neilston, Glasgow G78 3HH [E-mail: edwin.lowe50@ntlworld.com]	0141-580 5726
McBain, Margaret (Miss) DCS				33 Quarry Road, Paisley PA2 7RD	0141-884 2920
McColl, James C. BSc BD	(Johnstone: St Andrew's Trinity)	1966	2002	Greenways, Winton, Kirkby Stephen, Cumbria CA17 4HL	01768 372290
MacColl, John BD DipMin	Teacher: Religious Education	1989	2001	1 Birch Avenue, Johnstone PA5 0DD	01505 326506
McCully, M. Isobel (Miss) DCS	(Deacon)			10 Broadstone Avenue, Port Glasgow PA14 5BB [E-mail: mi.mccully@tesco.net]	01475 742240
McDonald, Alexander BA CMIWSC DUniv	Department of Ministry	1968	1988	36 Alloway Grove, Paisley PA2 7DQ [E-mail: amcdonald1@ntlworld.com]	0141-560 1937
McLachlan, Duncan MA BD ThM	(Paisley: Sherwood)	1955	1992	27 Penilee Road, Paisley PA1 3EU	0141-882 6353
McLachlan, Fergus C. BD	Hospital Chaplain: Inverclyde Royal	1982	2002	46 Queen Square, Glasgow G41 2AZ [E-mail: fergus.mclachlan@irh.scot.nhs.uk]	0141-423 3830
MacQuien, Durcan DCS	(Deacon)			2 Manor Crescent, Gourock PA19 1UY [E-mail: duncan@macquien.com]	01475 633407
Marshall, Fred J. BA	(Bermuda)	1946	1992	Flat 4, Varrich House, 7 Church Hill, Edinburgh EH10 4BG	0131-446 0205
Mathers, J. Allan C.	(Inchinnan)	1950	1989	19 Braemar Road, Inchinnan, Renfrew PA4 9QB	0141-561 2870
Moffet, James R. BA	(Paisley: St Matthew's)	1942	1979	Flat 49, Strathclyde House, 31 Shore Road, Skelmorlie PA17 5AN	
Montgomery, Robert A. MA	(Quarrier's Village: Mount Zion)	1955	1992	11 Myreton Avenue, Kilmacolm PA13 4LJ	01505 872028
Nicol, Joyce M. (Mrs) DCS	(Deacon)			93 Brisbane Street, Greenock PA16 8NY [E-mail: jnicol@surefish.co.uk]	01475 723235
O'Leary, Thomas BD	(Lochwinnoch)	1983	1998	1 Carters Place, Irvine KA12 0BU	
Palmer, S.W. BD	(Kilbarchan: East)	1980	1991	4 Bream Place, Houston PA6 7ZJ	01505 615280
Prentice, George BA BTh	(Paisley: Martyrs)	1964	1997	46 Victoria Gardens, Corsebar Road, Paisley PA2 9AQ [E-mail: g.prentice99@virgin.net]	0141-842 1585
Pyper, J. Stewart BA	(Greenock: St George's North)	1951	1986	39 Brisbane Street, Greenock PA16 8NR	01475 793234
Rule, James A.	(Renfrew: Moorpark)	1952	1991	6 St Andrew's Road, Renfrew PA4 0SN	0141-886 2896
Scott, Ernest M. MA	(Port Glasgow: St Andrew's)	1959	1992	17 Brueacre Road, Wemyss Bay PA18 6ER [E-mail: ernie.scott@ernest70.fsnet.co.uk]	01475 522267
Steele, Jean (Miss) DCS	(Deaconess)			93 George Street, Paisley PA1 2JX	0141-889 9512
Stone, W. Vernon MA BD	(Langbank)	1949	1985	36 Woodrow Court, Port Glasgow Road, Kilmacolm KA13 4QA [E-mail: stone@kilmacolm.fsnet.co.uk]	01505 872644
Whyte, John H. MA	(Gourock: Ashton)	1946	1986	6 Castle Levan Manor, Cloch Road, Gourock PA19 1AY	01475 636788

GREENOCK ADDRESSES

Gourock
Old Gourock
and Ashton   41 Royal Street
St John's   Bath Street x St John's Road

Greenock
Ardgowan   31 Union Street

Finnart St Paul's
Mount Kirk
Old West Kirk
St George's North
St Luke's
St Margaret's
St Ninian's
Wellpark Mid Kirk

Newark Street x Bentinck Street
Dempster Street at Murdieston Park
Esplanade x Campbell Street
George Square
9 Nelson Street
Finch Road x Kestrel Crescent
Warwick Road, Larkfield
Cathcart Square

Port Glasgow
Hamilton
Bardrainney

St Andrew's
St Martin's

Bardrainney Avenue x
Auchenbothie Road
Princes Street
Mansion Avenue

PAISLEY ADDRESSES

Abbey   Town Centre
Castlehead   Canal Street
Glenburn   Nethercraigs Drive off Glenburn Road
Laigh   Causeyside Street
Lylesland   Rowan Street off Neilston Road
Martyrs'   Broomlands

Oakshaw: Trinity
St Columba Foxbar
St James'
St Luke's
St Mark's Oldhall
St Ninian's Ferguslie

Churchill
Amochrie Road, Foxbar
Underwood Road
Neilston Road
Glasgow Road, Ralston
Blackstoun Road

Sandyford (Thread St)
Sherwood Greenlaw
Wallneuk North

Gallowhill
Glasgow Road
off Renfrew Road

(16) GLASGOW

Meets at New Govan Church, Govan Cross, Glasgow, on the second Tuesday of each month, except June when the meeting takes place on the third Tuesday. In January, July and August there is no meeting.

Clerk: REV. DAVID W. LUNAN MA BD   260 Bath Street, Glasgow G2 4JP   0141-332 6606 (Tel/Fax)
                                                     [E-mail: akph84@uk.uumail.com]
                                                     [E-mail: cofs.glasgow.presbytery@uk.uumail.com]

Hon. Treasurer: COPELAND KNIGHT Esq   [E-mail: glasgowpres@yahoo.co.uk]

1   **Banton linked with Twechar**
    Alexandra Farrington   2003   Manse of Banton, Kilsyth, Glasgow G65 0QL   01236 826129

2   **Bishopbriggs: Kenmure**
    Iain A. Laing MA BD   1971   1992   5 Marchfield, Bishopbriggs, Glasgow G64 3PP   0141-772 1468

3	**Bishopbriggs: Springfield** William Ewart BSc BD	1972 1978	39 Springfield Road, Bishopbriggs, Glasgow G64 1PL [E-mail: wmewart@ukonline.co.uk]	0141-772 1540
4	**Broom (0141-639 3528)** James Whyte BD	1981 1987	3 Laigh Road, Newton Mearns, Glasgow G77 5EX	0141-639 2916 0141-639 3528 (Fax)
	Margaret McLellan (Mrs) DCS		18 Broom Road East, Newton Mearns, Glasgow G77 5SD	0141-639 6853
5	**Burnside–Blairbeth (0141-634 4130)** David J.C. Easton MA BD	1965 1977	59 Blairbeth Road, Burnside, Glasgow G73 4JD [E-mail: david.easton3@ntlworld.com]	0141-634 1233 (Tel) 0141-634 7383 (Fax)
6	**Busby (0141-644 2073)** Jeremy C. Eve BSc BD	1998	17A Carmunnock Road, Busby, Glasgow G76 8SZ [E-mail: jerry.eve@btinternet.com]	0141-644 3670
7	**Cadder (0141-772 7436)** Graham S. Finch MA BD	1977 1999	6 Balmuildy Road, Bishopbriggs, Glasgow G64 3BS [E-mail: graham@gsf57.plus.com]	0141-772 1363
8	**Cambuslang: Flemington Hallside** Vacant		103 Overton Road, Cambuslang, Glasgow G72 7XA	0141-641 2097
9	**Cambuslang: Old** Lee Messeder	2003	74 Stewarton Drive, Cambuslang, Glasgow G72 8DG	0141-641 3261
10	**Cambuslang: St Andrew's** John Stevenson LTh	1998	37 Brownside Road, Cambuslang, Glasgow G72 8NH [E-mail: j.stevenson83@ntlworld.com]	0141-641 3847 (Tel) 0141-641 0773 (Fax)
	James Birch PGDip FRSA FIOC (Aux)	2001	1 Kirkhill Grove, Cambuslang, Glasgow G72 8EH	0141-583 1722
11	**Cambuslang: Trinity St Paul's** William Jackson BD CertMin	1994 2002	4 Glasgow Road, Cambuslang, Glasgow G72 7BW [E-mail: wiljcksn4@aol.com]	0141-641 3414
12	**Campsie (01360 310939)** David J. Torrance BD DipMin	1993	19 Redhills View, Lennoxtown, Glasgow G66 7BL	01360 312527
13	**Chryston (H)** Martin A.W. Allen MA BD ThM	1977	Main Street, Chryston, Glasgow G69 9LA [E-mail: allensall@hotmail.com]	0141-779 1436
	David J. McAdam BSc BD (Assoc)	1990 2000	12 Dunellan Crescent, Moodiesburn, Glasgow G69 0GA [E-mail: dmca29@aol.com]	01236 870472

14	**Eaglesham (01355 302047)** Vacant			The Manse, Cheapside Street, Eaglesham, Glasgow G76 0NS	01355 303495
15	**Fernhill and Cathkin** Margaret McArthur BD DipMin	1995	2002	82 Blairbeth Road, Rutherglen, Glasgow G73 4JA	0141-634 1508
16	**Gartcosh (H) (01236 873770) linked with Glenboig (01236 875625)** Alexander M. Fraser BD DipMin	1985		26 Inchknock Avenue, Gartcosh, Glasgow G69 8EA [E-mail: sandy@revfraser.freeserve.co.uk]	01236 872274
17	**Giffnock: Orchardhill (0141-638 3604)** Vacant				
18	**Giffnock: South (0141-638 2599)** Edward V. Simpson BSc BD	1972	1983	5 Langtree Avenue, Whitecraigs, Glasgow G46 7LN	0141-638 8767 (Tel) 0141-620 0605 (Fax)
19	**Giffnock: The Park** Calum D. Macdonald BD	1993	2001	41 Rouken Glen Road, Thornliebank, Glasgow G46 7JD [E-mail: calummcd@parkhoose.fsnet.co.uk]	0141-638 3023
20	**Glenboig** See Gartcosh				
21	**Greenbank (H) (0141-644 1841)** Jeanne Roddick	2003		Greenbank Manse, 38 Eaglesham Road, Clarkston, Glasgow G76 7DJ	0141-644 1395 (Tel) 0141-644 4804 (Fax)
22	**Kilsyth: Anderson** Charles M. MacKinnon BD	1989	1999	Anderson Manse, Kingston Road, Kilsyth, Glasgow G65 0HR [E-mail: cmmack@ukonline.co.uk]	01236 822345
23	**Kilsyth: Burns and Old** Vacant			The Grange, Glasgow Road, Kilsyth, Glasgow G65 9AE	01236 823116
24	**Kirkintilloch: Hillhead** Audrey Jamieson	2004		64 Waverley Park, Kensington Gate, Kirkintilloch, Glasgow G66 2BP	0141-776 6270
25	**Kirkintilloch: St Columba's (H)** David M. White BA BD	1988	1992	14 Crossdykes, Kirkintilloch, Glasgow G66 3EU [E-mail: david.m.white@ntlworld.com]	0141-578 4357

No.	Church / Minister		Address / E-mail	Tel
26	**Kirkintilloch: St David's Memorial Park (H)** Bryce Calder MA BD	1995 / 2001	2 Roman Road, Kirkintilloch, Glasgow G66 1EA [E-mail: ministry100@aol.com]	0141-776 1434
27	**Kirkintilloch: St Mary's** Mark E. Johnstone MA BD	1993 / 2001	St Mary's Manse, 60 Union Street, Kirkintilloch, Glasgow G66 1DH [E-mail: mark.johnstone2@ntlworld.com]	0141-776 1252
28	**Lenzie: Old (H)** Douglas W. Clark LTh	1993 / 2000	41 Kirkintilloch Road, Lenzie, Glasgow G66 4LB [E-mail: douglaswclark@hotmail.com]	0141-776 2184
29	**Lenzie: Union (H)** Daniel J.M. Carmichael MA BD	1994 / 2003	1 Larch Avenue, Lenzie, Glasgow G66 4HX [E-mail: djm@carmichael39.fsnet.co.uk]	0141-776 3831
30	**Maxwell Mearns Castle (Tel/Fax: 0141-639 5169)** David C. Cameron BD CertMin	1993	122 Broomfield Avenue, Newton Mearns, Glasgow G77 5JR [E-mail: maxwellmearns@hotmail.com]	0141-616 0642
31	**Mearns (H) (0141-639 6555)** Joseph A. Kavanagh BD DipPTh MTh	1992 / 1998	Manse of Mearns, Newton Mearns, Glasgow G77 5BU [E-mail: mearnskirk@hotmail.com]	0141-616 2410 (Tel/Fax)
32	**Milton of Campsie (H)** Diane E. Stewart BD	1988	33 Birdstone Road, Milton of Campsie, Glasgow G66 8BX [E-mail: diane.e.stewart@care4free.net]	01360 310548 (Tel/Fax)
33	**Netherlee (H)** Thomas Nelson BSc BD	1992 / 2002	25 Ormonde Avenue, Glasgow G44 3QY [E-mail: tomnelson@ntlworld.com]	0141-585 7502 (Tel/Fax)
	Daniel Frank (Assoc)	2003	106 Ormonde Crescent, Glasgow G44 3SW	0141-586 0875
34	**Newton Mearns (H) (0141-639 7373)** Angus Kerr BD CertMin ThM	1983 / 1994	28 Waterside Avenue, Newton Mearns, Glasgow G77 6TJ [E-mail: anguskerr@newtonmearns.ndo.co.uk]	0141-616 2079
35	**Rutherglen: Old (H)** Alexander Thomson BSc BD MPhil PhD	1973 / 1985	31 Highburgh Drive, Rutherglen, Glasgow G73 3RR [E-mail: alexander.thomson6@btopenworld.com]	0141-647 6178
36	**Rutherglen: Stonelaw (0141-647 5113)** Alistair S. May LLB BD PhD	2002	80 Blairbeth Road, Rutherglen, Glasgow G73 4JA [E-mail: alistair.may@ntlworld.com]	0141-583 0157

No.	Name			Address	Telephone
37	**Rutherglen: Wardlawhill** Ian Walker BD MEd DipMS	1973		26 Parkhill Drive, Rutherglen, Glasgow G73 2PW	0141-647 1374
38	**Rutherglen: West** John W. Drummond MA BD	1971	1986	12 Albert Drive, Rutherglen, Glasgow G73 3RT	0141-569 8547
39	**Stamperland (0141-637 4999) (H)** George C. MacKay BD CertMin	1994	2004	109 Ormonde Avenue, Glasgow G44 3SN	0141-637 4976 (Tel/Fax)
40	**Stepps (H)** Vacant			2 Lenzie Road, Stepps, Glasgow G33 6DX	0141-779 9556
41	**Thornliebank (H)** Robert M. Silver BA BD	1995		19 Arthurlie Drive, Giffnock, Glasgow G46 6UR	0141-620 2133
42	**Torrance (T) (01360 620970)** Nigel L. Barge BSc BD	1991		27 Campbell Place, Meadow Rise, Torrance, Glasgow G64 4HR [E-mail: nigel@nbarge.freeserve.co.uk]	01360 622379
43	**Twechar** See Banton				
44	**Williamwood** G. Hutton B. Steel MA BD	1982	1990	125 Greenwood Road, Clarkston, Glasgow G76 7LL [E-mail: huttonsteel@ntlworld.com]	0141-571 7949
45	**Glasgow: Anderston Kelvingrove (0141-221 9408)** Vacant			16 Royal Terrace, Glasgow G3 7NY	0141-332 3136
46	**Glasgow: Baillieston Mure Memorial (0141-773 1216)** Allan S. Vint BSc BD	1989	1996	28 Beech Avenue, Baillieston, Glasgow G69 6LF [E-mail: allan@vint.co.uk]	0141-771 1217
47	**Glasgow: Baillieston St Andrew's (0141-771 6629)** Robert Gehrke BSc BD CEng MIEE	1994	2001	55 Station Park, Baillieston, Glasgow G69 7XY	0141-771 1791
48	**Glasgow: Balshagray Victoria Park** Campbell Mackinnon BSc BD	1982	2001	20 St Kilda Drive, Glasgow G14 9JN	0141-954 9780
49	**Glasgow: Barlanark Greyfriars** David I.W. Locke MA MSc BD	2000		4 Rhindmuir Grove, Glasgow G69 6NE [E-mail: revdavidlocke@ntlworld.com]	0141-771 1240

50 Glasgow: Battlefield East (H) (0141-632 4206)
Alan C. Raeburn MA BD — 1971 1977 — 110 Mount Anman Drive, Glasgow G44 4RZ [E-mail: acraeburn@hotmail.com] — 0141-632 1514

51 Glasgow: Blawarthill
Ian M.S. McInnes BD DipMin — 1995 1997 — 46 Earlbank Avenue, Glasgow G14 9HL — 0141-579 6521

52 Glasgow: Bridgeton St Francis in the East (H) (L) (Church House: Tel: 0141-554 8045)
Howard R. Hudson MA BD — 1982 1984 — 10 Albany Drive, Rutherglen, Glasgow G73 3QN [E-mail: howard.hudson@ntlworld.com] — 0141-587 8667
Margaret S. Beaton (Miss) DCS — 64 Gardenside Grove, Fernlee Meadows, Carmyle, Glasgow G32 8EZ — 0141-646 2297

53 Glasgow: Broomhill (0141-334 2540)
William B. Ferguson BA BD — 1971 1987 — 27 St Kilda Drive, Glasgow G14 9LN [E-mail: revferg@aol.com] — 0141-959 3204

54 Glasgow: Calton Parkhead (0141-554 3866)
Ronald Anderson BD DipTh — 1992 — 98 Drumover Drive, Glasgow G31 5RP [E-mail: ron@anderson296.freeserve.co.uk] — 0141-556 2520
Karen Hamilton (Mrs) DCS — 6 Beckfield Gate, Glasgow G33 1SW — 0141-558 3195

55 Glasgow: Cardonald (0141-882 6264)
Eric McLachlan BD MTh — 1978 1983 — 133 Newyle Road, Paisley PA1 3LB [E-mail: eric.mclachlan@ntlworld.com] — 0141-561 1891

56 Glasgow: Carmunnock
G. Gray Fletcher BSc BD — 1989 2001 — The Manse, 161 Waterside Road, Carmunnock, Glasgow G76 9AJ — 0141-644 1578 (Tel/Fax)

57 Glasgow: Carmyle linked with Kenmuir Mount Vernon
Murdo Maclean BD CertMin — 1997 1999 — 3 Meryon Road, Glasgow G32 9NW [E-mail: murdo.maclean@ntlworld.com] — 0141-778 2625

58 Glasgow: Carntyne Old linked with Eastbank
Ronald A.S. Craig BACC BD — 1983 — 211 Sandyhills Road, Glasgow G32 9NB — 0141-778 1286

59 Glasgow: Carnwadric (E)
Graeme K. Bell BA BD — 1983 — 62 Loganswell Road, Glasgow G46 8AX — 0141-638 5884

60 Glasgow: Castlemilk: East (H) (0141-634 2444)
John D. Miller BA BD — 1971 — 15 Castlemilk Drive, Glasgow G45 9TL [E-mail: john@miller15.freeserve.co.uk] — 0141-631 1244

No.	Name	Ordained	Inducted	Address	Tel
61	**Glasgow Castlemilk: West (H) (0141-634 1480)** Janet P.H. MacMahon (Mrs) MSc BD	1992	2002	156 Old Castle Road, Glasgow G44 5TW	0141-637 5451
62	**Glasgow: Cathcart Old** Neil W. Galbraith BD CertMin	1987	1996	21 Courthill Avenue, Cathcart, Glasgow G44 5AA [E-mail: revneilgalbraith@hotmail.com]	0141-633 5248 (Tel/Fax)
63	**Glasgow: Cathcart Trinity (H) (0141-637 6658)** Ian Morrison BD	1991	2003	82 Merrylee Road, Glasgow G43 2QZ [E-mail: iain@morr.freeserve.co.uk]	0141-633 3744
	Wilma Pearson (Mrs) BD (Assoc)	2004		90 Newlands Road, Glasgow G43 2JR	0141-632 2491
64	**Glasgow: Cathedral (High or St Mungo's)** William Morris KCVO DD PhD LLD JP	1951	1967	1 Whitehill Grove, Newton Mearns, Glasgow G77 5DH	0141-639 6327
65	**Glasgow: Colston Milton (0141-772 1922)** Christopher D. Park BSc BD	1977	1994	118 Birsay Road, Glasgow G22 7QP [E-mail: chrispark8649@hotmail.com]	0141-772 1958
66	**Glasgow: Colston Wellpark (H)** Christine M. Goldie (Miss) LLB BD MTh	1984	1999	16 Bishop's Gate Gardens, Colston, Glasgow G21 1XS [E-mail: christine.goldie@ntlworld.com]	0141-589 8866
67	**Glasgow: Cranhill (H) (0141-774 5593)** Vacant			31 Lethamhill Crescent, Glasgow G33 2SH	0141-770 6873
68	**Glasgow: Croftfoot (H) (0141-637 3913)** John M. Lloyd BD CertMin	1984	1986	20 Victoria Road, Burnside, Rutherglen, Glasgow G73 3QG [E-mail: john.lloyd@croftfootparish.co.uk]	0141-647 5524
69	**Glasgow: Dennistoun Blackfriars (H)** Vacant			41 Broompark Drive, Glasgow G31 2JB	0141-554 8667
70	**Glasgow: Dennistoun Central (H) (0141-554 1350)** Vacant			45 Broompark Drive, Glasgow G31 2JB	0141-550 4487
71	**Glasgow: Drumchapel Drumry St Mary's (0141-944 1998)** Brian S. Sheret MA BD DPhil	1982	2002	8 Fruin Road, Glasgow G15 6SQ	0141-944 4493
72	**Glasgow: Drumchapel St Andrew's (0141-944 3758)** John S. Purves LLB BD	1983	1984	6 Firdon Crescent, Glasgow G15 6QQ [E-mail: john.s.purves@talk21.com]	0141-944 4566

No.	Church / Minister	Ord.	Ind.	Address	Telephone
73	**Glasgow: Drumchapel St Mark's** Alistair J. MacKichan MA BD	1984	2001	146 Garscadden Road, Glasgow G15 6PR	0141-944 5440
74	**Glasgow: Eastbank** See Carntyne Old				
75	**Glasgow: Easterhouse St George's and St Peter's (E) (0141-781 0800)** Malcolm Cuthbertson BA BD	1984		3 Barony Gardens, Baillieston, Glasgow G69 6TS [E-mail: malcuth@aol.com]	0141-573 8200 (Tel) 0141-773 4878 (Fax)
76	**Glasgow: Eastwood** Moyna McGlynn (Mrs) BD PhD	1999		54 Mansewood Road, Glasgow G43 1TL	0141-632 0724
77	**Glasgow: Gairbraid (H)** Ian C. MacKenzie MA BD	1970	1971	1515 Maryhill Road, Glasgow G20 9AB [E-mail: iancmackenzie@ntlworld.com]	0141-946 1568
78	**Glasgow: Gardner Street (GE)** Roderick Morrison MA BD	1974	1994	148 Beechwood Drive, Glasgow G11 7DX	0141-563 2638
79	**Glasgow: Garthamlock and Craigend East (E)** Valerie J. Duff (Miss) DMin	1993	1996	175 Tillycairn Drive, Garthamlock, Glasgow G33 5HS [E-mail: valduff@fish.co.uk]	0141-774 6364
80	**Glasgow: Gorbals** Ian F. Galloway BA BD	1976	1996	44 Riverside Road, Glasgow G43 2EF	0141-649 5250
81	**Glasgow: Govan Old (Tel/Fax: 0141-440 2466)** Norman J. Shanks MA BD	1983	2003	1 Marchmont Terrace, Glasgow G12 9LT	0141-339 4421
82	**Glasgow: Govanhill Trinity** Vacant			6 Darluith Park, Brookfield, Johnstone PA5 8DD	01505 320378
83	**Glasgow: High Carntyne (0141-778 4186)** Vacant			165 Smithycroft Road, Glasgow G33 2RD	0141-770 6464
84	**Glasgow: Hillington Park (H)** Vacant			61 Ralston Avenue, Glasgow G52 3NB	0141-882 7000
85	**Glasgow: Househillwood St Christopher's** May M. Allison (Mrs) BD	1988	2001	12 Leverndale Court, Crookston, Glasgow G53 7SJ	0141-810 5953

86 Glasgow: Hyndland (H) (0141-339 1804)
Vacant
24 Hughenden Gardens, Glasgow G12 9YH
0141-334 1002

87 Glasgow: Ibrox (H) (0141-427 0896)
C. Blair Gillon BD   1975   1980
3 Dargarvel Avenue, Glasgow G41 5LD
[E-mail: cb@gillon3.freeserve.co.uk]
0141-427 1282 (Tel/Fax)
07786 326905 (Mbl)

88 Glasgow: John Ross Memorial Church for Deaf People
(Voice Text: 0141-420 1759; Text Only: 0141-429 6682; Fax: 0141-429 6860; ISDN Video Phone: 0141-418 0579)
Richard C. Durno DSW CQSW   1989   1998
31 Springfield Road, Bishopbriggs, Glasgow G64 1PJ   (Voice/Text) 0141-772 1052
[E-mail: richard@durnada.freeserve.co.uk]
[www.deafconnections.co.uk]

89 Glasgow: Jordanhill (Tel: 0141-959 2496)
Colin C. Renwick BMus BD   1989   1996
96 Southbrae Drive, Glasgow G13 1TZ
[E-mail: jordchurch@btconnect.com]
0141-959 1310

90 Glasgow: Kelvin Stevenson Memorial (0141-339 1750)
Gordon Kirkwood BSc BD   1987   2003
94 Hyndland Road, Glasgow G12 9PZ
0141-334 5352

91 Glasgow: Kelvinside Hillhead
Jennifer Macrae (Mrs) MA BD   1998   2000
39 Athole Gardens, Glasgow G12 9BQ
[E-mail: jmacrae@supanet.com]
0141-339 2865

92 Glasgow: Kenmuir Mount Vernon See Carmyle

93 Glasgow: King's Park (H) (0141-632 1131)
G. Stewart Smith MA BD STM   1966   1979
1101 Aikenhead Road, Glasgow G44 5SL
[E-mail: ssmith99@ntlworld.com]
0141-637 2803 (Tel/Fax)

94 Glasgow: Kinning Park (0141-427 3063)
Margaret H. Johnston (Miss) BD   1988   2000
168 Arbroath Avenue, Cardonald, Glasgow G52 3HH
0141-810 3782

95 Glasgow: Knightswood St Margaret's (H)
Adam Dillon   2003
26 Airthrey Avenue, Glasgow G14 9LJ
[E-mail: adamdillon@ntlworld.com]
0141-959 7075

96 Glasgow: Langside (0141-632 7520)
David N. McLachlan BD   1985   2004
36 Madison Avenue, Glasgow G44 5AQ
0141-637 0797

97 Glasgow: Lansdowne
Roy J.M. Henderson MA BD DipMin   1987   1992
18 Woodlands Drive, Glasgow G4 9EH
[E-mail: roy.henderson7@ntlworld.com]
0141-339 2794

98	**Glasgow: Linthouse St Kenneth's** David A. Keddie MA BD	1966 2001	21 Ilay Road, Bearsden, Glasgow G61 1QG [E-mail: revked@hotmail.com]	0141-577 1408
99	**Glasgow: Lochwood (H) (0141-771 2649)** Stuart M. Duff BA	1997	42 Rhindmuir Road, Swinton, Glasgow G69 6AZ [E-mail: stuart@duff58.freeserve.co.uk]	0141-773 2756
100	**Glasgow: Martyrs', The** Ewen MacLean BA BD	1995	30 Louden Hill Road, Robroyston, Glasgow G33 1GA [E-mail: ewenmaclean@beeb.net]	0141-558 7451
101	**Glasgow: Maryhill (H) (0141-946 3512)** Anthony J.D. Craig BD	1987	111 Maxwell Avenue, Glasgow G61 1HT [E-mail: craig.glasgow@ntlworld.com]	0141-570 0642
	James Hamilton DCS		6 Beckfield Gate, Robroyston, Glasgow G33 1SW	0141-558 3195
102	**Glasgow: Merrylea (0141-637 2009)** David P. Hood BD CertMin DiplOB(Scot)	1997 2001	4 Pilmuir Avenue, Glasgow G44 3HX [E-mail: dphood3@ntlworld.com]	0141-637 6700
103	**Glasgow: Mosspark (H) (0141-882 2240)** Alan H. MacKay BD	2002	396 Kilmarnock Road, Glasgow G43 2DJ [E-mail: alanhmackay@aol.com]	0141-632 1247
104	**Glasgow: Mount Florida (H) (0141-561 0307)** Hugh M. Wallace MA BD	1981	90 Mount Annan Drive, Glasgow G44 4RZ	0141-589 5381
105	**Glasgow: New Govan (H)** Robert G. McFarlane BD	2001	19 Dumbreck Road, Glasgow G41 5LJ [E-mail: robertmcf@hotmail.com]	0141-427 3197
106	**Glasgow: Newlands South (H) (0141-632 3055)** John D. Whiteford MA BD	1989	24 Monreith Road, Glasgow G43 2NY [E-mail: jwhiteford@hotmail.com]	0141-632 2588
107	**Glasgow: North Kelvinside** William G. Alston	1961	41 Mitre Road, Glasgow G14 9LE	0141-954 8250
108	**Glasgow: Partick South** Alan L. Dunnett LLB BD	1994	17 Munro Road, Glasgow G13 1SQ [E-mail: dustydunnett@prtck.freeserve.co.uk]	0141-959 3732

109 Glasgow: Partick Trinity (H)			
Stuart J. Smith BEng BD	1994	99 Balshagray Avenue, Glasgow G11 7EQ [E-mail: stuart@stuartandelspeth.freeserve.co.uk]	0141-576 7149
110 Glasgow: Penilee St Andrew (H) (0141-882 2691)			
Alastair J. Cherry BA BD	1982	80 Tweedsmuir Road, Glasgow G52 2RX	0141-882 2460
111 Glasgow: Pollokshaws			
Margaret Whyte (Mrs) BA BD	1988	33 Mannering Road, Glasgow G41 3SW	0141-649 0458
112 Glasgow: Pollokshields (H)			
David R. Black MA BD	1986	36 Glencairn Drive, Glasgow G41 4PW	0141-423 4000
113 Glasgow: Possilpark			
W.C. Campbell-Jack BD MTh PhD	1979	108 Erradale Street, Lambhill, Glasgow G22 6PT	0141-336 6909
114 Glasgow: Priesthill and Nitshill			
Douglas M. Nicol BD CA	1987	36 Springkell Drive, Glasgow G41 4EZ	0141-427 7877
115 Glasgow: Queen's Park (0141-423 3654)			
T. Malcolm F. Duff MA BD	1985	5 Alder Road, Glasgow G43 2UY [E-mail: malcolm.duff@ntlworld.com]	0141-637 5491
116 Glasgow: Renfield St Stephen's (0141-332 4293; Fax: 0141-332 8482)			
Peter M. Gardner MA BD	1988	101 Hill Street, Glasgow G3 6TY	0141-353 0349
117 Glasgow: Robroyston (New Charge Development)			
Hilary MacDougall	2004	7 Beckfield Drive, Robroyston, Glasgow G33 1SR	0141-558 8355
118 Glasgow: Ruchazie (0141-774 2759)			
William F. Hunter MA BD	1986	18 Borthwick Street, Glasgow G33 3UU [E-mail: bhunter@fish.co.uk]	0141-774 6860
Janet Anderson (Miss) DCS	1999	338 Gartcraig Road, Glasgow G33 2TE	0141-774 5329
119 Glasgow: Ruchill (0141-946 0466)			
John C. Matthews MA BD	1992	9 Kirklee Road, Glasgow G12 0RQ [E-mail: jmatthews@kirklee9.fsnet.co.uk]	0141-357 3249
Paul McKeown BSc PhD BD (Community Minister)	2000	G/R, 10 Jedburgh Gardens, Glasgow G20 6BP	0141-946 6409
120 Glasgow: St Andrew's East (0141-554 1485)			
Janette G. Reid (Miss) BD	1991	43 Broompark Drive, Glasgow G31 2JB	0141-554 3620

121 Glasgow: St Columba (GE) (0141-221 3305)
Donald Michael MacInnes   2002   1 Reelick Avenue, Peterson Park, Glasgow G13 4NF   0141-952 0948

122 Glasgow: St David's Knightswood (0141-959 1024; E-mail: dringlis@stdavidschurch.freeserve.co.uk)
W. Graham M. Thain LLB BD   1988   1999   60 Southbrae Drive, Glasgow G13 1QD   0141-959 2904
                                                        [E-mail: graham_thain@btopenworld.com]

123 Glasgow: St Enoch's Hogganfield (H) (0141-770 5694; Fax: 0870 284 0084; E-mail: church@st-enoch.org.uk; Website: www.st-enoch.org.uk)
Vacant   43 Smithycroft Road, Glasgow G33 2RH   0141-770 7593
                                                                                                       0870 284 0085 (Fax)

124 Glasgow: St George's Tron (0141-221 2141)
William Philip   2004   12 Dargarvel Avenue, Glasgow G41 5LU   0141-427 1402
John Rushton BVMS BD (Assoc)   1983   29 Brent Avenue, Thornliebank, Glasgow G46 8JU   0141-638 0837
                                                        [E-mail: johnsusanrushton@talk21.com]

125 Glasgow: St James' (Pollok) (0141-882 4984)
John Mann   2004   30 Ralston Avenue, Glasgow G52 3NA   0141-883 7405
Ann Merrilees (Miss) DCS   0/1, 15 Crookston Grove, Glasgow G52 3PN   0141-883 2488

126 Glasgow: St John's Renfield (0141-339 7021; Website: www.stjohns-renfield.org.uk)
Dugald J.R. Cameron BD DipMin MTh   1990   1999   26 Leicester Avenue, Glasgow G12 0LU   0141-339 4637
                                                        [E-mail: dcameron@stjohns-renfield.org.uk]

127 Glasgow: St Luke's and St Andrew's
Ian C. Fraser BA BD   1983   10 Chalmers Street, Glasgow G40 2HA   0141-556 3883
                                                        [E-mail: stluke@cqm.co.uk]

128 Glasgow: St Margaret's Tollcross Park
George M. Murray LTh   1995   31 Kenmuir Avenue, Sandyhills, Glasgow G32 9LE   0141-778 5060
                                                        [E-mail: george.murray@ntlworld.com]

129 Glasgow: St Nicholas' Cardonald
Roderick I.T. MacDonald BD   1992   104 Lamington Road, Glasgow G52 2SE   0141-882 2065

130 Glasgow: St Paul's (0141-770 8559)
R. Russell McLarty MA BD   1985   38 Lochview Drive, Glasgow G33 1QF   0141-770 9611

131 Glasgow: St Rollox
Vacant   42 Melville Gardens, Bishopbriggs, Glasgow G64 3DE   0141-772 2848

132 Glasgow: St Thomas' Gallowgate
Peter R. Davidge   2003   12 Low Road, Paisley PA2 6AG   07834 191691

133 Glasgow: Sandyford Henderson Memorial (H) (L)
C. Peter White BVMS BD 1974 1997 66 Woodend Drive, Glasgow G13 1TG 0141-954 9013
[E-mail: revcpw@ntlworld.com]
Kenneth Macdonald (Aux) MA BA 5 Henderland Road, Glasgow G61 1AH 0141-943 1103

134 Glasgow: Sandyhills
John P.F. Martindale BD 1994 60 Wester Road, Glasgow G32 9JJ 0141-778 2174

135 Glasgow: Scotstoun (T)
Richard Cameron BD DipMin 2000 15 Northland Drive, Glasgow G14 9BE 0141-959 4637
[E-mail: rev.rickycam@virgin.net]

136 Glasgow: Shawlands (0141-649 2012)
Vacant 29 St Ronan's Drive, Glasgow G41 3SQ 0141-649 2034

137 Glasgow: Sherbrooke St Gilbert's (H) (0141-427 1968)
Thomas L. Pollock 1982 2003 114 Springkell Avenue, Glasgow G41 4EW 0141-427 2094
BA BD MTh FSAScot JP

138 Glasgow: Shettleston Old (T) (H) (0141-778 2484)
Vacant 57 Mansionhouse Road, Mount Vernon, Glasgow G32 0RP 0141-778 8904

139 Glasgow: South Carntyne (H) (0141-778 1343)
Gavin W. Forrest MA BD 1984 2002 47 Broompark Drive, Glasgow G31 2JB 0141-554 3275
[E-mail: gavinesque@bbm7.fsnet.co.uk]

140 Glasgow: South Shawlands (T) (0141-649 4656)
Fiona Gardner (Mrs) BD MA MLitt 1997 2000 391 Kilmarnock Road, Glasgow G43 2NU 0141-632 0013
[E-mail: fionandcolin@hotmail.com]

141 Glasgow: Springburn (H) (0141-557 2345)
Alan A. Ford BD 1977 2000 3 Tofthill Avenue, Bishopbriggs, Glasgow G64 3PA 0141-762 1844
[E-mail: alan@springburnchurch.freeserve.co.uk] 0771 045 5737 (Mbl)
Helen Hughes (Miss) DCS 2/2 Burnbank Terrace, Glasgow G20 6UQ 0141-333 9459

142 Glasgow: Temple Anniesland (0141-959 1814)
John Wilson BD 1985 2000 76 Victoria Park Drive North, Glasgow G14 9PJ 0141-959 5835
[E-mail: jwilson@crowroad0.freeserve.co.uk]

143 Glasgow: Toryglen (H)
Sandra Black (Mrs) BSc BD 1988 2003 36 Glencairn Drive, Glasgow G41 4PW 0141-423 0867

144 Glasgow: Trinity Possil and Henry Drummond
Richard G. Buckley BD MTh — 1990 1995 — 50 Highfield Drive, Glasgow G12 0HL — 0141-339 2870

145 Glasgow: Tron St Mary's
William T.S. Wilson BSc BD — 1999 — 3 Hurly Hawkin', Bishopbriggs, Glasgow G64 1YL — 0141-772 8555
[E-mail: william.mairi@ntlworld.com]

146 Glasgow: Victoria Tollcross
Vacant — 228 Hamilton Road, Glasgow G32 9QU — 0141-778 2413

147 Glasgow: Wallacewell
John B. MacGregor BD — 1999 — 54 Etive Crescent, Bishopbriggs, Glasgow G64 1ES — 0141-772 1453
[E-mail: johnmacgregor494@msn.com]
Joanna Love (Ms) DCS — 92 Everard Drive, Colston, Glasgow G21 1XQ — 0141-563 5859

148 Glasgow: Wellington (H) (0141-339 0454)
M. Leith Fisher MA BD — 1967 1990 — 27 Kingsborough Gardens, Glasgow G12 9NH — 0141-339 3627
[E-mail: leith@minister22.freeserve.co.uk]

149 Glasgow: Whiteinch (New Charge Development) (www.whiteinchcofs.co.uk)
Alan McWilliam BD — 1993 2000 — 65 Victoria Park Drive South, Glasgow G14 9NX — 0141-576 9020
[E-mail: alan@whiteinchcofs.co.uk]

150 Glasgow: Yoker (T)
Vacant — 15 Coldingham Avenue, Glasgow G14 0PX — 0141-952 3620

Name			Charge	Address	Phone
Aitken, Andrew J. BD APhS MTh PhD	1951	1981	(Tollcross Central with Park)	18 Dorchester Avenue, Glasgow G12 0EE	0141-357 1617
Alexander, Eric J. MA BD	1958	1997	(St George's Tron)	PO Box 14725, St Andrews KY16 8WB	ex-directory
Allan, A.G.	1959	1989	(Candlish Polmadie)	30 Dalrymple Drive, East Mains, East Kilbride, Glasgow G74 4LF	01355 226190
Anderson, Colin M. BA BD STM MPhil	1968	2003	(Inverness: St Stephen's with The Old High)	83 Marlborough Avenue, Glasgow G11 7BT	0141-357 2838
Barr, Alexander C. MA BD	1950	1992	(St Nicholas' Cardonald)	25 Fisher Drive, Phoenix Park, Paisley PA1 2TP	0141-848 5941
Beattie, John A.	1951	1984	(Dalmuir Overtoun)	0/1, 15 Kelvindale Gardens, Kelvindale Road, Glasgow G20 8DW	0141-946 5978
Bell, John L. MA BD FRSCM DUniv	1978	1988	(Iona Community)	Flat 2/1, 31 Lansdowne Crescent, Glasgow G20 6NH	0141-334 0688
Brain, Ernest J.	1955	1985	(Liverpool St Andrew's)	14 Chesterfield Court, 1240 Great Western Road, Glasgow G12 0BJ	0141-357 2249
Brain, Isobel J. (Mrs) MA	1987	1997	(Ballantrae)	14 Chesterfield Court, 1240 Great Western Road, Glasgow G12 0BJ	0141-357 2249
Brice, Dennis G. BSc BD	1981		(Taiwan)	8 Parkwood Close, Broxbourne, Herts EN10 7PF	
Brough, Robin BA	1968	2002	(Whitburn: Brucefield)	'Kildavanan', 10 Printers Lea, Lennoxtown, Glasgow G66 7GF	01360 310223
Bryden, William A. BD	1977	1984	(Yoker Old with St Matthew's)	145 Bearsden Road, Glasgow G13 1BS	0141-959 5213
Bull, Alister W. BD DipMin	1994	2001	Chaplain: Royal Hospital for Sick Children	Yorkhill NHS Trust, Yorkhill, Glasgow G3 8SJ	0141-201 0000
Campbell, A. Iain MA DipEd	1961	1997	(Busby)	430 Clarkston Road, Glasgow G44 3QF	0141-637 7460
Campbell, Colin MA BD	1940	1989	(Williamwood)	4 Golf Road, Clarkston, Glasgow G76 7LZ	0141-638 1215
Cartlidge, G.R.G. MA BD STM	1977	1993	Religious Education	5 Briar Grove, Newlands, Glasgow G43 2TD	0141-637 3228

Name	Ord.	Ind.	Position	Address	Telephone
Chester, Stephen J. BA BD	1999		RE Teacher, International Christian College	42 Drumlochy Road, Ruchazie, Glasgow G33 3RE	0141-774 4666
Coley, Richard LTh	1971	2004	(Glasgow: Victoria Tollcross)	146 Hamilton Road, Glasgow G32 9QR	0141-764 1259
Collard, John K. MA BD	1986	2003	Presbytery Congregational Facilitator	1 Nelson Terrace, East Kilbride, Glasgow G74 2EY	01355 520093
Cunningham, Alexander MA BD	1961	2002	(Presbytery Clerk)	The Glen, 103 Glenmavis Road, Airdrie ML6 0PQ	01236 763012
Cunningham, James S.A. MA BD BLitt PhD				'Kirkland', 5 Inveresk Place, Coatbridge ML5 2DA	01236 421541
Currie, Robert MA	1992	2000	(Glasgow: Barlanark Greyfriars)	Flat 3/2, 13 Redlands Road, Glasgow G12 0SJ	0141-334 5111
Currie, R. David BSc BD	1955	1990	(Community Minister)	69 Kethers Street, Motherwell ML1 3HN	
Dunnett, Linda (Mrs) DCS	1984	2004	(Cambuslang: Flemington Hallside)	759B Argyle Street, Glasgow G3 8DS	(Office) 0141-204 4800
			Frontier Youth Trust, West of Scotland Development Officer	17 Munro Road, Glasgow G13 1SQ	0141-959 3732
Ferguson, James B. LTh	1972	2002	(Lenzie: Union)	3 Bridgeway Place, Kirkintilloch, Glasgow G66 3HW	
Finlay, William P. MA BD	1969	2000	(Glasgow: Townhead Blochairn)	High Corrie, Brodick, Isle of Arran KA27 8JB	01770 810689
Forbes, George A.R. BD	1971	2000	(Kirkintilloch: Hillhead)	28 Murrayfield, Bishopbriggs, Glasgow G64 3DS	0141-762 0272
Galloway, Allan D. MA BD STM PhD FRSE	1948	1982	(University of Glasgow)	5 Sraid Bheag, Barremman, Clynder, Helensburgh G84 0QX	01436 831432
Galloway, Kathy (Mrs) BD	1977	2002	Leader: Iona Community	20 Hamilton Park Avenue, Glasgow G12 8UU	0141-357 4079
Gibson, H. Marshall MA BD	1957	1996	(St Thomas' Gallowgate)	39 Burntbroom Drive, Glasgow G69 7XG	0141-771 0749
Gibson, Michael BD STM	1974	2001	(Glasgow: Giffnock: The Park)	12 Mile End Park, Pocklington, York YO42 2TH	
Goss, Alister BD	1975	1998	Industrial Mission Organiser	79 Weymouth Crescent, Gourock PA19 1HR	01475 638944
Gray, Christine (Mrs)			(Deacon)	38 Cruachan Street, Glasgow G46 8LY	0141-571 1008
Gregson, Elizabeth M. (Mrs) BD	1996	2001	(Drumchapel: St Andrew's)	17 Westfields, Bishopbriggs, Glasgow G64 3PL	0141-563 1918
Grimstone, A. Frank MA	1949	1986	(Calton Parkhead)	144C Howth Drive, Parkview Estate, Anniesland, Glasgow G13 1RL	0141-954 1009
Haley, Derek BD DPS	1960	1999	(Chaplain: Gartnavel Royal)	9 Kinnaird Crescent, Bearsden, Glasgow G61 2BN	0141-942 9281
Harper, Anne J.M. (Miss) BD STM MTh CertSocPsych	1979	1990	Hospital Chaplain	122 Greenock Road, Bishopton PA7 5AS	01505 862466
Harvey, W. John BA BD	1965	2002	(Edinburgh: Corstorphine Craigsbank)	501 Shields Road, Glasgow G41 2RF	0141-429 3774
Haughton, Frank MA BD	1942	2000	(Kirkintilloch: St Mary's)	64 Regent Street, Kirkintilloch, Glasgow G66 1JF	0141-777 6802
Hope, Evelyn P. (Mrs) BA BD	1990	1990	(Wishaw: Thornlie)	Flat 0/1, 48 Moss-side Road, Glasgow G41 3UA	0141-649 1522
Houston, Thomas C.	1975	2004	(Glasgow: Priesthill and Nitshill)	110 Elder Crescent, Drumsagart, Glasgow G72 7GL	0141-641 1117
Hunter, Alastair G. MSc BD	1976	1980	University of Glasgow	487 Shields Road, Glasgow G41 2RG	0141-429 1687
Hutcheson, J. Murray MA	1943	1987	(Possilpark)	88 Ainslie Road, Kildrum, Cumbernauld, Glasgow G67 2ED	01236 631168
Hutchison, Henry MA BEd BD MLit PhD LLCM	1948	1993	(Carmunnock)	4A Briar Grove, Newlands, Glasgow G43 2TG	0141-637 2766
Irvine, Euphemia H.C. (Mrs) BD	1972	1988	(Milton of Campsie)	32 Baird Drive, Bargarran, Erskine PA8 6BB	0141-812 2777
Johnston, Robert W.M. MA BD STM	1964	1999	(Temple Anniesland)	13 Kilmardinny Crescent, Bearsden, Glasgow G61 3NP	0141-931 5862
Johnstone, H. Martin J. MA BD MTh	1989	2000	Urban Priority Areas Adviser	3 Herries Road, Glasgow G41 4DE	0141-423 3760
Jolly, John BA	1950	1990	(Old Partick)	10 Kensington Court, 20 Kensington Road, Glasgow G12 9NX	0141-339 8815
Jones, E. Gwynfai BA	1964	2002	(Glasgow: St Rollox)	50 Melville Gardens, Bishopbriggs, Glasgow G64 3DD	0141-563 1770
Langlands, Cameron H. BD MTh ThM	1995	1999	Hospital Chaplain	4 Langlook Place, Glasgow G53 7NS	0141-892 2080
Leask, Rebecca M. (Mrs)	1977	1985	(Callander: St Bride's)	1 Woodrow Court, 17 Woodrow Road, Glasgow G41 5TN	0141-427 2260
Levison, C.L. MA BD	1972	1998	Health Care Chaplaincy Training and Development Officer	5 Deaconsbank Avenue, Stewarton Road, Glasgow G46 7UN	0141-620 3492

Name	Charge / Appointment	Ord.	Dem.	Address	Tel.
Lewis, E.M.H. MA	(Drumchapel St Andrew's)	1962	1993	7 Cleveden Place, Glasgow G12 0HG	0141-334 5411
Liddell, Matthew MA BD	(St Paul's (Outer High) and St David's (Ramshorn))	1943	1982	17 Traquair Drive, Glasgow G52 2TB	0141-810 3776
Lindsay, W. Douglas BD CPS	(Eaglesham)	1978	2004	3 Drummond Place, Calderwood, East Kilbride, Glasgow G74 9AD	
Lodge, Bernard P. BD	(Glasgow: Govanhill Trinity)	1967	2004	6 Darluith Park, Brookfield, Johnstone PA5 8DD	01505 320378
Lunan, David W. MA BD	Presbytery Clerk	1970	2002	142 Hill Street, Glasgow G3 6UA	0141-353 3687
Lyall, Ann (Miss) DCS	Chaplain: Lodging House Mission	1950	2001	117 Barlia Drive, Glasgow G45 0AY	0141-631 3643
McAreavey, William BA	(Kelvin Stevenson Memorial)	1990	1998	12B East Donington Street, Darvel KA17 0JW	01560 320073
Macaskill, Marjory (Mrs) LLB BD	Chaplain: University of Strathclyde	1971	1993	44 Forfar Avenue, Cardonald, Glasgow G52 3JQ	0141-883 5956
MacBain, Iain W.	(Coatbridge: Coatdyke)			24 Thornyburn Drive, Baillieston, Glasgow G69 7ER	0141-771 7030
MacDonald, Anne (Miss) BA DCS	Hospital Chaplain	1995		62 Berwick Drive, Glasgow G52 3JA	0141-883 5618
MacFadyen, Anne M. (Mrs) BSc BD	(Auxiliary Minister)	1956	1992	295 Mearns Road, Glasgow G77 5LT	0141-639 3605
Macfarlane, Thomas G. BSc PhD BD	(South Shawlands)	1976	1996	Flat 0/2, 19 Corrour Road, Glasgow G43 2DY	0141-632 7966
McKenzie, Mary O. (Miss)	(Edinburgh Richmond Craigmillar)	1971	2001	4 Dunellan Avenue, Moodiesburn, Glasgow G69 0GB	01236 870180
McLaren, D. Muir MA BD MTh PhD	(Mosspark)	1989	2004	Flat 24, 28 Lethington Avenue, Glasgow G41 3HB	
McLay, Alastair D. BSc BD	(Kirkintilloch St David's Memorial)	1963	1988	42 Hawthorn Drive, Banknock, Bonnybridge FK4 1LF	01324 840667
MacLeod, William J. DipTh	(Hyndland)	1949	1989	62 Lauderdale Gardens, Glasgow G12 9QW	0141-339 1294
Macnaughton, J.A. MA BD				0/1, 104 Carside Street, Glasgow G42 9TQ	0141-616 6468
MacPherson, James B. DCS	(Deacon)				
MacQuarrie, Stuart BD BSc JP	Chaplain: Glasgow University	1984	2001	The Chaplaincy Centre, University of Glasgow, Glasgow G12 8QQ	0141-330 5419
Millar, David A.R. MA	(University of Glasgow)	1956	1989	310A Albert Drive, Glasgow G41 5RS	0141-429 2249
Millar, James	(Shawlands Old)	1949	1989	9 Glenbank Court, Glasgow G46 7EJ	0141-638 6250
Mitchell, David BD MSc DipPTheol	Chaplain: Marie Curie Hospice, Glasgow	1988	1998	48 Leglin Wood Drive, Wallacewell Park, Glasgow G21 3PL [E-mail: davidmitchell@chaplain48.freeserve.co.uk]	0141-558 4679
Morrice, Alastair M. MA BD	(Rutherglen: Stonelaw)	1968	2002	5 Brechin Road, Kirriemuir DD8 4BX	0141-647 2682
Morton, Thomas MA BD LGSM	(Rutherglen: Stonelaw)	1945	1986	54 Greystone Avenue, Burnside, Rutherglen, Glasgow G73 3SW	0141-779 2504
Muir, Fred C. MA BD ThM ARCM	(Stepps)	1961	1997	20 Alexandra Avenue, Stepps, Glasgow G33 6BP	01476 594430
Myers, Frank BA		1952	1978	18 Birmingham Close, Grantham NG31 8SD	0131-339 8855
Newlands, George M. MA BD PhD	University of Glasgow	1970	1986	12 Jamaica Street North Lane, Edinburgh EH3 6HQ	0141-942 1327
Philip, George M. MA	(Sandyford Henderson Memorial)	1953	1996	44 Beech Avenue, Bearsden, Glasgow G61 3EX	01225 333041
Philip, Robert A. BA BD	(Stepps: St Andrew's)	1937	1981	2 Hockley Court, Weston Park West, Bath BA1 4AR	0141-639 4169
Porter, Richard MA	(Govanhill)	1953	1988	58 Hillend Road, Glasgow G76 7XT	0141-776 2915
Ramsay, W.G.	(Springburn)	1967	1999	53 Kelvinvale, Kirkintilloch, Glasgow G66 1RD	0141-586 9925
Reid, Ian M.A. BD	Hospital Chaplain	1990	2001	16 Walker Court, Glasgow G11 6QP	0141-637 7572
Robertson, Archibald MA BD	(Eastwood)	1957	1999	19 Canberra Court, Braidpark Drive, Glasgow G46 6NS	
Robertson, Blair MA BD ThM	Chaplain: Southern General Hospital	1990	1998	c/o Chaplain's Office, Southern General Hospital, 1345 Govan Road, Glasgow G51 4TF	
Ross, Donald M. MA	(Industrial Mission Organiser)	1953	1994	14 Cartsbridge Road, Busby, Glasgow G76 8DH	0141-201 2156 / 0141-644 2220
Ross, James MA BD	(Kilsyth: Anderson)	1968	1998	53 Turnberry Gardens, Westerwood, Cumbernauld, Glasgow G68 0AY	01236 730501
Saunders, Keith BD	Hospital Chaplain	1983	1999	Western Infirmary, Dumbarton Road, Glasgow G11 6NT	0141-211 2000
Scrimgeour, Alice M. (Miss) DCS	(Deaconess)			265 Golfhill Drive, Glasgow G31 2PB	0141-564 9602
Shackleton, William	(Greenock: Wellpark West)	1960	1996	3 Tynwald Avenue, Burnside, Glasgow G73 4RN	0141-569 9407
Simpson, Neil A. BA BD PhD	(Glasgow: Yoker Old with Yoker St Matthew's)	1992	2001		

Name			Charge	Address	Telephone
Smith, A. McLaren	1971	1997	(Cumbrae)	27 Fenwick Road, Glasgow G46 6AU	0141-954 6497
Smith, Hilda C. (Miss) MA BD	1992	2001	Hospital Chaplain	107 Athelstane Road, Glasgow G13 3QY	0141-776 0870
Smith, J. Rankine MA BD	1945	1982	(Barmulloch)	44 Middlemuir Road, Lenzie, Glasgow G66 4ND	0141-883 9666
Smith, James S.A.	1956	1991	(Drongan, The Schaw Kirk)	146 Aros Drive, Glasgow G52 1TJ	01436 674493
Speed, David K. LTh	1969	2004	(Glasgow: Shettleston Old)	153 West Princes Street, Helensburgh G84 8EZ	0141-883 8973
Spence, Elisabeth G.B. (Miss) BD DipEd	1995	2000	Industrial Missioner: Glasgow Area	45 Selvieland Road, Glasgow G52 4AS	0141-638 0632 (Tel/Fax)
Spiers, John M. LTh MTh	1972	2004	(Giffnock: Orchardhill)	58 Woodlands Road, Thornliebank, Glasgow G46 7IQ	0141-637 6956
Stewart, Norma D. (Miss) MA MEd BD	1977	2000	(Glasgow: Strathbungo Queens Park)	127 Nether Auldhouse Road, Glagow G43 2YS	01236 731723
Sutherland, Denis I.	1963	1995	(Hutchesontown)	56 Lime Crescent, Cumbernauld, Glasgow G67 3PQ	01360 770154
Sutherland, Elizabeth W. (Miss) BD	1972	1996	(Balornock North with Barmulloch)	20 Kirkland Avenue, Blanefield, Glasgow G63 9BZ	0141-770 6027
Tait, Alexander	1967	1995	(St Enoch's Hogganfield)	129 Lochview Drive, Hogganfield, Glasgow G33 1LN	0141-424 0493
Turner, Angus BD	1976	1998	(Industrial Chaplain)	46 Keir Street, Pollokshields, Glasgow G41 2LA	01698 321108
Tuton, Robert M. MA	1957	1995	(Shettleston: Old)	6 Holmwood Gardens, Uddingston, Glasgow G71 7BH	01360 622281
Walker, A.I.	1955	1988	(Trinity Possil and Henry Drummond)	11 Dundas Avenue, Torrance, Glasgow G64 4BD	0141-420 3327
Walton, Ainslie MA MEd	1954	1995	(University of Aberdeen)	501 Shields Road, Glasgow G41 2RF [E-mail: revainslie@aol.com]	
White, Elizabeth (Miss) DCS			(Deaconess)	Woodside House, Rodger Avenue, Rutherglen, Glasgow G73 3QZ	
Younger, Adah (Mrs) BD	1978	2004	(Glasgow: Dennistoun Central)	Flat 0/1, 101 Greenhead Street, Glasgow G40 1HR	0141-550 0878

GLASGOW ADDRESSES

Banton	Kelvinhead Road, Banton	
Bishopbriggs		
Kenmure	Viewfield Road, Bishopbriggs	
Springfield	Springfield Road	
Broom	Mearns Road, Newton Mearns	
Burnside–Blairbeth	Church Avenue, Burnside	
Busby	Church Road, Busby	
Cadder	Cadder Road, Glasgow	
Cambuslang		
Flemington Hallside	265 Hamilton Road	
Old	Cairns Road	
St Andrew's	Main Street x Clydeford Road	
Trinity St Paul's	Main Street	
Campsie	Main Street, Lennoxtown	
Chryston	Main Street, Chryston	
Eaglesham	Montgomery Street, Eaglesham	
Gartcosh	113 Lochend Road, Gartcosh	
Giffnock		
Orchardhill	Church Road	
South	Eastwood Toll	
The Park	Ravenscliffe Drive	
Glenboig	138 Main Street, Glenboig	
Greenbank	Eaglesham Road, Clarkston	
Kilsyth		
Anderson	Kingston Road	
Burns and Old	Church Street	
Kirkintilloch		
Hillhead	Newdyke Road nr Old Aisle Road	
St Columba's	Waterside Road nr Old Aisle Road	
St David's Mem Pk	Alexander Street	
St Mary's	Cowgate	
Lenzie		
Old	Kirkintilloch Road x Garngaber Ave	
Union	Moncrieff Ave x Kirkintilloch Road	
Maxwell		
Mearns Castle	Waterfoot Road	
Mearns	Mearns Road, Newton Mearns	
Netherlee	Ormonde Drive x Ormonde Avenue	
Newton Mearns	Ayr Road, Newton Mearns	
Rutherglen		
Old	Main Street at Queen Street	
Stonelaw	Stonelaw Road x Dryburgh Avenue	
Wardlawhill	Hamilton Road	
West	Glasgow Road nr Main Street	
Stamperland	Stamperland Gardens, Clarkston	
Stepps	Whitehill Avenue	
Thornliebank	61 Spiersbridge Road	
Torrance	School Road, Torrance	
Twechar	Main Street, Twechar	
Williamwood	Vardar Avenue x Seres Ave, Clarkston	
Glasgow		
Anderston Kelvingrove	Argyle Street x Elderslie Street	
Baillieston		
Mure Memorial	Beech Avenue, Garrowhill	
St Andrew's	Bredisholm Road	
Balshagray Victoria Pk	Broomhill Cross	
Barlanark Greyfriars	Edinburgh Road x Hallhill Road	
Battlefield East	1216 Cathcart Road	
Blawarthill	Millbrix Avenue	

Bridgeton St Francis in the East	26 Queen Mary Street
Broomhill	Randolph Rd x Marlborough Ave
Calton Parkhead	122 Helenvale Street
Cardonald	2155 Paisley Road West
Carmunnock	Kirk Road, Carmunnock
Carmyle	South Carmyle Avenue
Carntyne	862 Shettleston Road
Carnwadric	556 Boydstone Road, Thornliebank
Castlemilk East	Bartia Terrace
Castlemilk West	Carmunnock Road
Cathcart Old	119 Carmunnock Road
Cathcart Trinity	92 Clarkston Road
Cathedral	Cathedral Square
Colston Milton	Egilsay Crescent
Colston Wellpark	1378 Springburn Road
Cranhill	Bellrock Crescent x Bellrock Street
Croftfoot	Croftpark Ave x Crofthill Road
Dennistoun Blackfriars	Whitehill Street
Dennistoun Central	Armadale Street
Drumchapel Drumry St Mary's	Drumry Road East
Drumchapel St Andrew's	Garscadden Road
Drumchapel St Mark's	Kinfauns Drive
Eastbank	679 Old Shettleston Road
Easterhouse St George's and St Peter's	Boyndie Street
Eastwood	Mansewood Road
Fernhill and Cathkin	Neilvaig Drive
Gairbraid	1517 Maryhill Road
Gardner Street	Gardner Street x Muirpark Street
Garthamlock and Craigend East	Porchester Street x Balveny Street
Gorbals	Eglinton Street x Cumberland Street
Govan Old	866 Govan Road
Govanhill Trinity	Daisy Street nr Allison Street
High Carntyne	358 Carntynehall Road
Hillington Park	24 Berryknowes Road

Househillwood St Christopher's	Meikle Road
Hyndland	Hyndland Road, opp Novar Drive
Ibrox	Carillon Road x Clifford Street
John Ross Memorial	100 Norfolk Street
Jordanhill	Woodend Drive x Munro Road
Kelvin Stevenson Mem	Belmont Street at Belmont Bridge
Kelvinside Hillhead	Huntly Gardens
Kenmuir Mount Vernon	London Road, Mount Vernon
King's Park	242 Castlemilk Road
Kinning Park	Eaglesham Place
Knightswood St Margaret's	Knightswood Cross
Langside	Ledard Road x Lochleven Road
Lansdowne	Gt Western Road at Kelvin Bridge
Linthouse St Kenneth's	9 Skipness Drive
Lochwood	Liff Place
Martyrs', The	St Mungo Avenue
Maryhill	1990 Maryhill Road
Merrylee	Merrylee Road
Mosspark	149 Ashkirk Drive
Mount Florida	1123 Cathcart Road
New Govan	Govan Cross
Newlands South	Riverside Road x Langside Drive
North Kelvinside	153 Queen Margaret Drive
Partick South	Dumbarton Road
Partick Trinity	20 Lawrence Street
Penilee St Andrew	Bowfield Cres x Bowfield Avenue
Pollokshaws	223 Shawbridge Street
Pollokshields	Albert Drive x Shields Road
Possilpark	124 Saracen Street
Priesthill and Nitshill	Priesthill Road x Muirshiel Cresc; Dove Street
Queen's Park	170 Queen's Drive
Renfield St Stephen's	260 Bath Street
Robroyston	34 Saughs Road
Ruchazie	Elibank Street x Milncroft Road
Ruchill	Shakespeare Street nr Maryhill Rd

St Andrew's East	681 Alexandra Parade
St Columba	300 St Vincent Street
St David's Knightswood	Boreland Drive nr Lincoln Avenue
St Enoch's Hogganfield	860 Cumbernauld Road
St George's Tron	163 Buchanan Street
St James' (Pollok)	Lyoncross Road x Byrebush Road
St John's Renfield	22 Beaconsfield Road
St Luke's and St Andrew's	Well Street at Bain Square
St Margaret's Tollcross Pk	179 Braidfauld Street
St Nicholas' Cardonald	Harlaw Crescent nr Gladsmuir Road
St Paul's Provanmill	Langdale Street x Greenrig Street
St Rollox	Fountainwell Road
St Thomas Gallowgate	Gallowgate opp Bluevale Street
Sandyford-Henderson Memorial	Kelvinhaugh Street at Argyle Street
Sandyhills	28 Baillieston Rd nr Sandyhills Rd
Scotstoun	Earlbank Avenue x Ormiston Avenue
Shawlands	Shawlands Cross
Sherbrooke St Gilbert's	Nithsdale Rd x Sherbrooke Avenue
Shettleston Old	99–111 Killin Street
South Carntyne	538 Carntyne Road
South Shawlands	Regwood Street x Deanston Drive
Springburn	Springburn Road x Atlas Street
Temple Anniesland	869 Crow Road
Toryglen	Glenmore Ave nr Prospecthill Road
Trinity Possil and Henry Drummond	Crowhill Street x Broadholm Street
Tron St Mary's	128 Red Road
Victoria Tollcross	1134 Tollcross Road
Wallacewell	57 Northgate Road; Ryehill Road x Quarrywood Road
Wellington	University Ave x Southpark Avenue
Whiteinch	St Paul's R.C. Primary School, Primrose Street
Yoker	Dumbarton Road at Hawick Street

(17) HAMILTON

Meets at Motherwell: Dalziel St Andrew's Parish Church Halls, on the first Tuesday of February, March, May, September, October, November, December, and on the third Tuesday of June.

Presbytery Office:	18 Haddow Street, Hamilton ML3 7HX [E-mail: akph54@uk.uumail.com]	01698 286837 (Tel/Fax)
Clerk:	REV. SHAW J. PATERSON BSc BD	
Treasurer:	15 Lethame Road, Strathaven ML10 6AD	01357 520019

1 **Airdrie Broomknoll (H) (Tel: 01236 762101; E-mail: airdrie-broomknoll@presbyteryofhamilton.co.uk)**
   linked with Calderbank (E-mail: calderbank@presbyteryofhamilton.co.uk)
   Andrew Thomson BA   1976   2000   38 Commonhead Street, Airdrie ML6 6NS   01236 602538

2 **Airdrie: Clarkston (E-mail: airdrie-clarkston@presbyteryofhamilton.co.uk)**
   Vacant   Clarkston Manse, Forrest Street, Airdrie ML6 7BE   01236 769676

3 **Airdrie: Flowerhill (H) (E-mail: airdrie-flowerhill@presbyteryofhamilton.co.uk)**
   Andrew Gardner BSc BD PhD   1997   31 Victoria Place, Airdrie ML6 9BX   01236 763025
                                          [E-mail: andrewgar@supanet.com]

4 **Airdrie: High (E-mail: airdrie-high@presbyteryofhamilton.co.uk)**
   Vacant   17 Etive Drive, Airdrie ML6 9QL   01236 762010

5 **Airdrie: Jackson (Tel: 01236 733508; E-mail: airdrie-jackson@presbyteryofhamilton.co.uk)**
   Sharon E.F. Colvin (Mrs)   1985   1998   48 Dunrobin Road, Airdrie ML6 8LR   01236 763154
   BD LRAM LTCL   [E-mail: dibley@hotmail.com]

6 **Airdrie: New Monkland (H) (E-mail: airdrie-newmonkland@presbyteryofhamilton.co.uk)**
   linked with Greengairs (E-mail: greengairs@presbyteryofhamilton.co.uk)
   Randolph Scott MA BD   1991   2001   3 Dykehead Crescent, Airdrie ML6 6PU   01236 763554
                                          [E-mail: rev.rs@tinyworld.co.uk]

7 **Airdrie: St Columba's (E-mail: airdrie-stcolumbas@presbyteryofhamilton.co.uk)**
   Margaret F. Currie BEd BD   1980   1987   52 Kennedy Drive, Airdrie ML6 9AW   01236 763173
                                          [E-mail: mfcstcol@surfaid.org]

8   **Airdrie: The New Wellwynd (H) (E-mail: airdrie-newwellwynd@presbyteryofhamilton.co.uk)**
Robert A. Hamilton BA BD   1995   2001   20 Arthur Avenue, Airdrie ML6 9EZ   01236 763022
[E-mail: revrob13@blueyonder.co.uk]

9   **Bargeddie (H) (E-mail: bargeddie@presbyteryofhamilton.co.uk)**
John Fairful BD   1994   2001   The Manse, Manse Road, Bargeddie, Baillieston, Glasgow G69 6UB   0141-771 1322

10   **Bellshill: Macdonald Memorial (E-mail: bellshill-macdonald@presbyteryofhamilton.co.uk) linked with Bellshill: Orbiston**
Alan McKenzie BSc BD   1988   2001   32 Adamson Street, Bellshill ML4 1DT   01698 849114
[E-mail: rev.a.mckenzie@btopenworld.com]

11   **Bellshill: Orbiston (E-mail: bellshill-orbiston@presbyteryofhamilton.co.uk)** See Bellshill: Macdonald Memorial

12   **Bellshill: West (H) (01698 747581) (E-mail: bellshill-west@presbyteryofhamilton.co.uk)**
Agnes A. Moore (Miss) BD   1987   2001   16 Croftpark Street, Bellshill ML4 1EY   01698 842877

13   **Blantyre: Livingstone Memorial (E-mail: blantyre-livingstone@presbyteryofhamilton.co.uk)**
Colin A. Sutherland LTh   1995   2003   286 Glasgow Road, Blantyre, Glasgow G72 9DB   01698 823794
[E-mail: colin.csutherland@btinternet.com]

14   **Blantyre: Old (H) (E-mail: blantyre-old@presbyteryofhamilton.co.uk)**
Rosemary A. Smith (Ms) BD   1997   The Manse, Craigmuir Road, High Blantyre, Glasgow G72 9UA   01698 823130
[E-mail: revrosieanne@btopenworld.com]

15   **Blantyre: St Andrew's (E-mail: blantyre-standrews@presbyteryofhamilton.co.uk)**
J. Peter N. Johnston BSc BD   2001   332 Glasgow Road, Blantyre, Glasgow G72 9LQ   01698 828633
[E-mail: peter.johnston@standrewsblantyre.com]

16   **Bothwell (H) (E-mail: bothwell@presbyteryofhamilton.co.uk)**
James M. Gibson TD LTh LRAM   1978   1989   Manse Avenue, Bothwell, Glasgow G71 8PQ   01698 853189 (Tel)
[E-mail: jamesgibson@msn.com]   01698 853229 (Fax)

17   **Calderbank** See Airdrie: Broomknoll

18   **Caldercruix and Longriggend (H) (E-mail: caldercruix@presbyteryofhamilton.co.uk)**
Vacant   Main Street, Caldercruix, Airdrie ML6 7RF   01236 842279

19   **Carfin (E-mail: carfin@presbyteryofhamilton.co.uk) linked with Newarthill (E-mail: newarthill@presbyteryofhamilton.co.uk)**
Douglas M. Main BD   1986   2003   Church Street, Newarthill, Motherwell ML1 5HS   01698 860316
[E-mail: revdmain@aol.com]

20   **Chapelhall (H) (E-mail: chapelhall@presbyteryofhamilton.co.uk)**
Vacant   Russell Street, Chapelhall, Airdrie ML6 8SG   01236 763439

21 Chapelton (E-mail: chapelton@presbyteryofhamilton.co.uk)
linked with Strathaven: Rankin (H) (E-mail: strathaven-rankin@presbyteryofhamilton.co.uk)
Shaw J. Paterson BSc BD   1991   15 Letham Road, Strathaven ML10 6AD   01357 520019 (Tel)
[E-mail: shaw@patersonsj.freeserve.co.uk]   01357 529316 (Fax)

22 Cleland (H) (E-mail: cleland@presbyteryofhamilton.co.uk)
John A. Jackson BD   1997   The Manse, Bellside Road, Cleland, Motherwell ML1 5NP   01698 860260
[E-mail: johnjackson@uk2.net]

23 Coatbridge: Blairhill Dundyvan (H) (E-mail: coatbridge-blairhill@presbyteryofhamilton.co.uk)
Patricia A. Carruth (Mrs) BD   1998   2004   18 Blairhill Street, Coatbridge ML5 1PG   01236 432304

24 Coatbridge: Calder (H) (E-mail: coatbridge-calder@presbyteryofhamilton.co.uk)
Amelia Davidson (Mrs) BD   2004   26 Bute Street, Coatbridge ML5 4HF   01236 421516
[E-mail: amelia@davidson1293.freeserve.co.uk]

25 Coatbridge: Clifton (H) (E-mail: coatbridge-clifton@presbyteryofhamilton.co.uk)
William G. McKaig BD   1979   2003   132 Muiryhall Street, Coatbridge ML5 3NH   01236 421181

26 Coatbridge: Middle (H) (E-mail: coatbridge-middle@presbyteryofhamilton.co.uk)
James Grier BD   1991   1996   47 Blair Road, Coatbridge ML5 1JQ   01236 432427

27 Coatbridge: Old Monkland (E-mail: coatbridge-oldmonkland@presbyteryofhamilton.co.uk)
Scott Raby LTh   1991   2003   2 Brandon Way, Coatbridge ML5 5QT   01236 423788
[E-mail: revscott@rabyfamily28.freeserve.co.uk]

28 Coatbridge: St Andrew's (E-mail: coatbridge-standrews@presbyteryofhamilton.co.uk)
Ian G. Wotherspoon BA LTh   1967   1994   77 Eglinton Street, Coatbridge ML5 3JF   01236 437271
[E-mail: wotherspoonrig@aol.com]

29 Coatbridge: Townhead (H) (E-mail: coatbridge-townhead@presbyteryofhamilton.co.uk)
Ecilo Selemani LTh MTh   2004   Crinan Crescent, Coatbridge ML5 2LH   01236 702914

30 Dalserf (E-mail: dalserf@presbyteryofhamilton.co.uk)
D. Cameron McPherson BSc BD   1982   Manse Brae, Dalserf, Larkhall ML9 3BN   01698 882195
[E-mail: dcameronmc@aol.com]

31 East Kilbride: Claremont (H) (Tel: 01355 238088; E-mail: ek-claremont@presbyteryofhamilton.co.uk)
Gordon R. Palmer MA BD STM   1986   2003   17 Deveron Road, East Kilbride, Glasgow G74 2HR   01355 248526
[E-mail: gkspalmer@blueyonder.co.uk]
Paul Cathcart DCS   50 Ardler Place, Greenhills, East Kilbride, Glasgow G75 9HP   01355 521906
[E-mail: paulcathcart@msn.com]

32 East Kilbride: Greenhills (E) (Tel: 01355 221746; E-mail: ek-greenhills@presbyteryofhamilton.co.uk)
John Brewster MA BD DipEd   1988   21 Turnberry Place, East Kilbride, Glasgow G75 8TB   01355 242564
[E-mail: johnbrewster1@activemail.co.uk]

33 East Kilbride: Moncreiff (H) (Tel: 01355 223328; E-mail: ek-moncreiff@presbyteryofhamilton.co.uk)
Alastair S. Lusk BD   1974   1983   16 Almond Drive, East Kilbride, Glasgow G74 2HX   01355 238639

34 East Kilbride: Mossneuk (E) (Tel: 01355 260954; E-mail: ek-mossneuk@presbyteryofhamilton.co.uk)
John L. McPake BA BD PhD   1986   2000   30 Eden Grove, Mossneuk, East Kilbride, Glasgow G75 8XU   01355 234196

35 East Kilbride: Old (H) (E-mail: ek-old@presbyteryofhamilton.co.uk)
Anne S. Paton BA BD   2001   40 Maxwell Drive, East Kilbride, Glasgow G74 4NG   01355 220732

36 East Kilbride: South (H) (E-mail: ek-south@presbyteryofhamilton.co.uk)
John C. Sharp BSc BD PhD   1980   7 Clamps Wood, East Kilbride, Glasgow G74 2HB   01355 247993
[E-mail: johncsharp@btinternet.com]

37 East Kilbride: Stewartfield (New Charge Development)
Douglas W. Wallace MA BD   1981   2001   8 Thistle Place, Stewartfield, East Kilbride, Glasgow G74 4RH   01355 260879

38 East Kilbride: West (H) (E-mail: ek-west@presbyteryofhamilton.co.uk)
Kenneth A.L. Mayne BA MSc CertEd   1976   2001   4 East Milton Grove, East Kilbride, Glasgow G75 8FN   01355 236639

39 East Kilbride: Westwood (H) (Tel: 01355 245657; E-mail: ek-westwood@presbyteryofhamilton.co.uk)
Kevin Mackenzie BD DPS   1989   1996   16 Inglewood Crescent, East Kilbride, Glasgow G75 8QD   01355 223992
[E-mail: kevin@westwood-church.org.uk]

40 Glasford (E-mail: glassford@presbyteryofhamilton.co.uk) linked with Strathaven: East (E-mail: strathaven-east@presbyteryofhamilton.co.uk)
William T. Stewart BD   1980   68 Townhead Street, Strathaven ML10 6BA   01357 521138

41 Greengairs See Airdrie: New Monkland

42 Hamilton: Burnbank (E-mail: hamilton-burnbank@presbyteryofhamilton.co.uk) linked with Hamilton: North (H) (E-mail: hamilton-north@presbyteryofhamilton.co.uk)
Raymond D. McKenzie BD   1978   1987   9 South Park Road, Hamilton ML3 6PJ   01698 424609

43 Hamilton: Cadzow (H) (Tel: 01698 428695; E-mail: hamilton-cadzow@presbyteryofhamilton.co.uk)
Arthur P. Barrie LTh   1973   1979   3 Carlisle Road, Hamilton ML3 7BZ   01698 421664 (Tel)   01698 891126 (Fax)

44 Hamilton: Gilmour and Whitehill (H) (E-mail: hamilton-gilmourwhitehill@presbyteryofhamilton.co.uk)
Ronald J. Maxwell Stitt LTh BA ThM BREd DMin FSAScot   1977   2000   86 Burnbank Centre, Burnbank, Hamilton ML3 0NA   01698 284201

45 **Hamilton: Hillhouse (E-mail: hamilton-hillhouse@presbyteryofhamilton.co.uk)**
David W.G. Burt BD DipMin   1989   1998   66 Wellhall Road, Hamilton ML3 9BY
                                                              [E-mail: dwgburt@blueyonder.co.uk]   01698 422300

46 **Hamilton: North** See Hamilton: Burnbank

47 **Hamilton: Old (H) (Tel: 01698 281905; E-mail: hamilton-old@presbyteryofhamilton.co.uk)**
John M.A. Thomson TD JP BD ThM   1978   2001   1 Chateau Grove, Hamilton ML3 7DS
                                                              [E-mail: jt@john1949.plus.com]   01698 422511

48 **Hamilton: St Andrew's (T) (E-mail: hamilton-standrews@presbyteryofhamilton.co.uk)**
Vacant   15 Bent Road, Hamilton ML3 6QB   01698 891361

49 **Hamilton: St John's (H) (Tel: 01698 283492; E-mail: hamilton-stjohns@presbyteryofhamilton.co.uk)**
Robert M. Kent MA BD   1973   1981   12 Castlehill Crescent, Hamilton ML3 7DG
                                                              [E-mail: robert@bobkent.fsnet.co.uk]   01698 425002

50 **Hamilton: South (H) (Tel: 01698 281014; E-mail: hamilton-south@presbyteryofhamilton.co.uk)
    linked with Quarter (E-mail: quarter@presbyteryofhamilton.co.uk)**
George MacDonald BTh   2004   The Manse, Limekilnburn Road, Quarter, Hamilton ML3 7XA
                                                              [E-mail: george.macdonald1@btinternet.com]   01698 424511

51 **Hamilton: Trinity (Tel: 01698 284254; E-mail: hamilton-trinity@presbyteryofhamilton.co.uk)**
Karen E. Harbison (Mrs) MA BD   1991   69 Buchan Street, Hamilton ML3 8JY   01698 425326

52 **Hamilton: West (H) (Tel: 01698 284670; E-mail: hamilton-west@presbyteryofhamilton.co.uk)**
William M. Murdoch BSc PhD BD STM   1980   2001   43 Bothwell Road, Hamilton ML3 0BB   01698 458770

53 **Holytown (E-mail: holytown@presbyteryofhamilton.co.uk)**
Vacant   Holytown, Motherwell ML1 5RU   01698 832622

54 **Kirk o' Shotts (H) (E-mail: kirk-o-shotts@presbyteryofhamilton.co.uk)**
Sheila M. Spence (Mrs) MA BD   1979   The Manse, Kirk o' Shotts, Salsburgh, Shotts ML7 4NS
                                                              [E-mail: sm_spence@hotmail.com]   01698 870208

55 **Larkhall: Chalmers (H) (E-mail: larkhall-chalmers@presbyteryofhamilton.co.uk)**
James S.G. Hastie CA BD   1990   Quarry Road, Larkhall ML9 1HH
                                                              [E-mail: jhastie@chalmers0.demon.co.uk]   01698 882238
                                                                                                         08700 562133 (Fax)

56 **Larkhall: St Machan's (H) (E-mail: larkhall-stmachans@presbyteryofhamilton.co.uk)**
Alastair McKillop BD DipMin   1995   2004   2 Orchard Gate, Larkhall ML9 1HG   01698 882457

57 **Larkhall: Trinity (E-mail: larkhall-trinity@presbyteryofhamilton.co.uk)**
Lindsay Schluter (Miss) ThE CertMin   1995   13 Machan Avenue, Larkhall ML9 2HE   01698 881401

58	**Motherwell: Crosshill (H) (E-mail: mwell-crosshill@presbyteryofhamilton.co.uk)**			
	W. Stuart Dunn LTh	1970	1982	15 Orchard Street, Motherwell ML1 3JE	01698 263410

Motherwell: Crosshill (H) (E-mail: mwell-crosshill@presbyteryofhamilton.co.uk)
W. Stuart Dunn LTh   1970   1982   15 Orchard Street, Motherwell ML1 3JE   01698 263410

Motherwell: Dalziel St Andrew's (H) (Tel: 01698 264097; E-mail: mwell-dalzielstandrews@presbyteryofhamilton.co.uk)
Derek W. Hughes BSc BD DipEd   1990   1996   4 Pollock Street, Motherwell ML1 1LP   01698 263414
[E-mail: derek@hughes04.freeserve.co.uk]

Motherwell: Manse Road (E-mail: mwell-manseroad@presbyteryofhamilton.co.uk)
Vacant   10 Hamilton Drive, Motherwell ML1 2QA   01698 267345

Motherwell: North (E-mail: mwell-north@presbyteryofhamilton.co.uk)
Derek H.N. Pope BD   1987   1995   Kirkland Street, Motherwell ML1 3JW   01698 266716
[E-mail: derekpopemotherwell@hotmail.com]

Motherwell: St Margaret's (E-mail: mwell-stmargarets@presbyteryofhamilton.co.uk)
Andrew M. Campbell BD   1984   70 Baron`s Road, Motherwell ML1 2NB   01698 263803
[E-mail: drewdorca@hotmail.com]

Motherwell: St Mary's (H) (E-mail: mwell-stmarys@presbyteryofhamilton.co.uk)
David W. Doyle MA BD   1977   1987   19 Orchard Street, Motherwell ML1 3JE   01698 263472

Motherwell: South Dalziel (H) (E-mail: mwell-southdalziel@presbyteryofhamilton.co.uk)
Phyllis M. Wilson (Mrs) DipCom DipRE   1985   1994   62 Manse Road, Motherwell ML1 2PT   01698 263054
[E-mail: phylandtomwilson@ukonline.co.uk]

Newarthill See Carfin

Newmains: Bonkle (H) (E-mail: bonkle@presbyteryofhamilton.co.uk)
linked with Newmains: Coltness Memorial (H) (E-mail: coltness@presbyteryofhamilton.co.uk)
Graham Raeburn MTh   2004   5 Kirkgate, Newmains, Wishaw ML2 9BT   01698 383858
[E-mail: grahamraeburn@tiscali.co.uk]

Newmains: Coltness Memorial See Newmains: Bonkle

New Stevenston: Wrangholm Kirk (E-mail: wrangholm@presbyteryofhamilton.co.uk)
George M Donaldson MA BD   1984   2003   222 Clydesdale Street, New Stevenston, Motherwell ML1 4JQ   01698 832533

Overtown (E-mail: overtown@presbyteryofhamilton.co.uk)
Nan Low (Mrs) BD   2002   The Manse, Main Street, Overtown, Wishaw ML2 0QP   01698 372330
[E-mail: nanlow@supanet.com]

Quarter See Hamilton: South

Shotts: Calderhead Erskine (E-mail: calderhead-erskine@presbyteryofhamilton.co.uk)
Ian G. Thom BSc PhD BD   1990   2000   The Manse, Kirk Road, Shotts ML7 5ET   01501 820042
[E-mail: the.thoms@btinternet.com]

72 **Stonehouse: St Ninian's (H) (E-mail: stonehouse@presbyteryofhamilton.co.uk)**
    Paul G.R. Grant BD MTh   2003   4 Hamilton Way, Stonehouse, Larkhall ML9 3PU   01698 792947
                                             [E-mail: agpg@surefish.co.uk]

73 **Strathaven: Avendale Old and Drumclog (H) (Tel: 01357 529748; E-mail: strathaven-avendaleold@presbyteryofhamilton.co.uk and**
    E-mail: drumclog@presbyteryofhamilton.co.uk)
    Alan W. Gibson BA BD   2001   Kirk Street, Strathaven ML10 6BA   01357 520077
                                             [E-mail: awgibson82@hotmail.com]

74 **Strathaven: East** See Glasford
75 **Strathaven: Rankin** See Chapelton

76 **Strathaven: West (E-mail: strathaven-west@presbyteryofhamilton.co.uk)**
    Una B. Stewart (Ms) BD DipEd   1995   2002   6 Avenel Crescent, Strathaven ML10 6JF   01357 529086
                                             [E-mail: rev.ubs@virgin.net]

77 **Uddingston: Burnhead (H) (E-mail: uddingston-burnhead@presbyteryofhamilton.co.uk)**
    Sandi Blackwood (Ms) BD   2002   90 Laburnum Road, Uddingston, Glasgow G71 5DB   01698 813716
                                             [E-mail: sandbox376-mail@yahoo.co.uk]

78 **Uddingston: Old (H) (Tel: 01698 814015; E-mail: uddingston-old@presbyteryofhamilton.co.uk)**
    Norman B. McKee BD   1987   1994   1 Belmont Avenue, Uddingston, Glasgow G71 7AX   01698 814757
                                             [E-mail: n.mckee1@btinternet.com]

79 **Uddingston: Park (T) (H) (E-mail: uddingston-park@presbyteryofhamilton.co.uk)**
    W. Bruce McDowall BA BD   1989   1999   25 Douglas Gardens, Uddingston, Glasgow G71 7HB   01698 817256

80 **Uddingston: Viewpark (H) (E-mail: uddingston-viewpark@presbyteryofhamilton.co.uk)**
    Michael G. Lyall BD   1993   2001   14 Holmbrae Road, Uddingston, Glasgow G71 6AP   01698 813113
                                             [E-mail: michaellyall@blueyonder.co.uk]

81 **Wishaw: Cambusnethan North (H) (E-mail: wishaw-cambusnethannorth@presbyteryofhamilton.co.uk)**
    Mhorag Macdonald (Ms) MA BD   1989   350 Kirk Road, Wishaw ML2 8LH   01698 381305
                                             [E-mail: mhorag@mhorag.force9.co.uk]

82 **Wishaw: Cambusnethan Old (E-mail: wishaw-cambusnethanold@presbyteryofhamilton.co.uk)**
    and Morningside (E-mail: wishaw-morningside@presbyteryofhamilton.co.uk)
    Iain C. Murdoch MA LLB DipEd BD   1995   22 Coronation Street, Wishaw ML2 8LF   01698 384235
                                             [E-mail: iaincmurdoch@btopenworld.com]

83 **Wishaw: Chalmers (H) (Tel: 01698 375306; E-mail: wishaw-chalmers@presbyteryofhamilton.co.uk)**
    Vacant   161 Kirk Road, Wishaw ML2 7BZ   01698 372464

84 Wishaw: Craigneuk and Belhaven (H) (E-mail: wishaw-craigneukbelhaven@presbyteryofhamilton.co.uk)
Vacant   100 Glen Road, Wishaw ML2 7NP   01698 372495

85 Wishaw: Old (H) (Tel: 01698 376080; E-mail: wishaw-old@presbyteryofhamilton.co.uk)
Vacant   130 Glen Road, Wishaw ML2 7NP   01698 375134

86 Wishaw: St Mark's (E-mail: wishaw-stmarks@presbyteryofhamilton.co.uk)
Henry J.W. Findlay MA BD   1965 1967   Coltness Road, Wishaw ML2 7EX   01698 384596 (Tel)
                                                                           01698 386025 (Fax)

87 Wishaw: Thornlie (H) (E-mail: wishaw-thornlie@presbyteryofhamilton.co.uk)
Klaus O.F. Buwert LLB BD   1984 1999   West Thornlie Street, Wishaw ML2 7AR   01698 372356 (Tel)
                                          [E-mail: k.buwert@btinternet.com]   07801 533548 (Mbl)

Name	Charge			Address	Tel
Anderson, Catherine B. (Mrs) DCS	(Deaconess)	1944	1984	13 Mosshill Road, Bellshill ML4 1NQ	01698 745907
Baird, George W. MA	(Crimond with St Fergus)	1951	1986	42 Neilsland Drive, Motherwell ML1 3EB	01698 262088
Beattie, William G. BD BSc	(Hamilton St Andrew's)	1963	2002	33 Dungavel Gardens, Hamilton ML3 7PE	01698 423804
Black, John M. MA BD	(Coatbridge: Blairhill Dundyvan)	1995	2003	3 Grantown Avenue, Airdrie ML6 8HH	01236 750638
Brown, Allan B BD MTh	(Chaplain: Shotts Prison)	1974	2001	18 Don Drive, Livingston EH54 5LN	01698 299600
Cook, J. Stanley. BD Dip PSS	(Hamilton: West)			Mansend, 137A Old Manse Road, Netherton, Wishaw ML2 0EW [E-mail: stancook@blueyonder.co.uk]	
Cowper, Macknight C. MA BD STM	(East Kilbride West)	1947	1983	17 Manor Place, Edinburgh EH3 7DH	0131-225 6214
Cullen, William T. BA LTh	(Kilmarnock: St John's Onthank)	1984	1996	6 Laurel Wynd, Cambuslang, Glasgow G72 7BA	0141-641 4337
Fraser, James P.	(Strathaven Avendale Old and Drumclog)	1951	1988	26 Hamilton Road, Strathaven ML10 6JA	01357 522758
Gilchrist, Kay (Miss) BD	(Chaplain: Rachel House)	1996	1999	45 Hawthorn Drive, Craigneuk, Airdrie ML6 8AP	
Handley, John	(Motherwell: Clason Memorial)	1954	1993	12 Airbles Crescent, Motherwell ML1 3AR	01698 262733
Hunter, James E. LTh	(Blantyre: Livingstone Memorial)	1974	1997	57 Dalwhinnie Avenue, Blantyre, Glasgow G72 9NQ	01698 826177
King, Crawford S. MA	(Glenboig)	1958	1984	77 Faskine Avenue, Airdrie ML6 9EA	01236 761753
McAlpine, John BSc	(Auxiliary Minister)	1998	2004	201 Bonkle Road, Newmans, Wishaw ML2 9AA	01698 384610
McCabe, George	(Airdrie: High)	1963	1996	Flat 8, Park Court, 2 Craighouse Park, Edinburgh EH10 5LD	0131-447 9522
McDonald, John A. MA BD	(Cumbernauld: Condorrat)	1978	1997	17 Thomson Drive, Bellshill ML4 3ND	
Martin, James MA BD DD	(Glasgow: High Carntyne)	1946	1987	9 Magnolia Street, Wishaw ML2 7EQ	01698 385825
Melrose, J.H. Loudon MA BD MEd	(Gourock: High Gourock & Ashton [Assoc])	1955	1996	24 Avonbridge Drive, Hamilton ML3 7EJ	01698 891033
Munton, James G BA	(Coatbridge: Old Monkland)	1969	2002	2 Moorcroft Drive, Airdrie ML6 8ES [E-mail: jacjim@supanet.com]	01236 754848
Nelson, James R. BD	(Chapelhall)	1986	2003	4 Glen Orchy Place, Airdrie ML6 8QT	01236 766685
Niven, William LTCL	(Lesmahagow: Old)	1955	1994	92 Linden Lea, Hamilton ML3 9AG	01698 420653
Price, Peter O. CBE QHC BA FPhS	(Blantyre: Old)	1960	1996	22 Old Bothwell Road, Bothwell, Glasgow G71 8AW [E-mail: peteroprice@aol.com]	01698 854032
Rogerson, Stuart D. BSc BD	(Strathaven: West)	1980	2001	17 Westfield Place, Strathaven ML10 6XH [E-mail: srogerson@cnetwork.co.uk]	01357 523321

Salmond, James S. BA BD MTh ThD	1979 2003	(Holytown)	165 Torbothie Road, Shotts ML7 5NE	01501 826852
Thorne, Leslie W. BA LTh	1987 2001	(Coatbridge: Clifton)	'Hatherleigh', 9 Chatton Walk, Coatbridge ML5 4FH	01236 432241
Wilson, James H. LTh	1970 1996	(Cleland)	21 Austine Drive, Hamilton ML3 7YE	01698 457042

[E-mail: wilsonjh@blueyonder.co.uk]

Wyllie, Hugh R. MA DD FCIBS	1962 2000	(Hamilton: Old)	18 Chantinghall Road, Hamilton ML3 8NP	01698 420002
Zambonini, James LlADip	1997	Auxiliary Minister	100 Old Manse Road, Wishaw ML2 0EP	01698 350887

HAMILTON ADDRESSES

Airdrie
Broomknoll	Broomknoll Street
Clarkston	Forrest Street
Flowerhill	89 Graham Street
High	North Bridge Street
Jackson	Glen Road
New Monkland	Glenmavis
St Columba's	Thrashbush Road
The New Wellwynd	Wellwynd

Coatbridge
Blairhill Dundyvan	Blairhill Street
Calder	Calder Street
Clifton	Muiryhall Street x Jackson Street
Middle	Bank Street
Old Monkland	Woodside Street
St Andrew's	Church Street
Townhead	Crinan Crescent

East Kilbride
Claremont	High Common Road, St Leonard's
Greenhills	Greenhills Centre
Moncreiff	Calderwood Road
Mossneuk	Eden Drive
Old	Montgomery Street
South	Baird Hill, Murray
West	Kittoch Street
Westwood	Belmont Drive, Westwood

Hamilton
Burnbank	High Blantyre Road
Cadzow	Woodside Walk
Gilmour and Whitehill	Glasgow Road, Burnbank
	Abbotsford Road, Whitehill
Hillhouse	Clerkwell Road
North	Windmill Road
Old	Leechlee Road
St Andrew's	Avon Street
St John's	Duke Street
South	Strathaven Road
Trinity	Neilsland Square off North Road
West	Burnbank Road

Motherwell
Crosshill	Windmillhill Street x Airbles Street
Dalziel St Andrew's	Merry Street and Muir Street
Manse Road	Gavin Street
North	Chesters Crescent
St Margaret's	Shields Road
St Mary's	Avon Street
South Dalziel	504 Windmillhill Street

Uddingston
Burnhead	Laburnum Road
Old	Old Glasgow Road
Park	Main Street
Viewpark	Old Edinburgh Road

Wishaw
Cambusnethan North	Kirk Road
Old	Kirk Road
Chalmers	East Academy Street
Craigneuk and Belhaven	Craigneuk Street
Old	Main Street
St Mark's	Coltness Road
Thornlie	West Thornlie Street

(18) DUMBARTON

Meets at Dumbarton in Riverside Church Halls, on the first Tuesday of February, March, April, May, October, November, December, and on the second Tuesday of June and September (and April when the first Tuesday falls in Holy Week).

Clerk:	REV. DAVID P. MUNRO MA BD STM	14 Birch Road, Killearn, Glasgow G63 9SQ	01360 550098 (Tel)
		[E-mail: akph43@uk.uumail.com]	01360 551198 (Fax)
		[E-mail: dmunro@uk.uumail.com]	

Alexandria
Elizabeth W. Houston (Miss) MA BD DipEd   1985   1995   32 Ledrish Avenue, Balloch, Alexandria   G83 8JB   01389 751933

Arrochar linked with Luss
H. Dane Sherrard BD DMin   1971   1998   The Manse, Luss, Alexandria   G83 8NZ   01436 860240
[E-mail: dane@cadder.demon.co.uk]   07801 939138 (Mbl)

Baldernock (H)
Andrew P. Lees BD   1984   2002   The Manse, Bardowie, Milngavie, Glasgow   G62 6ES   01360 620471
[E-mail: thereverend@alees.fsnet.co.uk]

Bearsden: Killermont (H)
Alan J. Hamilton LLB BD   2003   8 Clathic Avenue, Bearsden, Glasgow   G61 2HF   0141-942 0021
[E-mail: alanj@hamilton63.freeserve.co.uk]

Bearsden: New Kilpatrick (H) (0141-942 8827)
David D. Scott BSc BD   1981   1999   51 Manse Road, Bearsden, Glasgow   G61 3PN   0141-942 0035
[E-mail: nkbearsden@biopenworld.com]

Bearsden: North (H) (0141-942 2818)
Keith T. Blackwood BD Dip Min   1997   5 Fintry Gardens, Bearsden, Glasgow   G61 4RJ   0141-942 0366
[E-mail: k2blackwood@btinternet.com]   07961 442972 (Mbl)

Bearsden: South (H)
John W.F. Harris MA   1967   1987   61 Drymen Road, Bearsden, Glasgow   G61 2SU   0141-942 0507
[E-mail: jwfh@globalnet.co.uk]   07711 573877 (Mbl)

Bearsden: Westerton Fairlie Memorial (H) (0141-942 6960)
Eric V. Hudson LTh   1971   1990   3 Canniesburn Road, Bearsden, Glasgow   G61 1PW   0141-942 2672
[E-mail: evhudson@canniesburn.fsnet.co.uk]

Bonhill (H) (01389 756516)
Ian H. Miller BA BD   1975   1 Glebe Gardens, Bonhill, Alexandria   G83 9NZ   01389 753039
[E-mail: ianmiller@bonhillchurch.freeserve.co.uk]

Cardross (H) (01389 841322)
Andrew J. Scobie MA BD   1963   1965   The Manse, Main Road, Cardross, Dumbarton   G82 5LB   01389 841289
[E-mail: ascobie55@cardross.dunbartonshire.co.uk]   07889 670252 (Mbl)

Clydebank: Abbotsford (E-mail: abbotsford@lineone.net; Website: http://www.abbotsford.org.uk)
Roderick G. Hamilton MA BD   1992   1996   35 Montrose Street, Clydebank   G81 2PA   0141-952 5151
[E-mail: rghamilton@ntlworld.com]

Clydebank: Faifley
Gregor McIntyre BSc BD — 1991 — Kirklea, Cochno Road, Hardgate, Clydebank G81 6PT — 01389 876836
[E-mail: mail@gregormcintyre.com]
Agnes Tait (Mrs) DCS — 2003 — 2 Lennox Drive, Faifley, Clydebank G81 5JU — 01389 873196

Clydebank: Kilbowie St Andrew's
Peggy Roberts (Mrs) BA BD — 2003 — 5 Melfort Avenue, Clydebank G81 2HX — 0141-951 2455
[E-mail: peggy.r@ntlworld.com]

Clydebank: Radnor Park (H)
Margaret J.B.Yule (Mrs) BD — 1992 — Church Manse, Spencer Street, Clydebank G81 3AS — 0141-951 1007
[E-mail: mjbyule@yahoo.co.uk]

Clydebank: St Cuthbert's (T) linked with Duntocher (H)
David Donaldson MA BD — 1969 2002 — The Manse, Roman Road, Duntocher, Clydebank G81 6BT — 01389 873471
[E-mail: david.donaldson3@btopenworld.com]

Craigrownie linked with Rosneath: St Modan's (H)
Vacant — Edenkiln, Argyll Road, Kilcreggan, Helensburgh G84 0JW — 01436 842274

Dalmuir: Barclay (0141-941 3988)
Vacant — Parkhall Road, Dalmuir, Clydebank G81 3RJ — 0141-941 3317

Dumbarton: Riverside (H) (01389 742551)
Robert J. Watt BD — 1994 2002 — 5 Kirkton Road, Dumbarton G82 4AS — 01389 762512
[E-mail: robertjwatt@blueyonder.co.uk]

Dumbarton: St Andrew's (H)
Leslie G. Donaghy
BD DipMin PGCE FSAScot — 1990 1998 — 17 Mansewood Drive, Dumbarton G82 3EU — 01389 604259 / 07654 553473 (Pager)
[E-mail: info@bellsmyre.co.uk]

Dumbarton: West Kirk (H)
Christine Liddell (Miss) BD — 1999 — 3 Havoc Road, Dumbarton G82 4JW — 01389 604840
[E-mail: thewestkirk@blueyonder.co.uk]

Duntocher (H) See Clydebank: St Cuthbert's

Garelochhead (01436 810589)
Alastair S. Duncan MA BD — 1989 — Old School Road, Garelochhead, Helensburgh G84 0AT — 01436 810022
[E-mail: gpc@churchuk.fsnet.co.uk]

Helensburgh: Park (H) (01436 674825)
James H. Brown BD — 1977 — 35 East Argyle Street, Helensburgh G84 7EL — 01436 672209 / 07941 173299 (Mbl)
[E-mail: jh@jhbrown.freeserve.co.uk]

Helensburgh: St Columba (H)
Frederick M. Booth LTh — 1970 1982 — 46 Suffolk Street, Helensburgh G84 9QZ — 01436 672054

Helensburgh: The West Kirk (H) (01436 676880)
David W. Clark MA BD — 1975 1986 — 37 Campbell Street, Helensburgh G84 9NH
[E-mail: clarkdw@lineone.net] — 01436 674063

Jamestown (H)
Norma Moore (Ms) MA BD — 1995 2004 — 26 Kessog's Gardens, Balloch, Alexandria G83 8QJ
[E-mail: norma.moore5@btinternet.com] — 01389 756447

Kilmaronock Gartocharn
Vacant — Kilmaronock Manse, Alexandria G83 8SB — 01360 660295

Luss See Arrochar

Milngavie: Cairns (H) (0141-956 4868)
Andrew Frater BA BD — 1987 1994 — 4 Cairns Drive, Milngavie, Glasgow G62 8AJ
[E-mail: office@cairnschurch.org.uk] — 0141-956 1717

Milngavie: St Luke's (0141-956 4226)
Ramsay B. Shields BA BD — 1990 1997 — 70 Hunter Road, Milngavie, Glasgow G62 7BY
[E-mail: rbshields@ntlworld.com] — 0141-577 9171 (Tel) 0141-577 9181 (Fax)

Milngavie: St Paul's (H) (0141-956 4405)
Fergus C. Buchanan MA BD — 1982 1988 — 8 Buchanan Street, Milngavie, Glasgow G62 8DD
[E-mail: f.c.buchanan@ntlworld.com] — 0141-956 1043

Old Kilpatrick Bowling
Jeanette Whitecross (Mrs) BD — 2002 — The Manse, Dumbarton Road, Old Kilpatrick, Glasgow G60 5JQ
[E-mail: jeanettewx@yahoo.com] — 01389 873130

Renton: Trinity (H)
Ian Wilkie BD PGCE — 2001 — 38 Main Street, Renton, Dumbarton G82 4PU
[E-mail: rtpccofs@aol.com] — 01389 752017 07751 155552 (Mbl)

Rhu and Shandon (H)
J. Colin Caskie BA BD — 1977 2002 — 11 Ardenconnel Way, Rhu, Helensburgh G84 8LX
[E-mail: colin@jcaskie.freeserve.co.uk] — 01436 820213

Rosneath: St Modan's See Craigrownie

Name	Charge	Ord	App	Address	Tel
Crombie, W.M.D. MA BD	(Calton New with St Andrew's)	1947	1987	32 Westbourne Drive, Bearsden, Glasgow G61 4BH	0141-943 0235
Dalton, Mark F. BD DipMin	Chaplain: Royal Navy	2002		The Chaplaincy, HM Naval Base Clyde, Faslane, Helensburgh G84 8HL	01436 674321 ext. 6216
Davidson, Professor Robert MA BD DD FRSE	(University of Glasgow)	1956	1991	30 Dumgoyne Drive, Bearsden, Glasgow G61 3AP	0141-942 1810
Easton, I.A.G. MA FIPM	Lecturer	1945	1988	6 Edgehill Road, Bearsden, Glasgow G61 3AD	0141-942 4214
Ferguson, Archibald M. MSc PhD CEng FRINA	Auxiliary Minister with Clerk	1989	2004	The Whins, Barrowfield, Cardross, Dumbarton G82 5NL [E-mail: archieferguson@supanet.com]	01389 841517
Hamilton, David S.M. MA BD STM	(University of Glasgow)	1958	1996	2 Roselea Drive, Milngavie, Glasgow G62 8HQ	0141-956 1839
Houston, Peter M. FPhS	(Renfrew Old)	1952	1997	25 Honeysuckle Lane, Jamestown, Alexandria G83 8PL	01389 721165 (Mbl) 07770 390936
Jack, Robert MA BD	(Bearsden: Killermont)	1950	1996	142 Turnhill Drive, Erskine PA8 7AH	0141-812 8370
Lawson, Alexander H. ThM ThD FPhS	(Clydebank: Kilbowie)	1950	1988	1 Glebe Park, Manswood, Dumbarton G82 3HE	01389 742030
McFadzean, Iain MA BD	Chaplain: Royal Navy	1989	1999	Lochhaven, Portincaple, Garelochhead, Helensburgh G84 0EU	01436 810811
McIntyre, J. Ainslie MA BD	(University of Glasgow)	1963	1984	60 Bonnaughton Road, Bearsden, Glasgow G61 4DB [E-mail: jamcintyre@hotmail.com]	0141-942 5143 (Mbl) 07050 295103
Mackenzie, Ian M. MA	(BBC)	1967	1989	1 Glennan Gardens, Helensburgh G84 8XT	01436 673429
Morton, Andrew Q. MA BSc BD FRSE	(Culross and Torryburn)	1949	1987	4 Upper Adelaide Street, Helensburgh G84 7HT	01436 675152
Munro, David P. MA BD STM	(Bearsden: North)	1953	1996	14 Birch Road, Killearn, Glasgow G63 9SQ	01360 550098
Paul, Alison (Miss) MA BD Dip Theol	(Rhu and Shandon)	1986	2001	30 Perrays Drive, Lennox Gardens, Dumbarton G82 5HT	01389 733698
Rae, Scott M. MBE BD CPS	Chaplain: Royal Navy	1976	2002	HMS *Neptune*, Faslane, Helensburgh G84 8HL	
Ramage, Alistair E. BA ADB CertEd	Auxiliary Minister with Clerk	1996	2004	6 Claremont Gardens, Milngavie, Glasgow G62 6PG [E-mail: a.ramage@gcal.ac.uk]	0141-956 2897
Spence, C.K.O. MC TD MA BD	(Craigrownie)	1949	1983	8B Cairndhu Gardens, Helensburgh G84 8PG	01436 678838
Steven, Harold A.M. LTh FSA Scot	(Baldernock)	1970	2001	9 Cairnhill Road, Bearsden, Glasgow G61 1AT	0141-942 1598
Wright, Malcolm LTh	(Craigrownie with Rosneath St Modan's)	1970	2003	30 Clairinsh, Drumkinnon Gate, Balloch, Alexandria G83 8SE	010389 720338

DUMBARTON ADDRESSES

Clydebank
Abbotsford	Town Centre
Faifley	Faifley Road
Kilbowie St Andrew's	Kilbowie Road
Radnor Park	Radnor Street
St Cuthbert's	Linnvale

Dumbarton
Riverside	High Street
St Andrew's	Aitkenbar Circle
West Kirk	West Bridgend

Helensburgh
Park	Charlotte Street
St Columba	Sinclair Street
The West Kirk	Colquhoun Square

(19) ARGYLL

Meets at Inveraray or Ardrishaig or Tarbert, Loch Fyne on the first Tuesday or Wednesday of March, June, September and December.

Clerk:	MR IAN MACLAGAN LLB FSAScot	Carmonadh, Eastlands Road, Rothesay, Isle of Bute PA20 9JZ [E-mail: argyll.pres@uk.uumail.com]	01700 503015
Depute Clerk:	REV. GEORGE G. CRINGLES BD	St Oran's Manse, Connel, Oban PA37 1PJ [E-mail: george.cringles@btinternet.com]	01631 710242
Treasurer:	MRS PAM GIBSON	Allt Ban, Portsonachan, Dalmally PA33 1BJ [E-mail: lorraine.macgillivray@tesco.net]	01866 833344

Appin linked with Lismore
John A.H. Murdoch BA BD DPSS   1979   2001   The Manse, Appin PA38 4DD   01631 730206

Ardchattan (H)
Jeffrey A. McCormick BD   1984   Ardchattan Manse, Ardchattan, Oban PA37 1RG   01631 710364

Ardrishaig (H) linked with South Knapdale
David Carruthers BD   1998   The Manse, Park Road, Ardrishaig, Lochgilphead PA30 8HD   01546 603269

Campbeltown: Highland (H)
Michael J. Lind LLB BD   1984   1997   Highland Church Manse, Kirk Street, Campbeltown PA28 6BN
[E-mail: mijalind@hotmail.com]   01586 551146

Campbeltown: Lorne and Lowland (H)
Philip D. Burroughs   Castlehill, Campbeltown PA28 6AN   01586 552468

Coll linked with Connel
George G. Cringles BD   1981   2002   St Oran's Manse, Connel, Oban PA37 1PJ
[E-mail: george.cringles@btinternet.com]   01631 710242

Colonsay and Oronsay linked with Kilbrandon and Kilchattan (www.islandchurches.org.uk)
Freda Marshall (Mrs) BD FCII   1993   1997   The Manse, Winterton Road, Balvicar, Oban PA34 4TF
[E-mail: mail@freda.org.uk]   01852 300240

Connel See Coll

Craignish linked with Kilninver and Kilmelford
T. Alastair McLachlan BSc   1972   2004   The Manse, Kilmelford, Oban PA34 4XA
[E-mail: talastair@aol.com]   01852 200565

Cumlodden, Lochfyneside and Lochgair
Roderick MacLeod
MA BD PhD(Edin) PhD(Open)   1966   1985   Cumlodden Manse, Furnace, Inveraray PA32 8XU   01499 500288
[E-mail: revroddy@yahoo.co.uk]

Dunoon: St John's linked with Sandbank (H)
Joseph Stewart LTh   1979   1989   23 Bullwood Road, Dunoon PA23 7QJ   01369 702128

Dunoon: The High Kirk (H) linked with Innellan linked with Toward
David P. Anderson BSc BD   2002   7A Matheson Lane, Innellan, Dunoon PA23 7SH   01369 830276

Gigha and Cara (H) (GD)
Rosemary Legge (Mrs) BSc BD MTh   1992   2002   The Manse, Isle of Gigha PA41 7AA   01583 505245

Glassary and Kilmartin and Ford
Vacant   The Manse, Kilmichael Glassary, Lochgilphead PA31 8QA   01546 606926

Glenaray and Inveraray
W. Brian Wilkinson MA BD   1968   1993   The Manse, Inveraray PA32 8XT   01499 302060
[E-mail: brianwilkinson@freeuk.com]

Glenorchy and Innishael linked with Strathfillan
John Shedden CBE BD DipPSS   1971   2001   The Manse, Dalmally PA33 1AA   01838 200386
[E-mail: john@swonline.fsnet.co.uk]

Innellan (H)   See Dunoon: The High Kirk

Iona linked with Kilfinichen and Kilvickeon and the Ross of Mull
Sydney S. Graham BD DipYL MPhil   1987   2004   The Manse, Bunessan, Isle of Mull PA67 6DW   01681 700227
[E-mail: syd@graythorn.sol.co.uk]

Jura (GD)
Vacant   Church of Scotland Manse, Craighouse, Isle of Jura PA60 7XG   01496 820384

Kilarrow (H) linked with Kilmeny
Paul R. Read BSc MA   2000   2003   The Manse, Bowmore, Isle of Islay PA43 7LH   01496 810271
[E-mail: prr747@aol.com]

Kilberry linked with Tarbert (H)
William Gray LTh   1971   2003   Glenakil Cottage, Tarbert, Argyll PA29 6XX   01880 820156
[E-mail: gray98@hotmail.com]

Kilbrandon and Kilchattan See Colonsay and Oronsay

Kilcalmonell
Vacant — The Manse, Whitehouse, Tarbert, Argyll PA29 6XS — 01880 730224

Kilchoman (GD) linked with Portnahaven (GD)
Stephen Fulcher BA MA 1993 2003 — Main Street, Port Charlotte, Isle of Islay PA48 7TX — 01496 850241
[E-mail: scr@fish.co.uk]

Kilchrenan and Dalavich linked with Muckairn
Margaret R.M. Millar (Miss) BTh 1977 1996 — Muckairn Manse, Taynuilt PA35 1HW — 01866 822204
[E-mail: macoje@aol.com]

Kildalton and Oa (GD) (H)
Norman MacLeod BTh 1999 — Port Ellen, Isle of Islay PA42 7DB — 01496 302447
[E-mail: normanmacleod@btopenworld.com]

Kilfinan linked with Kyles (H)
David J. Kellas MA BD 1966 1998 — The Manse, Tighnabruaich PA21 2DX — 01700 811887 (Tel/Fax)
[E-mail: davidkellas@britishlibrary.net]

Kilfinichen and Kilvickeon and the Ross of Mull See Iona

Killean and Kilchenzie (H)
John H. Paton JP BSc BD 1983 1984 — The Manse, Muasdale, Tarbert, Argyll PA29 6XD — 01583 421249
[E-mail: jonymar@globalnet.co.uk]

Kilmeny See Kilarrow

Kilmodan and Colintraive
Robert M. Donald BA 1969 1998 — Kilmodan Manse, Glendaruel, Colintraive PA22 3AA — 01369 820232 (Tel/Fax)
[E-mail: robdon@colglen.freeserve.co.uk]

Kilmore (GD) and Oban
Andrew B. Campbell BD DPS MTh 1979 — Kilmore and Oban Manse, Ganavan Road, Oban PA34 5TU — 01631 562322
[E-mail: revabc@obancofs.freeserve.co.uk]
Elizabeth Gibson (Mrs) MA MLitt BD (Assoc) 2003 — Rudha-na-Cloiche, Esplanade, Oban PA34 5AQ — 01631 562759
[E-mail: egibson@fish.co.uk]

Kilmun (St Munn's) (H) linked with Strone (H) and Ardentinny
Franklin G. Wyatt MA MDiv DMin 1974 2004 — The Manse, Blairmore, Dunoon PA23 8TE — 01369 840313
[E-mail: mac84@tiscali.co.uk]

Kilninver and Kilmelford See Craignish

Kirn (H)
Grahame M. Henderson BD 1974 2004 Stewart Street, Kirn, Dunoon PA23 8DS 01369 702220
[E-mail: ghende5884@aol.com]

Kyles See Kilfinan
Lismore See Appin

Lochgilphead
Vacant Parish Church Manse, Manse Brae, Lochgilphead PA31 8QZ 01546 602238

Lochgoilhead (H) and Kilmorich
James Macfarlane PhD 1991 2000 The Manse, Lochgoilhead, Cairndow PA24 8AA 01301 703059
[E-mail: macfarlane-cofs@beeb.net]

Muckairn See Kilchrenan

Mull, Isle of, Kilninian and Kilmore linked with Salen (H) and Ulva
linked with Tobermory (GD) (H) linked with Torosay (H) and Kinlochspelvie
Alan T. Taylor BD 1980 Erray Road, Tobermory, Isle of Mull PA75 6PS 01688 302226
01688 302037 (Fax)
[E-mail: tobminister@aol.com]
Robert C. Nelson BA BD (Assoc) 1980 2003 Trewince, Western Road, Strongarbh, Tobermory, 01688 302356
Isle of Mull PA75 6RA
[E-mail: robertnelson@onetel.net.uk]

North Knapdale
Vacant Church of Scotland Manse, Tayvallich, Lochgilphead PA31 8PN 01546 870611

Portnahaven See Kilchoman

Rothesay: Trinity (H)
Samuel McC. Harris BA BD 1974 2004 12 Crichton Road, Rothesay, Isle of Bute PA20 9JR 01700 503010

Saddell and Carradale (H) linked with Skipness
Vacant The Manse, Carradale, Campbeltown PA28 6QN 01583 431253

Salen and Ulva See Mull
Sandbank See Dunoon: St John's
Skipness See Saddell and Carradale
South Knapdale See Ardrishaig

Southend (H)
Martin R. Forrest BA MA BD   1988   2001   St Blaans Manse, Southend, Campbeltown PA28 6RQ   01586 830274
[E-mail: jmr.forrest@btopenworld.com]

Strachur and Strathlachlan
Robert K. Mackenzie MA BD PhD   1976   1998   The Manse, Strachur, Cairndow PA27 8DG   01369 860246
[E-mail: rkmackenzie@strachurmanse.fsnet.co.uk]

Strathfillan See Glenorchy
Strone and Ardentinny See Kilmun

Tarbert See Kilberry

The United Church of Bute
Iain M. Goring BSc BD   1976   2003   10 Bishop Terrace, Rothesay, Isle of Bute PA20 9HF   01700 502407
[E-mail: iain.goring@ukonline.co.uk]

Tiree (GD)
Vacant   The Manse, Scarinish, Isle of Tiree PA77 6TN   01879 220377

Tobermory See Mull
Torosay and Kinlochspelvie See Mull
Toward (H) See Dunoon: The High Kirk

Name			Position	Address	Phone
Bristow, W.H.G. BEd HDipRE DipSpecEd	1951	2002	Part-time Hospital Chaplain: Campbeltown	Laith Cottage, Southend, Campbeltown PA28 6RU	01586 830667
Campbell, Margaret M. (Miss) DCS	1948	1991	(Deaconess)	Tigh-an-Rudha, Pier Road, Port Ellen, Isle of Islay PA42 7DJ	01496 302006
Carmichael, Robert C.M. MA	1957	1997	(Craignish with Kilninver and Kilmelford)	13 The Glebe, Kilmelford, Oban PA34 4AF	01852 200346
Cumming, David P.L. MA	1965	2004	(Kilmodan and Colintraive)	Shillong, Tarbat Ness Road, Portmahomack, Tain IV20 1YA	01862 871794
Dunlop, Alistair J. MA FSAScot	1986	2001	(Saddell and Carradale)	[E-mail: alistair.dunlop@ntlworld.com]	
Erskine, Austin U.			(Anwoth and Girthon with Borgue)	99 Sandhaven, Sandbank, Dunoon PA23 8QW [E-mail: austin@erskine81.freeserve.co.uk]	01369 701295
Fenemore, John H.C.	1980	1993	(Edinburgh Colinton Mains)	Seaford Cottage, 74E Shore Road, Innellan, Dunoon PA23 7TR	01369 830678
Forrest, Alan B. MA	1956	1993	(Uphall: South)	126 Shore Road, Innellan, Dunoon PA23 7SX	01369 830424
Forrest, Janice (Mrs) DCS			Part-time Hospital Chaplain: Campbeltown	St Blaans Manse, Southend, Campbeltown PA28 6RQ	01586 830274
Gibson, Frank S. BL BD STM DSWA DD	1963	1995	(Kilarrow with Kilmeny)	163 Gilbertstoun, Edinburgh EH15 2RG	0131-657 5208
Gisbey, John E. MA BD MSc	1964	2002	(Thornhill)	Kames Haven, Chapel Lane, Isle of Bute PA20 0LQ	01700 503346
Grainger, Ian G.	1985	1991	(Maxton with Newtown)	Seaview, Ardtun, Bunessan, Isle of Mull PA67 6DH	01681 700457
Hamilton, Patrick T.R. MA	1948	1979	(East Kilbride South)	La Madrugada, Tighnabruaich PA21 2BE	01700 811586
Henderson, Charles M.	1952	1989	(Campbeltown Highland)	Springbank House, Askomill Walk, Campbeltown PA28 6EP	01586 552759
Hood, H. Stanley C. MA BD	1966	2000	(London: Crown Court)	10 Dalriada Place, Kilmichael Glassary, Lochgilphead PA31 8QA	01546 606168
Inglis, Donald B.C. MA MEd BD	1975	2000	(Turriff St Andrew's)	'Lindores', 11 Bullwood Road, Dunoon PA23 7QJ [E-mail: dbcinglis@aol.com]	01369 701334

Name			(Parish)	Address	Tel.
Lamont, Archibald	1952	1994	(Kilcalmonell with Skipness)	8 Achlonan, Taynuilt PA35 1JJ	01866 822385
Lang, I. Pat (Miss) BSc	1996	2003	(Dunoon: The High Kirk)	37 Crawford Drive, Glasgow G15 6TW [E-mail: patlang@tinyworld.co.uk]	0141-944 2240
MacKechnie, J.M. MBE MA	1938	1978	(Kilchrenan and Dalavich)	Eastwing, Manton Grounds, Windermere, Cumbria	
Mackenzie, Iain MA BD	1967	2000	(Tarbat)	3 Southern Beeches, Sandbank, Dunoon PA23 8PD [E-mail: iandg@imackenzie.fsnet.co.uk]	01369 703507
Miller, Harry Galbraith MA BD	1941	1985	(Iona and Ross of Mull)	16 Lobnitz Avenue, Renfrew PA4 0TG	0141-886 2147
Montgomery, David	1961	1996	(North Knapdale)	Flat 1, 99 Quarry Street, Hamilton ML3 7AG	01698 200029
Morrison, Angus W. MA BD	1959	1999	(Kildalton and Oa)	1 Livingstone Way, Port Ellen, Isle of Islay PA42 7EP	01496 300043
Pollock, William MA BD PhD	1987	2002	(Isle of Mull Parishes)	Correay, Salen, Aros, Isle of Mull PA72 6JF [E-mail: wpollock@salen.freeserve.co.uk]	01680 300507
Ritchie, Malcolm A.	1955	1990	(kilbrandon and Kilchattan)	Roadside Cottage, Tayvallich, Lochgilphead PA31 8PN	01546 870616
Ritchie, Walter M.	1973	1999	(Uphall: South)	8 The Walled Garden, Achnaba, Lochgilphead PA31 8UG	01546 602941
Spencer, John MA BD	1962	2001	(Dumfries: Lincluden with Holywood)	Rhugarbh Cottage, North Shian, Appin PA38 4BA	01631 730416
Stewart, Jean E. (Mrs)	1983	1989	(Kildalton and Oa)	Tigh-na-Truain, Port Ellen, Isle of Islay PA42 7AH	01496 302068
Troup, Harold J.G. MA	1951	1980	(Garelochhead)	Tighshee, Isle of Iona PA76 6SP	01681 700309
Watson, James LTh	1968	1994	(Bowden with Lilliesleaf)	7 Lochan Avenue, Kirn, Dunoon PA23 8HT	01369 702851

Communion Sundays

Ardrishaig — 4th Apr, 1st Nov
Campbeltown
  Highland — 1st May, Nov
  Lorne and Lowland — 1st May, Nov
Craignish — 1st Jun, Nov
Cumlodden, Lochfyneside
  and Lochgair — 1st May, 3rd Nov
Dunoon
  St John's — 1st Mar, Jun, Nov
  The High Kirk — 1st Feb, Jun, Oct
Gigha and Cara — 1st May, Nov
Glassary, Kilmartin and Ford — 1st Apr, Sep
Glenaray and Inveraray — 1st Apr, Jul, Oct, Dec
Innellan — 1st Mar, Jun, Sep, Dec
Inverlussa and Bellanoch — 2nd May, Nov
Jura — Passion Sun., 2nd Jul, 3rd Nov

Kilarrow — 1st Mar, Jun, Sep, Dec
Kilberry with Tarbert — 1st May, Oct
Kilcalmonell — 1st Jul, 3rd Nov
Kilchoman — 1st Jul, 2nd Dec, Easter
Kildalton — Last Jan, Jun, Oct, Easter
Kilfinan — Last Apr, Oct
Killean and Kilchenzie — 1st Mar, Jul, Oct
Kilmeny — 2nd May, 3rd Nov
Kilmodan and
  Colintraive — 1st Apr, Sep
Kilmun — Last Jun, Nov
Kilninver and Kilmelford — Last Feb, Jun, Oct
Kirn — 2nd Jun, Oct
Kyles — 1st May, Nov
Lochgair — Last Apr, Oct
Lochgilphead — 2nd Oct (Gaelic), 1st Apr, Nov

Lochgoilhead and
  Kilmorich — 2nd Mar, Jun, Sep, Nov
North Knapdale — 1st Aug, Easter
Portnahaven — 3rd Oct, 2nd May
Rothesay Trinity — 3rd Jul
Saddell and Carradale — 1st Feb, May, Nov
Sandbank — 2nd May, 1st Nov
Skipness — 1st Jan, May, Nov
Southend — 2nd May, Nov
South Knapdale — 1st Jun, Dec
Strachur and Strathlachlan — 4th Apr, 1st Nov
Strone and Ardentinny — 1st Mar, Jun, Nov
Tayvallich — Last Feb, Jun, Oct
The United Church of Bute — 2nd May, Nov
Toward — 1st Feb, May, Nov
Last Feb, May, Aug, Nov

(22) FALKIRK

Meets at St Andrew's West, Falkirk, on the first Tuesday of September, October, November, December and March, and on the fourth Tuesday of January and June; and in Kildrum Church, Cumbernauld on the first Tuesday in May.

Clerk:	REV. IAN W. BLACK MA BD		Zetland Manse, Ronaldshay Crescent, Grangemouth FK3 9JH [E-mail: akph51@uk.uumail.com]	01324 472868 01324 471656 (Presby)
Depute Clerk:	REV. ROBERT S.T. ALLAN LLB DipLP BD		9 Major's Loan, Falkirk FK1 5QF	01324 625124
Treasurer:	MR. I. MACDONALD		1 Jones Avenue, Larbert FK5 3ER	01324 553603

Airth (H)
Richard J. Hammond BA BD	1993	2002	The Manse, Airth, Falkirk FK2 8LS	01324 831474

Blackbraes and Shieldhill
James H.D.C. Drysdale LTh	1987	1997	Shieldhill, Falkirk FK1 2EG [E-mail: jmdrysdl1@aol.com]	01324 621938

Bo'ness: Old (H)
David S. Randall BA BD	2003		10 Dundas Street, Bo'ness EH51 0DG	01506 822206

Bo'ness: St Andrew's
Albert O. Bogle BD MTh	1981		St Andrew's Manse, 11 Erngath Road, Bo'ness EH51 9DP [E-mail: a.bogle@blueyonder.co.uk] [Website: http://www.standonline.org.uk]	01506 822195

Bonnybridge: St Helen's (H) (01324 815756)
Alisdair T. MacLeod-Mair MEd DipTheol	2002		133 Falkirk Road, Bonnybridge FK4 1BA	01324 812621 (Tel/Fax)

Bothkennar and Carronshore
Vacant			11 Hunter Place, Greenmount Park, Carronshore, Falkirk FK2 8QS	01324 570525

Brightons (H)
Scott R.McL. Kirkland BD MAR	1996		The Manse, Maddiston Road, Brightons, Falkirk FK2 0JP [E-mail: scott@kirklands.net]	01324 712062 01324 713855 (2nd num)

Carriden (H)
R. Gordon Reid BSc BD AMIEE	1993		The Spires, Foredale Terrace, Carriden, Bo'ness EH51 9LW	01506 822141

Cumbernauld: Abronhill (H)
Joyce A. Keyes (Mrs) BD	1996	2003	26 Ash Road, Cumbernauld, Glasgow G67 3ED	01236 723833
Linda Black (Miss) DCS			148 Rowan Road, Cumbernauld, Glasgow G67 3DA	01236 786265

Cumbernauld: Condorrat (H)
Vacant
Janette McNaughton (Miss) DCS
11 Rosehill Drive, Cumbernauld, Glasgow G67 4FD — 01236 721464
4 Dunellan Avenue, Moodiesburn, Glasgow G69 0GB — 01236 870180

Cumbernauld: Kildrum (H)
Vacant
David Nicholson DCS
Clouden Road, Cumbernauld, Glasgow G67 2JQ — 01236 723204
2D Doon Side, Kildrum, Cumbernauld, Glasgow G67 2HX — 01236 732260
[E-mail: deacdave@btopenworld.com]

Cumbernauld: Old (H)
Catriona Ogilvie (Mrs) MA BD   1999
Valerie Cuthbertson (Miss) DCS
Baronhill, Cumbernauld, Glasgow G67 2SD — 01236 721912
105 Bellshill Road, Motherwell ML1 3SJ — 01698 259001

Cumbernauld: St Mungo's
Neil MacKinnon BD   1990   1999
The Manse, Fergusson Road, Cumbernauld, Glasgow G67 1LS — 01236 721513
[E-mail: neil@box200.fsnet.co.uk]
Ronald M. Mackinnon DCS
71 Cromarty Road, Cairnhill, Airdrie ML6 9RL — 01236 762024

Denny: Dunipace (H)
Jean W. Gallacher (Miss) BD CMin CTheol   1989
Dunipace Manse, Denny FK6 6QJ — 01324 824540

Denny: Old
John Murning BD   1988   2002
31 Duke Street, Denny FK6 6NR — 01324 824508

Denny: Westpark (H) (Website: http://www.westparkchurch.org.uk)
Andrew Barrie BSc BD   1984   2000
13 Baxter Crescent, Denny FK6 5EZ — 01324 876224
[E-mail: andrew.barrie@blueyonder.co.uk]

Falkirk: Bainsford
Michael R. Philip BD   1978   2001
1 Valleyview Place, Newcarron Village, Falkirk FK2 7JB — 01324 621087
[E-mail: mrphilip@btinternet.com]

Falkirk: Camelon
Stuart Sharp MTheol DipPA   2001
Margaret Corrie (Miss) DCS
30 Cotland Drive, Falkirk FK2 7GE — 01324 623631
44 Sunnyside Street, Falkirk FK1 4BH — 01324 670656

Falkirk: Erskine (H)
Glen D. Macaulay BD   1999
Burnbrae Road, Falkirk FK1 5SD — 01324 623701

Falkirk: Grahamston United (H)
Neil W. Barclay BSc BEd BD   1986   2001
30 Russel Street, Falkirk FK2 7HS — 01324 624461

Falkirk: Laurieston linked with Redding and Westquarter
Geoffrey H. Smart LTh — 1994 2002 — 11 Polmont Road, Laurieston, Falkirk FK2 9QQ — 01324 621196

Falkirk: Old and St Modan's (H)
Robert S.T. Allan LLB DipLP BD — 1991 2003 — 9 Major's Loan, Falkirk FK1 5QF — 01324 625124
Ronald W. Smith BA BEd BD (Assoc) — 1979 — 19 Neilson Street, Falkirk FK1 5AQ — 01324 621058

Falkirk: St Andrew's West (H)
Alastair M. Horne BSc BD — 1989 1997 — 1 Maggiewood's Loan, Falkirk FK1 5SJ — 01324 623308

Falkirk: St James'
Vacant — 13 Wallace Place, Falkirk FK2 7EN — 01324 622757

Grangemouth: Dundas
Vacant — 5 Abbotsgrange Road, Grangemouth FK3 9JD — 01324 482467
John J. Jenkinson JP LTCL — 1991 2002 — 8 Rosehall Terrace, Falkirk FK1 1PY — 01324 625498
ALCM DipEd DipSen (Aux)

Grangemouth: Kerse (H) (01324 482487)
Andrew C. Donald BD DPS — 1992 — 8 Naismith Court, Grangemouth FK3 9BQ — 01324 482109

Grangemouth: Kirk of the Holy Rood
David J. Smith BD DipMin — 1992 2003 — The Manse, Bowhouse Road, Grangemouth FK3 0EX — 01324 471595

Grangemouth: Zetland (H)
Ian W. Black MA BD — 1976 1991 — Ronaldshay Crescent, Grangemouth FK3 9JH — 01324 472868

Haggs (H)
Helen F. Christie (Mrs) BD — 1998 — 5 Watson Place, Dennyloanhead, Bonnybridge FK4 2BG — 01324 813786
David Wandrum (Aux) — 1993 2001 — 5 Cawder View, Carrickstone Meadows, Cumbernauld, Glasgow G68 0BN — 01236 723288

Larbert: East
Melville D. Crosthwaite BD DipEd DipMin — 1984 1995 — 1 Cortachy Avenue, Carron, Falkirk FK2 8DH — 01324 562402
Lorna MacDougall (Miss) MA (Aux) — 2003 — 34 Millar Place, Carron, Falkirk FK2 8QB — 01324 552739

Larbert: Old (H)
Clifford A.J. Rennie MA BD — 1973 1985 — The Manse, 38 South Broomage Avenue, Larbert FK5 3ED — 01324 562868

Larbert: West (H)
Gavin Boswell BTheol — 1993 1999 — 11 Carronvale Road, Larbert FK5 3LZ — 01324 562878

Muiravonside
Joan Ross (Miss) BSc BD PhD — 1999 — The Manse, South Brae, Main Road, Maddiston, Falkirk FK2 0LX — 01324 712876

Polmont: Old
Vacant — 3 Orchard Grove, Polmont, Falkirk FK2 0XE — 01324 713081

Redding and Westquarter See Falkirk: Laurieston

Slamannan
Raymond Thomson BD DipMin — 1992 — Slamannan, Falkirk FK1 3EN — 01324 851307

Stenhouse and Carron (H)
Robert K. Hardie MA BD — 1968 1969 — Stenhouse Church Manse, Church Street, Stenhousemuir, Larbert FK5 4BU — 01324 562393

Name	Year	Year	Position	Address	Phone
Blair, Douglas B. LTh	1969	2004	(Grangemouth: Dundas)	Flat 6, Hanover Grange, Forth Street, Grangemouth FK3 8LF	01324 484414
Brown, James BA BD DipHSW DipPsychol	1973	2001	(Abercorn with Dalmeny)	Fern Cottage, 3 Philpingstone Lane, Bo'ness EH51 9JP	01506 822454
Chalmers, George A. MA BD MLitt	1962	2002	(Catrine with Sorn)	3 Cricket Place, Brightons, Falkirk FK2 0HZ	01324 712030
Goodman, Richard A.	1976	1986	(Isle of Mull Associate)	13/2 Glenbrae Court, Falkirk FK1 1YT	01324 621315
Heriot, Charles R. JP BA	1962	1996	(Brightons)	20 Eastcroft Drive, Polmont, Falkirk FK2 0SU	01324 711352
Hill, Stanley LTh	1967	1998	(Muiravonside)	28 Creteil Court, Falkirk FK1 1UL	01324 634483
Holland, John C.	1998		(Strone and Ardentinny)	7 Polmont Park, Polmont, Falkirk FK2 0XT	01324 880109
Kellock, Chris N. MA BD	1976	1985	(Chaplain: RAF)	Chaplaincy Services, HQPTC, RAF Innsworth, Gloucester GL3 1EZ	
Kesting, Sheilagh M. (Miss) BA BD	1980	1993	(Ecumenical Relations)	12 Glenview Drive, Falkirk FK1 5JU	01324 671489
McCallum, John	1962	1998	(Falkirk: Irving Camelon)	11 Burnbrae Gardens, Falkirk FK1 5SB	01324 619766
McDonald, William G. MA BD	1959	1975	(Falkirk: Grahamston United)	38 St Mary Street, St Andrews KY16 8AZ	01334 470481
McDowall, Ronald J. BD	1980	2001	(Falkirk: Laurieston with Redding and Westquarter)	'Kailas', Windsor Road, Falkirk FK1 5EJ	01324 871947
Maclaren, William B. MA JP	1944	1983	(Bothkennar and Carronshore)	7 Malcolm Drive, Stenhousemuir, Larbert FK5 4JP	01324 551274
McMullin, Andrew MA	1960	1996	(Blackbraes and Shieldhill)	33 Eastcroft Drive, Polmont, Falkirk FK2 0SU	01324 624938
Martin, Neil DCS			(Deacon)	3 Strathmiglo Place, Stenhousemuir, Larbert FK5 4UQ	01324 551362
Mathers, Daniel L. BD	1982	2001	(Grangemouth: Charing Cross and West)	10 Ercall Road, Brightons, Falkirk FK2 0RS	01324 872253
Maxton, Ronald M. MA	1955	1995	(Dollar: Associate)	5 Rulley View, Denny FK6 6QQ	01324 825441
Miller, Elsie M. (Miss) DCS			(Deacon)	30 Swinton Avenue, Rowansbank, Baillieston, Glasgow G69 6JR	0141-771 0857
Munroe, Henry BA LTh LITl	1971	1988	(Denny Dunipace North with Old)	Viewforth, High Road, Maddiston, Falkirk FK2 0BL	01324 712446
Murray, Eric J.	1958	1995	(Larbert: East)	21 Redpath Drive, Greenmount Park, Carron, Falkirk FK5 8QL	01324 563764
Paul, Iain BSc PhD BD BD PhD	1976	1991	(Wishaw Craigneuk and Belhaven)	116 Tryst Road, Larbert FK5 4QJ	01324 562641
Scott, Donald H. BA BD	1987	2002	Prison Chaplain	Polmont Young Offenders' Institution, Newlands Road, Brightons, Falkirk FK2 0DE	01324 711558
Smith, Richard BD	1976	2002	(Denny Old)	Easter Wayside, 46 Kennedy Way, Airth, Falkirk FK2 8GB	01324 831386
Talman, Hugh MA	1943	1987	(Polmont Old)	Niagara, 70 Lawers Crescent, Polmont, Falkirk FK2 0RQ	01324 711240
Whiteford, Robert S. MA	1945	1986	(Shapinsay)	3 Wellside Court, Wellside Place, Falkirk FK1 5RG	01324 610562

FALKIRK ADDRESSES

Falkirk

Bainsford	Hendry Street, Bainsford	
Camelon	Dorrator Road and Glasgow Road	
Erskine	Cockburn Street x Hodge Street	
Grahamston	Bute Street	
Laurieston	Main Falkirk Road	
Old and St Modan's	Kirk Wynd	
St Andrew's West	Newmarket Street	
St James'	Thornhill Road x Firs Street	

Grangemouth

Charing Cross and West	Charing Cross
Dundas	Bo'ness Road
Kerse	Abbot's Road
Kirk of the Holy Rood	Bowhouse Road
Zetland	Ronaldshay Crescent

(23) STIRLING

Meets at the Moderator's Church on the second Thursday of September, and at Stirling Management Centre, Stirling University on the second Thursday of every other month except January, July and August when there is no meeting.

Clerk:	MOIRA G. MacCORMICK BA LTh Presbytery Office, St Columba's Church, Park Terrace, Stirling FK8 2NA 01786 449522 (Tel) 01786 473930 (Fax) (Mon–Fri: 9:30am–12 noon) [E-mail: akph75@uk.uumail.com] [E-mail: stirling-presbytery@uk.uumail.com]
Treasurer:	MR GILMOUR CUTHBERTSON 'Denovan', 1 Doune Road, Dunblane FK15 9AR 01786 823487

Aberfoyle (H) linked with Port of Menteith (H)

James Daniel Gibb BA LTh	1994	2000	The Manse, Loch Ard Road, Aberfoyle, Stirling FK8 3SZ [E-mail: rev.danny@gibb.fsworld.co.uk]	01877 382391

Alloa: North (H)

Elizabeth Clelland (Mrs) BD	2002	30 Claremont, Alloa FK10 2DF	01259 210403

Alloa: St Mungo's (H)

Alan F.M. Downie MA BD	1977	1996	37a Claremont, Alloa FK10 2DG [E-mail: alan@stmungos.freeserve.co.uk]	01259 213872
Marina Brown (Mrs) MA (Aux)	2000		3 Lover's Loan, Dollar FK14 7AB [E-mail: revmdb1711@btinternet.com]	01259 742870

Alloa: West

Irene C. Gillespie (Mrs) BD	1991	29 Claremont, Alloa FK10 2DF	01259 214204

Alva

James N.R. McNeil BSc BD	1990	1997	The Manse, 34 Ochil Road, Alva FK12 5JT	01259 760262

Balfron linked with Fintry (H)

John Turnbull LTh	1994	7 Station Road, Balfron, Glasgow G63 0SX	01360 440285

Balquhidder linked with Killin and Ardeonaig (H)

Minister				
John Lincoln MPhil BD	1986	1997	The Manse, Killin FK21 8TN [E-mail: gm0jol@zetnet.co.uk]	01567 820247

Bannockburn: Allan (H)

Jim Landels BD CertMin	1990	The Manse, Bogend Road, Bannockburn, Stirling FK7 8NP [E-mail: revjimlandels@btinternet.com]	01786 814692

Bannockburn: Ladywell (H)

Elizabeth M.D. Robertson (Miss) BD CertMin	1997	1997	57 The Firs, Bannockburn FK7 0EG [E-mail: lizr@tinyonline.uk]	01786 812467

Bridge of Allan (H) (01786 834155)

Vacant	19 Keir Street, Bridge of Allan, Stirling FK9 4QJ	01786 832093

Buchanan linked with Drymen

Alexander J. MacPherson BD	1986	1997	Buchanan Manse, Drymen, Glasgow G63 0AQ	01360 870212

Buchlyvie (H) linked with Gartmore (H)

Elaine H. MacRae (Mrs) BD	1985	2004	The Manse, Kippen, Stirling FK8 3DN	01786 871170

Callander (H) (Tel/Fax: 01877 331409)

Stanley A. Brook BD MTh	1977	2004	3 Aveland Park Road, Callander FK17 8FD [E-mail: stan_brook@hotmail.com]	01877 330097
June Cloggie (Mrs) (Aux)	1997	1998	11A Tulipan Crescent, Callander FK17 8AR	01877 331021

Cambusbarron: The Bruce Memorial (H)

Brian G. Webster BSc BD	1998	1998	14 Woodside Court, Cambusbarron, Stirling FK7 9PH [E-mail: revwebby@aol.com]	01786 450579

Clackmannan (H)

J. Gordon Mathew MA BD	1973	1999	The Manse, Port Street, Clackmannan FK10 4JH [E-mail: jgmathew@lineone.net]	01259 211255

Cowie (H) linked with Plean

Vacant	The Manse, Plean, Stirling FK7 8BX	01786 813287

Dollar (H) linked with Glendevon linked with Muckhart

Vacant	2 Manse Road, Dollar FK14 7AJ	01259 743432

Drymen See Buchanan

Dunblane: Cathedral (H)

Colin G. McIntosh BSc BD	1976	1988	Cathedral Manse, The Cross, Dunblane FK15 0AQ	01786 822205

Name	Ord	Ind	Address	Phone
Dunblane: St Blane's (H) Alexander B. Mitchell	1981	2003	49 Roman Way, Dunblane FK15 9DJ [E-mail: alex.mitchell6@btopenworld.com]	01786 822268
Fallin Eleanor D. Muir (Miss) MTheol DipPTheol	1986		4 King Street, Fallin, Stirling FK7 7JY	01786 812243
Fintry See Balfron				
Gargunnock linked with Kilmadock linked with Kincardine-in-Menteith Richard S. Campbell LTh	1993	2001	The Manse, Gargunnock, Stirling FK8 3BQ	01786 860678
Gartmore See Buchlyvie				
Glendevon See Dollar				
Killearn (H) Philip R.M. Malloch LLB BD	1970	1993	2 The Oaks, Killearn, Glasgow G63 9SF [E-mail: pmalloch@killearnkirk.freeserve.co.uk]	01360 550045
Killin and Ardeonaig (H) See Balquhidder				
Kilmadock See Gargunnock				
Kincardine-in-Menteith See Gargunnock				
Kippen (H) linked with Norrieston Gordon MacRae BA BD	1985	1998	The Manse, Kippen, Stirling FK8 3DN	01786 870229
Lecropt (H) William M. Gilmour MA BD	1969	1983	5 Henderson Street, Bridge of Allan, Stirling FK9 4NA	01786 832382
Logie (H) Regine U. Cheyne (Mrs) MA BSc BD	1988	2000	128 Causewayhead Road, Stirling FK9 5HJ	01786 463060
Menstrie (H) Vacant			The Manse, 7 Long Row, Menstrie FK11 7BA	01259 761461
Muckhart See Dollar				
Norrieston See Kippen				
Plean See Cowie				
Port of Menteith See Aberfoyle				
Sauchie and Coalsnaughton Alan T. McKean BD	1982	2003	19 Graygoran, Sauchie, Alloa FK10 3ET [E-mail: almack@freeuk.com]	01259 212037

Stirling: Allan Park South (H) linked with Church of the Holy Rude (H)
Morris C. Coull BD   1974   1996   22 Laurelhill Place, Stirling FK8 2JH   01786 473999

Stirling: Church of the Holy Rude (H) See Stirling: Allan Park South

Stirling: North (H)
Vacant   18 Shirra's Brae Road, Stirling FK7 0BA   01786 475378

Stirling: St Columba's (H) (01786 449516)
Kenneth G. Russell BD CCE   1986   2001   5 Clifford Road, Stirling FK8 2AQ
[E-mail: kenrussell11000@hotmail.com]   01786 475802

Stirling: St Mark's
Vacant   176 Drip Road, Stirling FK8 1RR   01786 473716

Stirling: St Ninian's Old (H)
Gary J. McIntyre BD DipMin   1993   1998   7 Randolph Road, Stirling FK8 2AJ   01786 474421

Stirling: Viewfield (T) (H)
Ian Taylor BD ThM   1995   7 Windsor Place, Stirling FK8 2HY
[E-mail: taylorian@btinternet.com]   01786 474534

Strathblane (H)
Alex H. Green MA BD   1986   1995   The Manse, Strathblane, Glasgow G63 9AQ   01360 770226

Tillicoultry (H)
James Cochrane LTh   1994   2000   The Manse, Dollar Road, Tillicoultry FK13 6PD
[E-mail: jc@cochranemail.co.uk]   01259 750340 / 01259 752951 (Fax)

Tullibody: St Serf's (H)
John Brown MA BD   1995   2000   16 Menstrie Road, Tullibody, Alloa FK10 2RG
[E-mail: john@browntj.fsnet.co.uk]   01259 213236

Aitken, E. Douglas MA	1961	1998	(Clackmannan)	1 Dolan Grove, Saline, Dunfermline KY12 9UP	01383 852730
Benson, James W. BA BD DipEd	1975	1996	(Balquhidder)	1 Sunnyside, Dunblane FK15 9HA	01786 822624
Blackley, Jean R.M. (Mrs) BD	1989	2001	(Banton with Twechar)	8 Rodders Grove, Alva, Clackmannan FK12 5RR	01259 760198
Burnett, John B.	1964	1985	(Dollar: Associate)	30 Manor House Road, Dollar FK14 7HB	01259 742892
Cheyne, Magnus	1963	1996	(Community Minister: Shetland)	128 Causewayhead Road, Stirling FK9 5HJ	01786 463060
Craig, Maxwell D. BD ThM	1966	2000	(Jerusalem: St Andrew's: Locum)	3 Queen's Avenue, Stirling FK8 2QY	01786 472319
Cruickshank, Alistair A.B. MA	1991	2004	(Auxiliary Minister)	2A Chapel Place, Dollar FK14 7DW	01259 742549
Doherty, Arthur James DipTh	1957	1993	(Fintry)	1 Murdiston Avenue, Callander FK17 8AY	

Name			Description	Address	Telephone
Fleming, Alexander F. MA BD	1966	1995	(Strathblane)	4 Horsburgh Avenue, Kilsyth, Glasgow G65 9BZ	01236 821461
Gallan, Alex MA	1955	1989	(Wishaw Cambusnethan North)	16 Dundas Road, Stirling FK9 5QQ	01786 470796
Izett, William A.F.	1968	2000	(Law)	1 Duke Street, Clackmannan FK10 4EF	01259 724203
Jamieson, G.T. BD	1936	1969	(Stirling: Viewfield)	10 Grendon Court, Snowdon Place, Stirling FK8 2JX	01786 461646
MacCormick, Moira G. BA LTh	1986	2003	(Buchlyvie with Gartmore)	12 Rankine Wynd, Tullibody, Alloa FK10 2UW	01259 724619
McIntosh, Hamish N.M. MA	1949	1987	(Fintry)	1 Forth Crescent, Stirling FK8 1LE	01786 470453
McRae, Malcolm H. MA PhD	1986	1994	(Coalsnaughton)	10B Victoria Place, Stirling FK8 2QU	
Nicol, John C. MA BD	1965	2002	(Bridge of Allan: Holy Trinity)	37 King O'Muirs Drive, Tullibody, Alloa FK10 3AY	01259 212305
Orrock, Archibald A. MA BD	1938	1982	(Teacher: Religious Instruction)	3 Kilbryde Court, Dunblane FK15 9AX	01786 822821
Ovens, Samuel B. BD	1982	1993	(Slamannan)	17 Swinburne Drive, Sauchie, Alloa FK10 3EQ	01259 222723
Paterson, John L. MA BD STM	1964	2003	(Linlithgow: St Michael's)	'Kirkmichael', 22 Waterfront Way, Stirling FK9 5GH [E-mail: lornandian.paterson@virgin.net]	01786 447165
Pryce, Stuart F.A.	1963	1997	(Dumfries: St George's)	36 Forth Park, Bridge of Allan, Stirling FK9 5NT	01786 831026
Reid, David T BA BD	1954	1993	(Cleish linked with Fossoway St Serf's and Devonside)	14 Argyle Park, Dunblane FK15 9DZ	01786 824863
Rennie, James B. MA	1959	1992	(Leochel Cushnie and Lynturk with Tough)	17 Oliphant Court, Riverside, Stirling FK8 1US	01786 841894
Robertson, Alex	1974	1993	(Baldernock)	4 Moray Park, Moray Street, Doune FK16 6DJ	
Sangster, Ernest G. BD ThM	1958	1997	(Alva)	6 Law Hill Road, Dollar FK14 7BG	01877 330565
Scott, James F.	1957	1997	(Dyce)	5 Gullipen View, Callander FK17 8HN	01786 825976
Scoular, J. Marshall	1954	1996	(Kippen)	2H Buccleuch Court, Dunblane FK15 0AH	
Sherry, George T. LTh	1977	2004	(Menstrie)	37 Moubray Gardens, Silver Meadows, Cambus, Alloa FK10 2NQ	01786 824944
Silcox, John R. BD	1976	1984	School Chaplain	Queen Victoria School, Dunblane FK15 0JA	01259 729001
Sinclair, James H. MA BD	1966	2004	(Auchencairn and Rerrick with Buittle and Kelton)	25 The Shielings, Cambus, Alloa FK10 2NN	
Stewart, Angus T. MA BD PhD	1962	1999	(Glasgow: Greenbank)	Mansefield, Station Road, Buchlyvie, Stirling FK8 3NE	01360 850117
Symington, Robert C. BA	1954	1997	(Community Minister: Lorn and Mull)	Flat 3, Belmont House, The Crescent, Dunblane FK15 0DW	01786 823902
Todd, A. Stewart MA BD DD	1952	1993	(Aberdeen: St Machar's Cathedral)	Ferntoun House, 11 Bedford Place, Alloa FK10 1LJ	01259 212737
Watson, Jean S. (Miss) MA	1993	2004	(Auxiliary Minister)	29 Strachan Crescent, Dollar FK14 7HL	01259 742872
Watt, Robert MA BD	1943	1982	(Aberdeen: Woodside South)	1 Coldstream Avenue, Dunblane FK15 9JN	01786 823632
Wright, John P. BD	1977	2000	(Glasgow: New Govan)	Plane Castle, Airth, Falkirk FK2 8SF	01786 480840

STIRLING ADDRESSES

Allan Park South	Dumbarton Road	St Columba's	Park Terrace	Viewfield	Barnton Street
Holy Rude	St John Street	St Mark's	Drip Road		
North	Springfield Road	St Ninian's Old	Kirk Wynd, St Ninians		

(24) DUNFERMLINE

Meets at Dunfermline, in the Abbey Church Hall, Abbey Park Place on the first Thursday of each month, except January, July and August when there is no meeting, and June when it meets on the last Thursday.

Clerk: REV. WILLIAM E. FARQUHAR BA BD   161 Main Street, Townhill, Dunfermline KY12 0EZ   01383 723835
[E-mail: akph46@uk.uumail.com]

Aberdour: St Fillan's (H)
Vacant   36 Bellhouse Road, Aberdour, Fife KY3 0TL   01383 860349

Ballingry and Lochcraig See Lochgelly: Macainsh: Team Ministry

Beath and Cowdenbeath: North (H)
David W. Redmayne BSc BD   2001   10 Stuart Place, Cowdenbeath KY4 9BN   01383 511033
[E-mail: david@redmayne.freeserve.co.uk]

Cairneyhill (H) (01383 882352) linked with Limekilns (H) (01383 873337)
Norman M. Grant BD   1990   The Manse, 10 Church Street, Limekilns, Dunfermline KY11 3HT   01383 872341
[E-mail: norman.grant@which.net]

Carnock and Oakley (H)
Elizabeth S.S. Kenny BD RGN SCM   1989   The Manse, Carnock, Dunfermline KY12 9JG   01383 850327
[E-mail: esskenny@ecosse.net]

Cowdenbeath: Trinity (H)
David G. Adams BD   1991   1999   66 Barclay Street, Cowdenbeath KY4 9LD   01383 515089
[E-mail: adams@cowden69.freeserve.co.uk]

Culross and Torryburn (H)
Thomas Moffat BSc BD   1976   2000   Culross, Dunfermline KY12 8JD   01383 880231
[E-mail: tsmoffat@fish.co.uk]

Dalgety (H) (01383 824092; E-mail: office@dalgety-church.co.uk; Website: http://www.dalgety-church.co.uk)
Donald G.B. McCorkindale BD DipMin   1992   2000   9 St Colme Drive, Dalgety Bay, Dunfermline KY11 9LQ   01383 822316 (Tel/Fax)
[E-mail: donald@dalgety-church.co.uk]

Dunfermline: Abbey (H) (Website: http://www.dunfabbey.freeserve.co.uk)
Alistair L. Jessamine MA BD   1979   1991   12 Garvock Hill, Dunfermline KY12 7UU   01383 721022

Dunfermline: Gillespie Memorial (H) (01383 621253; E-mail: gillespie.church@btopenworld.com)
A. Gordon Reid BSc BD   1982 1988   4 Killin Court, Dunfermline KY12 7XF   01383 723329
                                                                      [E-mail: reid501@fsmail.net]

Dunfermline: North
Gordon F.C. Jenkins MA BD PhD   1968 1998   13 Barbour Grove, Dunfermline KY12 9YB   01383 721061

Dunfermline: St Andrew's Erskine
Ann Allison BSc PhD BD   2000   71A Townhill Road, Dunfermline KY12 0BN   01383 734657
                                                                      [E-mail: ann.allison@dunfermline.presbytery.org.uk]

Dunfermline: St Leonard's (01383 620106)
Andrew J. Philip BSc BD   1996 2004   12 Torvean Place, Dunfermline KY11 4YY   01383 721054
                                                                      [E-mail: andrewphilip@minister.com]

Dunfermline: St Margaret's
Fiona Nicolson BA BD   1996   38 Garvock Hill, Dunfermline KY12 7UU   01383 723955

Dunfermline: St Ninian's
Elizabeth A. Fisk (Mrs) BD   1996   51 St John's Drive, Dunfermline KY12 7TL   01383 722256

Dunfermline: St Paul's East (New Charge Development)
Alan Childs BA BD MBA   2000 2003   9 Dover Drive, Dunfermline KY11 8HQ   01383 620704

Dunfermline: Townhill and Kingseat (H)
William E. Farquhar BA BD   1987   161 Main Street, Townhill, Dunfermline KY12 0EZ   01383 723835
                                                                      [E-mail: akph46@uk.uumail.com]

Inverkeithing: St John's linked with North Queensferry (T)
Vacant

Inverkeithing: St Peter's (01383 412626)
George G. Nicol BD DPhil   1982 1988   20 Struan Drive, Inverkeithing KY11 1AR   01383 410032
                                                                      [E-mail: ggnicol@totalise.co.uk]

Kelty (Website: www.keltykirk.org.uk)
Scott Burton BD DipMin   1999   15 Arlick Road, Kelty KY4 0BH   01383 830291
                                                                      [E-mail: sburton@supanet.com]

Limekilns See Cairneyhill

Lochgelly: Macainsh: Team Ministry
Irene A. Bristow (Mrs) BD (Team Leader)   1989   2002   82 Main Street, Lochgelly KY5 9AA   01592 780435
[E-mail: ibristow@btinternet.com]

Lochgelly: St Andrew's (T) (H) See Lochgelly: Macainsh: Team Ministry
North Queensferry See Inverkeithing: St John's

Rosyth
Violet C.C. McKay (Mrs) BD   1988   2002   42 Woodside Avenue, Rosyth KY11 2LA   01383 412776
[E-mail: v.mckay@btinternet.com]
Morag Crawford (Miss) DCS   118 Wester Drylaw Place, Edinburgh EH4 2TG   0131-332 2253
[E-mail: morag.crawford@virgin.net]

Saline and Blairingone
Robert P. Boyle LTh   1990   2003   8 The Glebe, Saline, Dunfermline KY12 9UT   01383 853062

Tulliallan and Kincardine
Jock Stein MA BD   1973   2002   62 Toll Road, Kincardine, Alloa FK10 4QZ   01259 730538
[E-mail: handsel@dial.pipex.com]
Margaret E. Stein (Mrs) DA BD DipRE   1984   2002   62 Toll Road, Kincardine, Alloa FK10 4QZ   01259 730538
[E-mail: handsel@dial.pipex.com]

Britchfield, Alison E.P. (Mrs) MA BD	1986	1992	Chaplain RN	13 Tregoning Road, Torpoint, Cornwall PL11 2LX	01752 818430
Brown, Peter MA BD FRAScot	1953	1987	(Holm)	24 Inchmickery Avenue, Dalgety Bay, Dunfermline KY11 5NF	01383 822456
Buckhaven (01592 715551999		2005			
Potatoes					
Campbell, John MA	1943	1978	(Urquhart)	15 Foulden Place, Dunfermline KY12 7TQ	01383 738055
Mackenzie, R.P. MA BD	1936	1980	(Dunfermline: St Leonard's)	23 Foulis Crescent, Juniper Green, Edinburgh EH14 5BN	0131-453 3599
Macpherson, Stewart M. MA	1953	1990	(Dunfermline: Abbey)	176 Halbeath Road, Dunfermline KY11 4LB	01383 722851
Munro, Sheila BD	1995	2003	Chaplain: RAF	Chaplain's Office, RAF Digby, Lincoln LN4 3LH	
Orr, J. McMichael MA BD PhD	1949	1986	(Aberfoyle with Port of Menteith)	9 Overhaven, Limekilns, Dunfermline KY11 3JH	01383 872245
Pogue, Victor C. BA BD	1945	1980	(Baird Research Fellow)	5/2 Plewlands Court, Edinburgh EH10 5JY	0131-445 1628
Reid, David MSc LTh FSAScot	1961	1992	(St Monans with Largoward)	North Lethans, Saline, Dunfermline KY12 9TE	01383 733144
Ross, Evan J. LTh	1986	1998	(Cowdenbeath: West with Mossgreen and Crossgates)		
Scott, John LTh	1969	1996	(Aberdour St Fillan's)	43 Auld Mart Road, Milnathort, Kinross KY13 7FR	01577 861484
Smith, T. Forrest	1959	1986	(Arbuthnott with Kinneff)	32 White's Quay, St David's Harbour, Dalgety Bay, Dunfermline	01383 82089
Stuart, Anne (Miss) DCS			(Deaconess)	71 Whitehills Gardens, Musselburgh EH21 6PH	01383 860049
Whyte, Isabel H. (Mrs) BD	1993		Chaplain: Queen Margaret Hospital, Dunfermline	19 St Colme Crescent, Aberdour, Burntisland KY3 0ST	
				14 Carlingnose Point, North Queensferry, Inverkeithing KY11 1ER	01383 410732

(25) KIRKCALDY

Meets at Kirkcaldy, in St Brycedale Hall, on the first Tuesday of February, March, April, May, November and December, on the second Tuesday of September, and on the fourth Tuesday of June.

Clerk:	MR ANDREW F. MOORE BL	Annandale, Linksfield Street, Leven KY8 4HX [E-mail: akph59@uk.numail.com]	**01333 422644**
Depute Clerk:	MR DOUGLAS HAMILL	41 Abbots Mill, Kirkcaldy KY2 5PE	**01592 267500**

Auchterderran: St Fothad's linked with Kinglassie

J. Ewen R. Campbell MA BD	1967	1977	7 Woodend Road, Cardenden, Lochgelly KY5 0NE	01592 720213

Auchtertool linked with Kirkcaldy: Linktown (H) (01592 641080)

Catriona M. Morrison (Mrs) MA BD	1995	2000	16 Raith Crescent, Kirkcaldy KY2 5NN	01592 265536

Buckhaven (01592 715577)

Wilma Cairns (Miss) BD	1999	2004	181 Wellesley Road, Buckhaven, Leven KY8 1JA	01592 712870

Burntisland (H)

Alan Sharp BSc BD	1980	2001	21 Ramsay Crescent, Burntisland KY3 9JL [E-mail: alansharp@compuserve.com]	01592 874303

Denbeath linked with Methilhill

Elizabeth F. Cranfield (Miss) MA BD	1988		9 Chemiss Road, Methilhill, Leven KY8 2BS	01592 713142

Dysart (H)

Tilly Wilson (Miss) MTh	1990	1998	1 School Brae, Dysart, Kirkcaldy KY1 2XB	01592 655887

Glenrothes: Christ's Kirk (H)

Vacant			12 The Limekilns, Glenrothes KY6 3QJ	01592 620536

Glenrothes: St Columba's (01592 752539)

Alistair G. McLeod	1988		40 Liberton Drive, Glenrothes KY6 3PB	01592 744558

Glenrothes: St Margaret's (H) (01592 610310)

John P. McLean BSc BPhil BD	1994		8 Alburne Park, Glenrothes KY7 5RB [E-mail: john@stmargaretschurch.org.uk]	01592 752241
Sarah McDowall (Mrs) DCS			116 Scott Road, Glenrothes KY6 1AE	

Glenrothes: St Ninian's (H) (01592 610560) (E-mail: st-ninians@tiscali.co.uk)

Linda J. Dunbar BSc BA BD PhD FRHS	2000		1 Cawdor Drive, Glenrothes KY6 2HN [E-mail: linda.dunbar0@ouvip.com]	01592 611963 (Tel/Fax)

Innerleven: East (H)
James L. Templeton BSc BD   1975   77 McDonald Street, Methil, Leven KY8 3AJ   01333 426310

Kennoway, Windygates and Balgonie: St Kenneth's (Tel: 01333 351372; E-mail: administration@st-kenneths.freeserve.co.uk)
Richard Baxter MA BD   1997   2 Fernhill Gardens, Windygates, Leven KY8 5DZ   01333 352329
                                                  [E-mail: richard-baxter@msn.com]

Kinghorn
James Reid BD   1985   1997   17 Myre Crescent, Kinghorn, Burntisland KY3 9UB   01592 890269
                                                  [E-mail: jim17reid@aol.com]

Kinglassie See Auchterderran: St Fothad's

Kirkcaldy: Abbotshall (H)
Vacant   83 Milton Road, Kirkcaldy KY1 1TP   01592 260315

Kirkcaldy: Linktown (01592 641080) See Auchtertool

Kirkcaldy: Pathhead (H) (Tel/Fax: 01592 204635; E-mail: pathhead@btinternet.com; Website: www.pathheadparishchurch.co.uk)
John D. Thomson BD   1985   1993   73 Loughborough Road, Kirkcaldy KY1 3DD   01592 652215
                                                  [E-mail: john.d.thomson@blueyonder.co.uk]
Maureen Paterson (Mrs) BSc (Aux) 1992   1994   91 Dalmahoy Crescent, Kirkcaldy KY2 6TA   01592 262300
                                                  [E-mail: m.e.paterson@btinternet.com]

Kirkcaldy: St Andrew's (H)
Donald M. Thomson BD   1975   2000   15 Harcourt Road, Kirkcaldy KY2 5HQ   01592 260816
                                                  [E-mail: dmaclthomson@aol.com]

Kirkcaldy: St Bryce Kirk (H) (Tel: 01592 640016; E-mail: office@stbee.freeserve.co.uk)
Ken Froude MA BD   1979   6 East Fergus Place, Kirkcaldy KY1 1XT   01592 264480
                                                  [E-mail: kenfroude@blueyonder.co.uk]

Kirkcaldy: St John's
Nicola Frail BLE MBA MDiv   2004   25 Bennochy Avenue, Kirkcaldy KY2 5QE   01592 263821

Kirkcaldy: Templehall (H)
Anthony J.R. Fowler BSc BD   1982   2004   The Manse, Appin Crescent, Kirkcaldy KY2 6EJ   01592 260156

Kirkcaldy: Torbain
Ian Elston BD MTh   1999   91 Sauchenbush Road, Kirkcaldy KY2 5RN   01592 263015

Kirkcaldy: Viewforth (H) linked with Thornton
Anne J. Job   2000   66 Viewforth Street, Kirkcaldy KY1 3DJ   01592 652502

Leslie: Trinity
Vacant   4 Valley Drive, Leslie, Glenrothes KY6 3BQ   01592 741008

Leven
Alan Miller BA MA BD   2000 2001   5 Forman Road, Leven KY8 4HH   01333 303339
[E-mail: millers@fish.co.uk]

Markinch
Alexander R. Forsyth TD BA MTh   1973 2002   7 Guthrie Crescent, Markinch, Glenrothes KY7 6AY   01592 758264

Methil (H)
Vacant   Alma House, 2 School Brae, Methilhill, Leven KY8 2BT   01592 713708

Methilhill See Denbeath
Thornton See Kirkcaldy: Viewforth

Wemyss
Kenneth W. Donald BA BD   1982 1999   33 Main Road, East Wemyss, Kirkcaldy KY1 4RE   01592 713260
[E-mail: kwdonald@4unet.co.uk]

Name			Charge/Role	Address	Phone
Connolly, Daniel BD DipTheol DipMin	1983		Army Chaplain	2 CS Reg, RLC, BFPO 47	
Cooper, M.W. MA	1944	1979	(Kirkcaldy: Abbotshall)	Applegarth, Sunny Park, Kinross KY13 7BX	01577 263204
Dick, James S. MA BTh	1988	1997	(Glasgow: Ruchazie)	1 Hawkmuir, Kirkcaldy KY1 2AN	01592 260289
Duncan, John C. BD MPhil	1987	2001	Army Chaplain	British Forces Episkopi Support Unit, BFPO 53	
Elston, Peter K.	1963	2000	(Dalgety)	6 Cairngorm Crescent, Kirkcaldy KY2 5RF	01592 205622
Ferguson, David J.	1966	2001	(Bellie with Speymouth)	4 Russell Gardens, Ladybank, Cupar KY15 7LT	01337 831406
Forrester, Ian L. MA	1964	1996	(Friockheim, Kinnell with Inverkeilor and Lunan)	8 Bennochy Avenue, Kirkcaldy KY2 5QE	01592 260251
Gatt, David W.	1981	1995	(Thornton)	15 Beech Avenue, Thornton, Kirkcaldy KY1 4AT	01592 774328
Gibson, Ivor MA	1957	1993	(Abercorn with Dalmeny)	15 McInnes Road, Glenrothes KY7 6BA	01592 759982
Gordon, Ian D. LTh	1972	2001	(Markinch)	2 Somerville Way, Glenrothes KY7 5GE	01592 742487
Howden, Margaret (Miss) DCS			(Deaconess)	38 Munro Street, Kirkcaldy KY1 1PY	01592 205913
McAlpine, Robin J. BDS BD	1988	1997	Adviser in Mission and Evangelism	10 Seton Place, Kirkcaldy KY2 6UX [E-mail: robin.mcalpine@virgin.net]	01592 643518
McDonald, Ian J.M. MA BD	1984	1996	Chaplain, Kirkcaldy Acute Hospitals	11 James Grove, Kirkcaldy KY1 1TN	01592 203775
McKenzie, Donald M. TD MA	1947	1986	(Auchtertool with Burntisland)	76 Forth Park Gardens, Kirkcaldy KY2 5TD	01592 263012
MacLeod, Norman	1960	1988	(Orwell with Portmoak)	324 Muirfield Drive, Glenrothes KY6 2PZ	01592 610281
McNaught, Samuel M. MA BD MTh	1968	2002	(Kirkcaldy: St John's)	6 Munro Court, Glenrothes KY7 5GD	01592 742352
Munro, Andrew MA BD PhD	1972	2000	(Glencaple with Lowther)	7 Dunvegan Avenue, Kirkcaldy KY2 5SG	01592 566129
Reid, Martin R.B.C. BD	1960	1990	(Falkirk: West)	13 Rothes Park, Leslie, Glenrothes KY6 3LL	01592 620053
Simpson, Gordon M. MA BD	1959	1996	(Leslie: Trinity)	37 Spottiswoode Gardens, St Andrews KY16 8SA	01334 473406
Sutherland, William	1964	1993	(Bo'ness Old)	88 Dunrobin Road, Kirkcaldy KY2 5YT	01592 205510
Taylor, John T.H.	1947	1983	(Glenrothes: Christ's Kirk on the Green)	9 Douglas Road, Leslie, Glenrothes KY6 3JZ	01592 741009

Thomson, Gilbert L. BA	1965 1996	(Glenrothes: Christ's Kirk)	3 Fortharfield, Freuchie, Cupar KY15 7JJ	01337 857431
Tomlinson, Bryan L. TD	1969 2003	(Kirkcaldy: Abbotshall)	2 Duddington Drive, Kirkcaldy KY2 6JP	01592 564843
			[E-mail: abbkirk@blueyonder.co.uk]	
Webster, Elspeth H. (Miss) DCS		(Deaconess)	82 Broomhill Avenue, Burntisland KY3 0BP	01592 873616
Young, W. Finlayson MA	1943 1979	(Kinglassie)	17 Whitecraig Road, Newburgh, Cupar KY14 6BP	01337 840646

KIRKCALDY ADDRESSES

Old	Kirk Wynd	Templehall	Beauly Place
Pathhead	Harriet Street x Church Street	Torbain	Lindores Drive
St Andrew's	Victoria Road x Victoria Gdns	Viewforth	Viewforth Street x Viewforth Terrace
St Bryce Kirk	St Brycedale Avenue x Kirk Wynd		
St John's	Elgin Street		

Abbotshall	Abbotshall Road
Linktown	Nicol Street x High Street

(26) ST ANDREWS

Meets at Cupar, in St John's Church Hall, on the second Wednesday of February, March, April, May, September, October, November and December, and on the last Wednesday of June.

Clerk: REV. DAVID I. SINCLAIR BSc BD PhD DipSW — Church and Nation Committee, Church of Scotland, 121 George Street, Edinburgh EH2 4YN — 0131-225 5239
[E-mail: akph74@uk.uumail.com]

Abdie and Dunbog (H) linked with Newburgh (H)
Lynn Brady (Miss) BD DipMin — 1996 2002 — 2 Guthrie Court, Cupar Road, Newburgh, Cupar KY14 6HA — 01337 842228
[E-mail: lynn@revbrady.freeserve.co.uk]

Anstruther
Ian A. Cathcart BSc BD — 1994 — The James Melville Manse, Anstruther KY10 3EX — 01333 311808

Auchtermuchty (H)
Ann G. Fraser (Mrs) BD CertMin — 1990 — 2 Burnside, Auchtermuchty, Cupar KY14 7AJ — 01337 828519
[E-mail: anmgilfraser@bushinternet.com]

Balmerino (H) linked with Wormit (H)
Vacant — 5 Westwater Place, Newport-on-Tay DD6 8NS — 01382 542626

Boarhills and Dunino linked with St Andrews: Martyrs'
J. Mary Henderson (Miss) MA BD DipEd PhD   1990   2000   49 Irvine Crescent, St Andrews KY16 8LG   01334 472948
[E-mail: jmh@smokeypuss.freeserve.co.uk]

Cameron linked with St Andrews: St Leonard's (01334 478702)
Alan D. McDonald LLB BD MTh   1979   1998   1 Cairnhill Gardens, St Andrews KY16 8UR   01334 472793
[E-mail: alan.d.mcdonald@talk21.com]

Carnbee linked with Pittenweem
Gordon W. Craig MBE MA BD   1972   2003   1 Beley Bridge, Dunino, St Andrews KY16 8LT   01334 880285

Cellardyke (H) linked with Kilrenny
David J.H. Laing BD DPS   1976   1999   Toll Road, Cellardyke, Anstruther KY10 3BH   01333 310810
[E-mail: davith@v21mail.co.uk]

Ceres and Springfield
Vacant   The Manse, St Andrews Road, Ceres, Cupar KY15 5NQ   01334 828233

Crail linked with Kingsbarns (H)
Michael J. Erskine MA BD   1985   2002   Church Manse, St Andrews Road, Crail, Anstruther KY10 3UH   01333 450358

Creich, Flisk and Kilmany linked with Monimail
Mitchell Collins BD CPS   1996   Creich Manse, Brunton, Cupar KY15 4PA   01337 870332
[E-mail: mitchell.collins@tesco.net]

Cupar: Old (H) and St Michael of Tarvit
Kenneth S. Jeffrey BA BD PhD   2002   76 Hogarth Drive, Cupar KY15 5YH   01334 653196
[E-mail: ksjeffrey@btopenworld.com]

Cupar: St John's
A. Sheila Blount (Mrs) BD BA   1978   2002   23 Hogarth Drive, Cupar KY15 5YH   01334 656408

Dairsie linked with Kemback linked with Strathkinness (H)
Alexander Strickland JP LTh   1971   1981   Dairsie Manse, Dairsie, Cupar KY15 4RS   01334 653283

Edenshead and Strathmiglo
Vacant   The Manse, Kirk Wynd, Strathmiglo, Cupar KY14 7QS   01337 860256

Elie (H) linked with Kilconquhar and Colinsburgh (H)
Iain F. Paton BD FCIS   1980   1998   30 Bank Street, Elie, Leven KY9 1BW   01333 330685
[E-mail: iain.paton@tesco.net]

Falkland (01337 858442) linked with Freuchie (H)
John W. Jarvie BD CertMin MTh   1990   1 Newton Road, Falkland, Cupar KY15 7AQ   01337 857696
[E-mail: jarvie@cwcom.net]

Freuchie (H) See Falkland

Howe of Fife
Marion J. Paton (Miss) BMus BD   1991   1994   83 Church Street, Ladybank, Cupar KY15 7ND   01337 830513
[E-mail: marion@marionpaton.f9.co.uk]

Kemback See Dairsie
Kilconquhar and Colinsburgh See Elie
Kilrenny See Cellardyke
Kingsbarns See Crail

Largo and Newburn (H) linked with Largo: St David's
Rosemary Frew (Mrs) MA BD   1988   The Manse, Church Place, Upper Largo, Leven KY8 6EH   01333 360286
[E-mail: rosemaryfrew@breathemail.net]

Largo: St David's See Largo and Newburn

Largoward linked with St Monans (H)
Donald G. MacEwan MA BD PhD   2001   The Manse, St Monans, Anstruther KY10 2DD   01333 730258
[E-mail: maiadona@fish.co.uk]

Leuchars: St Athernase
Caroline Taylor (Mrs) MA BD   1995   2003   7 David Wilson Park, Balmullo, St Andrews KY16 0NP   01334 870038
[E-mail: enilorac@fish.com.uk]

Monimail See Creich, Flisk and Kilmany
Newburgh See Abdie and Dunbog

Newport-on-Tay (H)
W. Kenneth Pryde DA BD   1994   57 Cupar Road, Newport-on-Tay DD6 8DF   01382 543165 (Tel/Fax)
[E-mail: wkpryde@hotmail.com]

Pittenweem See Carnbee

St Andrews: Holy Trinity
Rory MacLeod BA MBA BD   1994   2004   19 Priory Gardens, St Andrews KY16 8XX

St Andrews: Hope Park (H)
A. David K. Arnott MA BD   1971   1996   20 Priory Gardens, St Andrews KY16 8XX   01334 472912 (Tel/Fax)
[E-mail: adka@st-andrews.ac.uk]

St Andrews: Martyrs' (H) See Boarhills and Dunino

St Andrews: St Leonard's (H) See Cameron
St Monans See Largoward
Strathkinness See Dairsie

Tayport
Colin J. Dempster BD CertMin   1990   27 Bell Street, Tayport DD6 9AP   01382 552861
                                                         [E-mail: demps@tayportc.fsnet.co.uk]

Wormit See Balmerino

Name			Parish/Note	Address	Phone
Alexander, James S. MA BD BA PhD	1966	1973	University of St Andrews	5 Strathkinness High Road, St Andrews KY16 9RP	01334 472680
Bennett, G. A.estair A. TD MA	1938	1976	(Strathkinness)	7 Bonfield Park, Strathkinness, St Andrews KY16 9SY	01334 850249
Best, Ernest MA BD PhD DD	1949	1982	(University of Glasgow)	13 Newmill Gardens, St Andrews KY16 8RY	01334 473315
Bews, James MA	1942	1981	(Dundee: Craigiebank)	21 Balrymonth Court, St Andrews KY16 8XT	01334 476087
Blount, Graham K. LLB BD PhD	1976	1998	Parliamentary Officer	23 Hogarth Drive, Cupar KY15 5YH	01334 656408
Bogie, A.P. MA FSAScot	1944	1979	(Forgan)	7 Gourlay Wynd, St Andrews KY16 8HP	
Bradley, Ian MA BD DPhil	1990	1990	Lecturer: University of Aberdeen	4 Donaldson Gardens, St Andrews KY16 9DN	01334 475389
Brown, Lawson R. MA	1960	1997	(Cameron with St Andrew's St Leonard's)	10 Park Street, St Andrews KY16 8AQ	01334 473413
Buchan, Alexander MA BD	1975	1992	(North Ronaldsay with Sanday)	26 Allan Robertson Drive, St Andrews KY16 8EY	01334 473875
Cameron, James K.					
MA BD PhD FRHistS	1953	1989	(University of St Andrews)	Priorscroft, 71 Hepburn Gardens, St Andrews KY16 9LS	01334 473996
Casebow, Brian C. MA BD	1959	1993	(Edinburgh: Salisbury)	'The Rowans', 67 St Michael's Drive, Cupar KY15 5BP	01334 656385
Douglas, Peter C. JP	1966	1993	(Boarhills linked with Dunino)	The Old Schoolhouse, Flisk, Newburgh, Cupar KY14 6HN	01337 870218
Earnshaw, Philip BA BSc BD	1986	1996	(Glasgow: Pollokshields)	22 Castle Street, St Monans, Anstruther KY10 2AP	01333 730640
Edington, George L.	1952	1989	(Tayport)	64B Burghmuir Road, Perth PH1 1LH	
Fairlie, George BD BVMS MRCVS	1971	2002	(Crail with Kingsbarns)	41 Warrack Street, St Andrews KY18 8DR	01334 475868
Galloway, Robert W.C. LTh	1970	1998	(Cromarty)	22 Haughgate, Leven KY8 4SG	
Gibson, Henry M. MA BD PhD	1960	1999	(Dundee: The High Kirk)	4 Comerton Place, Drumoig, Leuchars, St Andrews KY16 0NQ	01382 542199
Gordon, Peter M. MA BD	1958	1995	(Airdrie West)	3 Cupar Road, Cuparmuir, Cupar KY15 5RH	01334 652341
				[E-mail: machrie@madasafish.com]	
Henney, William MA DD	1957	1996	(St Andrews Hope Park)	30 Doocot Road, St Andrews KY16 9LP	01334 472560
Hill, Roy MA	1962	1997	(Lisbon)	Forgan Cottage, Kinnessburn Road, St Andrews KY16 8AD	01334 472121
Howieson, R.A. JP MA	1937	1977	(Newport-on-Tay St Thomas's)	Flat 15, City Park, 18 City Road, St Andrews KY16 9XF	01334 473711
Kinnis, Robert L. MA BD	1931	1972	(Baillieston Mure Memorial)	Gibson House, St Andrews KY16 9JE	
Learmonth, Walter LTh	1968	1997	(Ceres with Springfield)	14 Marionfield Place, Cupar KY15 5JN	01334 656290
Lithgow, Thomas MA	1945	1982	(Banchory Devenick with Maryculter)	Pitlair House, Bow of Fife, Cupar KY15 5RF	
McCartney, Alexander C. BTh	1973	1995	(Caputh and Clunie with Kinclaven)	10 The Glebe, Crail, Anstruther KY10 3UT	01333 451194
McFadyen, Gavin J.	1963	1992	(Whiteinch)	62 Toll Court, Lundin Links, Leven KY8 6HH	01333 320434
McGregor, Duncan J. FIMA	1982	1996	(Channelkirk with Lauder Old)	14 Mount Melville, St Andrews KY16 8NG	01334 478314
Macintyre, William J. MA BD DD	1951	1989	(Crail with Kingsbarns)	Tigh a' Ghobhainn, Lochton, Crail, Anstruther KY10 3XE	01333 450327
McKane, William					
MA PhD DLitt DD FBA	1949	1990	(University of St Andrews)	51 Irvine Crescent, St Andrews KY16 8LG	01334 473797

Name	Charge			Address	Tel
Mackenzie, A. Cameron MA	(Biggar)	1955	1995	Hedgerow, 5 Shiels Avenue, Freuchie, Cupar KY15 7JD	01337 857763
Mackenzie, J.A.R. MA	(Largo: St David's)	1947	1987	West Lodge, Inverness Road, Nairn IV12 4SD	01667 452827
MacNab, Hamish S.D. MA	(Kilrenny)	1948	1987	Fairhill, Northmuir, Kirriemuir DD8 4PF	01575 572564
McPhail, Peter MA BD	(Creich, Flisk and Kilmany)	1940	1982	44 Doocot Road, St Andrews KY16 8QP	01334 473093
Meager, Peter MA BD CertMgmt(Open)	(Elie with Kilconquhar and Colinsburgh)	1971	1998	7 Lorraine Drive, Cupar KY15 5DY	01334 656991
Nicol, Robert M.	(Jersey: St Columba's)	1984	1996	35 Upper Greens, Auchtermuchty, Cupar KY14 7BX	01337 828327
Ord, J.K.	(Falkirk Condorrat)	1963		24 Forth Street, St Monance, Anstruther KY10 2AX	01333 730461
Patterson, John W. BA BD	(St Andrews: Martyrs)	1948	1989	34 Claybraes, St Andrews KY16 8RS	01334 473606
Portsmouth, Roland John NDD ATD	(Bendochy)	1980	1989	1 West Braes, Pittenweem, Anstruther KY10 2PS	01333 311448
Porteous, James K. DD	(Cupar: St John's)	1944	1997	16 Market Street, St Andrews KY16 9NS	
Reid, Alan A.S. MA BD STM	(Bridge of Allan: Chalmers)	1962	1995	Wayside Cottage, Bridgend, Ceres, Cupar KY15 5LS	01334 828509
Robb, Nigel J. FCP MA BD ThM MTh	(Director of Educational Services, Board of Ministry)	1981	1998	c/o 121 George Street, Edinburgh EH2 4YN [E-mail: nrobb@cofscotland.org.uk]	0131-225 5722
Robertson, Norma P. (Miss) BD DMin	(Kincardine O'Neil with Lumphanan)	1993	2002	82 Hogarth Drive, Cupar KY15 5YU [E-mail: normapr@fish.co.uk]	01334 650595
Roy, Alan J. BSc BD	(Aberuthven with Dunning)	1960	1999	14 Comerton Place, Drumoig, Leuchars, St Andrews KY16 0NQ [E-mail: roma.roy@btopenworld.com]	01382 542225
Salters, Robert B. MA BD PhD	(University of St Andrews)	1966	1971	Vine Cottage, 119 South Street, St Andrews KY16 9UH	01334 473198
Scott, J. Miller MA BD FSAScot DD	(Jerusalem)	1949	1988	St Martins, 6 Trinity Place, St Andrews KY16 8SG	01334 479518
Shaw, Duncan LTh CPS	Chaplain: RAF	1984		Chaplain's Office, RAF Leuchars, St Andrews KY16 0JX	
Sinclair, David I. BSc BD PhD DipSW	Secretary: Church and Nation Committee	1990	1998	42 South Road, Cupar KY15 5JF	01334 656957
Stevenson A.L. LLB MLitt DPA FPEA	(Balmerino linked with Wormit)	1984	1993	41 Main Street, Dairsie, Cupar KY15 4SR	01334 870582
Stoddart, David L.	(Laggan with Newtonmore)	1961	1987	3 Castle Street, Anstruther KY10 3DD	01333 310668
Strong, Clifford LTh	(Creich, Flisk and Kilmany with Monimail)	1983	1995		
Taylor, Ian BSc MA LTh DipEd	(Abdie and Dunbog with Newburgh)	1983	1997	60 Maryknowe, Gauldry, Newport-on-Tay DD6 8SL	01382 330445
Thomson, P.G. MA BD MTh ThD	(Irvine Fullarton)	1947	1989	Lundie Cottage, Arncroach, Anstruther KY10 2RN	01333 720222
Thrower, Charles G. BSc	(Carnbee with Pittenweem)	1965	2002	Fullarton, 2 Beech Walk, Crail, Anstruther KY10 3UN	01333 450423
				Grange House, Wester Grangemuir, Pittenweem, Anstruther KY10 2RB [E-mail: craigroundh@aol.com]	01333 312631
Torrance, Alan J. MA BD DrTheol	University of St Andrews	1984	1999	Kincaple House, Kincaple, St Andrews KY16 9SH	(Home) 01334 850755 (Office) 01334 462843
Turnbull, James J. MA	(Arbirlot with Colliston)	1940	1981	Woodlands, Beech Avenue, Ladybank, Cupar KY15 7NG	01337 830279
Walker, James B. MA BD DPhil	Chaplain: University of St Andrews	1975	1993	1 Gillespie Terrace, The Scores, St Andrews KY16 9AT [E-mail: jbw1@st-andrews.ac.uk]	(Tel) 01334 477471 (Fax) 01334 462697
Whyte, James A. MA LLD DD DUniv	(University of St Andrews)	1945	1987	13 Hope Street, St Andrews KY16 9HJ	01334 472323
Wilson, Robert McL. MA BD PhD DD FBA	(University of St Andrews)	1946	1983	10 Murrayfield Road, St Andrews KY16 9NB	01334 474331
Wright, Lynda (Miss) BEd DCS	Deacon: Retreat Leader, Key House	1946	1983	6 Key Cottage, High Street, Falkland, Cupar KY15 7BD	01337 857705
Young, Evelyn M. (Mrs) BSc BD	(Kilmun (St Munn's) with Strone and Ardentinny)	1984	2003	2 Priestden Place, St Andrews KY16 8DP	01334 479662

(27) DUNKELD AND MEIGLE

Meets at Pitlochry on the first Tuesday of September and December, on the third Tuesday of February, April and October, and at the Moderator's church on the third Tuesday of June.

Clerk:	REV. JOHN RUSSELL MA	Kilblaan, Gladstone Terrace, Birnam, Dunkeld PH8 0DP [E-mail: akph47@uk.uumail.com]	01350 728896

Aberfeldy (H) linked with Amulree and Strathbraan linked with Dull and Weem
Alexander M Gunn MA BD 1967 1986 Taybridge Terrace, Aberfeldy PH15 2BS [E-mail: sandy@aberfeldypc.co.uk] 01887 820656 (Tel/Fax)

Alyth (H)
Neil N. Gardner MA BD 1991 1998 Cambridge Street, Alyth, Blairgowrie PH11 8AW [E-mail: nng@surfaid.org] 01828 632104

Amulree and Strathbraan See Aberfeldy

Ardler, Kettins and Meigle
Linda Stewart (Mrs) BD 2001 The Manse, Dundee Road, Meigle, Blairgowrie PH12 8SB 01828 640278

Bendochy linked with Coupar Angus: Abbey
Bruce Dempsey BD 1997 Caddam Road, Coupar Angus, Blairgowrie PH13 9EF [E-mail: revbruce.dempsey@btopenworld.com] 01828 627331

Blair Atholl and Struan linked with Tenandry
Brian Ian Murray BD 2002 Blair Atholl, Pitlochry PH18 5SX [E-mail: athollkirks@yahoo.co.uk] 01796 481213

Blairgowrie
Donald Macleod BD LRAM DRSAM 1987 2002 The Manse, Upper David Street, Blairgowrie PH10 6HB [E-mail: donmac@fish.co.uk] 01250 872146

Braes of Rannoch linked with Foss and Rannoch (H)
Vacant Kinloch Rannoch, Pitlochry PH16 5QA 01882 632381

Caputh and Clunie (H) linked with Kinclaven (H) (T)
Vacant Caputh Manse, Caputh, Perth PH1 4JH 01738 710520

Coupar Angus: Abbey See Bendochy
Dull and Weem See Aberfeldy

Dunkeld (H)

R. Fraser Penny BA BD	1984	2001	Cathedral Manse, Dunkeld PH8 0AW [E-mail: fraserpenn@aol.com]	01350 727249 01350 727102 (Fax)

Fortingall and Glenlyon linked with Kenmore and Lawers

Anne J. Brennan BSc BD MTh	1999	The Manse, Balnaskeag, Kenmore, Aberfeldy PH15 2HB [E-mail: annebrennan@yahoo.co.uk]	01887 830218

Foss and Rannoch See Braes of Rannoch

Grantully, Logierait and Strathtay

Christine M. Creegan (Mrs) MTh	1993	2000	The Manse, Strathtay, Pitlochry PH9 0PG [E-mail: christine@creegans.co.uk] 01887 840251

Kenmore and Lawers (H) See Fortingall and Glenlyon
Kinclaven See Caputh and Clunie

Kirkmichael, Straloch and Glenshee linked with Rattray (H)

Vacant	The Manse, Alyth Road, Rattray, Blairgowrie PH10 7HF	01250 872462

Pitlochry (H) (01796 472160)

Malcolm Ramsay BA LLB DipMin	1986	1998	Manse Road, Moulin, Pitlochry PH16 5EP [E-mail: amramsay@aol.com] 01796 472774

Rattray See Kirkmichael, Straloch and Glenshee
Tenandry See Blair Atholl and Struan

Name			(Last charge)	Address	Tel
Barbour, Robin A.S. KCVO MC BD STM DD	1954	1982	(University of Aberdeen)	Fincastle Village, Pitlochry PH16 5RJ	01796 473209
Cassells, Alexander K. MA BD	1961	1997	(Leuchars St Athernase and Guardbridge)	Tighaness, Keltney Burn, Aberfeldy PH15 2LS	01887 830758
Dick, Tom MA	1951	1990	(Dunkeld)	Mo Dhachaidh, Callybrae, Dunkeld PH8 0EP	01350 727338
Duncan, James BTh FSAScot	1980	1995	(Blair Atholl and Struan)	25 Knockard Avenue, Pitlochry PH16 5JE	01796 474096
Forsyth, David Stuart MA	1948	1992	(Belhelvie)	Birchlea, 38 Fonab Crescent, Pitlochry PH16 5SR	01796 473708
Fulton, Frederick H. MA	1942	1983	(Clunie, Lethendy and Kinloch)	Grampian Cottage, Chapel Brae, Braemar, Ballater AB35 5YT	01339 741277
Hamilton, David G. MA BD	1971	2004	(Braes of Rannoch with Foss and Rannoch)	79 Finlay Rise, Milngavie, Glasgow G62 5QA [E-mail: davidhamilton@onetel.net.uk]	0141-956 4202
Henderson, John D. MA BD	1953	1992	(Cluny with Monymusk)	Aldersyde, George Street, Blairgowrie PH10 6HP	01250 875181
Knox, John W. MTheol	1992	1997	(Lochgelly: Macainsh)	Heatherlea, Main Street, Ardler, Blairgowrie PH12 8SR	01828 640731
McAlister, D.J.B. MA BD PhD	1951	1989	(North Berwick: Blackadder)	2 Duff Avenue, Moulin, Pitlochry PH16 5EN	01796 473591
MacVicar, Kenneth MBE DFC TD MA	1950	1990	(Kenmore with Lawers with Fortingall & Glenlyon)	Illeray, Kenmore, Aberfeldy PH15 2HE	01887 830514
Ormiston, Hugh C. BSc BD MPhil PhD	1969	2004	(Kirkmichael, Straloch and Glenshee with Rattray)	Cedar Lea, Main Road, Woodside, Blairgowrie PH13 9NP	01828 670539

Robertson, Iain M. MA	(Carriden)	1967 1992	St Colme's, Perth Road, Birnam, Dunkeld PH8 0BH	01350 727455
Robertson, Matthew LTh	(Cawdor with Croy and Dalcross)	1968 2002	Inver, Strathtay, Pitlochry PH9 0PG	01887 840780
Russell, John MA	(Tillicoultry)	1959 2000	Kilblaan, Gladstone Terrace, Birnam, Dunkeld PH8 0DP	01350 728896
Shannon, W.G.H. MA BD	(Pitlochry)	1955 1998	19 Knockard Road, Pitlochry PH16 5HJ	01796 473533
Stewart, Walter T.A.	(Barry)	1964 1999	7A Tummel Crescent, Pitlochry PH16 5DF	01796 473422
Tait, Thomas W. BD	(Rattray)	1972 1997	20 Cedar Avenue, Blairgowrie PH10 6TT	01250 874833
White, Brock A. LTh	(Kirkcaldy: Templehall)	1971 2001	1 Littlewood Gardens, Blairgowrie PH10 6XZ	01250 870399
Whyte, William B. BD	(Nairn: St Ninian's)	1973 2003	The Old Inn, Park Hill Road, Rattray, Blairgowrie PH10 7DS	01250 874401
Young, G. Stuart	(Blairgowrie: St Andrew's)	1961 1996	7 James Place, Stanley, Perth PH1 4PD	01738 828473

(28) PERTH

Meets at Scone: Old, at 7:00pm, in the Elizabeth Ashton Hall, on the second Tuesday of every month except January, July and August, when there is no meeting, and on the last Tuesday of June, when it meets in the church of the incoming Moderator.

Clerk:	**Rev. DEREK G. LAWSON LLB BD**		
Presbytery Office:	209 High Street, Perth PH1 5PB	**01738 451177 (Tel)**
	[E-mail: akph70@uk.uumail.com]	**01738 638226 (Fax)**

Abernethy and Dron linked with Arngask

Kenneth G. Anderson MA BD	1967	1988	Manse Road, Abernethy, Perth PH2 9JP	01738 850607
			[E-mail: mgtanderson@aol.com]	

Almondbank Tibbermore

Donald Campbell BD	1998		The Manse, Pitcairngreen, Perth PH1 3LU	01738 583217
			[E-mail: revdonald@almondbankchurch.co.uk]	

Ardoch (H) linked with Blackford (H)

Vacant	Manse of Ardoch, Feddal Road, Braco, Dunblane FK15 9RE	01786 880217

Arngask See Abernethy and Dron

Auchterarder (H)

Michael R.R. Shewan MA BD CPS	1985	1998	24 High Street, Auchterarder, Perth PH3 1DF	01764 662210
			[E-mail: michael.shewan@lineone.net]	

Auchtergaven and Moneydie

Vacant	Bankfoot, Perth PH1 4BS	01738 787235

Blackford See Ardoch

Cargill Burrelton linked with Collace
Jose R. Carvalho BD — 2002
Manse Road, Woodside, Blairgowrie PH13 9NQ
[E-mail: jrcarvalho@aol.com]
01828 670352

Cleish (H) linked with Fossoway: St Serf's and Devonside
A. David Macleod MA BD — 1993 1994
The Manse, Cleish, Kinross KY13 7LR
[E-mail: david@mcleodcleish.freeserve.co.uk]
01577 850231 (Tel/Fax)

Collace See Cargill and Burrelton

Comrie (H) linked with Dundurn (H)
Peter D. Thomson MA BD — 1968 1978
The Manse, Comrie, Crieff PH6 2HE
[E-mail: revpdt@the-manse.freeserve.co.uk]
01764 670269

Crieff (H)
James W. MacDonald BD — 1976 2002
8 Strathearn Terrace, Crieff PH7 3AQ
[E-mail: revup@tesco.net]
01764 653907

Dunbarney (H) linked with Forgandenny
W. Duncan Stenhouse MA BD — 1989
Dunbarney Manse, Bridge of Earn, Perth PH2 9DY
[E-mail: duncan@stenhouse58.freeserve.co.uk]
01738 812463

Dundurn See Comrie

Errol (H) linked with Kilspindie and Rait
Vacant
South Bank, Errol, Perth PH2 7PZ
01821 642279

Forgandenny See Dunbarney
Fossoway: St Serf's and Devonside See Cleish

Fowlis Wester linked with Madderty linked with Monzie
Alexander F. Bonar LTh LRIC — 1988 1996
Beechview, Abercairney, Crieff PH7 3NF
[E-mail: sandy.bonar@btinternet.com]
01764 652116

Gask (H) linked with Methven and Logiealmond (H)
Brian Bain LTh — 1980 1986
Sauchob Road, Methven, Perth PH1 3QD
[E-mail: brian@methvenmanse.freeserve.co.uk]
01738 840274 (Tel/Fax)

Kilspindie and Rait See Errol

Kinross (H)
John P.L. Munro MA BD PhD — 1977 1998
15 Station Road, Kinross KY13 8TG
[E-mail: john@lochleven.freeserve.co.uk]
01577 862952

Madderty See Fowlis Wester
Methven and Logiealmond See Gask
Monzie See Fowlis Wester

Muthill (H) linked with Trinity Gask and Kinkell
John Oswald BSc PhD BD   1997   2002   Muthill, Crieff PH5 2AR   01764 681205
[E-mail: revdocoz@bigfoot.com]

Orwell (H) linked with Portmoak (H)
Robert G.D.W. Pickles BD MPhil   2003   3 Perth Road, Milnathort, Kinross KY13 9XU   01577 863461
[E-mail: robert.pickles@btopenworld.com]

Perth: Craigie (H)
William Thomson   2001   46 Abbot Street, Perth PH2 0EE   01738 623748

Perth: Kinnoull (H)
David I. Souter BD   1996   2001   1 Mount Tabor Avenue, Perth PH2 7BT   01738 626046
[E-mail: d.souter@virgin.net]

Perth: Letham St Mark's (H)
James C. Stewart BD DipMin   1997   35 Rose Crescent, Perth PH1 1NT   01738 624167
[E-mail: jimstewartrev@lineone.net]
Kenneth McKay DCS   11F Balgowan Road, Perth PH1 2JG   01738 621169
[E-mail: kennydandcs@hotmail.com]

Perth: Moncreiffe (T)
Isobel Birrell (Mrs) BD   1994   1999   2 Rhynd Lane, Perth PH2 8QT   01738 625694
[E-mail: isobel.birrell@tiscali.co.uk]

Perth: North (01738 622298)
David W. Denniston BD DipMin   1981   1996   127 Glasgow Road, Perth PH2 0LU   01738 625728
[E-mail: david.denniston@blueyonder.co.uk]
Brian R. Hendrie BD (Assoc)   1992   2000   98 Duncansby Way, Perth PH1 5XF   01738 441029
[E-mail: brianandyvonne@98duncansby.freeserve.uk]

Perth: Riverside (New Charge Development)
Alfred G. Drummond BD DMin   1991   2000   44 Hay Street, Perth PH1 5HS   01738 621305
[E-mail: ncdriverside@uk.uumail.com]

Perth: St John the Baptist's (H) (01738 626159)
David D. Ogston MA BD   1970   1980   15 Comely Bank, Perth PH2 7HU   01738 621755
[E-mail ogston@cwcom.net]
Elizabeth Brown (Mrs)   1996   25 Highfield Road, Scone, Perth PH2 6RN   01738 552391 (Tel/Fax)
[E-mail: liz.brown@blueyonder.co.uk]

Perth: St Leonard's-in-the-Fields and Trinity (H) (01738 632238)
Gilbert C. Nisbet CA BD   1993   2000   5 Strathearn Terrace, Perth PH2 0LS   01738 621709
[E-mail: gcnisbet@stleonardsmanse.fsnet.co.uk]

Perth: St Matthew's (Office: 01738 636757; Vestry: 01738 630725)
Ewen J. Gilchrist BD DipMin DipComm   1982   1988   23 Kincarrathie Crescent, Perth PH2 7HH   01738 626828
[E-mail: hobgoblins@kincarrathie.fsnet.co.uk]

Portmoak See Orwell

Redgorton linked with Stanley
Derek G. Lawson LLB BD   1998   22 King Street, Stanley, Perth PH1 4ND   01738 828247
[E-mail: lawson@stanley9835.freeserve.co.uk]

St Madoes and Kinfauns
Marc F. Bircham BD MTh   2000   Glencarse, Perth PH2 7NF   01738 860837
[E-mail: mark.bircham@btinternet.com]

St Martin's linked with Scone: New (H) (01738 553900)
Robert Sloan BD   1997   2001   24 Victoria Road, Scone, Perth PH2 6JW   01738 551467
[E-mail: robertsloan@lineone.net]

Scone: New See St Martin's

Scone: Old (H)
J. Bruce Thomson JP MA BD   1972   1983   Burnside, Scone, Perth PH2 6LP   01738 552030
[E-mail: jock.tamson@talk21.com]

Stanley See Redgorton

The Stewartry of Strathearn (H) (Tel: 01738 621674; Fax: 01738 643321; E-mail: stewartry@beeb.net)
Colin R. Williamson LLB BD   1972   2000   Manse of Aberdalgie, Aberdalgie, Perth PH2 0QD   01738 625854
[E-mail: stewartry@beeb.net]

Trinity Gask and Kinkell See Muthill

Barr, George K. ARIBA BD PhD	1967	1993	(Uddingston: Viewpark)	7 Tay Avenue, Comrie, Crieff PH6 2PE	01764 670454
				[E-mail: gbarr2@compuserve.com]	
Barr, T. Leslie LTh	1969	1997	(Kinross)	8 Fairfield Road, Kelty KY4 0BY	01383 839330
Bartholomew, Julia (Mrs) BSc BD	2002		Auchterarder: Associate	Kippenhill, Dunning, Perth PH2 0RA	01764 684929
Bertram, Thomas A.	1972	1995	(Patna Waterside)	3 Scrimgeours Corner, 29 West High Street, Crieff PH7 4AP	01764 652066

Name	Charge			Address	Tel
Birrell, John M. MA LLB BD	Hospital Chaplain: Perth Royal Infirmary	1974	1996	2 Rhynd Lane, Perth PH2 8QT [E-mail: john.birrell@tuht.scot.nhs.uk]	01738 625694
Bonomy, William MA BD	(Inverkip)	1946	1987	Viewlands House, Viewlands Road, Perth PH1 1BL	
Buchan, William DipTheol BD	(Kilwinning Abbey)	1987	2001	34 Bridgewater Avenue, Auchterarder PH3 1DQ	01764 660306
Carr, W. Stanley MA	(Largs: St Columba's)	1951	1991	16 Gannochy Walk, Perth PH2 7LW	01738 627422
Coleman, Sidney H. BA BD MTh	(Glasgow: Merrylea)	1961	2001	'Blaven', 11 Clyde Place, Perth PH2 0EZ	01738 565072
Cowie, J.L. MA	(Edinburgh: Richmond Craigmillar)	1950	1977	16 Curate Wynd, Kinross KY13 7DX	01577 864762
Denniston, Jane MA BD	Board of Parish Education	2002		127 Glasgow Road, Perth PH2 0LU	01738 565379
Donaldson, Robert B. BSocSc	(Kilchoman with Portnahaven)	1953	1997	11 Strathearn Court, Crieff PH7 3DS	01764 654976
Elders, I. Alasdair MA BD	(Edinburgh: Broughton St Mary's)	1964	2002	The Limes, Ancaster Lane, Comrie, Crieff PH6 2DT	01764 679588
Ferguson, John F. MA BD	(Perth: Kinnoull)	1987	2001	71 Burghmuir Road, Perth PH1 1LH	01738 561945
Fleming, Hamish K. MA	(Banchory Ternan East)	1966	2001	36 Earnmuir Road, Comrie, Crieff PH6 2EY	01764 679178
Galbraith, W. James L. BSc BD MICE	(Kilchrenan and Dalavich with Muckairn)	1973	1996	19 Mayfield Gardens, Kinross KY13 7GD	01577 863887
Gaston, A. Ray C. MA BD	(Leuchars: St Athernase)	1969	2002	'Hamewith', 13 Manse Road, Dollar FK14 7AL	01259 743202
Gordon, Elinor J. (Miss) BD	Board of World Mission	1988	2001	Kildrum Manse, Clouden Road, Cumbernauld, Glasgow G67 2JQ	01236 723204
Gregory, J.C. LTh	(Blantyre St Andrew's)	1968	1992	2 Southlands Road, Auchterarder PH3 1BA	01764 664594
Grimson, John A. MA	(Glasgow Wellington: Associate)	1950	1986	29 Highland Road, Turret Park, Crieff PH7 4LE	01764 653063
Halliday, Archibald R. BD MTh	(Duffus, Spynie and Hopeman)	1964	1999	2 Pittenzie Place, Crieff PH7 3JL	01764 656464
Henry, Malcolm N. MA BD	(Perth Craigie)	1951	1987	Kelton, Castle Douglas DG7 1RU	01556 504144
Houston, Alexander M.	(Tibbermore)	1939	1977	120 Glasgow Road, Perth PH2 0LU	01738 628056
Hughes, Clifford E. MA BD	(Haddington: St Mary's)	1993	2001	Pavilion Cottage, Briglands, Rumbling Bridge, Kinross KY13 0PS	01577 840506
Kelly, T. Clifford	(Ferintosh)	1973	1995	7 Bankfoot Park, Scotlandwell, Kinross KY13 7JP	01592 840387
Lacey, Eric R. BD	(Creich with Rosehall)	1971	1992	The Bungalow, Forteviot, Perth PH2 9BT	01764 684041
Lawson, James B. MA BD	(South Uist)	1961	2002	4 Cowden Way, Comrie, Crieff PH6 2NW	01764 679180
Lawson, Ronald G. MA BD	(Greenock: Wellpark Mid Kirk)	1964	1999	6 East Brougham Street, Stanley, Perth PH1 4NJ	01738 828871
Low, J.E. Stewart MA	(Tarbat)	1957	1997	15 Stormont Place, Scone, Perth PH2 6SR	
McCormick, Alastair F.	(Creich with Rosehall)	1962	1998	14 Balmanno Park, Bridge of Earn, Perth PH2 9RJ	01738 813588
Macdonald, W.U. JP MA	(Aberdalgie and Dupplin with Forteviot)	1939	1984	30 Muircroft West Terrace, Perth PH1 1DY	01738 627948
McGregor, William LTh	(Auchtergaven and Moneydie)	1987	2003	Ard Choille, 7 Taypark Road, Luncarty, Perth PH1 3FE [E-mail: bill.mcgregor@ukonline.co.uk]	01738 827866
MacKenzie, Donald W. MA	(Auchterarder The Barony)	1941	1983	81 Kingswell Terrace, Perth PH1 2DA	01738 633716
MacLean, Nigel R. MA BD	(Perth: St Paul's)	1940	1986	9 Hay Street, Perth PH1 5HS	01738 626728
MacMillan, Riada M. (Mrs) BD	(Perth: Craigend Moncreiffe with Rhynd)	1991	1998	73 Muirend Gardens, Perth PH1 1JR	01738 628867
McNaughton, David J.H. BA CA	(Killin and Ardeonaig)	1976	1995	30 Hollybush Road, Crieff PH7 3HB	01764 653028
MacPhee, Duncan P.	(Braemar with Crathie: Associate)	1951	1980	Braemar Cottage, Ben Alder Place, Kirkcaldy KY2 5RH	01592 201984
McQuilken, John E. MA BD	(Glenaray and Inveraray)	1969	1992	18 Clark Terrace, Crieff PH7 3QE	01764 655764
Millar, Alexander M. MA BD MBA	Secretary Deputy: National Mission	1980	2001	17 Mapledene Road, Scone, Perth PH2 6NX [E-mail: millar@millar62.freeserve.co.uk]	01738 550270
Millar, Archibald E. DipTh	(Perth: St Stephen's)	1965	1991	7 Maple Place, Perth PH1 1RT	01738 621813
Munro, Gillian (Miss) BSc BD	Head of Department of Spiritual Care	1989	2003	Royal Dundee Liff Hospital, Liff, Dundee DD2 5ND	
Ritchie, Bruce BSc BD	Board of World Mission	1977	2001	2 Laurel Avenue, Crieff PH7 3EN [E-mail: brucecrieff@compuserve.com]	01764 652531
Robertson, Thomas G.M. LTh	(Edenshead and Strathmiglo)	1971	2004	25 Muirend Road, Perth PH1 1JL	
Shirra, James MA	(St Martin's with Scone New)	1945	1987	17 Dunbarney Avenue, Bridge of Earn, Perth PH2 9BP	01738 812610

Simpson, James A. BSc BD STM DD	1960 2000	(Dornoch Cathedral)	'Dornoch', Perth Street, Bankfoot, Perth PH1 4ED	01738 787710
Stewart, Gordon G. MA	1961 2000	(Perth: St Leonard's-in-the-Fields and Trinity)	'Balnoe', South Street, Rattray, Blairgowrie PH10 7BZ	01250 870626
Stewart, Robin J. MA BD STM	1959 1995	(Orwell with Portmoak)	Oakbrae, Perth Road, Murthly, Perth PH1 4HF	01738 710220
Tait, Henry A.G. MA BD	1966 1997	(Crieff: South and Monzievaird)	14 Shieling Hill Place, Crieff PH7 4ER	01764 652325
Taylor, A.H.S. MA BA BD	1957 1992	(Brydekirk with Hoddam)	41 Anderson Drive, Perth PH1 1LF	01764 626579

PERTH ADDRESSES

Craigie	Abbot Street	St John's	St John's Street
Kinnoull	Dundee Rd near Queen's Bridge	St Leonard's-in-the-Fields and Trinity	Marshall Place
Letham St Mark's	Rannoch Road	St Matthew's	Tay Street
Moncreiffe	Glenbruar Crescent		
North	Mill Street near Kinnoull Street		
Riverside	Bute Drive		

(29) DUNDEE

Meets at Dundee, Meadowside St Paul's Church Halls, Nethergate, on the second Wednesday of February, March, May, September, October, November and December; and on the fourth Wednesday of June.

Clerk: REV. JAMES A. ROY MA BD   [E-mail: akph45@uk.uumail.com]
Presbytery Office: Nicoll's Lane, Dundee DD2 3HG   01382 611415

Abernyte linked with Inchture and Kinnaird linked with Longforgan (H)
Diana Hobson (Mrs) BA BD   2002   The Manse, Longforgan, Dundee DD2 5EU   01382 360238
Elizabeth Kay (Miss) DipYCS (Aux)   1993 1999   1 Kintail Walk, Inchture, Perth PH14 9RY   01828 686029
    [E-mail: lizkay@clara.co.uk]

Auchterhouse (H) linked with Murroes and Tealing (T)
Vacant
Gordon Campbell MA CDipAF DipHSM MCMI MIHM MRIN ARSGS FRGS FSAScot (Aux)   The Manse, Balgray, Tealing, Dundee DD4 0QZ   01382 380224
    2 Falkland Place, Kingoodie, Invergowrie, Dundee DD2 5DY   01382 561383

Dundee: Balgay (H)
George K. Robson LTh DPS BA   1983 1987   150 City Road, Dundee DD2 2PW   01382 668806
    [E-mail: gkrobson@rev-balgay.freeserve.co.uk]

Dundee: Barnhill St Margaret's (H)
Fraser M.C. Stewart BSc BD   1980 2000   The Manse, Invermark Terrace, Broughty Ferry, Dundee DD5 2QU   01382 779278

Dundee: Broughty Ferry East (H) (01382 738264)
Vacant
8 West Queen Street, Broughty Ferry, Dundee DD5 1AR
01382 778972

Dundee: Broughty Ferry St Aidan's (T) (H)
Vacant
63 Collingwood Street, Barnhill, Dundee DD5 2UF
01382 736828

Dundee: Broughty Ferry St James' (H)
Vacant

Dundee: Broughty Ferry St Luke's and Queen Street
C. Graham Taylor BSc BD FIAB   2001
22 Albert Road, Broughty Ferry, Dundee DD5 1AZ
01382 779212

Dundee: Broughty Ferry St Stephen's and West (H)
John U. Cameron BA BSc PhD BD ThD   1974
33 Camperdown Street, Broughty Ferry, Dundee DD5 3AA
01382 477403

Dundee: Camperdown (H) (01382 623958)
Vacant
Camperdown Manse, Myrekirk Road, Dundee DD2 4SF
01382 621383
James H. Simpson BSc (Aux)   1996
11 Claypotts Place, Broughty Ferry, Dundee DD5 1LG
01382 776520

Dundee: Chalmers Ardler (H)
Kenneth D. Stott MA BD   1989 1997
The Manse, Turnberry Avenue, Dundee DD2 3TP
[E-mail: arkstotts@aol.com]
01382 827439
Jane Martin (Miss) DCS
12A Carnoustie Court, Ardler, Dundee DD2 3RB
01382 813786

Dundee: Clepington and Fairmuir
James G. Redpath BD DipPTh   1988 2003
9 Abercorn Street, Dundee DD4 7HY
[E-mail: james.redpath1@btinternet.com]
01382 458314

Dundee: Craigiebank (H) (01382 457951) linked with Douglas and Angus (01382 739884)
Michael V.A. Mair MA BD   1967 1998
244 Arbroath Road, Dundee DD4 7SB
01382 452337
Edith F. McMillan (Mrs) MA BD (Assoc)   1981 1999
19 Americanmuir Road, Dundee DD3 9AA
[E-mail: edith.stewart-macmillan@ukonline.co.uk]
01382 812423

Dundee: Douglas and Angus (01382 739884) See Dundee: Craigiebank

Dundee: Downfield South (H) (01382 810624)
Lezley J. Kennedy (Mrs) BD ThM MTh   2000
15 Elgin Street, Dundee DD3 8NL
[E-mail: kennedy@lezley.freeserve.co.uk]
01382 889498

Dundee: Dundee (St Mary's) (H) (01382 226271)
Keith F. Hall MA BD   1980 1994
33 Strathern Road, West Ferry, Dundee DD5 1PP
01382 778808

Dundee: Lochee Old and St Luke's (T)
Hazel Wilson (Ms) MA BD DipEd DMS   1991 2004
32 Clayhills Drive, Dundee DD2 1SX
[E-mail: hazel@feddal.freeserve.co.uk]
01382 561989

Dundee: Lochee West (H)
James A. Roy MA BD — 1965 — 1973 — Beechwood, 7 Northwood Terrace, Wormit, Newport-on-Tay DD6 8PP [E-mail: j.roy@btinternet.com] — 01382 543578

Dundee: Logie and St John's Cross (H)
David S. Scott MA BD — 1987 — 1999 — 7 Hyndford Street, Dundee DD2 1HQ — 01382 641572

Dundee: Mains (H) (01382 812166)
John M. Pickering BSc BD DipEd — 1997 — 2004 — 9 Elgin Street, Dundee DD3 8NL — 01382 825562
Jean Allan (Mrs) DCS — 12C Hindmarsh Avenue, Dundee DD3 7LW — 01382 827299

Dundee: Mains of Fintry (01382 508191)
Colin M. Brough BSc BD — 1998 — 2002 — 4 Clive Street, Dundee DD4 7AW [E-mail: colin.brough@btinternet.com] — 01382 458629

Dundee: Meadowside St Paul's (H) (01382 225420)
Maudeen I. MacDougall (Miss) BA BD — 1978 — 1984 — 36 Blackness Avenue, Dundee DD2 1HH — 01382 668828

Dundee: Menzieshill
Harry J. Brown LTh — 1991 — 1996 — The Manse, Charleston Drive, Dundee DD2 4ED [E-mail: harrybrown@aol.com] — 01382 667446
David Sutherland (Aux) — 6 Cromarty Drive, Dundee DD2 2UQ — 01382 621473

Dundee: Mid Craigie (T) (01382 506147)
Vacant — 96 Forfar Road, Dundee DD4 7BG — 01382 453926

Dundee: St Andrew's (H) (01382 224860)
Ian D. Petrie MA BD — 1970 — 1986 — 77 Blackness Avenue, Dundee DD2 1JN — 01382 641695

Dundee: St David's High Kirk (H) (01382 224433)
William B. Ross LTh CPS — 1988 — 2000 — 6 Adelaide Place, Dundee DD3 6LF — 01382 322955

Dundee: Steeple (H) (01382 223880)
David M. Clark MA BD — 1989 — 2000 — 128 Arbroath Road, Dundee DD4 7HR — 01382 455411

Dundee: Stobswell (H)
Jane L. Barron (Mrs) BA DipEd BD MTh — 1999 — 23 Shamrock Street, Dundee DD4 7AH [E-mail: jane.ian@virgin.net] — 01382 459119

Dundee: Strathmartine (H) (01382 825817)
Stewart McMillan BD — 1983 — 1990 — 19 Americanmuir Road, Dundee DD3 9AA [E-mail: edith.stewart-macmillan@ukonline.co.uk] — 01382 812423

Dundee: Trinity (H) (01382 459997)
James MacMillan BD — 1997 2003 — 5 Castlewood Avenue, Emmock Woods, The Barns of Clave, Dundee DD4 9FP — 01382 501334

Dundee: West
Andrew T. Greaves BD — 1985 2000 — 22 Hyndford Street, Dundee DD2 1HX [E-mail: andrew@greaves49.fsnet.co.uk] — 01382 646586

Dundee: Whitfield (E) (H) (01382 503012) (New Charge Development)
James L. Wilson BD CPS — 1986 2001 — 53 Old Craigie Road, Dundee DD4 7JD [E-mail: r3vjw@aol.com] — 01382 459249

Fowlis and Liff linked with Lundie and Muirhead of Liff (H) (01382 580550)
Donna M. Hays (Mrs) MTheol DipEd DipTMHA — 2004 — 149 Coupar Angus Road, Muirhead of Liff, Dundee DD2 5QN [E-mail: dmhays32@aol.com] — 01382 580210

Inchture and Kinnaird See Abernyte

Invergowrie (H)
Robert J. Ramsay LLB NP BD — 1986 1997 — 2 Boniface Place, Invergowrie, Dundee DD2 5DW [E-mail: robert@r-j-ramsay.fsnet.co.uk] — 01382 561118

Longforgan See Abernyte
Lundie and Muirhead of Liff See Fowlis and Liff

Monifieth: Panmure (H)
David B. Jamieson MA BD STM — 1974 — 8A Albert Street, Monifieth, Dundee DD5 4JS — 01382 532772

Monifieth: St Rule's (H)
Robert W. Massie LTh — 1989 1999 — Church Street, Monifieth, Dundee DD5 4JP [E-mail: revrwm@lineone.net] — 01382 532607

Monifieth: South
Donald W. Fraser MA — 1958 1959 — Queen Street, Monifieth, Dundee DD5 4HG — 01382 532646

Monikie and Newbigging
Vacant — 59B Broomwell Gardens, Monikie, Dundee DD5 3QP — 01382 370200

Murroes and Tealing See Auchterhouse

Barrett, Leslie M. BD FRICS — 1991 2001 — Chaplain: University of Abertay, Dundee — 26 Shoregate, Crail, Anstruther KY10 3SU [E-mail: leslie@abertay.ac.uk] — 01333 451599

Clarkson, Robert G. — 1950 1989 — (Dundee: Strathmartine) — 320 Strathmartine Road, Dundee DD3 8QG [E-mail: rob.gov@virgin.net] — 01382 825380

Name	Ord	Ind	Charge	Address	Tel
Craig, Iain R. MA	1948	1988	(Invergowrie)	Hope View, Burton Row, Brent Knoll, Highbridge, Somerset TA9 4BX	01278 760719
Craik, Sheila (Mrs) BD	1989	2001	(Dundee: Camperdown)	35 Haldane Terrace, Dundee DD3 0HT	01382 802078
Cramb, Erik M. LTh	1973	1989	Industrial Mission Organiser	65 Clepington Road, Dundee DD4 7BQ [E-mail: erikcramb@aol.com]	01382 458764
Douglas, Fiona C. (Miss) MA BD PhD	1989	1997	Chaplain: University of Dundee	10 Springfield, Dundee DD1 4JE	01382 344157
Gammack, George BD	1985	1999	(Dundee: Whitfield)	13A Hill Street, Broughty Ferry, Dundee DD5 2JP	01382 778636
Hawdon, John E. BA MTh AICS	1961	1995	(Dundee: Clepington)	53 Hillside Road, Dundee DD2 1QT [E-mail: jandjhawdon@btopenworld.com]	01382 646212
Hudson, J. Harrison DipTh MA BD	1961	1999	(Dundee: St Peter's McCheyne)	22 Hamilton Avenue, Tayport DD6 9BW	01382 552052
Ingram, J.R.	1954	1978	(Chaplain: RAF)	48 Marlee Road, Broughty Ferry, Dundee DD5 3EX	01382 736400
Laidlaw, John J. MA	1964	1973	(Adviser in Religious Education)	14 Dalhousie Road, Barnhill, Dundee DD5 2SQ	01382 477458
McLeod, David C. BSc MEng BD	1969	2001	(Dundee: Fairmuir)	6 Carseview Gardens, Dundee DD2 1NE [E-mail: david@mcleod6098.freeserve.co.uk]	01382 641371
Malvenan, Dorothy DCS	1964	1990	The Deaf Association, Dundee	Flat 19, 6 Craigie Street, Dundee DD4 6PF	01382 462495
Miller, Charles W. MA	1953	1994	(Fowlis and Lift)	'Palm Springs', Parkside, Auchterhouse, Dundee DD3 0RS	01382 320407
Milroy, Tom	1960	1992	(Monifieth: St Rule's)	9 Long Row, Westhaven, Carnoustie DD7 6BE	01241 856654
Mitchell, Jack MA BD CTh	1987	1996	(Dundee: Menzieshill)	10 Invergowrie Drive, Dundee DD2 1RF	01382 642301
Mowat, Gilbert M. MA	1948	1986	(Dundee: Albany-Butterburn)	7 Dunmore Gardens, Dundee DD2 1PP	01382 566013
Powrie, James E. LTh	1969	1995	(Dundee: Chalmers Ardler)	3 Kirktonhill Road, Kirriemuir DD8 4HU	01575 572503
Rae, Robert LTh	1968	1983	Chaplain: Dundee Acute Hospitals	14 Neddertoun View, Liff, Dundee DD3 5RU	01382 581790
Robertson, Thomas P.	1963	2001	(Dundee: Broughty Ferry St James')	20 Kilnburn, Newport-on-Tay DD6 8DE [E-mail: tp.robertson@ukonline.co.uk]	01382 542422
Rogers, James M. BA DB DCult	1955	1996	(Gibraltar)	24 Mansion Drive, Dunclaverhouse, Dundee DD4 9DD	01382 506162
Scroggie, John C.	1951	1985	(Mains)	4 Bell Tree Gardens, Balmossie, Dundee DD5 2LJ	01382 739354
Scoular, Stanley	1963	2000	(Rosyth)	31 Duns Crescent, Dundee DD4 0RY	01382 501653
Smith, Lilian MA DCS			(Deaconess)	6 Fintry Mains, Dundee DD4 9HF	01382 500052

DUNDEE ADDRESSES

Balgay	200 Lochee Road
Barnhill St Margaret's	10 Invermark Terrace
Broughty Ferry	
East	370 Queen Street
St Aidan's	408 Brook Street
St James'	5 Fort Street
St Luke's and Queen Street	5 West Queen Street
St Stephen's and West	96 Dundee Road
Camperdown	22 Brownhill Road
Chalmers Ardler	Turnberry Avenue
Clepington	Isla Street x Main Street
Craigiebank	Craigie Avenue at Greendyke Road
Douglas and Angus	Balbeggie Place
Downfield South	Haldane Street off Strathmartine Road
Dundee (St Mary's)	Nethergate
Fairmuir	329 Clepington Road
Lochee	
Old and St Luke's	Bright Street, Lochee
West	191 High Street, Lochee
Logie and St John's (Cross)	Shaftsbury Rd x Blackness Ave
Mains	Foot of Old Glamis Road
Mains of Fintry	Fintry Road x Fintry Drive
Meadowside St Paul's	114 Nethergate
Menzieshill	Charleston Drive, Lochee
Mid Craigie	Longtown Terrace
St Andrew's	2 King Street
St David's High Kirk	119A Kinghorne Road and 273 Strathmore Avenue
Steeple	Nethergate
Stobswell	Top of Albert Street
Strathmartine	513 Strathmartine Road
Trinity	73 Crescent Street
West	130 Perth Road
Whitfield	Haddington Crescent

(30) ANGUS

Meets at Forfar in St Margaret's Church Hall, on the first Tuesday of each month, except June when it meets on the last Tuesday, and January, July and August when there is no meeting.

Clerk:	REV. MALCOLM I.G. ROONEY DPE BEd BD		
Depute Clerk:	MRS HELEN McLEOD MA		
Presbytery Office:		St Margaret's Church, West High Street, Forfar DD8 1BJ	01307 464224
		[E-mail: akph36@uk.uumail.com]	

Aberlemno linked with Guthrie and Rescobie
Brian Ramsay BD DPS   1980   1984   The Manse, Guthrie, Forfar DD8 2TP   01241 828243

Airlie Ruthven Kingoldrum linked with Glenisla (H) Kilry Lintrathen
Ben Pieterse BA BTh LTh   2001   Balduff House, Kilry, Blairgowrie PH11 8HS   01575 560260
                                                                        [E-mail: benhp@tesco.net]

Arbirlot linked with Carmyllie
Ian O. Coltart CA BD   1988   2004   The Manse, Arbirlot, Arbroath DD11 2NX   01241 434479

Arbroath: Knox's (H) linked with Arbroath: St Vigeans (H)
Ian G. Gough MA BD MTh DMin   1974   1990   The Manse, St Vigeans, Arbroath DD11 4RD   01241 873206
                                                                        [E-mail: ianggough@btinternet.com]

Arbroath: Old and Abbey (H)
Valerie L. Allen (Ms) BMus MDiv   1990   1996   51 Cliffburn Road, Arbroath DD11 5BA   01241 872196 (Tel/Fax)
                                                                        [E-mail: vl2allen@aol.com]

Arbroath: St Andrew's (H)
W. Martin Fair BA BD DMin   1992   Albert Street, Arbroath DD11 1RA   01241 873238 (Tel/Fax)
                                                                        [E-mail: martinfair@aol.com]

Arbroath: St Vigeans See Arbroath: Knox's

Arbroath: West Kirk (H)
Alasdair G. Graham BD DipMin   1981   1986   1 Charles Avenue, Arbroath DD11 2EY   01241 872244
                                                                        [E-mail: alasdair.graham@lineone.net]

Barry linked with Carnoustie
Michael S. Goss BD DPS   1991   2003   44 Terrace Road, Carnoustie DD7 7AR   01241 410194 (Tel/Fax)
                                                                        [E-mail: mikegoss@aol.com]

Brechin: Cathedral (H)
Scott Rennie MA BD STM — 1999 — Chanonry Wynd, Brechin DD9 6JS [E-mail: scott@brechincathedral.freeserve.co.uk] — 01356 622783

Brechin: Gardner Memorial (H)
Moira Herkes (Mrs) BD — 1985 1999 — 36 Park Road, Brechin DD9 7AP [E-mail: mossherkes@aol.com] — 01356 622789

Carmyllie See Arbirlot
Carnoustie See Barry

Carnoustie: Panbride
Matthew S. Bicket BD — 1989 — 8 Arbroath Road, Carnoustie DD7 6BL [E-mail: matthew@bicket.freeserve.co.uk] — 01241 854478 (Tel) / 01241 855088 (Fax)

Colliston linked with Friockheim Kinnell linked with Inverkeilor and Lunan
Peter Phillips — 2004 — 18 Middlegate, Friockheim, Arbroath DD11 4TS — 01241 828781

Dun linked with Hillside
Vacant — 4 Manse Road, Hillside, Montrose DD10 9FB — 01674 830288

Dunnichen, Letham and Kirkden
Allan F. Webster MA BD — 1978 1990 — 7 Braehead Road, Letham, Forfar DD8 2PG [E-mail: allanfwebster@aol.com] — 01307 818916
Shirley Thomas (Mrs) (Aux) — 2000 2002 — 14 Kirkgait, Letham, Forfar DD8 2XQ [E-mail: martyn-shirley@thomas447.fsnet.net.uk] — 01307 818084

Eassie and Nevay linked with Newtyle
Carleen Robertson (Miss) BD — 1992 — 2 Kirkton Road, Newtyle, Blairgowrie PH12 8TS [E-mail: carleen.robertson@tesco.net] — 01828 650461

Edzell Lethnot (H) linked with Fern, Careston and Menmuir linked with Glenesk
Alan G.N. Watt MTh — 1996 2003 — Glenesk Cottage, Dunlappie Road, Edzell, Brechin DD9 7UB [E-mail: alangnwatt@aol.com] — 01356 648455

Farnell
Vacant — 01674 672060

Fern, Careston and Menmuir See Edzell Lethnot

Forfar: East and Old (H)
Graham Norrie MA BD — 1967 1978 — The Manse, Lour Road, Forfar DD8 2BB — 01307 464303

Forfar: Lowson Memorial (H)
Robert McCrum BD — 1982 — 1 Jamieson Street, Forfar DD8 2HY
[E-mail: robert.mccrum@virgin.net] — 01307 462248

Forfar: St Margaret's (H)
Jean B. Montgomerie (Miss) MA BD — 1973 1998 — 15 Potters Park Crescent, Forfar DD8 1HH
[E-mail: revjean@montgomerie.wanadoo.co.uk] — 01307 466390 (Tel/Fax)

Friockheim Kinnell See Colliston

Glamis, Inverarity and Kinnettles (T)
Vacant — 10 Kirk Wynd, Glamis, Forfar DD8 1RT — 01307 840206

Glenesk See Edzell Lethnot
Glenisla Kilry Lintrathen See Airlie Ruthven Kingoldrum

Glens, The and Kirriemuir: Old
Malcolm I.G. Rooney DPE BEd BD — 1993 1999 — 20 Strathmore Avenue, Kirriemuir DD8 4DJ
[E-mail: malcolm@gkopc.co.uk] — 01575 573724 / 07909 993233 (Mbl) / 01575 574937
Harry Mowbray (Aux) — 2003 — Viewlands, Beechwood Place, Kirriemuir DD8 5DZ

Guthrie and Rescobie See Aberlemno
Hillside See Dun

Inchbrayock linked with Montrose: Melville South
David S. Dixon MA BD — 1976 — The Manse, Ferryden, Montrose DD10 9SD
[E-mail: davidsdixon@ukonline.co.uk] — 01674 672108

Inverkeilor and Lunan See Colliston

Kirriemuir: St Andrew's linked with Oathlaw Tannadice
David J. Taverner MCIBS ACIS BD — 1996 2002 — 26 Quarry Park, Kirriemuir DD8 4DR
[E-mail: rahereuk@hotmail.com] — 01575 575561

Montrose: Melville South See Inchbrayock

Montrose: Old and St Andrew's
Laurence A.B. Whitley MA BD PhD — 1975 1985 — 2 Rosehill Road, Montrose DD10 8ST
[E-mail: labwhitley@btinternet.com] — 01674 672447

Newtyle See Eassie and Nevay
Oathlaw Tannadice See Kirriemuir: St Andrew's

Name			Parish	Address	Phone
Anderson, James W. BSc MTh	1986	1997	(Kincardine O'Neil with Lumphanan)	47 Glebe Road, Arbroath DD11 4HJ	01356 626222
Broadley, Linda J. (Mrs) LTh DipEd	1996	2004	(Caputh and Clunie with Kinclaven)	Maybank House, Panmure Street, Brechin DD9 6AP	01241 873298
Brodie, James BEM MA BD STM	1955	1974	(Hurlford)	25A Keptie Road, Arbroath DD11 3ED	01241 873062
Brownlie, Gavin D. MA	1955	1990	(Arbroath: Ladyloan St Columba's)	12 Cliffburn Road, Arbroath DD11 5BB	01241 411078
Bruce, William C. MA BD	1961	1995	(Motherwell: Dalziel)	31 Kirkton Terrace, Carnoustie DD7 7BZ	01241 828030
Butters, David	1964	1998	(Turriff: St Ninian's and Forglen)	68A Millgate, Friockheim, Arbroath DD11 4TN	01241 828717
Douglas, Iain M. MA BD MPhil DipEd	1960	2002	(Farnell with Montrose St Andrew's)	Old School House, Kinnell, Friockheim, Arbroath DD11 4UL	01356 625201
Drysdale James P.R.	1967	1999	(Brechin: Gardner Memorial)	51 Airlie Street, Brechin DD9 6JX	01575 573973
Duncan, Robert F. MTheol	1986	2001	(Lochgelly: St Andrew's)	25 Rowan Avenue, Kirriemuir DD8 4TB	01674 675522
Finlay, Quintin BA BD	1975	1996	(North Bute)	1 Brougham Square, Northesk Road, Montrose DD10 8TD	01307 461944
Hodge, William N.T.	1966	1995	(Longside)	'Tullochgorum', 61 South Street, Forfar DD8 2BS	01307 463193
Jones, William	1952	1987	(Kirriemuir: St Andrew's)	14 Muir Street, Forfar DD8 3JY	01241 854928
Milton, Eric G.	1963	1994	(Blairdaff)	16 Bruce Court, Links Parade, Carnoustie DD7 7JE	01307 818741
Perry, Joseph B.	1955	1989	(Farnell)	19 Guthrie Street, Letham, Forfar DD8 2PS	01307 818416
Reid, Albert B. BD BSc	1996	2001	(Ardler, Kettins and Meigle)	1 Dundee Street, Letham, Forfar DD8 2PQ	01241 872794
Searle, David C. MA DipTh	1965	2003	(Warden: Rutherford House)	12 Cairnie Road, Arbroath DD11 3DY	01307 818973
Smith, Hamish G.	1965	1993	(Auchterless with Rothienorman)	11A Guthrie Street, Letham, Forfar DD8 2PS	
Stevens, David MA	1935	1972	(Glenesk)	c/o Brown, Easter Coates Farm Cottage, Newburn, Upper Largo, Leven KY8 6JG	
Thomas, Martyn R.H. CEng MIStructE	1987	2002	(Fowlis and Liff with Lundie and Muirhead of Liff)	14 Kirkgait, Letham, Forfar DD8 2XQ	01307 818084
Tyre, Robert	1960	1998	(Aberdeen: St Ninian's with Stockethill)	8 Borrowfield Crescent, Montrose DD10 9BR	01674 676961
Warnock, Denis MA	1952	1990	(Kirkcaldy: Torbain)	19 Keptie Road, Arbroath DD11 3ED	01241 872740
Weatherhead, James L. CBE MA LLB DD	1960	1996	(Principal Clerk)	59 Brechin Road, Kirriemuir DD8 4DE	01575 572237
Youngson, Peter	1961	1996	(Kirriemuir: St Andrew's)	Coreen, Woodside, Northmuir, Kirriemuir DD8 4PG	01575 572832

ANGUS ADDRESSES

Arbroath

Old and Abbey	West Abbey Street
Knox's	Howard Street
St Andrew's	Hamilton Green
West Kirk	Keptie Street

Brechin

Cathedral	Bishops Close
Gardner Memorial	South Esk Street

Carnoustie

	Dundee Street
Panbride	Arbroath Road

Forfar

East: Old	East High Street
Lowson Memorial	Jamieson Street
St Margaret's	West High Street

Kirriemuir

Old	High Street
St Andrew's	Glamis Road

Montrose

Melville South	Castle Street
Old and St Andrew's	High Street

(31) ABERDEEN

Meets at St Mark's Church, Rosemount Viaduct, Aberdeen, on the first Tuesday of February, March, April, May, September, October, November and December, and on the fourth Tuesday of June.

Clerk:	REV. IAN A. McLEAN BSc BD		
Presbytery Office:	Mastrick Church, Greenfern Road, Aberdeen AB16 6TR [E-mail: akph34@uk.uumail.com]		01224 690494 (Tel/Fax)
Hon. Treasurer:	MR A. SHARP	27 Hutchison Terrace, Aberdeen AB10 7NN	01224 315702

Aberdeen: Beechgrove (H) (01224 632102)

| Iain M. Forbes BSc BD | 1964 | 2000 | 156 Hamilton Place, Aberdeen AB15 5BB [E-mail: beechgro@fish.co.uk] | 01224 642615 |

Aberdeen: Bridge of Don Oldmachar (01224 709299) (New Charge Development)

| Vacant | | | 60 Newburgh Circle, Aberdeen AB22 8QZ | 01224 708137 |

Aberdeen: Cove (E)

| Vacant | 1998 | | 4 Charleston Way, Cove, Aberdeen AB12 3FA | 01224 898030 |
| Mark Johnston (Assoc) | 2003 | | 5 Bruce Walk, Redmoss, Nigg, Aberdeen AB12 3LX [E-mail: ncdcove2@uk.uumail.com] | 01224 874269 |

Aberdeen: Craigiebuckler (H) (01224 315649)

| Kenneth L. Petrie MA BD | 1984 | 1999 | 185 Springfield Road, Aberdeen AB15 8AA [E-mail: patandkenneth@aol.com] | 01224 315125 |

Aberdeen: Denburn (H)

| James Patterson BSc BD | 2003 | | 122 Desswood Place, Aberdeen AB15 4DQ [E-mail: jimandmegan@btopenworld.com] | 01224 641033 |

Aberdeen: Ferryhill (H) (01224 213093)

| John H.A. Dick MA MSc BD | 1982 | | 54 Polmuir Road, Aberdeen AB11 7RT [E-mail: jhadick@fish.co.uk] | 01224 586933 |

Aberdeen: Garthdee (H)

| Vacant | | | 27 Ramsay Gardens, Aberdeen AB10 7AE | 01224 317452 |

Aberdeen: Gilcomston South (H) (01224 647144)

| D. Dominic Smart BSc BD MTh | 1988 | 1998 | 37 Richmondhill Road, Aberdeen AB15 5EQ [E-mail: smartdd@btconnect.com] | 01224 314326 |

Aberdeen: Greyfriars John Knox (T) (01224 644719)
Vacant — 41 Gray Street, Aberdeen AB10 6JD — 01224 584594

Aberdeen: High Hilton (H) (01224 494717)
A. Peter Dickson BSc BD — 1996 — 24 Rosehill Drive, Aberdeen AB24 4JJ [E-mail: peter@highhilton.com] — 01224 484155

Aberdeen: Holburn Central (H) (01224 580967)
George S. Cowie BSc BD — 1991 1999 — 6 St Swithin Street, Aberdeen AB10 6XE [E-mail: gscowie@aol.com] — 01224 593302

Aberdeen: Holburn West (H) (01224 571120)
Duncan C. Eddie MA BD — 1992 1999 — 31 Cranford Road, Aberdeen AB10 7NJ [E-mail: nacnud@ceddie.freeserve.co.uk] — 01224 325873

Aberdeen: Mannofield (H) (01224 310087)
John F. Anderson MA BD FSAScot — 1966 1975 — 21 Forest Avenue, Aberdeen AB15 4TU [E-mail: mannofieldchurch@lineone.net] — 01224 315748

Aberdeen: Mastrick (H) (01224 694121) (E-mail: mastrick.church@btconnect.com)
Vacant — 8 Corse Wynd, Kingswells, Aberdeen AB15 8TP

Aberdeen: Middlefield (H)
Vacant — 73 Manor Avenue, Aberdeen AB16 7UT — 01224 685214
Michael Phillippo (Aux) — 25 Deeside Crescent, Aberdeen AB15 7PT — 01224 318317

Aberdeen: New Stockethill (New Charge Development)
Ian M. Aitken MA BD — 1999 — 52 Ashgrove Road West, Aberdeen AB16 5EE [E-mail: ncdstockethill@uk.uumail.com] — 01224 686929

Aberdeen: North of St Andrew (T) (01224 643567)
Vacant — 51 Osborne Place, Aberdeen AB25 2BX — 01224 646429

Aberdeen: Northfield
Scott C. Guy BD — 1989 1999 — 28 Byron Crescent, Aberdeen AB16 7EX [E-mail: scguy@xalt.co.uk] — 01224 692332
Duncan Ross DCS — 64 Stewart Crescent, Aberdeen AB16 5SR [E-mail: dross@fish.co.uk] — 01224 692519

Aberdeen: Queen's Cross (H) (01224 644742)
Robert F. Brown MA BD ThM — 1971 1984 — 1 St Swithin Street, Aberdeen AB10 6XH [E-mail: minister@queenscrosschurch.org.uk] — 01224 322549

Aberdeen: Rosemount (H) (01224 620111)
A. David M. Graham BA BD — 1971 1983 — 22 Osborne Place, Aberdeen AB25 2DA — 01224 648041

Aberdeen: Rubislaw (H) (01224 645477)
Andrew G.N. Wilson MA BD DMin   1977   1987   45 Rubislaw Den South, Aberdeen AB15 4BD   01224 314878
[E-mail: agn.wilson@virgin.net]

Aberdeen: Ruthrieston South (H) (01224 211730)
Hugh F. Kerr MA BD   1968   1985   39 Gray Street, Aberdeen AB10 6JD   01224 586762

Aberdeen: Ruthrieston West (H)
Sean Swindells BD DipMin   1996   451 Great Western Road, Aberdeen AB10 6NL   01224 313075
[E-mail: seanswinl@aol.com]

Aberdeen: St Columba's Bridge of Don (H) (01224 825653)
Louis Kinsey BD DipMin   1991   151 Jesmond Avenue, Aberdeen AB22 8UG   01224 705337
[E-mail: revkinsey@aol.com]

Aberdeen: St George's Tillydrone (H) (01224 482204)
James Weir BD   1991   2003   127 Clifton Road, Aberdeen AB24 3RH   01224 483976
Ann V. Luncie (Miss) DCS   20 Langdykes Drive, Cove, Aberdeen AB12 3HW   01224 898416

Aberdeen: St John's Church for Deaf People (H) (01224 494566)
John R. Osbeck BD   1979   1991   15 Deeside Crescent, Aberdeen AB15 7PT   (Voice/Text) 01224 315595
[E-mail: info@aneds.org.uk]

Aberdeen: St Machar's Cathedral (H) (01224 485988)
Alan D. Falconer MA BD DLitt   18 The Chanonry, Old Aberdeen AB24 1RQ   01224 483688

Aberdeen: St Mark's (H) (01224 640672)
John M. Watson LTh   1989   65 Mile-end Avenue, Aberdeen AB15 5PU   01224 622470
[E-mail: jomwat@aol.com]

Aberdeen: St Mary's (H) (01224 487227)
Elsie Fortune (Mrs) BSc BD   2003   456 King Street, Aberdeen AB24 3DE   01224 633778

Aberdeen: St Nicholas Uniting, Kirk of (H) (01224 643494)
J. Ross McLaren MBE   1964   2002   8 Hilton Street, Aberdeen AB24 4QX   01224 491160

Aberdeen: St Nicholas Kincorth, South of
Edward C. McKenna BD DPS   1989   2002   The Manse, Kincorth Circle, Aberdeen AB12 5NX   01224 872820

Aberdeen: St Ninian's (T) (01224 319519)
Alison J. Swindells (Mrs) LLB BD   1998   2000   451 Great Western Road, Aberdeen AB10 6NL   01224 317667
[E-mail: alisonswindells@aol.com]

Aberdeen: St Stephen's (H) (01224 624443)
James M. Davies BSc BD   1982   1989   6 Belvidere Street, Aberdeen AB25 2QS   01224 635694
[E-mail: daviesjim@btinternet.com]

Aberdeen: Summerhill (H)
Ian A. McLean BSc BD — 1981 — 36 Stronsay Drive, Aberdeen AB15 6JL
[E-mail: iamclean@lineone.net] — 01224 324669

Aberdeen: Torry St Fittick's (H) (01224 899183)
Iain C. Barclay — 1976 1999 — 11 Devanha Gardens East, Aberdeen AB11 7UH
MBE TD MA BD MTh MPhil PhD
[E-mail: st.fittick@virgin.net] — 01224 588245 / 07968 131930 (Mbl) / 07625 383830 (Pager)

Aberdeen: Woodside (H) (01224 277249)
Vacant — 322 Clifton Road, Aberdeen AB24 4HQ — 01224 484562
Ann V. Lundie DCS — 20 Langdykes Drive, Cove, Aberdeen AB12 3HW — 01224 898416

Buckburn Stoneywood (H) (01224 712411)
Nigel Parker BD MTh — 1994 — 25 Gilbert Road, Bucksburn, Aberdeen AB21 9AN
[E-mail: nigel@revparker.fsnet.co.uk] — 01224 712635

Cults: East (T) (H) (01224 869028)
Vacant — Cults, Aberdeen AB15 9TD — 01224 867587

Cults: West (H) (01224 869566)
Vacant — 3 Quarry Road, Cults, Aberdeen AB15 9EX — 01224 867417

Dyce (H) (01224 771295)
Russel Moffat BD MTh PhD — 1986 1998 — 144 Victoria Street, Dyce, Aberdeen AB21 7BE
[E-mail: russelbrenda@dyce144.freeserve.co.uk] — 01224 722380

Kingswells
Vacant — Kingswells Manse, Lang Stracht, Aberdeen AB15 8PL — 01224 740229

Newhills (H) (Tel/Fax: 01224 716161)
Norman Maciver MA BD DMin — 1976 — Newhills Manse, Bucksburn, Aberdeen AB21 9SS
[E-mail: newhillsnm@aol.com] — 01224 712655

Peterculter (H) (01224 735845)
John A. Ferguson BD DipMin — 1988 1999 — 7 Howie Lane, Peterculter, Aberdeen AB14 0LJ
[E-mail: jc.ferguson@virgin.net] — 01224 735041

Name				
Aitchison, James W. BD	1993		Chaplain: Army	HQ Briticon, UNFICUP, BFPO 567
Alexander, William M. BD	1971	1998	(Berriedale and Dunbeath with Latheron)	110 Fairview Circle, Danestone, Aberdeen AB22 8YR — 01224 703752
Ballantyne, Samuel MA BD	1941	1982	(Rutherford)	26 Cairncry Road, Aberdeen AB16 5DP — 01224 483049

Name			Charge	Address	Tel
Beattie, Walter G. MA BD	1956	1995	(Arbroath Old and Abbey)	126 Seafield Road, Aberdeen AB15 7YQ	01224 329259
Bryden, Agnes Y. (Mrs) DCS			(Deaconess)	9 Rosewell Place, Aberdeen AB15 6HN	01224 315042
Campbell, W.M.M. BD CPS	1970	2003	(Hospital Chaplain)	43 Murray Terrace, Aberdeen AB11 7SA	07761 235815
Coutts, Fred MA BD	1973	1989	(Hospital Chaplain)	9A Millburn Street, Aberdeen AB11 6SS	01224 583805
Cowie, Marion (Mrs) MA BD MTh	1990	2003	(Hospital Chaplain)	6 St Swithin Street, Aberdeen AB10 6XE	01224 593302
Crawford, Michael S.M. LTh	1966	2002	(Aberdeen: St Mary's)	9 Craigton Avenue, Aberdeen AB15 7RR	01224 208341
Deans, John Bell	1951	1986	(Hospital Chaplain)	14 Balmoral Avenue, Ellon AB41 9EW	01358 721539
Dickson, John C. MA	1950	1987	(Aberdeen St Fittick's)	36 Queen Victoria Park, Inchmarlo, Banchory AB31 4AL	01330 826236
Douglas, Andrew M. MA	1957	1995	(High Hilton)	219 Countesswells Road, Aberdeen AB15 7RD	01224 311932
Falconer, James B. BD	1982	1991	(Hospital Chaplain)	3 Brimmond Walk, Westhill AB32 6XH	01224 744621
Finlayson, Ena (Miss) DCS			(Deaconess)	16E Denwood, Aberdeen AB15 6JF	01224 321147
Goldie, George D. ALCM	1953	1995	(Greyfriars)	27 Broomhill Avenue, Aberdeen AB10 6JL	01224 322503
Gordon, Laurie Y.	1960	1995	(John Knox)	1 Alder Drive, Portlethen, Aberdeen AB12 4WA	01224 782703
Grainger, Harvey L. LTh	1975	2004	(Kingswells)	13 St Ronan's Crescent, Peterculter, Aberdeen AB14 0RL	01224 733563
				[E-mail: harveygrainger@tiscali.co.uk]	
Grubb, Anthony J. MA BD	1937	1986	(Deer)	Ardier House, Oakdale Terrace, Aberdeen AB15 7PT	01224 352177
Haddow, Angus BSc	1963	1999	(Methlick)	25 Lerwick Road, Aberdeen AB16 6RF	01224 696362
Hamilton, Helen (Miss) BD	1991	2003	(Glasgow: St James' Pollok)	The Cottage, West Tilbouries, Maryculter, Aberdeen AB12 5GD	01224 739632
Hutchison, A. Scott MA BD DD	1957	1991	(Hospital Chaplain)	Ashfield, Drumoak, Banchory AB31 5AG	01330 811309
Hutchison, Alison M. (Mrs) BD DipMin	1988	1988	Hospital Chaplain	Ashfield, Drumoak, Banchory AB31 5AG	01330 811309
				[E-mail: amhutch62@aol.com]	
Hutchison, David S. BSc BD ThM	1991	1999	(Aberdeen: Torry St Fittick's)	51 Don Street, Aberdeen AB24 1UH	01224 276122
Jack, David LTh	1984	1999	(West Mearns)	7 Cromwell Road, Aberdeen AB15 4UH	01224 325355
Johnstone, William MA BD	1963	2001	(University of Aberdeen)	9/5 Mount Alvernia, Edinburgh EH16 6AW	0131-664 3140
McCallum, Moyra (Miss) MA BD DCS			(Deaconess)	176 Hilton Drive, Aberdeen AB24 4LT	01224 486240
				[E-mail: moymac@aol.com]	
Main, Alan TD MA BD STM PhD	1963	2001	(University of Aberdeen)	Kirkfield, Barthol Chapel, Inverurie AB51 8TD	01651 806773
				[E-mail: amain@fish.co.uk]	
Mirrilees, J.B. MA BD	1937	1977	(High Hilton)	22 King's Gate, Aberdeen AB15 4EJ	01224 638351
Richardson, Thomas C. LTh ThB	1971	2004	(Cults: West)	19 Kinkell Road, Aberdeen AB15 8HR	01224 315328
				[E-mail: thomas.richardson7@btinternet.com]	
Rodgers, D. Mark BA BD MTh	1987	2003	Hospital Chaplain	152D Gray Street, Aberdeen AB10 6JW	01224 210810
Russell, Andrew M. MA BD *	1940	1976	(Woodside North)	3 Hill Place, Alloa FK10 2LP	01259 213115
Sefton, Henry R MA BD STM PhD	1957	1992	(University of Aberdeen)	25 Albury Place, Aberdeen AB11 6TQ	01224 572305
Skakle, George S. MA	1945	1987	(Aberdeen Powis)	30 Whitehall Terrace, Aberdeen AB25 2RY	01224 646478
Smith, Angus MA LTh	1965	1991	Industrial Chaplain	1 Fa'burn Terrace, Lumphanan, Banchory AB31 4AG	01339 883395
Stewart, James C. MA BD STM	1960	2000	(Aberdeen: Kirk of St Nicholas)	54 Murray Terrace, Aberdeen AB11 7SB	01224 587071
Strachan, Ian M. MA BD	1959	1994	(Ashkirk with Selkirk)	'Cardenwell', Glen Drive, Dyce, Aberdeen AB21 7EN	01224 772028
Swinton, John BD PhD	1999		University of Aberdeen	51 Newburgh Circle, Bridge of Don, Aberdeen AB22 8XA	01224 825637
				[E-mail: j.swinton@abdn.ac.uk]	
Watt, William G.	1970	1977	(South of St Nicholas Kincorth)	50 Rosewell Gardens, Aberdeen AB15 6HZ	01224 321915
Wilkie, William E. LTh	1978	2001	(Aberdeen: St Nicholas Kincorth, South of)	38 St Anne's Crescent, Newtonhill, Stonehaven AB39 3WZ	01569 731630
Wood, James L.K.	1967	1995	(Ruthrieston West)	1 Glen Drive, Dyce, Aberdeen AB21 7EN	01224 722543

ABERDEEN ADDRESSES

Beechgrove	Beechgrove Avenue	
Bridge of Don		
Oldmachar	Ashwood Park	
Cove	Loirston Primary School, Loirston Avenue	
Craigiebuckler	Springfield Road	
Cults East	North Deeside Road, Cults	
Cults West	Quarry Road, Cults	
Denburn	Summer Street	
Dyce	Victoria Street, Dyce	
Ferryhill	Fonthill Road x Polmuir Road	
Garthdee	Ramsay Gardens	
Gilcomston South	Union Street x Summer Street	
Greyfriars John Knox	Broad Street	
High Hilton	Hilton Drive	
Holburn	Holburn Street	
Central	Great Western Road	
West	Old Skene Road, Kingswells	
Kingswells	Great Western Road x Craigton Road	
Mannofield	Greenfern Road	
Mastrick	Manor Avenue	
Middlefield		
New Stockethill		
North Church of St Andrew	Queen Street	
Northfield	Byron Crescent	
Peterculter	Craigton Crescent	
Queen's Cross	Albyn Place	
Rosemount	Rosemount Place	
Rubislaw	Queen's Gardens	
Ruthrieston		
South	Holburn Street	
West		Broomhill Road
St Columba's		Braehead Way, Bridge of Don
St George's		Hayton Road, Tillydrone
St John's for the Deaf		Smithfield Road
St Machar's		The Chanonry
St Mark's		Rosemount Viaduct
St Mary's		King Street
St Nicholas Kincorth, South of		Kincorth Circle
St Nicholas Uniting, Kirk of		Union Street
St Ninian's		Mid Stocket Road
St Stephen's		Powis Place
Summerhill		Stronsay Drive
Torry St Fittick's		Walker Road
Woodside		Church Street, Woodside

(32) KINCARDINE AND DEESIDE

Meets at Fetteresso, Stonehaven on the first Tuesday of February, the last Tuesday of March, the first Tuesday of May, the last Tuesday of June, the last Tuesday of September, the first Tuesday of November and the first Tuesday of December at 7pm.

Clerk: REV. JACK HOLT BSc BD   The Manse, Finzean, Banchory AB31 6PB   01330 850339
[E-mail: akph58@uk.uumail.com]
[E-mail: kincardinedeeside.presbytery@uk.uumail.com]

Aberluthnott linked with Laurencekirk (H)   1985   2001
Ronald Gall BSc BD   Aberdeen Road, Laurencekirk AB30 1AJ   01561 378838
[E-mail: ronniegall@aol.com]

Aboyne – Dinnet (H)
Vacant   49 Charlton Crescent, Charlton Park, Aboyne AB34 5GN   01339 886447

Arbuthnott linked with Bervie
Vacant   10 Kirkburn, Inverbervie, Montrose DD10 0RT   01561 362633

Banchory-Devenick and Maryculter/Cookney

Bruce K. Gardner MA BD PhD	1988	2002	The Manse, Kirkton of Maryculter, Aberdeen AB12 5FS [E-mail: ministerofbdmc@aol.com]	01224 735776

Banchory-Ternan: East (H) (Tel: 01330 820380; E-mail: eastchurch@banchory.fsbusiness.co.uk)

Mary M. Haddow (Mrs) BD		2001	East Manse, Station Road, Banchory AB31 5YP [E-mail: mary_haddow@ntlworld.com]	01330 822481
Anthony Stephen MA BD (Assistant Minister and Youth Leader)		2001	72 Grant Road, Banchory AB31 5UU	01330 825038

Banchory-Ternan: West (H)

Donald K. Walker BD	1979	1995	2 Wilson Road, Banchory AB31 5UY [E-mail: btw@uk2.net]	01330 822811
Anthony Stephen MA BD (Assistant Minister and Youth Leader)		2001	72 Grant Road, Banchory AB31 5UU	01330 825038

Bervie See Arbuthnott

Birse and Feughside

Jack Holt BSc BD	1985	1994	The Manse, Finzean, Banchory AB31 6PB [E-mail: jack@finzean.freeserve.co.uk]	01330 850237

Braemar linked with Crathie

Robert P. Sloan MA BD	1968	1996	Manse, Crathie, Ballater AB35 5UL	01339 742208

Crathie See Braemar

Cromar

Lawrie I. Lennox MA BD DipEd	1991	2001	Aberdeen Road, Tarland, Aboyne AB34 4UA	01339 881464

Drumoak (H) and Durris (H)

James Scott MA BD	1973	1992	Manse, Durris, Banchory AB31 6BU [E-mail: jimscott@durrismanse.freeserve.co.uk]	01330 844557

Glenmuick (Ballater) (H)

Anthony Watts BD DipTechEd JP		1999	The Manse, Craigendarroch Walk, Ballater AB35 5ZB	01339 754014

Kinneff linked with Stonehaven: South (H)

David J. Stewart BD MTh DipMin		2000	South Church Manse, Cameron Street, Stonehaven AB39 2HE [E-mail: brigodon@ifb.co.uk]	01569 762576

Laurencekirk See Aberluthnott

Mearns Coastal

George I. Hastie MA BD	1971	1998	The Manse, Kirkton, St Cyrus, Montrose DD10 0BW	01674 850880 (Tel/Fax)

Mid Deeside
Norman Nicoll BD | 2003 | The Manse, Torphins, Banchory AB31 4GQ | 01339 882276

Newtonhill
Hugh Conkey BSc BD | 1987 2001 | 39 St Ternans Road, Newtonhill, Stonehaven AB39 3PF | 01569 730143
[E-mail: conkey@tesco.net]

Portlethen (H) (01224 782883)
Flora J. Munro (Mrs) BD | 1993 2004 | 18 Rowanbank Road, Portlethen, Aberdeen AB12 4QY | 01224 780211

Stonehaven: Dunnottar (H)
Gordon Farquharson MA BD DipEd | 1998 | Dunnottar Manse, Stonehaven AB39 3XL | 01569 762874
[E-mail: gfarqu@lineone.net]

Stonehaven: Fetteresso (H) (Tel: 01569 767689; E-mail: office@fetteressokirk.org.uk)
John R. Notman BSc BD | 1990 2001 | 11 South Lodge Drive, Stonehaven AB39 2PN | 01569 762876
[E-mail: jr.notman@virgin.net]

Stonehaven: South See Kinneff

West Mearns
Catherine A. Hepburn (Miss) BA BD | 1982 2000 | West Mearns Parish Church Manse, Fettercairn, Laurencekirk AB30 1UE | 01561 340203
[E-mail: chepburn@fish.co.uk]

Name			Charge	Address	Phone
Brown, Alastair BD	1986	1992	(Glenmuick, Ballater)	52 Henderson Drive, Kintore, Inverurie AB51 0FB	01467 632787
Brown, J.W.S. BTh	1960	1995	(Cromar)	10 Forestside Road, Banchory AB31 5ZH	01330 824353
Caie, Albert LTh	1983	1997	(Glenmuick [Ballater])	34 Ringwell Gardens, Stonehouse, Larkhall ML9 3QW	
Christie, Andrew C. LTh	1975	2000	(Banchory-Devenick and Maryculter/Cookney)	17 Broadstraik Close, Elrick, Aberdeen AB32 6JP	01224 746888
Forbes, John W.A. BD	1973	1999	(Edzell Lethnot with Fern, Careston and Menmuir with Glenesk)	Mid Clune, Finzean, Banchory AB31 6PL	01330 850283
Gray, Robert MA BD	1942	1982	(Stonehaven Fetteresso)	4 Park Drive, Stonehaven AB39 2NW	01569 767027
Hood, E.C.P. MA	1946	1989	(Methlick)	1 Silver Gardens, Stonehaven AB39 2LH	
Kinniburgh, Elizabeth B.F. (Miss) MA BD	1970	1986	(Birse with Finzean with Strachan)	7 Huntly Cottages, Aboyne AB31 5HD	01339 886757
Lamb, A. Douglas MA	1964	2002	(Dalry: St Margaret's)	130 Denstrath Road, Edzell Woods, Brechin DD9 7XF [E-mail: lamb.edzell@talk21.com]	01356 648139
MacLeod, Kenneth	1950	1986	(Bourtreebush with Portlethen)	30 Woodlands Place, Inverbervie, Montrose DD10 0SL	01561 362414
Nicholson, William	1949	1986	(Banchory-Ternan: East with Durris)	10 Pantoch Gardens, Banchory AB31 5ZD	01330 823875
Rennie, Donald B. MA	1956	1996	(Lumphanan)	Mernis Howe, Inverurie Street, Auchenblae, Laurencekirk AB30 1XS	01561 320622
Skinner, Silvester MA	1941	1979	(Industrial Chaplain)	29 Silverbank Gardens, Banchory AB31 3YZ	01330 823032
Smith, J.A. Wemyss MA	1947	1983	(Garvock St Cyrus)	30 Greenbank Drive, Edinburgh EH10 5RE	0131-447 2205

Taylor, Peter R. JP BD	1977 2001	(Torphins)	42 Beltie Road, Torphins, Banchory AB31 4JT	01339 882780
Tierney, John P. MA	1945 1985	(Peterhead West Associate)	3 Queenshill Drive, Aboyne AB34 5DG	01339 886741
Urie, D.M.L. MA BD PhD	1940 1980	(Kincardine O'Neil)	5 Glebe Park, Kincardine O'Neil, Aboyne AB34 5ED	01339 884204
Watt, William D. LTh	1978 1996	(Aboyne – Dinnet)	2 West Toll Crescent, Aboyne AB34 5GB	01339 886943

(33) GORDON

Meets at various locations on the first Tuesday of February, March, April, May, September, October, November and December, and on the fourth Tuesday of June.

Clerk: REV. G. EUAN D. GLEN BSc BD   The Manse, 26 St Ninian's, Monymusk, Inverurie AB51 7HF   01467 651941
[E-mail: akph52@uk.uumail.com]

Barthol Chapel linked with Tarves
Vacant   8 Murray Avenue, Tarves, Ellon AB41 7LZ   01651 851250

Belhelvie (H)
Vacant   Belhelvie Manse, Balmedie, Aberdeen AB23 8YR   01358 742227

Blairdaff linked with Chapel of Garioch
Kim Cran (Mrs) MDiv BA   1993   2000   The Manse, Chapel of Garioch, Inverurie AB51 5HE   01467 681619
[E-mail: blairdaff.chapelofgariochparish@btinternet.com]

Chapel of Garioch See Blairdaff

Cluny (H) linked with Monymusk (H)
G. Euan D. Glen BSc BD   1992   The Manse, 26 St Ninian's, Monymusk, Inverurie AB51 7HF   01467 651470
[E-mail: euanglen@aol.com]

Culsalmond and Rayne linked with Daviot (H)
Mary M. Cranfield (Miss) MA BD DMin   1989   The Manse, Daviot, Inverurie AB51 0HY   01467 671241
[E-mail: marymc@ukgateway.net]

Cushnie and Tough (T) (H)
Margaret J. Garden (Miss) BD   1993   2000   The Manse, Muir of Fowlis, Alford AB33 8JU   01975 581239
[E-mail: m.garden@virgin.net]

Daviot See Culsalmond and Rayne

Drumblade linked with Huntly Strathbogie
Neil I.M. MacGregor BD   1995   Deveron Road, Huntly AB54 5DU   01466 792702

Echt linked with Midmar (T)
Alan Murray BSc BD PhD
2003
The Manse, Echt, Westhill AB32 7AB
[E-mail: ladecottage@btinternet.com]
01330 860004

Ellon
Eleanor E. Macalister (Mrs) BD
1994 1999
The Manse, Union Street, Ellon AB41 9BA
[E-mail: maca1lster@aol.com]
01358 720476

Sheila Craggs (Mrs) (Aux)
2001
7 Morar Court, Ellon AB41 9GG
01358 723055

Fintray and Kinellar linked with Keithhall
Dolly Purnell BD
2003
20 Kinmhor Rise, Blackburn, Aberdeen AB21 0LJ
[E-mail: dolly@npurnell.freeserve.co.uk]
01224 790701

Foveran
Neil Gow BSc MEd BD
1996 2001
The Manse, Foveran, Ellon AB41 6AP
[E-mail: the-gows@lineone.net]
01358 789288

Howe Trinity
John A. Cook MA BD
1986 2000
The Manse, 110 Main Street, Alford AB33 8AD
[E-mail: j-a-cook@howe-trinity.freeserve.co.uk]
01975 562282

Huntly Cairnie Glass
Thomas R. Calder LLB BD WS
1994
The Manse, Queen Street, Huntly AB54 8EB
01466 792630

Huntly Strathbogie See Drumblade

Insch-Leslie-Premnay-Oyne (H)
Jane C. Taylor (Miss) BD DipMin
1990 2001
22 Western Road, Insch AB52 6JR
01464 820914

Inverurie: St Andrew's
T. Graeme Longmuir KSJ MA BEd
1976 2001
St Andrew's Manse, 1 Ury Dale, Inverurie AB51 3XW
[E-mail: standrew@ukonline.co.uk]
01467 620468

Risby, Lesley P. (Mrs) BD (Assistant)
1994 2002
Middle Pitmunie, Monymusk, Inverurie AB51 7HX
01467 651791

Inverurie: West
Ian B. Groves BD CPS
1989
West Manse, 42 Westfield Road, Inverurie AB51 3YS
[E-mail: i.groves@inveruriewestchurch.org]
01467 620285

Keithhall See Fintray and Kinellar

Kemnay
John P. Renton BA LTh
1976 1990
Kemnay, Inverurie AB51 9ND
[E-mail: johnrenton@btinternet.com]
01467 642219 (Tel/Fax)

Kintore (H)
Alan Greig BSc BD — 1977 1992 — 6 Forest Road, Kintore, Inverurie AB51 0XG [E-mail: greig@kincarr.free-online.co.uk] — 01467 632219 (Tel/Fax)

Meldrum and Bourtie
Hugh O'Brien CSS MTheol — 2001 — The Manse, Urquhart Road, Oldmeldrum, Inverurie AB51 0EX [E-mail: minister@meldrum-bourtiechurch.org] — 01651 872250

Methlick
Albert E. Smith BD FSAScot — 1983 1999 — Methlick, Ellon AB41 0DS [E-mail: aesmethlick@aol.com] — 01651 806215

Midmar See Echt
Monymusk See Cluny

New Machar
Manson C. Merchant BD CPS — 1992 2001 — The Manse, Disblair Road, Newmachar, Aberdeen AB21 0RD [E-mail: mcmerchant@btopenworld.com] — 01651 862278

Noth
John McCallum BD DipPTh — 1989 — The Manse of Noth, Kennethmont, Huntly AB54 4NP [E-mail: rev.john@btopenworld.com] — 01464 831244

Skene (H)
Iain U. Thomson MA BD — 1970 1972 — The Manse, Kirkton of Skene, Skene AB32 6LX — 01224 743277
Marion G. Stewart (Miss) DCS — Kirk Cottage, Kirkton of Skene, Skene AB32 6XE — 01224 743407

Tarves See Barthol Chapel

Udny and Pitmedden
George R. Robertson LTh — 1985 — Manse Road, Udny Green, Udny, Ellon AB41 0RS — 01651 842052

Upper Donside (H)
Vacant — Lumsden, Huntly AB54 4GQ — 01464 861757

Name			Note	Address	Phone
Andrew, John MA BD DipRE DipEd	1961	1995	(Teacher: Religious Education)	Cartar's Croft, Midmar, Inverurie AB51 7NJ	01330 833208
Bowie, Alfred LTh	1974	1998	(Alford with Keig with Tullynessle Forbes)	17 Stewart Road, Alford AB33 8UD	01975 563824
Collie, Joyce P. (Miss) MA PhD	1966	1994	(Corgarff Strathdon and Glenbuchat Towie)	35 Foudland Court, Insch AB52 6LG	01464 820945
Dryden, Ian MA DipEd	1988	2001	(New Machar)	16 Glenhome Gardens, Dyce, Aberdeen AB21 7FG	01224 722820
Hawthorn, Daniel MA BD DMin	1965	2004	(Belhelvie)	7 Crimond Drive, Ellon AB41 8BT [E-mail: donhawthorn@compuserve.com]	(Mbl) 07971 906146
Jones, Robert A. LTh CA	1966	1997	(Marnoch)	13 Gordon Terrace, Inverurie AB51 4GT	01467 622691
Lister, Douglas	1945	1986	(Largo and Newburn)	Gowanbank, Port Elphinstone, Inverurie AB51 3UN	01467 621262
Macallan, Gerald B.	1954	1992	(Kintore)	82 Angusfield Avenue, Aberdeen AB15 6AT	01224 316125

McLean, John MA BD	1967	2003	(Bathgate: Boghall)	16 Eastside Drive, Westhill AB32 6QN	01224 747701
McLeish, Robert S.	1970	2000	(Insch-Leslie-Premnay-Oyne)	19 Western Road, Insch AB52 6JR	01464 820749
Mack, John C. JP (Aux)	1985	2001	Presbytery Auxiliary Minister	The Willows, Auchleven, Insch AB52 6QD	01464 820387
Mellis, Robert J. BTh CA	1982	1998	(Shapinsay)	81 Western Avenue, Ellon AB41 9EX	01358 721929
Milligan, Rodney	1949	1985	(Culsalmond with Rothienorman)	Cameron House, Culduthel Road, Inverness IV2 4YG	01463 243241
Rodger, Matthew A. BD	1978	1999	(Ellon)	57 Eilean Rise, Ellon AB41 9NF	01358 724556
Scott, Allan D. BD	1977	1989	(Culsalmond with Daviot with Rayne)	20 Barclay Road, Inverurie AB51 3QP	01467 625161
Stewart, George C. MA	1952	1995	(Drumblade with Huntly Strathbogie)	104 Scott Drive, Huntly AB54 5PF	
Stoddart, A. Grainger	1975	2001	(Meldrum and Bourtie)	6 Mayfield Gardens, Insch AB52 6XL	01464 821124
Wallace, R.J. Stuart MA	1947	1986	(Foveran)	Manse View, Manse Road, Methlick, Ellon AB41 7DW	01651 806843

(34) BUCHAN

Meets at St Kane's Centre, New Deer, Turriff on the first Tuesday of each month with the exception of January, July and August.

Clerk:	MR G.W. BERSTAN			Faithlie, Victoria Terrace, Turriff AB53 4GE [E-mail: akph41@uk.uumail.com]	01888 562392

Aberdour linked with Pitsligo linked with Sandhaven
Vacant — The Manse, 49 Pitsligo Street, Rosehearty, Fraserburgh AB43 7JL — 01346 571237

Auchaber United linked with Auchterless
Alison Jaffrey (Mrs) MA BD — 1990 1999 — The Manse, Auchterless, Turriff AB53 8BA [E-mail: alison.jaffrey@bigfoot.com] — 01888 511217

Auchterless See Auchaber United

Banff linked with King Edward
Alan Macgregor BA BD — 1992 1998 — 7 Colleonard Road, Banff AB45 1DZ [E-mail: alan.macgregor@banff98.freeserve.co.uk] — 01261 812107 (Tel) / 01261 818526 (Fax)

Crimond linked with Lonmay linked with St Fergus
Vacant — The Manse, Crimond, Fraserburgh AB43 8QJ — 01346 532431

Cruden
Rodger Neilson JP BSc BD — 1972 1974 — Hatton, Peterhead AB42 0QQ [E-mail: r.neilson@tiscali.co.uk] — 01779 841229 (Tel) / 01779 841822 (Fax)

Deer (H)
James Wishart JP BD — 1986 — Old Deer, Peterhead AB42 5JB [E-mail: jimmy_wishart@lineone.net] — 01771 623582

Fordyce
Iain A. Sutherland BSc BD — 1996 2000 — Seafield Terrace, Portsoy, Banff AB45 2QB [E-mail: revsuthy@aol.com] — 01261 842272

Fraserburgh: Old
Douglas R. Clyne BD — 1973 — The Old Parish Church Manse, 4 Robbies Road, Fraserburgh AB43 7AF [E-mail: manse1@supanet.com] — 01346 518536

Fraserburgh: South (H) linked with Inverallochy and Rathen: East
Ronald F. Yule — 1982 — 15 Victoria Street, Fraserburgh AB43 9PJ — 01346 518244 (Tel) / 0870 055 4665 (Fax)

Fraserburgh: West (H) linked with Rathen: West
B. Andrew Lyon LTh — 1971 1978 — 23 Strichen Road, Fraserburgh AB43 9SA [E-mail: balyon@tiscali.co.uk] — 01346 513303 (Tel) / 01346 512398 (Fax)

Fyvie linked with Rothienorman
Robert J. Thorburn BD — 1978 2004 — The Manse, Fyvie, Turriff AB53 8RD — 01651 891230

Gardenstown
Donald N. Martin BD — 1996 — The Manse, Fernie Brae, Gardenstown, Banff AB45 3YL [E-mail: d.n.martin@virgin.net] — 01261 851256 (Tel) / 01261 851022 (Fax)

Inverallochy and Rathen: East See Fraserburgh: South
King Edward See Banff

Longside
Norman A. Smith MA BD — 1997 — 9 Anderson Drive, Longside, Peterhead AB42 4XG [E-mail: norm@smith1971.fsnet.co.uk] — 01779 821224

Lonmay See Crimond

Macduff
David J. Randall MA BD ThM — 1971 — Manse of Doune, Banff AB45 3QL [E-mail: djrandall@macduff.force9.co.uk] — 01261 832316 (Tel) / 01261 832301 (Fax)

Marnoch
Vacant — Aberchirder, Huntly AB54 7TS — 01466 780276

Maud and Savoch linked with New Deer: St Kane's
Alistair P. Donald MA PhD BD — 1999 — The Manse, New Deer, Turriff AB53 6TD — 01771 644216

Monquhitter and New Byth linked with Turriff: St Andrew's

James Cook MA MDiv	1999	2002	Balmellie Road, Turriff AB53 4SP [E-mail: therev@jimmiecook.freeserve.co.uk]	01888 560304

New Deer: St Kane's See Maud and Savoch

New Pitsligo linked with Strichen and Tyrie

Vacant	Kingsville, Strichen, Fraserburgh AB43 6SQ	01771 637365 (Tel) 01771 637941 (Fax)

Ordiquhill and Cornhill (H) linked with Whitehills

Vacant	6 Craigneen Place, Whitehills, Banff AB45 2NE	01261 861671

Peterhead: Old

Vacant	1 Hawthorn Road, Peterhead AB42 2DW

Peterhead: St Andrew's (H)

David G. Pitkeathly LLB BD	1996	1 Landale Road, Peterhead AB42 1QN [E-mail: davidgp@fish.co.uk]	01779 472141

Peterhead: Trinity

L. Paul McClenaghan BA	1973	1996	18 Landale Road, Peterhead AB42 1QP [E-mail: paul.mcclenaghan@virgin.net]	01779 472405 (Tel) 01779 471174 (Fax)

Pitsligo See Aberdour
Rathen: West See Fraserburgh: West
Rothienorman See Fyvie
St Fergus See Crimond
Sandhaven See Aberdour
Strichen and Tyrie See New Pitsligo
Turriff: St Andrew's See Monquhitter and New Byth

Turriff: St Ninian's and Forglen

Murdo C. MacDonald MA BD	2002	4 Deveronside Drive, Turriff AB53 4SP	01888 563850

Whitehills See Ordiquhill and Cornhill

Bell, Douglas W. MA LLB	1975 1993	(Alexandra: North)	3 Cairnbaan Lea, Cairnbaan, Lochgilphead PA31 8BA	01771 623299
Birnie, Charles J. MA	1969 1995	(Aberdour and Tyrie)	'The Dookit', 23 Water Street, Strichen, Fraserburgh AB43 6ST	01771 637775
Blaikie, James BD	1972 1997	(Berwick-on-Tweed: St Andrew's Wallace Green and Lowick)	57 Glenugie View, Peterhead AB42 2BW	01779 490625

Name			Congregation	Address	Telephone
Douglas, Iar P. LTh	1974	1998	(Aberdeen: Craigiebuckler)	1 Torterston Drive, Blackhills, Peterhead AB42 7LB	01779 474728
Dunlop, M. William B. LLB BD	1981	1995	(Peterhead: St Andrew's)	18 Iona Avenue, Peterhead AB42 1NZ	01779 479189
Fawkes, G.M. Allan BA BSc JP	1979	2000	(Lonmay with Rathen West)	3 Northfield Gardens, Hatton, Peterhead AB42 0SW	01779 841814
McKay, Margaret (Mrs) MA BD MTh	1991	2003	(Auchaber United with Auchterless)	The Smithy, Knowes of Elrick, Aberchirder, Huntly AB54 7PP [E-mail: mgt.mckay@yahoo.com.uk]	01466 780208 (Tel) 01466 780015 (Fax)
Mackenzie, Seoras L. BD	1996	1998	Chaplain: Army	1 RHF, BFPO 38	
McMillan, William J. CA LTh BD	1969	2004	(Sandsting and Aithsting with Walls and Sandness)	7 Ardinn Drive, Turriff AB53 4PR	01888 560727
Noble, George S. DipTh	1972	2000	(Carfin with Newarthill)	Craigowan, 3 Main Street, Inverallochy, Fraserburgh AB43 8XX	01346 582749
Ross, David S. MSc PhD BD	1978	2003	Prison Chaplain Service	3–5 Abbey Street, Old Deer, Peterhead AB42 5LN [E-mail: padsross@btinternet.com]	01771 623994
Taylor, William MA MEd	1984	1996	(Buckie North)	23 York Street, Peterhead AB42 6SN	01779 481798
Walker, Colin D.	1977	1982	(Auchindoir and Kildrummy)	c/o Walter Gerrard & Co., 31 Duff Street, Macduff AB44 1QL	

(35) MORAY

Meets at St Andrew's-Lhanbryd and Urquhart on the first Tuesday of February, March, April, May, September, October, November, December; and at the Moderator's Church on the fourth Tuesday of June.

Clerk:	REV. G. MELVYN WOOD MA BD	3 Seafield Place, Cullen, Buckie AB56 4UU [E-mail: akph67@uk.uumail.com]	01542 841851 (Tel) 07974 095840 (Mbl)

Aberlour (H)

Elizabeth M. Curran (Miss) BD	1995	1998	Mary Avenue, Aberlour AB38 9QN [E-mail: ecurran8@aol.com]	01340 871027

Alves and Burghead linked with Kinloss and Findhorn

Vacant		Dunbar Street, Burghead, Elgin IV30 5XB	01343 830365

Bellie linked with Speymouth

Alison C. Mehigan BD DPS	2003	11 The Square, Fochabers IV32 7DG [E-mail: alison@mehigan-ug.fsnet.co.uk]	01343 820256

Birnie and Pluscarden linked with Elgin High

Vacant	5 Forteath Avenue, Elgin IV30 1TQ	01343 542449

Buckie: North (H)

Vacant	14 St Peter's Road, Buckie AB56 1DL	01542 831328

Buckie: South and West (H) linked with Enzie

John D. Hegarty LTh ABSC	1988	2002	41 East Church Street, Buckie AB56 1ES [E-mail: john.hegarty@tesco.net]	01542 832103

Cullen and Deskford
G. Melvyn Wood MA BD   1982   1997   3 Seafield Place, Cullen, Buckie AB56 4UU   01542 841851 (Tel)
                                                          [E-mail: melvynwood@cullenmanse.freeserve.co.uk]   01542 841991 (Fax)
                                                                                                             07974 095840 (Mbl)

Dallas linked with Forres: St Leonard's (H) linked with Rafford
Paul Amed LTh DPS   1992   2000   St Leonard's Manse, Nelson Road, Forres IV36 1DR   01309 672380
                                                          [E-mail: paulamed@stleonardsmanse.freeserve.co.uk]

Duffus, Spynie and Hopeman (H)
Bruce B. Lawrie BD   1974   2001   The Manse, Duffus, Elgin IV30 5QP   01343 830276
                                                          [E-mail: blawrie@zetnet.co.uk]

Dyke linked with Edinkillie
Gordon R. Mackenzie BScAgr BD   1977   2003   Manse of Dyke, Brodie, Forres IV36 2TD   01309 641239
                                                          [E-mail: rev.g.mackenzie@btopenworld.com]

Edinkillie See Dyke
Elgin: High See Birnie and Pluscarden

Elgin: St Giles' (H) and St Columba's South (01343 551501)
George B. Rollo BD   1974   1986   (Office and Church Halls: Greyfriars Street, Elgin IV30 1LF)   01343 547208
                                                          18 Reidhaven Street, Elgin IV30 1QH
                                                          [E-mail: gbrstgiles@hotmail.com]
Norman R. Whyte BD DipMin (Assoc)   1982   2000   2 Hay Place, Elgin IV30 1LZ   01343 540143
                                                          [E-mail: burraman@msn.com]

Enzie See Buckie South and West

Findochty linked with Portknockie linked with Rathven
Graham Austin BD   1997   20 Netherton Terrace, Findochty, Buckie AB56 4QD   01542 833484
                                                          [E-mail: grahamaustin1@btopenworld.com]

Forres: St Laurence (H)
Barry J. Boyd LTh DPS   1993   12 Mackenzie Drive, Forres IV36 2JP   01309 672260
                                                                                                             07778 731018 (Mbl)

Forres: St Leonard's See Dallas

Keith: North, Newmill, Boharm and Rothiemay (H) (01542 886390)
T. Douglas McRoberts BD CPS FRSA   1975   2002   North Manse, Church Road, Keith AB55 5BR   01542 882559
                                                          [E-mail: doug.mcroberts@btinternet.com]
Ian Cunningham DCS   The Manse, Rothiemay, Huntly AB54 7NE   01466 711334
                                                          [E-mail: icunninghamdcs@btinternet.com]

Keith: St Rufus, Botriphnie and Grange (H)
Ranald S.R. Gauld MA LLB BD   1991 1995   Church Road, Keith AB55 5BR   01542 882799
Kay Gauld (Mrs) BD STM PhD (Assoc)   1999   Church Road, Keith AB55 5BR   01542 882799
[E-mail: kay_gauld@strufus.fsnet.co.uk]

Kinloss and Findhorn See Alves and Burghead

Knockando, Elchies and Archiestown (H) linked with Rothes
Robert J.M. Anderson BD   1993 2000   Manse Brae, Rothes, Aberlour AB38 7AF   01340 831381 (Tel/Fax)
[E-mail: robert@carmanse.freeserve.co.uk]

Lossiemouth: St Gerardine's High (H)
Thomas M. Bryson BD   1997 2002   The Manse, St Gerardine's Road, Lossiemouth IV31 6RA   01343 813146
[E-mail: thomas@bryson547.fsworld.co.uk]

Lossiemouth: St James'
Graham W. Crawford BSc BD STM   1991 2003   The Manse, Prospect Terrace, Lossiemouth IV31 6JS   01343 810676
[E-mail: pictishreiver@aol.com]

Mortlach and Cabrach (H)
Hugh M.C. Smith LTh   1973 1982   The Manse, Church Street, Dufftown, Keith AB55 4AR   01340 820380

Pluscarden See Birnie
Portknockie See Findochty
Rafford See Dallas
Rathven See Findochty
Rothes See Knockando, Elchies and Archiestown

St Andrew's-Lhanbryd (H) and Urquhart
Rolf H. Billes BD   1996 2001   39 St Andrews Road, Lhanbryde, Elgin IV30 8PU   01343 843995
[E-mail: rolf.billes@lineone.net]

Speymouth See Bellie

Cowie, Gordon S. MA LLB	1986	1992	(Birnie with Pluscarden)	Strathspey, Lower Inchberry, Orton, Fochabers IV32 7QH	01343 880377
Davidson, A.A.B. MA BD	1960	1997	(Grange with Rothiemay)	11 Sutor's Rise, Nairn IV12 5BU	
Diack, Peter MA	1951	1994	(Elgin South)	3A Gordon Street, Elgin IV30 1JQ	01343 542545
Douglas, Christina A. (Mrs)	1987	1993	(Inveraven and Glenlivet)	White Cottage, St Fillans, Crieff PH6 2ND	
Evans, John W. MA BD	1945	1984	(Elgin High)	15 Weaver Place, Elgin IV30 1HB	01343 543607
Henig, Gordon BSc BD	1997	2003	(Bellie with Speymouth)	59 Woodside Drive, Forres IV36 2UF	01309 672558
King, Margaret R. (Miss) MA DCS	2002			56 Murrayfield, Fochabers IV32 7EZ	01343 820937
				[E-mail: margaretrking@aol.com]	
Macaulay, Alick Hugh MA	1943	1981	(Bellie with Speymouth)	5 Duke Street, Fochabers IV32 7DN	
McMillan, Charles D. LTh	1979	2004	(Elgin: High)	11 Troon Terrace, The Orchard, Dundee DD2 3FX	01343 820726

Miller, William B.	1950	1987	(Cawdor with Croy and Dalcross)	10 Kirkhill Drive, Lhanbryde, Elgin IV30 8QA	01343 842368
Morton, Alasdair J. MA BD DipEd FEIS	1960	2000	(Bowden with Newtown)	16 St Leonard's Road, Forres IV36 1DW [E-mail: alasgilmor@compuserve.com]	01309 671719
Morton, Gillian M. (Mrs) MA BD PGCE	1983	1996	(Hospital Chaplain)	16 St Leonard's Road, Forres IV36 1DW [E-mail: alasgilmor@compuserve.com]	01309 671719
Poole, Ann McColl (Mrs) DipEd ACE LTh	1983	2003	(Dyke with Edinkillie)	Kirkside Cottage, Dyke, Forres IV36 0TS	01309 641046
Robertson, John T. FPhS	1961	1993	(Keith: North, Newmill and Boharm)	43 Nelson Terrace, Keith AB55 5EF	01542 886339
Scotland, Ronald J. BD	1993	2003	(Birnie with Pluscarden)	7A Rose Avenue, Elgin IV30 1NX	01343 543086
Spence, Alexander	1944	1989	(Elgin St Giles': Associate)	16 Inglis Court, Edzell, Brechin DD9 7SR	01356 648502
Wright, David L. MA BD	1957	1998	(Stornoway: St Columba)	84 Wyvis Drive, Nairn IV12 4TP	01667 451613
Thomson, James M. BA	1952	2000	(Elgin: St Giles' and St Columba's South: Associate)	48 Mayne Road, Elgin IV30 1PD	01343 547664

(36) ABERNETHY

Meets at Boat of Garten on the first Tuesday of February, March, April, June, September, October, November and December.

Clerk: REV. JAMES A.I. MACEWAN MA BD   The Manse, Nethy Bridge PH25 3DG   **01479 821280**
[E-mail: akph35@uk.uumail.com]

Abernethy (H) linked with Cromdale (H) and Advie
James A.I. MacEwan MA BD   1973   The Manse, Nethy Bridge PH25 3DG   01479 821280
[E-mail: manse@nethybridge.freeserve.co.uk]

Alvie and Insh (T) (H)
Vacant   Kincraig, Kingussie PH21 1NA

Boat of Garten (H) and Kincardine linked with Duthil (H)
David W. Whyte LTh   1993 1999   Deshar Road, Boat of Garten PH24 3BN   01479 831252
[E-mail: djwhyte@fish.co.uk]

Cromdale and Advie See Abernethy

Dulnain Bridge (H) linked with Grantown-on-Spey (H)
Morris Smith BD   1988   The Manse, Golf Course Road, Grantown-on-Spey PH26 3HY   01479 872084
[E-mail: mosmith.themanse@virgin.net]

Duthil See Boat of Garten and Kincardine

Grantown-on-Spey See Dulnain Bridge

Kingussie (H)
Helen Cook (Mrs) BD   1974   2003   The Manse, West Terrace, Kingussie PH21 1HA   01540 661311
[E-mail: bhja@cookville.freeserve.co.uk]

Laggan linked with Newtonmore (H)
Douglas F. Stevenson BD DipMin   1991   2001   The Manse, Fort William Road, Newtonmore PH20 1DG   01540 673238
[E-mail: dfstevenson@aol.com]

Newtonmore See Laggan

Rothiemurchus and Aviemore (H)
Ron C. Whyte BD CPS   1990   Dalfaber Park, Aviemore PH22 1QF   01479 810280
[E-mail: ron4xst@aol.com]

Tomintoul (H), Glenlivet and Inveraven
Sven S. Bjarnason CandTheol   1975   1992   The Manse, Tomintoul, Ballindalloch AB37 9HA   01807 580254
[E-mail: sven@bjarnason-org.uk]

(37) INVERNESS

Meets at Inverness, in the Dr Black Memorial Hall, on the first Tuesday of February, March, April, May, September, October, November and December, and at the Moderator's church on the fourth Tuesday of June.

Clerk: REV. ALASTAIR S. YOUNGER BScEcon ASCC   3 Elm Park, Inverness IV2 4WN   **01463 232462 (Tel/Fax)**
[E-mail: akph55@uk.uumail.com]
[E-mail: inverness.presbytery@uk.uumail.com]

Ardclach linked with Auldearn and Dalmore
Vacant   Auldearn, Nairn IV12 5SX   01667 453180

Ardersier (H) linked with Petty
Alexander Whiteford LTh   1996   Ardersier, Inverness IV2 7SX   01667 462224
[E-mail: a.whiteford@ukonline.co.uk]

Auldearn and Dalmore See Ardclach

Cawdor (H) linked with Croy and Dalcross (H)
Janet S. Mathieson MA BD   2003   The Manse, Croy, Inverness IV2 5PH   01667 493217
[E-mail: jan@mathieson99.fsnet.co.uk]

Croy and Dalcross See Cawdor

Culloden: The Barn (H)
James H. Robertson BSc BD   1975   1994   45 Oakdene Court, Culloden IV2 7XL   01463 790504
[E-mail: revjimrobertson@netscape.net]

Daviot and Dunlichity linked with Moy, Dalarossie and Tomatin
Reginald F. Campbell BD DipChEd   1979   2003   The Manse, Daviot, Inverness IV2 5XL   01463 772242

Dores and Boleskine
Vacant   The Manse, Foyers, Inverness IV2 6XU   01456 486206

Inverness: Crown (H) (01463 238929)
Peter H. Donald MA PhD BD   1991   1998   39 Southside Road, Inverness IV2 4XA   01463 230537
[E-mail: crownchurch@tesco.net]
Willis A. Jones BA MDiv DMin (Assoc)   1964   2003   4 Beechwood, Wellington Road, Nairn IV12 4RE

Inverness: Dalneigh and Bona (GD) (H)
Fergus A. Robertson MA BD   1971   1999   9 St Mungo Road, Inverness IV3 5AS   01463 232339

Inverness: East (H)
Aonghas I. MacDonald MA BD   1967   1981   2 Victoria Drive, Inverness IV2 3QD   01463 231269
[E-mail: aonghas@ukonline.co.uk]

Inverness: Hilton
Duncan MacPherson LLB BD   1994   4 Tomatin Road, Inverness IV2 4UA   01463 231417
[E-mail: duncan@hiltonchurch.freeserve.uk]

Inverness: Inshes (H)
Alistair Malcolm BD DPS   1976   1992   48 Redwood Crescent, Milton of Leys, Inverness IV2 6HB   01463 772402
[E-mail: alimalcolm@7inverness.freeserve.co.uk]

Inverness: Kinmylies (E) (H)
Peter M. Humphris BSc BD   1976   2001   2 Balnafettack Place, Inverness IV3 8TQ   01463 709893
[E-mail: peter@humphris.co.uk]

Inverness: Ness Bank (T) (H)
S. John Chambers OBE BSc   1972   1998   15 Ballifeary Road, Inverness IV3 5PJ   01463 234653
[E-mail: chambers@ballifeary.freeserve.co.uk]

Inverness: Old High St Stephen's
Peter W. Nimmo BD ThM   1996   2004   24 Damfield Road, Inverness IV2 3HU   01463 250802
[E-mail: peternimmo@minister.com]

Inverness: St Columba High (H)
Alastair S. Younger BScEcon ASCC — 1969 1976 — 3 Elm Park, Inverness IV2 4WN [E-mail: asyounger@aol.com] — 01463 232462 (Tel/Fax)

Inverness: Trinity (H)
Alistair Murray BD — 1984 2004 — 60 Kenneth Street, Inverness IV3 5PZ [E-mail: ally.murray@btopenworld.com] — 01463 234756

Kilmorack and Erchless
George Duthie BSc MSc PhD BD — 1998 — 'Roselynn', Croyard Road, Beauly IV4 7DJ [E-mail: gduthie@tinyworld.co.uk] — 01463 782260

Kiltarlity linked with Kirkhill
Fraser K. Turner LTh — 1994 2002 — Wardlaw Manse, Wardlaw Road, Kirkhill, Inverness IV5 7NZ [E-mail: fraseratq@yahoo.co.uk] — 01463 831662

Kirkhill See Kiltarlity

Moy, Dalarossie and Tomatin See Daviot and Dunlichity

Nairn: Old (H)
Ian W.F. Hamilton BD LTh ALCM AVCM — 1978 1986 — 3 Manse Road, Nairn IV12 4RN [E-mail: reviwfh@btinternet.com] — 01667 452203

Nairn: St Ninian's (H)
Vacant — 7 Queen Street, Nairn IV12 4AA — 01667 452202

Petty See Ardersier

Urquhart and Glenmoriston (H)
Hugh F. Watt BD DPS — 1986 1996 — Blairbeg, Drumnadrochit, Inverness IV3 6UG [E-mail: hw@tinyworld.co.uk] — 01456 450231

Black, Archibald T. BSc	1964	1997	(Inverness: Ness Bank)	16 Elm Park, Inverness IV2 4WN	01463 230588
Brown, Derek G. BD DipMin DMin	1989	1994	Chaplain: Raigmore Hospital and Highland Hospice	Cathedral Manse, Choc-an-Lobht, Dornoch IV25 3HN [E-mail: revsbrown@aol.com]	01862 810296
Buell, F. Bart BA MDiv	1980	1995	(Urquhart and Glenmoriston)	6 Towerhill Place, Cradlehall, Inverness IV1 2FN [E-mail: bart@tower22.freeserve.co.uk]	01463 794634
Charlton, George W.	1952	1992	(Fort Augustus with Glengarry)	61 Drumfield Road, Inverness IV2 4XL	01463 242802
Chisholm, Archibald F. MA	1957	1997	(Braes of Rannoch with Foss and Rannoch)	32 Seabank Road, Nairn IV12 4EU	01667 452001
Christie, James LTh	1993	2003	(Dores and Boleskine)	20 Wester Inshes Crescent, Inverness IV2 5HL	01463 710534
Donaldson, Moses	1972	2000	(Fort Augustus with Glengarry)	'Tabgha', 10 Garden Place, Beauly IV4 7AW	(Tel/Fax) 01463 783701
Donn, Thomas M. MA	1932	1969	(Duthil)	Clachnaharry Residential Home, Inverness	
Frizzell, R. Stewart BD	1961	2000	(Wick Old)	98 Boswell Road, Inverness IV2 3EW	01463 231907
Gibbons, Richard BD	1997		Adviser in Mission and Evangelism	3 Holm Burn Place, Inverness IV2 6WT [E-mail: nmadvisernorth@uk.uumail.com]	01463 226889
Henderson, Roderick B.	1973	1982	(Kingswells)	Isobel Fraser Residential Home, Mayfield Road, Inverness	

Name	Years	Note	Address	Telephone
Jeffrey, Stewart D. BSc BD	1962 1997	(Banff with King Edward)	10 Grigor Drive, Inverness	01667 455126
Livesley, Anthony LTh	1979 1997	(Kiltearn)	87 Beech Avenue, Nairn IV12 5SX	01463 790226
Logan, Robert J.V. MA BD	1962 2001	(Abdie and Dunbog with Newburgh)	Lindores, 1 Murray Place, Smithton, Inverness IV2 7PX [E-mail: rjvlogan@aol.com]	
Macaskill, Duncan	1952 1974	(Lochs-in-Bernera)	71 Smithton Park, Inverness IV2 7PD	01463 791376
Macritchie, Iain A.M. BSc BD STM PhD	1987 1998	Chaplain: Inverness Hospitals	7 Merlin Crescent, Inverness IV2 3TE	01463 235204
Morrison, Hector BSc BD MTh	1981 1994	Lecturer: Highland Theological College	24 Oak Avenue, Inverness IV2 4NX	01463 238561
Prentice, Donald K. BSc BD	1989 1992	Army Chaplain	Fort George, Inverness IV1 2TD	
Rettie, James A. BTh	1981 1999	(Melness and Eriboll with Tongue)	2 Trantham Drive, Westhill, Inverness IV2 5QT	01463 798896
Robb, Rodney P.T.	1995 2004	(Stirling: St Mark's)	2A Mayfield Road, Inverness IV2 4AE	
Stirling, G. Alan S. MA	1960 1999	(Leochel Cushnie and Lynturk linked with Tough)		
Waugh, John L. LTh	1973 2002		97 Lochlaan Road, Culloden, Inverness IV2 7HS	01463 798313
			58 Wyvis Drive, Nairn IV12 4TP [E-mail: jswaugh@care4free.net]	(Tel/Fax) 01667 456397
Wilson, Ian M.	1988 1993	(Cawdor with Croy and Dalcross)	3 Kilravock Crescent, Nairn IV12 4QZ	01667 452977

INVERNESS ADDRESSES

Inverness

Crown	Kingsmills Road x Midmills Road	Inshes	Inshes Retail Park
Dalneigh and Bona	St Mary's Avenue	Kinmylies	Kinmylies Way
East	Academy Street x Margaret Street	Ness Bank	Ness Bank x Castle Road
Hilton	Druid Road x Tomatin Road	St Columba High	Bank Street x Fraser Street
		St Stephen's	Old Edinburgh Road x Southside Road
The Old High	Church Street x Church Lane		
Trinity	Huntly Place x Upper Kessock Street		

Nairn

Old	Academy Street x Seabank Road
St Ninian's	High Street x Queen Street

(38) LOCHABER

Meets at Caol, Fort William, in Kilmallie Church Hall at 7pm, on the first Tuesday of September, December and February, the last Tuesday in October and the fourth Tuesday in March. The June meeting is held on the first Tuesday in the church of the incoming Moderator.

Clerk:	REV. DAVID M. ANDERSON MSc FCOptom	'Mirlos', 1 Dumfries Place, Fort William PH33 6UQ [E-mail: akph62@uk.uumail.com]	01397 703203

Acharacle (H) linked with Ardnamurchan

Ian R. Pittendreigh BA BD	2002	The Manse, Acharacle, Argyll PH36 4JU [E-mail: jipitt@ekit.com]	01967 431561

Ardgour linked with Strontian

James A. Carmichael LTh	1976	The Manse, Ardgour, Fort William PH33 7AH	01855 841230

Ardnamurchan See Acharacle

Arisaig and the Small Isles
Alan H.W. Lamb BA MTh (Locum) 1959 1992 The Manse, Mid Road, Arisaig PH39 4NJ 01687 450227
[E-mail: a.lamb@tinyonline.co.uk]

Duror (H) linked with Glencoe: St Munda's (H) (T)
Alison H. Burnside (Mrs) MA BD 1991 2002 The Manse, Ballachulish PH49 4JG 01855 811998
[E-mail: alisonskyona@aol.com]

Fort Augustus linked with Glengarry
Adrian P.J. Varwell BA BD PhD 1983 2001 The Manse, Fort Augustus PH32 4BH 01320 366210
[E-mail: a-varwell@ecosse.net]

Fort William: Duncansburgh (H) linked with Kilmonivaig
Donald A. MacQuarrie BSc BD 1979 1990 The Manse of Duncansburgh, The Parade, Fort William PH33 6BA 01397 702297
[E-mail: pdmacq@ukgateway.net]

Fort William: MacIntosh Memorial (H)
Alan Ramsay MA 1967 The Manse, 26 Riverside Park, Lochyside, Fort William PH33 7RB 01397 702054
[E-mail: linandalan@btopenworld.com]
David M. Anderson MSc FCOptom (Aux) 1984 2001 'Mirlos', 1 Dumfries Place, Fort William PH33 6UQ 01397 703203
[E-mail: david@mirlos.co.uk]

Glencoe: St Munda's See Duror
Glengarry See Fort Augustus

Kilmallie
Vacant Kilmallie Manse, Corpach, Fort William PH33 7JS 01397 772210

Kilmonivaig See Fort William: Duncansburgh

Kinlochleven (H) linked with Nether Lochaber (H)
Archibald Speirs BD 1995 2002 Lochaber Road, Kinlochleven, Argyll PA40 4QW 01855 831227
[E-mail: archiespeirs1@aol.com]

Mallaig: St Columba and Knoydart
Vacant The Manse, Mallaig PH41 4RG 01687 462256

Morvern
Alicia Ann Winning MA BD 1984 The Manse, Lochaline, Morvern, Oban PA34 5UU 01967 421267
[E-mail: annw@morvern12.fslife.co.uk]

Nether Lochaber See Kinlochleven
Strontian See Ardgour

Beaton, Jamesina (Miss) DCS		(Deaconess)	Farhills, Fort Augustus PH32 4DS	01320 366252
Burnside, William A.M. MA BD PGCE	1990	Teacher: Religious Education	The Manse, Ballachulish PH49 4JG	01855 811998
Millar, John L. MA BD	1981 1990	(Fort William: Duncansburgh with Kilmonivaig)	17 Whittingehame Court, 1350 Great Western Road, Glasgow G12 0BH	0141-339 4098
Olsen, Heather C. (Miss) BD	1978 2003	(Creich with Rosehall)	4 Riverside Park, Lochyside, Coull, Fort William PH33 7RA	01397 700023
Rae, Peter C. BSc BD	1968 2000	(Beath and Cowdenbeath North)	Rodane, Badabrie, Banavie, Fort William PH33 7LX	01397 772603

LOCHABER Communion Sundays

Acharacle	1st Mar, Jun, Sep, Dec	Kilmonivaig	1st May, Nov
Ardgour	1st Jun, Sep, Dec, Easter	Kinlochleven	1st Feb, Apr, Jun, Oct, Dec
Ardnamurchan	1st Apr, Aug, Dec	Mallaig	4th May, 3rd Nov
Arisaig and Moidart	1st May, Nov	Morvern	Easter, 1st Jul, 4th Sep, 1st Dec
Duror	2nd Jun, 3rd Nov	Nether Lochaber	1st Apr, Oct
Fort Augustus	1st Jan, Apr, Jul, Oct	Strontian	1st Jun, Sep, Dec
Fort William			
Duncansburgh	1st Apr, Jun, Oct		
M'Intosh Memorial	1st Mar, Jun, Sep, Dec		
Glencoe	1st Apr, Oct		
Glengarry	1st Jan, Apr, Jul, Oct		
Kilmallie	3rd Mar, May, Sep, 1st Dec		

(39) ROSS

Meets in Dingwall on the first Tuesday of each month, except January, May, July and August.

Clerk:	REV. THOMAS M. McWILLIAM MA BD		Guidhadden, 7 Woodholme Crescent, Culbokie, Dingwall IV7 8JH [E-mail: akph71@uk.uumail.com]	01349 877014

Alness

Ronald Morrison BD	1996	27 Darroch Brae, Alness IV17 0SD	01349 882238

Avoch linked with Fortrose and Rosemarkie

Samuel Torrens BD	1995	5 Nessway, Fortrose IV10 8SS [E-mail: sam@nessway5.fsnet.co.uk]	01381 620068

Contin
Vacant

	The Manse, Contin, Strathpeffer IV14 9ES	01997 421380

Cromarty

John Tallach MA MLitt	1970 1999	Denny Road, Cromarty IV11 8YT [E-mail: john.t@ecosse.net]	01381 600802

Dingwall: Castle Street (H) Vacant			16 Achany Road, Dingwall IV15 9JB	01349 863167
Dingwall: St Clement's (H) Russel Smith BD	1994		8 Castlehill Road, Dingwall IV15 9PB	01349 861011
Fearn Abbey and Nigg linked with Tarbat John Macgregor BD	2001		The Manse, Fearn, Tain IV20 1TN	01862 832626
Ferintosh Vacant			Ferintosh Manse, Leanaig Road, Conon Bridge, Dingwall IV7 8BE	01349 861275
Fodderty and Strathpeffer Ivan C. Warwick MA BD	1980	1999	The Manse, Strathpeffer IV14 9DL	01997 421398
Fortrose and Rosemarkie See Avoch				
Invergordon Kenneth Donald Macleod BD CPS	1989	2000	The Manse, Cromlet Drive, Invergordon IV18 0BA	01349 852273
Killearnan linked with Knockbain Iain Ramsden BTh	1999		The Church of Scotland Manse, Coldwell Road, Artafallie, North Kessock, Inverness IV1 3ZE [E-mail: s4rev@cqm.co.uk]	01463 731333
Kilmuir and Logie Easter Kenneth J. Pattison MA BD STM	1967	1996	Delny, Invergordon IV18 0NW [E-mail: ken@thepattisons.fsnet.co.uk]	01862 842280
Kiltearn (H) Donald A. MacSween BD	1991	1998	Kiltearn, Evanton, Dingwall IV16 9UY	01349 830472
Knockbain See Killearnan				
Lochbroom and Ullapool (GD) James Gemmell BD MTh	1999		The Manse, Garve Road, Ullapool IV26 2SX [E-mail: JasGemmell@aol.com]	01854 612050
Resolis and Urquhart (T) C.J. Grant Bell	1983	2002	The Manse, Culbokie, Conon Bridge, Dingwall IV7 8JN	01349 877452
Rosskeen Robert Jones BSc BD	1990		Rosskeen Manse, Perrins Road, Alness IV17 0SX [E-mail: rob-jones@freeuk.com]	01349 882265

Tain
Douglas A. Horne BD   1977   14 Kingsway Avenue, Tain IV19 1BN   01862 894140
[E-mail: douglas@kingswayavenue.freeserve.co.uk]

Tarbat (T) See Fearn Abbey and Nigg

Urray and Kilchrist
J. Alastair Gordon BSc BD   2000   The Manse, Corrie Road, Muir of Ord IV6 7TL   01463 870259
[E-mail: jagordon.pci@virgin.net]

Buchan, John BD MTh	1968	1993	(Fodderty and Strathpeffer)	'Faithlie', 45 Swanston Avenue, Inverness IV3 6QW	01463 713114
Dupar, Kenneth W. BA BD PhD	1965	1993	(Christ's College, Aberdeen)	The Old Manse, The Causeway, Cromarty IV11 8XJ	01381 600428
Forsyth, James LTh	1970	2000	(Fearn Abbey with Nigg Chapelhill)	Rhivs Lodge, Golspie, Sutherland KW10 6DD	
Glass, Alexander OBE MA	1998		Auxiliary Minister: Attached to Presbytery Clerk	Craigton, Tulloch Avenue, Dingwall IV15 9TU	01349 863258
Harries, David A.	1950	1990	(British Sailors' Society)	Odessey, 5 Farm Lane, Englands Road, Acle, Norfolk	
Holroyd, Gordon BTh FPhS FSAScot	1959	1993	(Dingwall: St Clement's)	22 Stuarthill Drive, Maryburgh, Dingwall IV15 9HU	01349 863379
Liddell, Margaret (Miss) BD DipTh	1987	1997	(Contin)	20 Wyvis Crescent, Conon Bridge, Dingwall IV7 8BZ	01349 865997
McGowan, Prof. Andrew T.B. BD STM PhD	1979	1994	Highland Theological College	4 Kintail Place, Dingwall IV15 9RL	
Mackenzie, A. Ian	1945	1986	(Glenelg with Glenshiel with Kintail)	4 St Mary's Well, Tain IV19 1LS	01862 893305
Mackinnon, R.M. LTh	1968	1995	(Kilmuir and Logie Easter)	27 Riverford Crescent, Conon Bridge, Dingwall IV7 8HL	01349 866293
MacLennan, Alasdair J. BD DCE	1978	2001	(Resolis and Urquhart)	Airdale, Seaforth Road, Muir of Ord IV6 7TA	01463 870704
Macleod, John MA	1959	1993	(Resolis and Urquhart)	'Benview', 19 Balvaird, Muir of Ord IV6 7RG	01463 871286
McWilliam, Thomas M. MA BD	1964	2003	(Contin)	Guidhadden, 7 Woodholme Crescent, Culbokie, Dingwall IV7 8JH	01349 877014
Niven, William W. BTh	1982	1995	(Alness)	4 Obsdale Park, Alness IV17 0TP	01349 882427
Rutherford, Ellen B. (Miss) MBE DCS			(Deaconess)	41 Duncanston, Conon Bridge, Dingwall IV7 8JB	01349 877439

(40) SUTHERLAND

Meets at Lairg on the first Tuesday of March, May, September, November and December, and on the first Tuesday of June at the Moderator's church.

Clerk: REV. J.L. GOSKIRK LTh   The Manse, Lairg, Sutherland IV27 4EH   01549 402373
[E-mail: akph76@uk.uumail.com]

Altnaharra and Farr
John M. Wilson MA BD   1965   1998   The Manse, Bettyhill, Thurso KW14 7SZ   01641 521208

Charge / Minister	Ord.	Ind.	Address	Tel.
Assynt and Stoer Vacant			Canisp Road, Lochinver, Lairg IV27 4LH	01571 844342
Clyne (H) Ian W. McCree BD	1971	1987	Golf Road, Brora KW9 6QS [E-mail: ian.mccree@lineone.net]	01408 621239
Creich linked with Rosehall Vacant			Church of Scotland Manse, Dornoch Road, Bonar Bridge, Ardgay IV24 3EB	01863 766256
Dornoch Cathedral (H) Susan M. Brown (Mrs) BD DipMin	1985	1998	Cnoc-an-Lobht, Dornoch IV25 3HN [E-mail: revsbrown@aol.com]	01862 810296
Durness and Kinlochbervie John T. Mann BSc BD	1990	1998	Manse Road, Kinlochbervie, Lairg IV27 4RG [E-mail: jtmklb@aol.com]	01971 521287
Eddrachillis John MacPherson BSc BD	1993		Church of Scotland Manse, Scourie, Lairg IV27 4TQ	01971 502431
Golspie William D. Irving LTh	1985	2003	The Manse, Fountain Road, Golspie KW10 6TH	01408 633295
Kildonan and Loth Helmsdale (H) Vacant			Church of Scotland Manse, Helmsdale KW8 6HT	01431 821674
Kincardine Croick and Edderton Graeme W.M. Muckart MTh MSc FSAScot	1983	2004	The Manse, Ardgay IV24 3BG [E-mail: gw2m@clara.net]	01863 766285
Lairg (H) linked with Rogart (H) J.L. Goskirk LTh	1968		The Manse, Lairg IV27 4EH	01549 402373
Melness and Tongue (H) John F. Mackie BD	1979	2000	New Manse, Glebelands, Tongue, Lairg IV27 4XL [E-mail: john.mackie1@virgin.net]	01847 611230
Rogart See Lairg				
Rosehall See Creich				

Wilson, Mary D. (Mrs) RGN SCM DTM	1990	1998	Auxiliary Minister	The Manse, Bettyhill, Thurso KW14 7SZ	01641 521208

(41) CAITHNESS

Meets alternately at Wick and Thurso on the first Tuesday of February, March, May, September, November and December, and the third Tuesday of June.

Clerk:	MRS MYRTLE A. GILLIES MBE			Ardachadh, Halladale, Forsinard, Sutherland KW13 6YT [E-mail: akph42@uk.uumail.com]	01641 571241
Berriedale and Dunbeath linked with Latheron					
Vacant				Ross Manse, Dunbeath KW6 6EA	01593 731228
Bower linked with Watten					
Vacant				Station Road, Watten, Wick KW1 5YN	01955 621220
Canisbay linked with Keiss					
Iain Macnee LTh BD MA PhD	1975	1998		The Manse, Canisbay, Wick KW1 4YH [E-mail: i.macnee@amserve.com]	01955 611309
Dunnet linked with Olrig					
James F. Todd BD CPS	1984	1999		Olrig, Castletown, Thurso KW14 8TP	01847 821221
Halkirk and Westerdale					
Kenneth Warner BD DA DipTD	1981			Abbey Manse, Halkirk KW12 6UU [E-mail: wrmkenn@aol.com]	01847 831227
Keiss See Canisbay					
Latheron See Berriedale and Dunbeath					
Lybster and Bruan (T)					
Vacant				Central Manse, Lybster KW3 6BN	01593 721231
Olrig See Dunnet					
Reay linked with Strathy and Halladale (H)					
Vacant				Church of Scotland Manse, Reay, Thurso KW14 7RE	
Strathy and Halladale See Reay					
Thurso: St Peter's and St Andrew's (H)					
Kenneth S. Borthwick MA BD	1983	1989		46 Rose Street, Thurso KW14 7HN [E-mail: kennysamuel@aol.com]	01847 895186

Thurso: West (H)

Ronald Johnstone BD	1977	1984	Thorkel Road, Thurso KW14 7LW	01847 892663
			[E-mail: ronaldjohnstone@onetel.net.uk]	

Watten See Bower

Wick: Bridge Street

A.A. Roy MA BD	1955	Mansefield, Miller Avenue, Wick KW1 4DF	01955 602822

Wick: Old (H) (L)

Vacant	The Old Manse, Miller Avenue, Wick KW1 4DF	01955 604252

Wick: Pulteneytown (H) and Thrumster

William F. Wallace BDS BD	1968	1974	The Manse, Coronation Street, Wick KW1 5LS	01955 603166
			[E-mail: williamwallace39@btopenworld.com]	

Craw, John DCS	1961	1998	(Bower with Watten)	'Craiglockhart', Latheronwheel, Latheron KW5 6DW	01593 741779
Mappin, Michael G. BA	2001	2004	Chaplain: RN	Mundays, Banks Road, Watten, Wick KW1 5YL	01955 621720
Thomson, Steven				

CAITHNESS Communion Sundays

Berriedale and Dunbeath	2nd Mar, Jun, Sep, Dec
Bower	1st Jul, Dec
Canisbay	1st Jun, Nov
Dunnet	last May, Nov
Halkirk	Oct, Apr, Jul
Keiss	1st May, 3rd Nov
Latheron	1st Jul, 2nd Sep, 1st Dec, 2nd Mar
Lybster and Bruan	3rd Jun, Nov, Easter
Olrig	last May, Nov
Reay	last Apr, Sep
Strathy and Halladale	1st Jun, last Nov, Easter
Thurso	
St Peter's and	
St Andrew's	
West	
Watten	1st Jul, Dec
Westerdale	Apr, Oct, 4th Dec
Wick	
Bridge Street	1st Apr, Oct
Old	4th Apr, Sep
Pulteneytown and	
Thrumster	1st Mar, Jun, Sep, Dec

(42) LOCHCARRON – SKYE

Meets in Kyle on the first Tuesday of each month, except January, May, July and August.

Clerk:	REV. ALLAN J. MACARTHUR BD	High Barn, Croft Road, Lochcarron, Strathcarron IV54 8YA	01520 722278 (Tel)
		[E-mail: akph63@uk.uumail.com]	01520 722674 (Fax)
		[E-mail: a.macarthur@btinternet.com]	

Charge / Minister		Year	Address	Telephone
Applecross, Lochcarron and Torridon (GD)				
George M. Martin MA BD		1987	The Manse, Lochcarron, Strathcarron IV54 8YD	01520 722829
David V. Scott BTh (Assoc)		1994	Camusterrach, Applecross, Strathcarron IV54 8LU	01520 744263 (Tel/Fax)
Bracadale and Duirinish (GD)				
Gary Wilson BD		1996	Kinloch Manse, Dunvegan, Isle of Skye IV55 8WQ [E-mail: gary@shalom55.fsnet.co.uk]	01470 521457
Gairloch and Dundonnell				
Derek Morrison		1995	Church of Scotland Manse, The Glebe, Gairloch IV21 2BT [E-mail: derekmorrison@tinyworld.co.uk]	01445 712053 (Tel/Fax)
Glenelg and Kintail				
Vacant			Church of Scotland Manse, Inverinate, Kyle IV40 8HE	01599 511245
Kilmuir and Stenscholl (GD)				
Ivor MacDonald BSc MSc BD		1993	Staffin, Portree, Isle of Skye IV51 9JX [E-mail: ivormacd@aol.com]	01470 562759 (Tel/Fax)
Lochalsh				
John M. Macdonald		2002	The Church of Scotland Manse, Main Street, Kyle IV40 8DA [E-mail: jmmd@jmacdonald10.fsnet.co.uk]	01599 534294
Portree (GD)				
John M. Nicolson BD DipMin		1997	Viewfield Road, Portree, Isle of Skye IV51 9ES [E-mail: johnjehunicolson@aol.com]	01478 611868
Snizort (H) (GD)				
Iain M. Greenshields BD DipRS ACMA MSc MTh		1985	The Manse, Kensaleyre, Snizort, Portree, Isle of Skye IV51 9XE [E-mail: rev_imaclg@hotmail.com]	01470 532260
Strath and Sleat (GD)				
Ben Johnstone MA BD DMin		1973	The Manse, 6 Upper Breakish, Isle of Skye IV42 8PY [E-mail: benonskye@onetel.com]	01471 820063
John D. Urquhart BA BD		1998	The Manse, The Glebe, Kilmore, Teangue, Isle of Skye IV44 8RG [E-mail: jurquh8218@aol.com]	01471 844469
Beaton, Donald MA BD MTh	1961 2002	(Glenelg and Kintail)	Kilmaluag Croft, North Duntulm, Isle of Skye IV51 9UF	01470 552296
Ferguson, John LTh BD DD	1973 2002	(Portree)	9 Braeview Park, Beauly, Inverness IV4 7ED	01463 783900
Macarthur, Allan J. BD	1973 1998	(Applecross, Lochcarron and Torridon)	High Barn, Croft Road, Lochcarron, Strathcarron IV54 8YA (Tel)	01520 722278
			(Fax)	01520 722674
McCulloch, Alen J.R. MA BD	1990 1995	Chaplain: Army	Vimy Barracks, Catterick Garrison, North Yorkshire DL9 3PS	

MacDonald, Kenneth | 1965 1992 | (Associate: Applecross l/w Lochcarron) | Tighary, Main Street, Lochcarron, Strathcarron IV54 8YB | 01520 722433
MacDougall, Angus | 1940 1982 | (Sleat) | Tigh Ard, Earlish, Portree, Isle of Skye IV51 9XL | 01470 542466
Macleod, Donald LTh | 1988 2000 | (Snizort) | 20 Caulfield Avenue, Cradlehall, Inverness IV1 2GA | 01463 798093
Matheson, James G. MA BD DD | 1936 1979 | (Portree) | The Elms, 148 Whitehouse Loan, Edinburgh EH9 2EZ | 0131-446 6211
Murray, John W. | 2003 | Auxiliary Minister | Totescore, Kilmuir, Portree, Isle of Skye IV51 9YN | 01470 542297
Williamson, Tom MA BD | 1941 1982 | (Dyke with Edinkillie) | 16 Cove, Inverasdale, Poolewe, Achnasheen IV22 2LT | 01445 781423

LOCHCARRON – SKYE   Communion Sundays

Applecross	4th Jun	Kilmuir	1st Mar, Sep	Portree	Easter, Pentecost, Christmas,
Arnisort	1st Sep	Kintail	3rd Apr, Jul		2nd Mar, Aug, 1st Nov
Bracadale	3rd Mar, Sep	Kyleakin	Easter, 1st Nov	Sleat	2nd Jun, Dec
Duirinish	3rd Jan, Easter, 2nd Jun, 3rd Sep	Lochalsh and		Snizort	1st Jan, 4th Mar
Dundonnell	4th Jun	Stromeferry	4th Jan, Jun, Sep, Christmas, Easter	Stenscholl	1st Jun, Dec
Gairloch	3rd Jun, Nov	Lochcarron		Strath	2nd Mar, Sep
Glenelg	2nd Jun, Nov	and Shieldaig	Easter, 3rd Jun, 1st Oct	Torridon	2nd May
Glenshiel	1st Jul	Plockton and Kyle	2nd May, 1st Oct	and Kinlochewe	

(43) UIST

Meets on the fourth Wednesday of January, March, September and November in Berneray, and the fourth Wednesday of June in Leverburgh.

Clerk: REV. MURDO SMITH MA BD | Scarista, Isle of Harris HS3 3HX | **01859 550200**
[E-mail: akph77@uk.uumail.com]

Barra (GD)
Vacant | Cuithir, Castlebay, Isle of Barra HS9 5XD | 01871 810230

Benbecula (GD) (H)
Vacant | Griminish, Isle of Benbecula HS7 5QA | 01870 602180

Berneray and Lochmaddy (GD) (H)
Vacant | Lochmaddy, Isle of North Uist HS6 5BD | 01876 500414

Carinish (GD) (H)
Thomas J.R. Mackinnon LTh DipMin   1996   1998 | Clachan, Isle of North Uist HS6 5HD | 01876 580219
[E-mail: tmackinnon@aol.com]

Kilmuir and Paible (GE)
Vacant | Paible, Isle of North Uist HS6 5ED | 01876 510310

Manish-Scarista (GD) (H)
Murdo Smith MA BD   1988   Scarista, Isle of Harris HS3 3HX   01859 550200
                                                [E-mail: akph77@uk.uumail.com]

South Uist (GD)
Vacant   Daliburgh, Isle of South Uist HS8 5SS   01878 700265

Tarbert (GE) (H)
Norman MacIver BD   1976   1988   The Manse, Manse Road, Tarbert, Isle of Harris HS3 3DF   01859 502231
                                                [E-mail: norman@n-cmaciver.freeserve.co.uk]

MacDonald, Angus J. BSc BD	1995	2001	(Lochmaddy and Trumisgarry)	7 Memorial Avenue, Stornoway, Isle of Lewis HS1 2QR	01851 706634
MacInnes, David MA BD	1966	1999	(Kilmuir and Paible)	9 Golf View Road, Kinmylies, Inverness IV3 8SZ	01463 717377
Macpherson, Kenneth J. BD	1988	2002	(Benbecula)	70 Baile na Cille, Balivanich, Isle of Benbecula HS7 5ND	01870 602751
Macrae, D.A. JP MA	1942	1988	(Tarbert)	5 Leverhulme Road, Tarbert, Isle of Harris HS3 3DD	01859 502310
Macrae, William DCS			(Deacon)	6 Park View Terrace, Isle of Scalpay, Tarbert, Isle of Harris HS4 3XX	01859 540288
Morrison, Donald John		2001	Auxiliary Minister	Lagnam, Brisgean 22, Kyles, Isle of Harris HS3 3BS	01859 502341
Muir, Alexander MA BD	1982	1996	(Carinish)	14 West Mackenzie Park, Inverness IV2 3ST	01463 712096
Smith, John M.	1956	1992	(Lochmaddy)	Hamersay, Clachan, Isle of North Uist HS6 5HD	01876 580332

UIST Communion Sundays

Barra	Easter, Pentecost, Christmas	Kilmuir and Paible	1st Jun, 3rd Nov	South Uist – Iochdar	1st Mar
Benbecula	2nd Mar, Sep	Manish-Scarista	3rd Apr, 1st Oct	Howmore	1st Jun
Berneray and Lochmaddy	4th Jun, 1st Nov			Daliburgh	1st Sep
Carinish	4th Mar, Aug			Tarbert	2nd Mar, 3rd Sep

(44) LEWIS

Meets at Stornoway, in St Columba's Church Hall, on the last Tuesday of January, February, March, June, September and November. It also meets if required in April and December on dates to be decided.

Clerk: REV. THOMAS S. SINCLAIR MA LTh BD   Martin's Memorial Manse,   01851 702206 (Tel/Fax)
                                                Matheson Road, Stornoway, Isle of Lewis HS1 2LR   07766 700110 (Mbl)
                                                [E-mail: akph61@uk.uumail.com]
                                                [E-mail: thomas@sinclair0438.freeserve.co.uk]

Barvas (GD) (H)
Thomas MacNeil MA BD — 2002 — Barvas, Isle of Lewis HS2 0QY
[E-mail: tommymacneil@hotmail.com] — 01851 840218

Carloway (GD) (H)
Murdo M. Campbell BD DipMin — 1997 — Carloway, Isle of Lewis HS2 9AU
[E-mail: murdocampbell@hotmail.com] — 01851 643255

Cross Ness (GE) (H)
Ian Murdo M. Macdonald DPA BD — 2001 — Cross Manse, Swainbost, Ness, Isle of Lewis HS2 0TB
[E-mail: ianmurdo@crosschurch.fsnet.co.uk] — 01851 810375

Kinloch (GE) (H)
Donald Angus MacLennan — 1975 1989 — Laxay, Lochs, Isle of Lewis HS2 9LA
[E-mail: maclennankinloch@btinternet.com] — 01851 830218 / 07799 668270 (Mbl)

Knock (GE) (H)
Fergus J. MacBain BD DipMin — 1999 2002 — Knock Manse, Garrabost, Point, Isle of Lewis HS2 0PW — 01851 870362

Lochs-Crossbost (GD) (H)
Andrew W.F. Coghill BD DPS — 1993 — Leurbost, Lochs, Isle of Lewis HS2 9NS
[E-mail: andcoghill@aol.com] — 01851 860243 (Tel/Fax) / 07776 480748 (Mbl)

Lochs-in-Bernera (GD) (H)
Vacant — Bernera, Isle of Lewis HS2 9LU — 01851 612371

Stornoway: High (GD) (H)
William B. Black MA BD — 1972 1998 — 1 Goathill Road, Stornoway, Isle of Lewis HS1 2NJ
[E-mail: willieblack@lineone.net] — 01851 703106

Stornoway: Martin's Memorial (H)
Thomas Suter Sinclair MA LTh BD — 1966 1976 — Matheson Road, Stornoway, Isle of Lewis HS1 2LR
[E-mail: thomas@sinclair0438.freeserve.co.uk]
[E-mail: akph61@uk.uumail.com] — 01851 702206 (Tel/Fax) / 07766 700110 (Mbl)

Stornoway: St Columba (GD) (H)
Angus Morrison MA BD PhD — 1979 2000 — Lewis Street, Stornoway, Isle of Lewis HS1 2JF
[E-mail: angusmorrison@lineone.net] — 01851 703350

Uig (GE) (H)
William Macleod — 1957 1964 — Miavaig, Uig, Isle of Lewis HS2 9HW — 01851 672216 (Tel/Fax)

Macaulay, Donald OBE JP — 1968 1992 — (Park) — 6 Kirkibost, Bernera, Isle of Lewis HS2 9RD
[E-mail: garymilis@talk21.com] — 01851 612341

Macdonald, Alexander — 1957 1991 — (Cross Ness) — 5 Urquhart Gardens, Stornoway, Isle of Lewis HS1 2TX — 01851 702825
Macdonald, James LTh CPS — 1984 2001 — (Knock) — Elim, 8A Lower Bayble, Point, Isle of Lewis HS2 0QA — 01851 870173

Maclean, Donald A. DCS			(Deacon)	8 Upper Barvas, Barvas, Isle of Lewis HS2 0QX	01851 840454
MacRitchie, Murdanie	1958	1969	(Acharacle)	15A New Garrabost, Isle of Lewis HS2 0PR	01851 870763
MacSween, Norman	1952	1986	(Kinloch)	7 Balmerino Drive, Stornoway, Isle of Lewis HS1 2TD	01851 703369

LEWIS   Communion Sundays

Barvas	3rd Mar, Sep		
Carloway	1st Mar, last Sep		
Cross, Ness	2nd Mar, Oct		
Kinloch	3rd Mar, 2nd Jun, 2nd Sep		
Knock	1st Apr, Nov		
Lochs-Crossbost	4th Mar, Sep	Stornoway	
Lochs-in-Bernera	1st Apr, 2nd Sep	St Columba	3rd Feb, last Aug
Stornoway		Uig	3rd Jun, 1st Sep
High	3rd Feb, last Aug		
Martin's Memorial	3rd Feb, last Aug, 1st Dec, Easter		

(45) ORKNEY

Normally meets at Kirkwall, in the East Church King Street Halls, on the first Tuesday of September, on the second Tuesday of February and May, and on the last Tuesday of November.

Clerk: REV. TREVOR G. HUNT BA BD   The Manse, Finstown, Orkney KW17 2EG   01856 761328 (Tel/Fax)
[E-mail: akph68@uk.uumail.com]   07753 423333 (Mbl)
[E-mail (personal): trevorghunt@yahoo.co.uk]

Birsay, Harray and Sandwick
Andrea E. Price (Mrs)   1997   2001   The Manse, North Biggings Road, Dounby, Orkney KW17 2HZ   01856 771803
[E-mail: andrea-neil@ukonline.co.uk]

Deerness linked with Holm linked with St Andrews
Joan H. Craig (Miss) MTheol   1986   1993   Holm, Orkney KW17 2SB   01856 781422 (Tel/Fax)
[E-mail: joanhcraig@bigfoot.com]

Eday linked with Stronsay: Moncur Memorial (H)
Vacant   Stronsay, Orkney KW17 2AF   01857 616311

Evie linked with Firth (H) linked with Rendall
Trevor G. Hunt BA BD   1986   Finstown, Orkney KW17 2EG   01856 761328 (Tel/Fax)
[E-mail: trevorghunt@yahoo.co.uk]   07753 423333 (Mbl)

Firth (01856 761117)   See Evie

Flotta linked with Hoy and Walls Vacant			South Isles Manse, Longhope, Stromness, Orkney KW16 3PG	01856 701325
Holm See Deerness				
Hoy and Walls See Flotta				
Kirkwall: East (H) Allan McCafferty BSc BD	1993		Thom Street, Kirkwall, Orkney KW15 1PF [E-mail: amccafferty@beeb.net]	01856 875469
Kirkwall: St Magnus Cathedral (H) G. Fraser H. Macnaughton MA BD	1982	2002	Berstane Road, Kirkwall, Orkney KW15 1NA [E-mail: fmacnaug@fish.co.uk]	01856 873312
North Ronaldsay linked with Sanday (H) John L. McNab MA BD	1997	2002	Sanday, Orkney KW17 2BW	01857 600429
Orphir (H) linked with Stenness (H) Thomas L. Clark BD	1985		Stenness, Stromness, Orkney KW16 3HH [E-mail: toml.clark1@btopenworld.com]	01856 761331
Papa Westray linked with Westray Iain D. MacDonald BD	1993		The Manse, Hilldavale, Westray, Orkney KW17 2DW [E-mail: macdonald@rapnessmanse.freeserve.co.uk]	01857 677357 (Tel/Fax) 07710 443780 (Mbl)
Rendall See Evie				
Rousay Continuing Vacancy				
St Andrew's See Deerness				
Sanday See North Ronaldsay				
Shapinsay (50 per cent part-time) Vacant				
South Ronaldsay and Burray Graham D.S. Deans MA BD MTh	1978	2002	St Margaret's Manse, Church Road, St Margaret's Hope, Orkney KW17 2SR [E-mail: graham.deans@btopenworld.com]	01856 831288
Stenness See Orphir				

Stromness (H)
Fiona L. Lillie (Mrs) BA BD MLitt   1995   1999   5 Manse Lane, Stromness, Orkney KW16 3AP   01856 850203
[E-mail: fiona@lilliput23.freeserve.co.uk]

Stronsay: Moncur Memorial See Eday
Westray See Papa Westray

Brown, R. Graeme BA BD   1961 1998   (Birsay with Rousay)   Bring Deeps, Orphir, Orkney KW17 2LX   (Tel/Fax) 01856 811707
[E-mail: grasibrown@bringdeeps.fsnet.co.uk]
Cant, H.W.M. MA BD STM   1951 1990   (Kirkwall: St Magnus Cathedral)   Quoylobs, Holm, Orkney KW17 2RY   01856 781300

(46) SHETLAND

Meets at Lerwick on the first Tuesday of March, April, June, September, October, November and December.

Clerk: REV. CHARLES H.M. GREIG MA BD   **The Manse, Sandwick, Shetland ZE2 9HW**   **01950 431244**
    [E-mail: akph72@uk.uumail.com]

Burra Isle linked with Tingwall
Edgar J. Ogston BSc BD   1976   2001   Park Neuk, Meadowfield Place, Scalloway, Shetland ZE1 0UE   01595 880865
[E-mail: edgar.ogston@ntlworld.com]

Delting linked with Northmavine
Winnie Munson (Ms) BD   1996   2001   The Manse, Grindwell, Brae, Shetland ZE2 9QJ   01806 522219

Dunrossness and St Ninian's inc. Sandwick, Cunningsburgh and Quarff
Fair Isle linked with Sandwick,
Charles H.M. Greig MA BD   1976   1997   The Manse, Sandwick, Shetland ZE2 9HW   01950 431244
[E-mail: chm.greig@btopenworld.com]

Fetlar linked with Unst linked with Yell
R. Alan Knox MA LTh Alnst AM   1965   2000   The Manse, Mid Yell, Shetland ZE2 9BN   01957 702283

Lerwick and Bressay
Gordon Oliver BD   1979   2002   The Manse, 82 St Olaf Street, Lerwick, Shetland ZE1 0ES   01595 692125
[E-mail: gordon@cofslerwick.freeserve.co.uk]

Nesting and Lunnasting linked with Whalsay and Skerries

Irene A. Charlton (Mrs) BTh   1994   1997   The Manse, Marrister, Symbister, Whalsay, Shetland ZE2 9AE   01806 566767
[E-mail: irene.charlton@virgin.net]

Richard M. Charlton (Aux)   2001   The Manse, Marrister, Symbister, Whalsay, Shetland ZE2 9AE   01806 566767
[E-mail: richardm.charlton@virgin.net]

Northmavine See Delting

Sandsting and Aithsting linked with Walls and Sandness

Vacant   Westside Manse, Effirth, Bixter, Shetland ZE2 9LY   01595 810386

Sandwick, Cunningsburgh and Quarff See Dunrossness and St Ninian's
Tingwall See Burra Isle
Unst See Fetlar
Walls and Sandness See Sandsting and Aithsting
Whalsay and Skerries See Nesting and Lunnasting
Yell See Fetlar

Blair, James N.	1962	1986	(Sandsting and Aithsting with Walls)	2 Swinister, Sandwick, Shetland ZE2 9HH 01950 431472
Douglas, Marilyn (Miss) DCS	1988	2004	Presbytery Assistant	Heimdal, Quarff, Shetland ZE2 9EZ 01950 477584
Kirkpatrick, Alice H. (Miss) MA BD FSAScot	1987	2000	(Northmavine)	6 Valladale, Urafirth, Shetland ZE2 9RW
Smith, Catherine (Mrs) DCS	1964	2003	(Presbytery Assistant)	21 Lingaro, Bixter, Shetland ZE2 9NN 01595 810207
Williamson, Magnus J.C.	1982	1999	(Fetlar with Yell)	Creekhaven, Houll Road, Scalloway, Shetland ZE1 0XA 01595 880023
Wilson, W. Stewart DA	1980	1997	(Kirkcudbright)	Aesterhoull, Fair Isle, Shetland ZE2 9JU 01595 760273

(47) ENGLAND

Meets at London, in Crown Court Church, on the second Tuesday of March and December, and at St Columba's, Pont Street, on the second Tuesday of June and October.

Clerk: REV. W.A. CAIRNS BD   6 Honiton Gardens, Corby, Northants NN18 8BW   01536 203175
[E-mail: akph14@uk.uumail.com]
[E-mail: englandpresbytery@uk.uumail.com]

Corby: St Andrew's (H)
W. Alexander Cairns BD   1978   2001   6 Honiton Gardens, Corby, Northants NN18 8BW   01536 203175
[E-mail: englandpresbytery@uk.uumail.com]

Marjory Burns (Mrs) DCS   2003   1998   25 Barnsley Square, Corby, Northants NN18 0PQ   01536 264819
[E-mail: mburns8069@aol.com]

Corby: St Ninian's (H) (01536 265245)
Melvyn J. Griffiths BTh DipTheol   1978   2002   46 Glyndebourne Gardens, Corby, Northants NN18 0PZ   01536 747378
[E-mail: thehavyn@tiscali.co.uk]

Marjory Burns (Mrs) DCS   2003   1998   25 Barnsley Square, Corby, Northants NN18 0PQ   01536 264819
[E-mail: mburns8069@aol.com]

Guernsey: St Andrew's in the Grange (H)
Graeme W. Beebee BD   1993   2003   The Manse, Le Villocq, Castel, Guernsey GY5 7SB   01481 257345
[E-mail: beehive@cwgsy.net]

Jersey: St Columba's (H)
James G. Mackenzie BA BD   1980   1997   18 Claremont Avenue, St Saviour, Jersey JE2 7SF   01534 730659
[E-mail: jgmackenzie@jerseymail.com]

Liverpool: St Andrew's
Continued Vacancy
Session Clerk: Mr Robert Cottle   0151-524 1915

London: Crown Court (H) (020 7836 5643)
Sigrid Marten   1997   2001   53 Sidmouth Street, London WC1H 8JX   020 7278 5022
[E-mail: minister@crowncourtchurch.org.uk]
Timothy Fletcher BA FCMA (Aux)   1998   37 Harestone Valley Road, Caterham, Surrey CR3 6HN   01883 340826

London: St Columba's (H) (020 7584 2321) linked with Newcastle: St Andrew's (H)
Barry W. Dunsmore MA BD   1982   2000   29 Hollywood Road, Chelsea, London SW10 9HT   020 7376 5230
[E-mail: office@stcolumbas.org.uk]
Dorothy Lunn (Aux)   2001   14 Bellerby Drive, Ouston, Co. Durham DH2 1TW   0191-492 0647
Patricia Munro (Miss) BSc DCS   2002   11 Hurlingham Square, Peterborough Road, London SW6 3DZ   020 7610 6994
[E-mail: patmunro@tiscali.co.uk]

Newcastle: St Andrews See London: St Columba's

Bowie, A. Glen CBE BA BSc   1954   1984   (Principal Chaplain: RAF)   16 Weir Road, Hemingford Grey, Huntingdon PE18 9EH   01480 381425
Brown, Scott J. BD   1993   Chaplain: RN   4 Darwin Close, Lee-on-Solent, Hants PO13 8LS   02392 554116
[E-mail: leeonsolent@hotmail.com]
Cameron, R. Neil   1975   1981   Chaplain: Community   The Church Centre, Rhine Area Support Unit, BFPO 40   0049 2161 472770
Coulter, David G. BA BD PhD   1989   1994   Chaplain: Army   14 Fairfield, Lisburn, Co. Antrim BT27 4EE   02890 427540
[E-mail: padrecoulter@aol.com]
Craig, Gordon T. BD   1988   1988   Chaplain: RAF
Devenney, David J. BD   1997   2003   Chaplain: RN   8 Hunton Close, Lympstone, Exmouth, Devon EX8 5JG   01395 266570
[E-mail: davidjdevenney@freeuk.com]
Dowswell, James A.M.   1991   2001   (Lerwick and Bressay)   Mill House, High Street, Staplehurst, Tonbridge, Kent TN12 0AV   01580 891271

Name			Role	Address	(Tel)/(Fax)
Drummond, J.S. MA	1946	1978	(Corby: St Ninian's)	77 Low Road, Hellesdon, Norwich NR6 5AG	01603 417736
Duncan, Denis M. BD PhD	1944	1986	(Editor: *The British Weekly*)	80A Woodland Rise, London N10 3UJ	020 8883 1831 (Tel) 020 8374 4708 (Fax) 020 8201 1397
Fields, James MA BD STM	1988	1997	School Chaplain	The Bungalow, The Ridgeway, Mill Hill, London NW7 1QX	
Fyall, Robert S. MA BD PhD	1986	1989	Tutor: St John's College, Durham	7 Briardene, Durham DH1 4QU	
Hood, Adam J.J. MA BD DPhil	1989		Lecturer	67A Farquhar Road, Edgbaston, Birmingham B15 2QP [E-mail: adamhood1@hotmail.com]	0121-452 2606
Hughes, O. Tudor MBE BA	1934	1976	(Guernsey: St Andrew's in the Grange)	4 Belcher Court, Dorchester on Thames, Oxon	01865 340779
Jolly, Andrew J. BD	1989	1996	Chaplain: RAF	Chaplaincy Services, RAF Uxbridge, Middlesex UB10 0RX [E-mail: andrewchrissiejolly@btopenworld.com]	01895 815387
Lugton, George L. MA BD	1955	1997	(Guernsey: St Andrew's in the Grange)	6 Clos de Beauvoir, Rue Cohu, Guernsey GY5 7TE	01481 254285
McEnhill, Peter BD PhD	1992	1996	Lecturer	Westminster College, Madingley Road, Cambridge CB3 0AA	01223 353997
Macfarlane, Peter T. BA LTh	1970	1994	(Chaplain: Army)	4 rue de Rives, 37160 Abilly, France	
McIndoe, John H. MA BD STM DD	1966	2000	(London: St Columba's with Newcastle: St Andrew's		
MacLeod, Angus BD	1996		Chaplain: Army	5 Dunlin, Westerlands Park, Glasgow G12 0FE RMA Sandhurst, Camberley, Surrey GU15 4PQ [E-mail: padrermas@btconnect.com]	0141-579 1366 01276 691498
MacLeod, R.N. MA BD	1986	1992	Chaplain: Army	St Andrew's Garrison Church, Queen's Avenue, Aldershot, Hants GU11 2BY	01252 331123
Majcher, Philip L. BD	1982	1987	Chaplain: Army	18 Britannia Drive, Cempshott Park, Basingstoke RE22 4FN	01256 398868
Martin, Anthony M. BA BD	1989	1989	Chaplain: Army	Army Technical Foundation College, Rowcroft Barracks, Arborfield, Reading, Berks RG2 9NJ [E-mail: am_km_martin@hotmail.com]	01189 763409
Milloy, A. Miller DPE LTh DipTrMan	1979	1998	Regional Secretary: United Bible Societies	United Bible Societies, Allied Dunbar House, East Park, Crawley, West Sussex RH10 6AS	01444 257989
Mills, Peter W. BD CPS	1984		Principal Chaplain: RAF	Chaplaincy Services RAF, HQ PTC Innsworth, Gloucs GL3 1EZ	01452 510828
Milton, A. Leslie MA BD PhD	1996	2001	Lecturer	Ripon College, Cuddesdon, Oxford OX4 9HP	01865 877408
Norwood, David W. BA	1948	1980	(Lisbon)	6 Kempton Close, Thundersley, Benfleet, Essex SS7 3SG	01268 747219
Rennie, Alistair M. BD	1939	1986	(Kincardine Croick and Edderton)	Noble's Yard, St Mary's Gate, Wirksworth, Derbyshire DE4 4DQ	01629 820289
Richmond, James MA BD PhD	1956	1994	(Lancaster University)	10 Wallace Lane, Forton, Preston, Lancs PR3 0BA	01524 791705
Shackleton, Scott S.S. BA BD PhD	1993		Chaplain: Royal Navy	RM Stonehouse, Plymouth, Devon	01752 836397
Stewart, Charles E. BSc BD PhD	1976	2000	(Chaplain of the Fleet)	The Royal Hospital School, Holbrook, Ipswich IP9 2RX	01473 326200
Trevorrow, James A. LTh	1971	2003	(Glasgow: Cranhill)	12 Test Green, Corby, Northants NN17 2HA [E-mail: jimtrevorrow@compuserve.com]	01536 264018
Walker, R. Forbes BSc BD ThM	1987	2000	School Chaplain	2 Holmleigh, Priory Road, Ascot, Berks SL5 8EA	01344 883272
Wallace, Donald S.	1950	1980	(Chaplain: RAF)	7 Dellfield Close, Watford, Herts WD1 3BL	01923 223289
White, Earlsley M. BA	1957	1998	(Uddingston: Park)	11 Keble Lawns, Fairford, Gloucs GL7 4BQ	
Whitton, John P.	1977	1999	Assistant Chaplain General	115 Sycamore Road, Farnborough, Hants GU14 6RE	01262 674488

ENGLAND – Church Addresses

Corby
St Andrew's — Occupation Road
St Ninian's — Beanfield Avenue

Liverpool — The Western Rooms, Anglican Cathedral

London
Crown Court — Crown Court WC2
St Columba's — Pont Street SW1

Newcastle — Sandyford Road

(48) EUROPE

Clerk: REV. JOHN A. COWIE BSc BD   **Jan Willem Brouwersstraat 9, NL-1071 LH Amsterdam**   **Tel: 0031 20 672 2288**
[E-mail: j.cowie@chello.nl]   **Fax: 0031 842 221513**

Amsterdam John A. Cowie BSc BD	1983	1989	Jan Willem Brouwersstraat 9, NL-1071 LH Amsterdam, The Netherlands [E-mail: j.cowie@chello.nl]	0031 20 672 2288 Fax: 0031 842 221513
Brussels (E-mail: secretary@churchofscotland.be) Vacant			23 Square des Nations, B-1000 Brussels, Belgium	0032 2 672 40 56
Budapest Kenneth I. Mackenzie BD CPS	1990	1999	St Columba's Scottish Mission, Vorosmarty utca 51, H-1064 Budapest, Hungary Oltvany Arok 25, H-1112 Budapest, Hungary (Manse) [E-mail: mackenzie@mail.datanet.hu]	0036 1 343 8479 0036 1 246 2258
Costa del Sol Vacant			Astighi 2, Fifth Floor, Number 4, Fuengirola 29640, Malaga, Spain	0034 952 582836
Geneva Ian A. Manson BA BD	1989	2001	20 Ancienne Route, 1218 Grand Saconnex, Geneva, Switzerland (Office) [E-mail: cofsg@pingnet.ch]	0041 22 798 29 09 0041 22 788 08 31
Gibraltar Stewart J. Lamont BSc BD	1972	2003	St Andrew's Manse, 29 Scud Hill, Gibraltar [E-mail: lamont@gibraltar.gi]	00350 77040
Lausanne Vacant			26 Avenue de Rumine, CH-1005 Lausanne, Switzerland (Tel/Fax) [E-mail: scotskirklausanne@bluewin.ch]	0041 21 323 98 28
Lisbon Vacant			The Manse, Rua da Arriaga 11, 1200-608 Lisbon, Portugal (Tel/Fax) [E-mail: st.andrewschurch@clix.pt]	00351 21 395 7677
Malta David Morris		2002	La Romagnola, 13 Triq is-Seiqia, Mosra Kola, Attard (Tel/Fax) BZN 05, Malta [E-mail: djlmorris@onvol.net] Church address: 210 Old Baker Street, Valletta, Malta	00356 214 15465

Paris				
William M. Reid MA BD	1966	1993	10 Rue Thimmonier, F-75009 Paris, France [E-mail: scotskirk@wanadoo.fr]	0033 1 48 78 47 94
Rome: St Andrew's				
William B. McCulloch BD	1997	2002	Via XX Settembre 7, 00187 Rome, Italy [E-mail: revwbmcculloch@hotmail.com]	(Tel) 0039 06 482 7627 (Fax) 0039 06 487 4370
Rotterdam				
Robert A. Calvert BSc BD DMin	1983	1995	Gelebrem 59, NL-3068 TJ Rotterdam, The Netherlands [E-mail: scotsintchurch@cs.com]	0031 10 220 4199
Joanne Evans-Boiten (Community Minister)	2004		Oude Veerdam 2, NL-3212 MA Simonshaven, The Netherlands	
Turin				
Robert A. Mackenzie LLB BD	1993	2001	Via Sant Anselmo 6, 10125 Turin, Italy [E-mail: valdese.english@arpnet.it]	0039 011 650 9467
Conference of European Churches				
Matthew Z. Ross LLB BD MTh FSAScot	1998	2003	Church and Society Commission, Ecumenical Centre, Rue Joseph II 174, B-1000 Brussels, Belgium [E-mail: mzr@cec-kek.be]	(Tel) 0032 2 230 1732 (Fax) 0032 2 231 1413 (Mbl) 0044 7711 706950
World Alliance of Reformed Churches				
Paraic Raemonn BA BD	1982	1993	WARC, 150 Route de Ferney, CH-1211 Geneva 2, Switzerland [E-mail: par@warc.ch]	0041 22 791 62 43
CORRESPONDING MEMBERS				
James M. Brown MA BD	1982		Neustrasse 15, D-4630 Bochum, Germany [E-mail: j.brown@web.de]	0049 234 133 65
Dr Virgil Cruz	1956	1996	(Senior Professor of New Testament: Louisville Presbyterian Theological Seminary) Geelvinckstraat 21, NL-1901 AE Castricum, The Netherlands	
R. Graeme Dunphy	1988	1993	Institut für Anglistik, Universitätsstrasse 31, D-93053 Regensburg, Germany	
Rhona Dunphy (Mrs)				
Professor A.I.C. Heron BD DTheol	1975	1987	University of Erlangen, Kochstrasse 6, D-91054 Erlangen, Germany [E-mail: arheron@theologie.uni-erlangen.de]	0049 9131 852202
Jane H. Howitt (Miss) MA BD	1996		Scripture Union, PO Box 476, LV-1050 Riga, Latvia [E-mail: janesu@com.latnet.lv]	00371 7 220877
Bertalan Tamas			St Columba's Scottish Mission, Vorosmarty utca 51, H-1064 Budapest, Hungary [E-mail: rch@mail.elender.hu]	0036 1 343 8479

Derek Yarwood

(Rome)	David F. Huie MA BD	1962	(2001)	Chaplain's Department, Garrison HQ, Princess Royal Barracks, BFPO 47, Germany	0044 5241 77924
	David V.F. Kingston BD	1993		9 Kennedy Crescent, Alverstoke, Gosport, Hants PO12 2NL	02392 529310
				Army Chaplain: 20 Armoured Brigade, Paderborn, Germany	
				[E-mail: d.v.f.k@btinternet.com]	
(Brussels)	A.J. Macleod MA BD	1943	(1974)	72A Cathcart Road, London SW10 9DJ	
(Brussels)	Charles C. McNeill OBE BD	1962	(1991)	17 All Saints Way, Beachamwell, Swaffham, Norfolk PE37 8BU	
(Lausanne)	Douglas R. Murray MA BD	1965	2004	Flat 9, 4 Bonnington Gait, Edinburgh EH6 5NZ	0131-553 4398
(Gibraltar)	John R. Page BD DipMin	1988	2003	Astighi 2, Fifth Floor, Number 4, E-29640 Fuengirola, Malaga, Spain	0034 952 582836
(Gibraltar)	D. Stuart Philip MA	1952	(1990)	6 St Bernard's Crescent, Edinburgh EH4 1NP	0131-332 7499
(Brussels)	Thomas C. Pitkeathly MA CA BD	1984	2004	1 Lammermuir Court, Gullane EH31 2HU	01620 843373
(Rotterdam)	Joost Pot BSc (Aux)	1992	2004	[E-mail: j.pot@wanadoo.nl]	

(49) JERUSALEM

Jerusalem: St Andrew's

Clarence W. Musgrave BA BD ThM	1966	2000	PO Box 8619, 91086 Jerusalem, Israel	(Tel) 00972 2 673 2401
			[E-mail: standjer@netvision.net.il]	(Fax) 00972 2 673 1711

Tiberias: St Andrew's

Frederick W. Hibbert BD	1986	1995	St Andrew's, Galilee, PO Box 104, 14100 Tiberias, Israel	(Tel) 00972 4 672 1165
			[E-mail: scottie@netvision.net.il]	(Fax) 00972 4 679 0145

SECTION 6

Additional Lists
of Personnel

LIST A – AUXILIARY MINISTERS

NAME	ORD	ADDRESS	TEL	PR
Anderson, David M. MSc FCOptom	1984	1 Dumfries Place, Fort William PH33 6UQ	01397 703203	38
Birch, Jim PGDip FRSA FIOC	2001	1 Kirkhill Grove, Cambuslang, Glasgow G72 8EH	0141-583 1722	16
Brown, Elizabeth (Mrs) JP RGN	1996	25 Highfield Road, Scone, Perth PH2 6RN	01738 552391	28
Campbell, Gordon MA CDipAF DipHSM MCMI MIHM MRIN ARSGS FRGS FSAScot	2001	2 Falkland Place, Kingoodie, Invergowrie, Dundee DD2 5DY	01382 561383	29
Charlton, Richard	2001	The Manse, Symbister, Whalsay, Shetland ZE2 9AE	01806 566767	46
Cloggie, June (Mrs)	1997	11A Tulipan Crescent, Callander FK17 8AR	01877 331021	23
Craggs, Sheila (Mrs)	2001	7 Morar Court, Ellon AB41 9GG	01358 723055	33
Cruikshank, Alistair A.B. MA	1991	Thistle Cottage, 2A Chapel Place, Dollar FK14 7DW	01259 742549	23
Durno, Richard C. DSW CQSW	1989	Durnada House, 31 Springfield Road, Bishopbriggs, Glasgow G64 1PJ	0141-772 1052	16
Ferguson, Archibald M. MSc PhD CEng FRINA	1989	The Whins, Barrowfield, Station Road, Cardross, Dumbarton G82 5NL	01389 841517	18
Fletcher, Timothy E.G. BA FCMA	1998	37 Hareston Valley Road, Caterham, Surrey CR3 6HN	01883 340826	47
Glass, Alexander OBE MA	1998	Craigton, Tulloch Avenue, Dingwall IV15 9TU	01349 863258	39
Howie, Marion L.K. (Mrs) MA ARCS	1992	51 High Road, Stevenston KA20 3DY	01294 466571	12
Jenkinson, John J. JP LTCL ALCM DipEd DipSen	1991	8 Rosehall Terrace, Falkirk FK1 1PY	01324 625498	22
Kay, Elizabeth (Miss) Dip YCS	1993	1 Kintail Walk, Inchture, Perth PH14 9RY	01828 686029	29
Lunn, Dorothy	2002	14 Bellerby Drive, Ouston, Co. Durham DH2 1TN	0191-492 0647	47
McAlpine, John BSc	1988	Braeside, 201 Bonkle Road, Newmains, Wishaw ML2 9AA	01698 384610	17
McCann, George McD. BSc ATI	1994	Rosbeg, Parsonage Road, Galashiels TD1 3HS	01896 752055	4
MacDonald, Kenneth MA BA	2001	5 Henderland Road, Bearsden, Glasgow G61 1AH	0141-943 1103	16
MacDougall, Lorna	2003	34 Miller Place, Greenmount Park, Falkirk FK2 9QB	01324 552739	22
Mack, Elizabeth (Miss) Dip PEd	1994	24 Roberts Crescent, Dumfries DG2 7RS	01387 264847	8
Mack, John C. JP	1985	The Willows, Auchleven, Insch AB52 6QD	01464 820387	33
Mailer, Colin	2000	Innis Chonain, Back Row, Polmont, Falkirk FK2 0RD	01324 712401	22
Manson, Eileen (Mrs) DCE	1994	1 Cambridge Avenue, Gourock PA19 1XT	01475 632401	14
Moore, Douglas T.	2003	9 Midton Avenue, Prestwick KA9 1PU	01292 671352	10
Morrison, Donald John	2001	22 Kyles Harris, Isle of Harris HS3 3BS	01859 502341	43
Mowbray, Harry	2003	Viewlands, Beechwood Place, Kirriemuir DD8 5DZ		30
Munro, Mary (Mrs) BA	1993	High Barbeth, Leswalt, Stranraer DG9 0QS	01776 870250	9
Murray, John W.	2003	Totescore, Kilmuir, Portree, Isle of Skye IV51 9YN	01470 542297	42
Paterson, Andrew E. JP	1994	6 The Willows, Kelty KY4 0FQ	01383 830998	24
Paterson, Maureen (Mrs) BSc	1992	91 Dalmahoy Crescent, Kirkcaldy KY2 6TA	01592 262300	25
Phillippo, Michael	2003	25 Deeside Crescent, Aberdeen AB15 7PT		31
Pot, Joost BSc	1992	Rijksstraatweg 12, NL-2988 BJ Ridderkerk, The Netherlands	0031 18 042 0894	48
Ramage, Alistair E. BA	1996	16 Claremont Gardens, Milngavie, Glasgow G62 6PG	0141-956 2897	18
Riddell, Thomas S. BSc CEng FIChemE	1993	4 The Maltings, Linlithgow EH49 6DS	01506 843251	2
Ritchie, Christine (Mrs)	2002	Throughgate, 78 High Street, Dunbar EH42 1JH	01368 863141	3

Name	Year	Address	Phone	Page
Shaw, Catherine A.M. MA	1998	40 Merrygreen Place, Stewarton, Kilmarnock KA3 5EP	01560 483352	11
Simpson, James H. BSc	1996	11 Claypotts Place, Broughty Ferry, Dundee DD5 1LG	01382 776520	29
Sutherland, David	2001	6 Cromarty Drive, Dundee DD2 2UQ	01382 621473	29
Thomas, Shirley A. (Mrs) Dip Soc Sci AMIA	1988	14 Kirkgait, Letham, Forfar DD8 2XQ	01307 818084	30
Wandrum, David	1993	5 Cawder View, Carrickstone Meadows, Cumbernauld, Glasgow G68 0BN	01236 723288	22
Watson, Jean S. (Miss) MA	1993	29 Strachan Crescent, Dollar FK14 7HL	01259 742872	23
Wilson, Mary D. (Mrs) RGN SCM DTM	1990	The Manse, Bettyhill, Thurso KW14 7SS	01641 521208	40
Zambonini, James LIADip	1997	100 Old Manse Road, Netherton, Wishaw ML2 0EP	01698 350889	17

LIST B – CHAPLAINS TO HM FORCES

NAME	ORD	COM	BCH	ADDRESS
Abeledo, Benjamin J.A. BTh DipTh PTh	1991	1999	A	3rd Bn The Parachute Regiment, Hyderabad Barracks, Mersea Road, Colchester CO2 7TB
Aitchison, James W. BD	1993	1993	A	7th Armoured Brigade HQ. BFPO 30
Britchfield, Alison E.P. (Mrs) MA BD	1987	1992	RN	Room 014, Victory Building, HM Naval Base, Portsmouth PO1 3LS
Brown, Scott J. BD	1993	1993	RN	c/o The Chaplaincy, Jago Road, HM Naval Base, Portsmouth PO1 3LU
Cameron, Robert N.	1975	1981	A	Church Centre, Rhine Garrison, BFPO 40
Cobain, Alan R. BD	2000		A	2nd Bn The Parachute Regiment, Meanee Barracks, Colchester CO2 7TA
Connolly, Daniel BD DipTheol DipMin	1983		A	1 Bn Scots Guards, BFPO 17
Coulter, David G. BA BD PhD	1989	1994	A	Senior Chaplain, HQ Northern Ireland, BFPO 825
Craig, Gordon T. BD DipMin	1988	1988	RAF	Senior Chaplain, Chaplain's Office, RAF Cottesmore, Oakham LE15 8BL
Dailly, J.R. BD DipPS	1979	1979	A	DACG, HQ 42 (NW) Bde, Fulwood Barracks, Preston PR2 8AA
Dalton, Mark BD DipMin	2002	2002	RN	HMS Neptune, Faslane, Helensburgh, Argyll and Bute G84 8HL
Devenney, David BD	1997	2002	RN	The Chaplaincy, Commando Training Centre RM, Lympstone, Exeter EX8 5AR
Duncan, John C. BD MPhil	1987	2001	A	1Bn Kings Own Royal Border Regiment, Salimanker Barracks, BFPO 53
Jolly, Andrew J. BD CertMin	1983	1996	RAF	Chaplaincy Centre, RAF Uxbridge UB10 0RX
Kellock, Chris N. MA BD	1998		RAF	Chaplain's Office, RAF Cranwell, Sleaford NG34 8HB
Kennon, Stan MA BD	1992	2000	RN	c/o The Chaplaincy, Jago Road, HM Naval Base, Portsmouth PO1 3LU
Kingston, David V.F. BD	1993	1993	A	Senior Chaplain, HQ20, Armoured Brigade, BFPO 31
McCulloch, Alen J.R. MA BD	1990	1995	A	Senior Chaplain, 2nd BN ITC, Vimy Barracks, Catterick Garrison, North Yorks DL9 4HH
McFadzean, Iain MA BD	1989	1999	RN	Belmore House, HM Naval Base Clyde, Argyll and Bute G84 8HL
Mackenzie, Secras L. BD	1996	1998	A	Royal Armoured Corps Training Regiment, Borington, Wareham, Dorset BH20 6JA
MacLeod, Charles A. MA BD	1996	1996	A	Royal Military Academy, Camberley, Surrey GU15 4PQ
MacLeod, Roderick N. MA BD	1986	1992	A	101 Logistic Brigade, Buller Barracks, Aldershot, Hants GU11 2BX
MacLeod, Rory A.R. BA BD MBA	1994	1998	RN	1 Assistant Gp Royal Marines, Hamworthy Barracks, Dorset BH15 4NQ
MacPherson Duncan J. BSc BD	1993	2002	A	1 Bn The Black Watch, BFPO 38
Majcher, Philip L. BD	1982	1987	A	HQ 4th Division, Steele's Road, Aldershot GU11 2DP
Martin, Anthony M. BA BD	1989	1989	A	AFT College, Rowcroft Barracks, Arobfield, Reading, Berks RG2 9NJ
Mills, Peter W. BD CPS	1984	1984	RAF	Principal Chaplain, Chaplaincy Services, RAF Innsworth, Gloucester GL3 1EZ
Munro, Sheila BD	1995	2003	RAF	Chaplaincy Centre, RAF Odiham, Hook RG29 1QT

NAME		ORD	COM	ADDRESS	TEL
Prentice, Donald K. BSc BD	A	1987	1992	1 Bn Royal Irish Regiment, Fort George, Ardersier, Inverness IV1 2TD	
Rae, Scott M. MBE BD CPS	RN	1976	1981	HMS *Neptune*, Faslane, Helensburgh G84 8HL	
Shackleton, Scott J.S. BA BD	RN	1993	1993	Staff Chaplain Commandant General Royal Navy Marines, RM Barracks, Stonehouse, Plymouth PL1 3QS	
Shaw, Duncan LTh CPS	RAF	1984	1984	Senior Chaplain, Chaplain's Office, RAF Lossiemouth IV31 6SD	
Whitton, John P. MA BD	A	1977	1977	Deputy Chaplain General, MOD Chaplains (Army), Trenchard Lines, Upavon, Pewsey, Wilts SN9 6BE	

CHAPLAINS TO HM FORCES (Territorial Army)

NAME	ORD	COM	ADDRESS	TEL
Barclay, Iain C. MBE TD	1976	1982	HQ 2 Division, South Queensferry EH30 9TN	0131-310 2124
Blakey, Stephen A.	1977	1996	32 (Scottish) Signal Regiment (Volunteers), Glasgow G20 6JU	0141-224 5025
Forsyth, Alex R. TD	1973	1983	71 Engineer Regiment (Volunteers), RAF Leuchars KY16	01334 839471
Kinsey, Louis	1991	1992	205 (Scottish) Field Hospital (Volunteers), Glasgow G51 6JU	0141-224 5172
Swindells, Sean	1996	2001	225 Field Ambulance (Volunteers), Dundee DD4 7DL	0131-310 4760
Thomson, John M.A.	1978	1992	105 Regiment RA (Volunteers), Glasgow G20 8LQ	0141-224 5025
Warwick, Ivan C.	1980	1990	51 Highland Regiment (Volunteers), Perth PH1 5BT	0131-310 8547

CHAPLAINS TO HM FORCES (Army Cadet Force)

NAME	ORD	COM	ADDRESS	TEL
Almond, David M.	1996	1998	West Lowland Bn ACF, Ayr KA8 9HX	01292 264612
Andrews, J. Edward	1985	1998	Glasgow & Lanarkshire Bn ACF, Glasgow G72 8YP	0141-641 0858
Barclay, Iain C. MBE TD	1976	1996	Black Watch Bn ACF, Perth PH1 5BT	01738 626571
Campbell, Roderick D.M. TD	1975	1998	Argyll & Sutherland Highlands Bn ACF, Dumbarton G82 2DG	01389 763451
Fisk, Elizabeth A.	1996	1999	Black Watch Bn ACF, Perth PH1 5BT	01738 626571
Keyes, Joyce	1996	2000	Orkney (Independent) Bty ACF, Kirkwall KW1 5LP	01856 872661
Sherratt, Arthur	1994	1999	West Lowland Bn ACF, Ayr KA8 9HX	01292 264612
Sutherland, Iain A.	1996	1999	2 Bn Highlands ACF, Aberdeen AB24 8DV	01224 826239
Thom, D.J.	2000	2003	Cumbria ACF	01228 819832
Thomson, Stephen	2001	2003	1 Bn Highlands ACF, Inverness IV2 4SU	01463 231829

LIST C – HOSPITAL CHAPLAINS ('Full-time' Chaplains are listed first in each area)

LOTHIAN

EDINBURGH – LOTHIAN UNIVERSITY HOSPITALS

ROYAL INFIRMARY

Name	Address	Tel
Rev. Alexander Young	19B Craigour Drive, Edinburgh EH17 7NY	0131-242 1997
Rev. Iain Telfer	32 Alnwickhill Park, Edinburgh EH16 6UH	0131-242 1991
Ms Anne Mulligan	27A Craigour Avenue, Edinburgh EH17 1NH	0131-242 1996

WESTERN GENERAL HOSPITAL [0131-537 1000]

Name	Address	Tel
Rev. Alistair K. Ridland	13 Stewart Place, Kirkliston EH29 2BQ	0131-537 1401

LOTHIAN PRIMARY CARE

ROYAL EDINBURGH HOSPITAL [0131-537 6734]

Name	Address	Tel
Rev. Murray Chalmers		
Rev. Lynne MacMurchie	25 Greenbank Road, Edinburgh EH10 5RX	
Rev. Patricia Allen		

ROYAL HOSPITAL FOR SICK CHILDREN [0131-536 0000]

Name	Address	Tel
Rev. Caroline Upton	1 Westgate, Dunbar EH42 1JL	

EDINBURGH COMMUNITY MENTAL HEALTH

Rev. Caroline Upton	10 (3FL) Montagu Terrace, Edinburgh EH3 5QX	0131-536 0144
Rev. Lynne MacMurchie	41 George IV Bridge, Edinburgh EH1 1EL	0131-220 5150
Rev. Iain Whyte	41 George IV Bridge, Edinburgh EH1 1EL	0131-220 5150

LIVINGSTON – WEST LOTHIAN HEALTHCARE NHS TRUST [01506 419666]

Name	Address	Tel
Rev. John McMahon	28/2 Saughton Road, Edinburgh EH11 3PT	
Rev. Dr Georgina Nelson	6 Pentland Park, Craigshill, Livingston EH54 5NR	

HOSPICES

MARIE CURIE CENTRE — Rev. Tom Gordon	Frogston Road West, Edinburgh EH10 7DR	
ST COLUMBA'S HOSPICE — Rev. Alison Wagstaff	Challenger Lodge, 15 Boswall Road, Edinburgh EH5 3RW	(Tel) 0131-445 2141 / 0131-445 5845 (Fax) 0131-551 1381

HOSPITALS

Hospital	Name	Address	Tel
CORSTORPHINE	Rev. J. William Hill	33/9 Murrayfield Road, Edinburgh EH12 6EP	0131-554 1842
EASTERN GENERAL	Rev. John Tait	52 Pilrig Street, Edinburgh EH6 5AS	
LINLITHGOW ST MICHAEL'S	Rev. James Francis	Cross House, Kirkgate, Linlithgow EH49 7AL	01506 842665
BELHAVEN	Rev. Laurence H. Twaddle	The Manse, Belhaven Road, Dunbar EH42 1NH	01368 863098
EDENHALL	Rev. Anne M. Jones	7 North Elphinstone Farm, Tranent EH33 2ND	01875 614442
HERDMANFLAT	Rev. Anne M. Jones	7 North Elphinstone Farm, Tranent EH33 2ND	01875 614442
LOANHEAD	Mrs Susan Duncan	35 Kilmaurs Road, Edinburgh EH16 5DB	0131-667 2995

ROODLANDS	Rev. Kenneth D.F. Walker	The Manse, Athelstaneford, North Berwick EH39 5BE	01620 880378
ROSSLYNLEE	Rev. John W. Fraser	North Manse, Penicuik EH26 8AG	01968 672213
	Mrs Diane Kettles	10 Millway, Pencaitland, Tranent EH34 5HQ	07812 032226

BORDERS

MELROSE – BORDERS GENERAL HOSPITAL [01896 754333]	Rev. J. Ronald Dick	Chaplaincy Centre, Borders General Hospital, Melrose TD6 9BS	
DINGLETON	Rev. John Riddell	42 High Street, Jedburgh TD8 6NQ	01835 863223
HAY LODGE, PEEBLES	Rev. James H. Wallace	Innerleithen Road, Peebles EH45 8BD	01721 721749
KNOLL	Rev. Andrew Morrice	The Manse, Castle Street, Duns TD11 3DG	01361 883755
INCH	Rev. Robin McHaffie	Kirk Yetholm, Kelso TD5 8RD	01573 420308

DUMFRIES AND GALLOWAY

DUMFRIES HOSPITALS [01387 246246]	Rev. Alexander E. Strachan	2 Leafield Road, Dumfries DG1 2DS	01387 279460
THOMAS HOPE, LANGHOLM	Rev. Robert Milne	The Manse, Langholm DG13 0BL	01896 668577
LOCHMABEN	Rev. Alexander Stoddart	The Manse, Hightae, Lockerbie DG11 1JL	01387 811499
MOFFAT	Rev. David McKay	The Manse, Moffat DG10 9LR	01683 220128
NEW ANNAN	Rev. Mairi Byers	Meadowbank, Plumdon Road, Annan DG12 6SJ	01461 206512
CASTLE DOUGLAS	Rev. Robert Malloch	1 Castle View, Castle Douglas DG7 1BG	01556 502171
DUMFRIES AND GALLOWAY ROYAL INFIRMARY	Mrs Morven Archer	1 Gilloch Drive, Dumfries DG1 4DP	01387 263946
KIRKCUDBRIGHT	Rev. Douglas R. Irving	6 Bourtree Avenue, Kirkcudbright DG6 4AU	01557 330489
THORNHILL	Rev. Donald Keith	The Manse, Mansepark, Thornhill D63 5ER	01848 331191
DALRYMPLE	Rev. Gordon Kennedy	The Manse, London Road, Stranraer DG9 9AB	01776 702443
GARRICK	Rev. Gordon Kennedy	The Manse, London Road, Stranraer DG9 9AB	01776 702443
NEWTON STEWART	Rev. Neil Campbell	The Manse, Newton Stewart DG8 6HH	01671 402259

AYRSHIRE AND ARRAN

Location	Chaplain	Address
AYRSHIRE AND ARRAN PRIMARY CARE [01292 513023] AILSA HOSPITAL, AYR	Rev. Sheila Mitchell	Chaplaincy Centre, Dalmellington Road, Ayr KA6 6AB

AYRSHIRE AND ARRAN ACUTE HOSPITALS
[01563 521133]

CROSSHOUSE HOSPITAL KILMARNOCK			
AYR/BIGGART HOSPITALS [01292 610555]	Rev. Judith Huggett	4 Westmoor Crescent, Kilmarnock KA1 1TX	01292 442554
ARROL PARK	Rev. Roderick H. McNidder	6 Hollow Park, Alloway, Ayr KA7 4SR	
AYR	Mrs Norma Livingstone	31 Victoria Drive, Troon KA10 6JF	01292 478788
BALLOCHMYLE	Rev. Kenneth Elliott	68 St Quivox Road, Prestwick KA9 1JF	01292 269161
DAVIDSON	Rev. Robert Bell	87 Forehill Road, Ayr KA7 3JR	01465 831282
HOLMHEAD	Rev. John Paterson	The Manse, Ballantrae, Girvan KA26 0UH	01290 420769
CROSSHOUSE	Rev. John Urquhart	33 Barrhill Road, Cumnock KA18 1PJ	01863 538289
	Mrs Norma Livingstone	9 Standalane, Kilmaurs, Kilmarnock KA3 2NB	
	Rev. James McNaughtan	31 Victoria Drive, Troon KA10 6JF	01563 521665
	Rev. Paul Russell	35 South Gargieston Drive, Kilmarnock KA1 1TB	01292 570272
	Mrs Iris Gooding	4 Hamilton Place, Coylton, Ayr KA6 6JQ	
KIRKLANDSIDE	Mrs Barbara Urquhart	58 Wilson Avenue, Troon KA10 7AJ	01863 538289
STRATHLEA	Mrs Barbara Urquhart	9 Standalane, Kilmaurs, Kilmarnock KA3 2NB	01863 538289
AYRSHIRE CENTRAL	Rev. Hugh M. Adamson	9 Standalane, Kilmaurs, Kilmarnock KA3 2NB	01294 279916
	Mrs Norma Livingstone	Mure Church Manse, West Road, Irvine KA12 8RE	
BROOKSBY HOUSE, LARGS	Rev. Stephen J. Smith	31 Victoria Drive, Troon KA10 6JF	01475 672370
WAR MEMORIAL, ARRAN	Rev. Elizabeth Watson	31 Douglas Street, Largs KA30 8PT	01770 700289
LADY MARGARET, MILLPORT	Rev. Marjory H. Mackay	The Manse, Whiting Bay, Isle of Arran KA27 8RE	01475 530416
		The Manse, Millport, Isle of Cumbrae KA28 0ED	

LANARKSHIRE

LOCKHART	Rev. Catherine Collins	2 Friarsdene, Lanark ML11 9EJ	01555 663363
	Rev. Bruce Gordon	The Rectory, Cleghorn Road, Lanark ML11 7QT	
CLELAND	Rev. John Jackson	The Manse, Bellside Road, Cleland, Motherwell ML1 5NP	01698 860260
KELLO	Post Vacant		
LADY HOME	Rev. Bryan Kerr	The Manse, Douglas, Lanark ML11 0RB	01555 851213
ROADMEETINGS	Rev. Geoff McKee	Kirkstyle Manse, Church Street, Carluke ML8 4BA	01698 882238
WISHAW GENERAL	Rev. James S.G. Hastie	Chalmers Manse, Quarry Road, Larkhall ML9 1HH	01698 372356
	Rev. Klaus Buwert	The Manse, West Thornlie Street, Wishaw ML2 7AR	01698 372657
	Rev. J. Allardyce	6 Kelso Crescent, Wishaw ML2 7HD	01355 663363
	Rev. David Collins	Greyfriars Manse, Friarsdene, Lanark ML11 9EJ	01236 763154
	Rev. Sharon Colvin	48 Dunrobin Road, Airdrie ML6 8LR	01698 381305
STRATHCLYDE	Rev. Mhorag MacDonald	350 Kirk Road, Wishaw ML2 8LH	01698 263472
HAIRMYRES	Rev. David W. Doyle	19 Orchard Street, Motherwell ML1 3JE	01355 242564
	Rev. John Brewster	21 Turnberry Place, East Kilbride, Glasgow G75 8TB	01355 234196
	Rev. Dr John McPake	30 Eden Grove, East Kilbride, Glasgow G75 8XY	01357 520643
	Rev. Marjorie Taylor	1 Kirkhill Road, Strathaven ML10 6HN	01698 882238
KIRKLANDS	Rev. James S.G. Hastie	Chalmers Manse, Quarry Road, Larkhall ML9 1HH	01698 823130
STONEHOUSE	Rev. Rosemary Smith	Blantyre Old Manse, High Blantyre, Glasgow G72 9UA	
	Rev. James P. Fraser	26 Hamilton Road, Strathaven ML10 6JA	01357 522758

UDSTON	Rev. J. Stanley Cook	137A Old Manse Road, Netherton, Wishaw ML2 0EW	01698 299600
COATHILL	Rev. William Beattie	33 Dungavel Gardens, Hamilton ML3 7PE	01698 423804
MONKLANDS GENERAL	Rev. William McKaig	132 Muiryhall Street, Coatbridge ML5 3NH	01236 421181
	Rev. James Munton	2 Moorcroft Drive, Airdrie ML6 8ES	01236 754848
	Rev. Andrew Thomson	38 Commonhead Street, Airdrie ML6 6NS	01236 602538
WESTER MOFFAT	Rev. James Grier	47 Blair Road, Coatbridge ML5 1JQ	01236 432427
HARTWOODHILL	Rev. James Munton	2 Moorcroft Drive, Airdrie ML6 8ES	01263 754848
	Rev. Henry J.W. Findlay	St Mark's Manse, Coltness Road, Wishaw ML2 7EX	01698 384596
	Rev. Colin Cuthbert	Yieldshields Farm, Carluke ML8 4QB	
HATTONLEA	Rev. Agnes Moore	16 Croftpark Street, Bellshill ML4 1EY	01698 842877
MOTHERWELL PSYCHIATRIC	Rev. John Handley	12 Airbles Crescent Motherwell ML1 3AR	01698 262733
COMMUNITY MENTAL HEALTH CARE	Rev. J. Stanley Cook	137A Old Manse Road, Netherton, Wishaw ML2 0EW	01698 299600
	Rev. Sharon Colvin	48 Dunrobin Road, Airdrie ML6 8LR	01236 763154
	Rev. Rosemary Smith	Blantyre Old Manse, High Blantyre, Glasgow G72 9UA	01698 823130

GREATER GLASGOW

NORTH GLASGOW UNIVERSITY HOSPITALS			
GLASGOW ROYAL INFIRMARY [0141-211 4000/4661]	Rev. Patricia McDonald	4 Whithope Terrace, Glasgow G53 7LT	
	Rev. Anne J.M. Harper	122 Greenock Road, Bishopton PA7 5AS	
WESTERN INFIRMARY [0141-211 2000]	Rev. Keith Saunders	1 Beckfield Drive, Robroyston, Glasgow G33 1SR	0141-211 2000/2812
GARTNAVEL GENERAL [0141-211 3000]	Rev. Keith Saunders	1 Beckfield Drive, Robroyston, Glasgow G33 1SR	0141-211 3000/3026
GLASGOW HOMEOPATHIC [0141-211 1600]	Rev. Keith Saunders	1 Beckfield Drive, Robroyston, Glasgow G33 1SR	0141-211 1600
GREATER GLASGOW PRIMARY CARE	Rev. Cameron H. Langlands: Co-ordinator		
GARTNAVEL ROYAL HOSPITAL [0141-211 3686]	Rev. Gordon B. Armstrong: North/East Sector	Chaplain's Office, Old College of Nursing, Stobhill Hospital, 133 Balornock Road, Glasgow G21 3UW	0141-232 0609
	Ms Anne MacDonald: South Sector	Chaplain's Office, Leverndale Hospital, 510 Crookston Road, Glasgow G53 7TU	0141-211 6695
SOUTH GLASGOW UNIVERSITY HOSPITALS			
SOUTHERN GENERAL HOSPITAL [0141-201 2156]	Rev. Ann Purdie		
	Rev. Blair Robertson: Co-ordinator		
VICTORIA INFIRMARY	Rev. Iain Reid	Chaplain's Office, Langside Road, Glasgow G42 9TT	0141-201 5164
YORKHILL NHS TRUST [0141-201 0595]	Rev. Alistair Bull	Royal Hospital for Sick Children, Glasgow G3 8SG	
	Rev. Hilda Smith	Royal Hospital for Sick Children, Glasgow G3 8SG	
GREATER GLASGOW PRIMARY CARE	Rev. David Torrance	19 Redhills View, Lennoxtown, Glasgow G65 7BL	
	Rev. Alastair MacDonald	42 Roman Way, Dunblane FK15 9DJ	01360 312527

ROYAL INFIRMARY	Mrs Sandra Bell	62 Loganswell Road, Thornliebank, Glasgow G46 8AX	0141-637 6956
STOBHILL	Rev. Norma Stewart	127 Nether Auldhouse Road, Glasgow G43 2YS	0141-772 1453
	Rev. Elizabeth W. Sutherland	54 Etive Crescent, Bishopbriggs, Glasgow G54 1ES	
LEVERNDALE	Rev. John Beaton	33 North Birbiston Road, Lennoxtown, Glasgow G65 7LZ	0141-647 6250
DARNLEY COURT	Rev. Kenneth Coulter	8 Abbotsford Avenue, Rutherglen, Glasgow G73 3NX	0141-883 5618
VICTORIA INFIRMARY/MEARNSKIRK	Miss Anne MacDonald	62 Berwick Drive, Glasgow G52 3JA	
GARTNAVEL GENERAL/WESTERN	Rev. Alan Raeburn	110 Mount Annan Drive, Glasgow G44 4RZ	0141-632 1514
BLAWARTHILL	Mrs Deirdre Lyon	14 Melfort Avenue, Clydebank, Glasgow G81 2HX	
KNIGHTSWOOD/DRUMCHAPEL	Mrs Deirdre Lyon	14 Melfort Avenue, Clydebank, Glasgow G81 2HX	0141-959 7158
RUTHERGLEN TAKARE	Rev. Andrew McMillan	1 Swallow Gardens, Glasgow G13 4QD	0141-643 0234
	Rev. J.W. Drummond	21 Albert Drive, Rutherglen, Glasgow G73 3RT	0141-647 6178
	Rev. Alexander Thomson	31 Highburgh Drive, Rutherglen, Glasgow G73 3RR	0141-429 5599
PRINCE AND PRINCESS OF WALES HOSPICE	Rev. Alan Donald	71 Carlton Place, Glasgow G5 9TD	0141-762 1844
FOURHILLS NURSING HOME	Rev. W.G. Ramsay	3 Tofthill Avenue, Bishopbriggs, Glasgow G64 3PN	0141-558 2555
HUNTERS HILL MARIE CURIE CENTRE	Rev. David Mitchell	1 Belmont Road, Glasgow G21 3AY	0141-427 2094
COMMON SERVICES AGENCY	Rev. Thomas Pollock	114 Springkell Avenue, Glasgow G41 4EW	0141-637 5451
	Rev. Janet McMahon	156 Old Castle Road, Glasgow G44 5TW	

ARGYLL AND CLYDE

INVERCLYDE ROYAL HOSPITAL (Whole-time)	Rev. Fergus McLachlan	Chaplain's Office, Inverclyde Royal Hospital,	
GREENOCK [01475 633777]		Larkfield Road, Greenock PA16 0XN	
(Part-time)	Mrs Joyce Nicol	93 Brisbane Street, Greenock PA16 8NY	01475 723235
DYKEBAR	Rev. Alistair Morrison	36 Newtyle Road, Paisley PA1 3JX	0141-889 4279
	Rev. Alexander MacDonald	The Manse, Neilston, Glasgow G78 3NP	0141-881 1958
	Rev. George Mackay	10 Hawick Avenue, Paisley PA2 9LD	0141-884 8903
	Miss Margaret McBain	33 Quarry Road, Paisley PA2 7RD	0141-854 2920
HAWKHEAD	Rev. Georgina Baxendale	The Manse, Main Street, Houston, Johnstone PA6 7EL	01505 612569
MERCHISTON HOUSE	Rev. Thomas Cant	18 Oldhall Road, Paisley PA1 3HL	0141-882 2277
JOHNSTONE	Rev. Thomas Cant	18 Oldhall Road, Paisley PA1 3HL	0141-882 2277
ROYAL ALEXANDRA	Rev. Arthur Sherratt	West Manse, Kilbarchan, Johnstone PA10 2JR	01805 702669
	Rev. Douglas Ralph	24 Kinpurnie Road, Paisley PA1 3HH	0141-883 3505
	Rev. Ian S. Currie	9 Hawkhead Road, Paisley PA1 3ND	0141-887 0884
	Rev. Alexander Wark	31 Gibson Road, Renfrew PA4 0RH	0141-886 2005
	Rev. Ritchie Gillon	31 Southfield Avenue, Paisley PA2 8BX	0141-884 6215
	Rev. E. Lorna Hood (Mrs)	North Manse, 1 Alexandra Drive, Renfrew PA4 8UB	0141-886 2074
	Rev. Owain Jones	East Manse, Kilbarchan PA10 2JQ	01505 702621
RAVENSCRAIG	Rev. James H. Simpson	76 Finnart Street, Greenock PA16 8HJ	01475 722338
	Rev. Douglas Cranston	6 Churchill Road, Kilmacolm PA13 4LH	01505 873271

DUMBARTON JOINT			
VALE OF LEVEN GENERAL	Rev. Christine Liddell	3 Havoc Road, Dumbarton G82 4JW	01389 604840
VALE OF LEVEN GERIATRIC	Rev. Ian Miller	1 Glebe Gardens, Bonhill, Alexandria G83 9HB	01389 753039
CAMPBELTOWN	Rev. Ian Wilkie	38 Main Street, Renton, Dumbarton G82 4PU	01389 752017
LOCHGILPHEAD	Mrs Janice Forrest	The Manse, Southend, Campbeltown PA28 6RQ	01586 830274
ISLAY	Mrs Margaret Sinclair	2 Quarry Park, Furnace, Inveraray PA32 8XW	01499 500633
DUNOON	Rev. Norman Macleod	The Manse, Port Ellen, Isle of Islay PA42 7DB	01496 302447
DUNOON ARGYLL UNIT	Rev. Austin Erskine	99 Sandhaven, Sandbank, Dunoon PA23 8QW	01369 701295
ROTHESAY	Rev. Austin Erskine	99 Sandhaven, Sandbank, Dunoon PA23 8QW	01369 701295
LORN AND THE ISLANDS	Mr Raymond Deans	60 Ardmory Road, Rothesay PA20 0PG	01700 504893
DISTRICT GENERAL	Rev. Elizabeth Gibson	Rudha-na-Cloiche, The Esplanade, Oban PA34 5AQ	01631 562759

FORTH VALLEY

BELLSDYKE	Rev. Ann Smith	16 Mannerston Holdings, Linlithgow EH49 7ND	01506 834350
	Rev. Henry Munroe	Viewforth, High Road, Maddiston, Falkirk FK2 0BL	01324 712446
	Rev. Robert MacLeod	13 Cannons Way, Falkirk FK2 7QG	01324 631008
BO'NESS	Rev. Stuart Webster	36 Blair Avenue, Bo'ness EH51 0QT	01506 204485
BONNYBRIDGE	Rev. Alisdair MacLeod-Mair	133 Falkirk Road, Bonnybridge FK4 1BA	01324 812621
FALKIRK ROYAL INFIRMARY	Rev. Joanne Finlay	6 Herd Green, Livingston EH54 8PU	01324 813786
	Rev. Helen Christie	5 Watson Place, Dennyloanhead, Bonnybridge FK4 2BG	0131-337 7153
	Rev. Margery Collin	2 Saughtonhall Crescent, Edinburgh EH12 5RF	01324 861252
RSNH LARBERT	Rev. Robert Philip	Congregational Church Manse, Avonbridge, Falkirk FK1 2LU	01786 814692
BANNOCKBURN	Rev. James Landels	Allan Manse, Bogend Road, Bannockburn, Stirling FK7 8NP	01259 212836
CLACKMANNAN COUNTY	Rev. Eleanor Forgan	18 Alexandra Drive, Alloa FK10 2DQ	01786 823902
KILDEAN	Rev. Robert Symington	3 Belmont House, The Crescent, Dunblane FK15 0DW	01786 465547
SAUCHIE	Rev. Malcolm MacRae	10b Victoria Place, Stirling FK8 2QU	01786 831026
STIRLING ROYAL INFIRMARY	Rev. Stuart Pryce	36 Forth Park, Bridge of Allan FK9 5NT	01786 474421
	Rev. Gary McIntyre	7 Randolph Road, Stirling FK8 2AJ	01786 475802
	Rev. Kenneth Russell	5 Clifford Road, Stirling FK8 2QU	

FIFE

QUEEN MARGARET HOSPITAL, DUNFERMLINE [01383 674136]	Rev. Isabel Whyte	Fife Acute Hospitals, Queen Margaret Hospital, Whitefield Road, Dunfermline KY12 0SU	
VICTORIA HOSPITAL, KIRKCALDY [01592 643355]			
LYNEBANK	Rev. Ian J.M. McDonald	11 James Grove, Kirkcaldy KY1 1TN	01592 203775
CAMERON	Rev. Elizabeth Frisk	51 St John's Drive, Dunfermline KY12 7TL	01383 720256
	Rev. James L. Templeton	Innerleven Manse, McDonald Street, Methil, Leven KY8 3AJ	01333 426310
	Rev. Kenneth Donald	33 Main Road, East Wemyss, Kirkcaldy KY1 4RE	01592 713260

Hospital	Chaplain	Address	Telephone
GLENROTHES	Rev. Ian D. Gordon	7 Guthrie Crescent, Markinch, Glenrothes KY7 6AY	01592 758264
RANDOLPH WEMYSS	Rev. Elizabeth Cranfield	9 Chemiss Road, Methilhill, Leven KY8 2BS	01592 713142
ADAMSON, CUPAR	Rev. Lynn Brady	2 Guthrie Court, Cupar Road, Newburgh, Cupar KY14 6HA	01337 842228
NETHERLEA, NEWPORT	Rev. Colin Dempster	27 Bell Street, Tayport DD6 9AP	01382 552861
STRATHEDEN, CUPAR	Rev. Dr Henry Gibson	4 Comerton Place, Drumoig, St Andrews KY16 0NQ	01382 542199
	Miss Margaret Browning	4 Wellpark Terrace, Newport-on-Tay DD6 8HT	01382 542140
ST ANDREWS MEMORIAL	Rev. David Arnott	20 Priory Gardens, St Andrews KY16 8XX	01334 472912

TAYSIDE

Hospital	Chaplain	Address	Telephone
DUNDEE NINEWELLS HOSPITAL [01382 660111]	Rev. David J. Gordon		
PERTH ROYAL INFIRMARY [01738 473896]	Rev. John M. Birrell	2 Rhynd Lane, Perth PH2 8TP	01738 625694
	Rev. Anne Findlay	Balcraig House, Scone, Perth PH2 7PG	01738 552237
ABERFELDY	Rev. Alexander M. Gunn	The Manse, Taybridge Terrace, Aberfeldy PH15 2BS	01887 820656
BLAIRGOWRIE RATTRAY	Rev. Ian Knox	Heatherlea, Main Street, Ardler, Blairgowrie PH12 8SR	01828 640731
IRVINE MEMORIAL	Rev. Ian Murray	The Manse, Blair Atholl, Pitlochry PH18 5SX	01796 481213
CRIEFF COTTAGE	Rev. Gillian Munro		01382 423116
MACMILLAN HOSPICE	Rev. Anne Findlay	Balcraig House, Scone, Perth PH2 7PG	01738 552237
MURRAY ROYAL	Rev. Peter Meager	7 Lorraine Drive, Cupar KY15 5DY	01334 656991
	Rev. Isobel Birrell	2 Rhynd Lane, Perth PH2 8TP	01738 625694
ST MARGARET'S COTTAGE	Rev. Randal MacAlister	St Kessog's Rectory, High Street, Auchterarder PH3 1AD	01764 662525
ASHLUDIE	Rev. Roy Massie	St Rule's Manse, 8 Church Street, Monifieth DD5 4JP	01382 532607
	Rev. David Jamieson	Panmure Manse, 8A Albert Street, Monifieth DD5 4JS	01382 532772
TAYSIDE ORTHOPAEDIC AND REHAB. CENTRE	Rev. Thomas P. Robertson	20 Kilnburn, Newport-on-Tay DD6 8DE	01382 542422
DUNDEE, ROYAL LIFF	Rev. Gillian Munro		01382 423116
ROYAL VICTORIA	Rev. Janet Foggie	39 Tullidelph Road, Dundee DD2 2JD	01382 660152
NINEWELLS	Rev. Tom Milroy	9 Long Row, Westhaven, Carnoustie DD7 6BE	01241 856654
STRATHMARTINE	Rev. Gillian Munro		01382 423116
ARBROATH INFIRMARY	Rev. Alasdair G. Graham	1 Charles Avenue, Arbroath DD11 2EZ	01241 872244
BRECHIN INFIRMARY	Mr Gordon Anderson	33 Grampian View, Montrose DD10 9SU	01674 674915
FORFAR INFIRMARY	Rev. Graham Norrie	East Manse, Lour Road, Forfar DD8 2BB	01307 464303
LITTLE CAIRNIE	Rev. Iain G. Gough	St Vigeans Manse, Arbroath DD11 4RD	01241 873206
MONTROSE ROYAL	Rev. Iain Coltart	The Manse, Arbirlot, Arbroath DD11 2NX	01241 434479
STRACATHRO	Mr Gordon Anderson	33 Grampian View, Montrose DD10 9SU	01674 674915
SUNNYSIDE ROYAL	Mr Gordon Anderson	33 Grampian View, Montrose DD10 9SU	01674 674915

GRAMPIAN

GRAMPIAN UNIVERSITY HOSPITALS
ABERDEEN ROYAL INFIRMARY
[01224 681818]

Rev. Fred Coutts	9a Milburn Street, Aberdeen AB11 6SS	01224 553166
Rev. James Falconer	3 Brimmond Walk, Westhill, Skene AB32 6XH	01224 554905
Rev. Sylvia Spencer (Chaplain's Assistant)		
Miss Monica Stewart (Chaplain's Assistant)		

WOODEND HOSPITAL [01224 557293]

Rev. Alison Hutchison	9 Craigton Avenue, Aberdeen AB15 7RD	01224 554907
Rev. Mark Rodgers	'Ashfield', Drumoak, Banchory AB31 3AA	01224 556788
Rev. Marion Cowie		

GRAMPIAN PRIMARY CARE
ROYAL CORNHILL and
WOODLANDS HOSPITAL [01224 557293]

Rev. Muriel Knox	35 Valentine Drive, Aberdeen AB22 8YF	01224 553316
Mr Donald Meston	20 Rosehill Place, Aberdeen AB2 2LE	01224 557484
Miss Pamela Adam (Chaplain's Assistant)	409 Holburn Street, Aberdeen AB10 7GS	

ABERDEEN CITY	Rev. Marian Cowie	6 St Swithin Street, Aberdeen AB10 6XE	01224 593302
KINCARDINE COMMUNITY	Rev. Gordon Farquharson	Dunnottar Manse, Stonehaven AB39 3XL	01569 762874
	Rev. David Stewart	South Church Manse, Cameron Street, Stonehaven AB39 2HE	01569 762576
GLEN O' DEE	Rev. Donald Walker	2 Wilson Road, Banchory AB31 3UY	01330 822811
INVERURIE	Rev. Ian B. Groves	West Manse, Inverurie AB51 9YS	01467 620285
JUBILEE	Rev. Thomas Calder	The Manse, Queen Street, Huntly AB54 5EB	01466 792630
CAMPBELL	Rev. Iain Sutherland	The Manse, Portsoy, Banff AB45 2QB	01261 842272
CHALMERS	Rev. David Randall	Manse of Doune, Banff AB45 3QL	01261 832316
FRASERBURGH	Rev. Andrew Lyon	23 Strichen Road, Fraserburgh AB43 9SA	01346 513303
MAUD	Rev. Alastair Donald	New Deer Manse, Turriff AB53 6TG	01771 644216
PETERHEAD COTTAGE	Rev. David S. Ross	3–5 Abbey Street, Deer, Peterhead AB42 5LN	01771 623994
TURRIFF	Rev. Sylvia Dyer	The Shieling, Westfield Road, Turriff AB53 4AF	01888 562530
UGIE	Rev. David Pitkeathly	1 Landale Road, Peterhead AB42 1QN	01779 472141
DR GRAY'S	Rev. George B. Rollo	18 Reidhaven Street, Elgin IV30 1QH	01343 547208
FLEMING COTTAGE	Rev. Ruth Tait	30 Mayne Road, Elgin IV30 1PB	
LEANCHOIL	Post Vacant		
SPYNIE	Rev. Ray Hall	21 St Peter's Road, Duffus, Elgin IV30 5QL	01343 830985
SEAFIELD	Rev. John Hegarty	The Manse, East Church Street, Buckie AB56 1ES	01542 832103
STEPHEN AND COUNTY HOSPITALS	Rev. Hugh M.C. Smith	The Manse, Church Street, Dufftown, Keith AB55 4AR	01340 820380
TURNER MEMORIAL	Rev. Dr Kay Gauld	The Manse, Church Road, Keith AB55 5BR	01542 882799

HIGHLAND

THE RAIGMORE HOSPITAL [01463 704000]

Rev. Iain MacRitchie	7 Merlin Crescent, Inverness IV2 3TE	
Rev. Derek Brown	Cathedral Manse, Dornoch IV25 3HV	

IAN CHARLES	Rev. Morris Smith	Golfcourse Road, Grantown-on-Spey PH26 3HY	01479 872084
ST VINCENT	Rev. Helen Cook	The Manse, West Terrace, Kingussie PH21 1HA	01340 661311
NEW CRAIGS	Rev. Michael Hickford	15 Ardross Street, Inverness IV3 5NS	01463 870395
NAIRN TOWN AND COUNTY	Rev. Ian Hamilton	3 Manse Road, Nairn IV12 4RN	01667 452203
BELFORD AND BELHAVEN	Rev. Donald A. MacQuarrie	Manse of Duncansburgh, Fort William PH33 6BA	01397 702297
GLENCOE	Rev. Alison Burnside	The Manse, Ballachulish PH49 4JG	01855 811998
ROSS MEMORIAL, DINGWALL	Rev. Russel Smith	8 Castlehill Road, Dingwall IV15 9PB	01349 861011
	Rev. Grahame M. Henderson	16 Achany Road, Dingwall IV15 9JB	01349 863167
INVERGORDON COUNTY	Rev. Kenneth D. Macleod	The Manse, Cromlet Drive, Invergordon IV18 0BA	01349 852273
LAWSON MEMORIAL	Rev. Eric Paterson	Free Church Manse, Golspie KW10 6TT	01408 633529
MIGDALE	Rev. Kenneth Hunter	Free Church Manse, Gower Street, Brora KW9 6PU	01408 621271
CAITHNESS GENERAL	Rev. A.A. Roy	Mansefield, Miller Avenue, Wick KW1 4DF	01955 602822
	Rev. Steven Thomson	The Manse, Miller Avenue, Wick KW1 4DF	01955 604252
DUNBAR	Rev. Kenneth Borthwick	46 Rose Street, Thurso KW14 7HN	01847 895186
	Rev. Ronald Johnstone	West Church Manse, Thorkel Road, Thurso KW14 7LW	01847 892663
BROADFORD MACKINNON MEMORIAL	Rev. Dr Ben Johnstone	The Shiants, 5 Upper Breakish, Breakish, Isle of Skye IV42 8PY	01471 822538
GESTO	Rev. Iain Greenshields	The Manse, Kensaleyre, Snizort, Portree, Isle of Skye IV51 9XE	01470 532260

WESTERN ISLES HEALTH BOARD

UIST AND BARRA HOSPITAL	Rev. Thomas MacKinnon	The Manse, Clachan, Isle of North Uist HS6 5HD	01876 580219
WESTERN ISLES, STORNOWAY	Rev. James MacDonald	8A Lower Bayble, Point, Lewis HS2 0QA	01851 870173

ORKNEY HEALTH BOARD

BALFOUR AND EASTBANK	Rev. Thomas Clark	Stenness, Stromness, Orkney KW16 3HN	01856 761331

LIST D – FULL-TIME INDUSTRIAL CHAPLAINS

EDINBURGH (Edinburgh City Mission Appointment)	Mr John Hopper	26 Mulberry Drive, Dunfermline KY11 5BZ	01383 737189

EDINBURGH (Methodist Appointment)	Rev. Linda Bandelier	5 Dudley Terrace, Edinburgh EH6 4QQ	0131-554 1636
EDINBURGH (part-time)	Mrs Dorothy Robertson	15/1 Meadowhouse Road, Edinburgh EH12 7HW	0131-334 5440
GLASGOW (part-time)	Rev. Elisabeth Spence	45 Selvieland Road, Glasgow G52 4ES	0141-883 8973 / 0141-883 1714 (Office)
	Mr William Shirlaw	194 Redpath Drive, Glasgow G52 2ER	0141-332 4458 (Office)
WEST OF SCOTLAND	Rev. Alister Goss	79 Weymouth Crescent, Gourock PA19 1HR	01475 638944 / 01475 629383
OFFSHORE OIL INDUSTRY	Rev. Angus Smith	1 Fa'burn Terrace, Lumphanan, Banchory AB31 4AG	01339 883395 / 01224 297532 (Office)
ABERDEEN CITY CENTRE (part-time)	Mrs Cate Adams	15 Rousay Place, Aberdeen AB15 6HG	01224 643494/647470
NORTH OF SCOTLAND	Mr Lewis Rose DCS	16 Gean Drive, Blackburn, Aberdeen AB21 0YN	01224 790145
TAYSIDE and NATIONAL CO-ORDINATOR	Rev. Erik M. Cramb	65 Clepington Road, Dundee DD4 7BQ	01382 458764

LIST E – PRISON CHAPLAINS

CO-ORDINATOR (NATIONAL)	Rev. William Taylor	HM Prison, Edinburgh EH11 3LN	0131-444 3082
ABERDEEN CRAIGINCHES	Rev. Dr David Ross	HM Prison, Aberdeen AB1 2NE	01224 238300
CASTLE HUNTLY	Rev. David MacLeod	6 Carseview Gardens, Dundee DD2 1NE	01382 641371
	Rev. Diane Hobson	The Manse, Longforgan, Dundee DD2 5EU	01382 360238
CORNTON VALE	Post Vacant		
DUMFRIES	Rev. Dennis S. Rose	The Manse, Kirkmahoe, Dumfries DG1 1ST	01387 710572
EDINBURGH: SAUGHTON	Rev. Colin Reed	Chaplaincy Centre, HMP Edinburgh EH11 3LN	0131-444 3115
	Rev. William Taylor	HM Prison, Edinburgh EH11 3LN	0131-444 3082
	Rev. Robert Ackroyd	HM Prison, Edinburgh EH11 3LN	0131-444 3115
	Mr Timothy Bell	HM Prison, Edinburgh EH11 3LN	0131-444 3115

	Rev. C. Blair Gillon	3 Dargarvel Avenue, Glasgow G41 5LD	0141-427 1282
	Rev. Ian McInnes	46 Earlbank Avenue, Glasgow G14 9HL	0141-954 0328
	Rev. Douglas Clark	41 Kirkintilloch Road, Lenzie, Glasgow G66 4LB	0141-770 2184
	Rev. Russell McLarty	38 Lochview Drive, Glasgow G33 1QF	0141-770 9611
	Rev. Alexander Wilson	HM Prison, Barlinnie, Glasgow G33 2QX	0141-770 2059
LOW MOSS	Rev. William B. Moore	Chaplaincy Centre, HMP Low Moss, Glasgow G64 2QB	0141-762 4848
GLENOCHIL	Rev. Malcolm MacRae	10B Victoria Place, Stirling FK8 2QU	01786 465547
	Rev. Alan F.M. Downie	37A Claremont, Alloa FK10 2DG	01259 213872
GREENOCK	Rev. James Munro	80 Bardrainney Avenue, Port Glasgow PA14 6UD	01475 701213
INVERNESS	Rev. James Robertson	45 Oakdene Court, Culloden, Inverness IV2 7XZ	01463 790504
	Rev. Alexander Shaw	HM Prison, Inverness IV2 3HN	01463 229000
	Rev. Christopher Smart	HM Prison, Inverness IV2 3HN	01463 229000
KILMARNOCK	Rev. Andrew A. Downie	HMP Bowhouse, Mauchline Road, Kilmarnock KA1 5AA	01563 548928
	Rev. Morag Dawson	206 Bank Street, Irvine KA12 0YB	01294 211403
NORANSIDE	Mrs Helen Scott	HM Prison, Noranside DD8 3QV	01356 650217
PERTH INCLUDING FRIARTON	Rev. Graham Matthews	Chaplaincy Centre, HMP Perth PH2 8AT	01738 622293
	Mrs Deirdre Yellowlees	Ringmill House, Gannochy Farm, Perth PH2 7JH	01738 633773
	Rev. Isobel Birrell	2 Rhynd Lane, Perth PH2 8TP	01738 625694
PETERHEAD	Rev. Dr David Ross	HM Prison, Peterhead AB42 6YY	01779 479101
POLMONT	Rev. Donald H. Scott	Chaplaincy Centre, HMYOI Polmont, Falkirk FK2 0AB	01324 711558
	Rev. Daniel L. Mathers	36 Thistle Avenue, Grangemouth FK3 8YQ	01324 474511
SHOTTS	Rev. Andrew Campbell	70 Baron's Road, Motherwell ML1 2NB	01698 263803
	Rev. Allan Brown	Chaplaincy Centre, HMP Shotts ML7 4LE	01501 824071

LIST F – UNIVERSITY CHAPLAINS

ABERDEEN	Easter Smart MDiv	01224 484271
ABERTAY, DUNDEE	Leslie M. Barrett BD FRICS	01382 308447
CALEDONIAN	Rev. J. Owain Jones MA BD FSAScot (Visiting)	0141-637 0797

CAMBRIDGE	Keith Riglin (U.R.C. and C. of S.)	01223 503726
DUNDEE	Fiona C. Douglas BD PhD	01382 344157
EDINBURGH	Diane Williams	0131-650 2595
GLASGOW	Stuart D. MacQuarrie JP BD BSc	0141-330 5419
HERIOT-WATT	Howard G. Taylor BSc BD	0131-449 5111 (ext 4508)
NAPIER	Deryck Collingwood	0131-455 4694
OXFORD	Susan Durber (U.R.C. and C. of S.)	01865 554358
PAISLEY		
ROBERT GORDON	George Cowie BSc BD (Honorary)	01224 262000 (ext 3506)
ST ANDREWS	James B. Walker MA BD DPhil	01334 462866
STIRLING	Regine U. Cheyne MA BSc BD (Honorary)	01786 463060
STRATHCLYDE	Marjory Macaskill LLB BD	0141-553 4144

LIST G – THE DIACONATE

NAME	COM	APP	ADDRESS	TEL	PRES
Allan, Jean (Mrs) DCS	1989	1988	12C Hindmarsh Avenue, Dundee DD3 7LW	01382 827299	29
Anderson, Janet (Miss) DCS	1979	1982	1/1, 338 Gartcraig Road, Glasgow G33 2TE	0141-774 5329	16
Beaton, Margaret (Miss) DCS	1989	1988	64 Gardenside Grove, Carmyle, Glasgow G32 8EZ	0141-646 2297	16
Bell, Sandra (Mrs)	2001		62 Loganswell Road, Thornliebank, Glasgow G46 8AX	0141-638 5884	16
Black, Linda (Miss) BSc DCS	1993	2001	148 Rowan Road, Abronhill, Cumbernauld, Glasgow G67 3DA [E-mail: blcklind@aol.com]		22
Buchanan, John (Mr) DCS	1988	1994	19 Gillespie Crescent, Edinburgh EH10 4HJ	0131-229 0794	3
Buchanan, Marion (Mrs) DCS	1983	1997	6 Hamilton Terrace, Edinburgh EH15 1NB	0131-669 5312	1
Burns, Marjorie (Mrs) DCS	1997	1998	25 Barnsley Square, Corby, Northants NN18 0PQ [E-mail: mburns8069@aol.com]	01536 264819 / 07989 148464 (Mbl)	47
Carson, Christine (Miss) MA DCS	1992	2000	1FR, 7 Kirkwood Street, Cessnock, Glasgow G51 1QQ	0141-427 2349	16
Cathcart, John Paul (Mr) DCS	1998		50 Alder Place, Greenhills, East Kilbride, Glasgow G75 9HP [E-mail: johnpaul.cathcart@ntlworld.com]	0141-569 6865	17
Corrie, Margaret (Miss) DCS	1989	1988	44 Sunnyside Street, Camelon, Falkirk FK1 4BH	01324 670656	22
Craw, John (Mr) DCS	1998		'Craiglockhart', Latheronwheel, Latheron KW5 6DW	01593 741779	41
Crawford, Morag (Miss) DCS	1977	1998	118 Wester Drylaw Place, Edinburgh EH4 2TG [E-mail: morag.crawford@virgin.net]	0131-332 2253 (Tel/Fax) / 07970 982563 (Mbl)	24
Crocker, Elizabeth (Mrs) DCS DipComEd	1985	1992	77C Craigcrook Road, Edinburgh EH4 3PH [E-mail: crock@crook77c.freeserve.co.uk]	0131-332 0227	1
Cunningham, Ian (Mr) DCS	1994		The Manse, Rothiemay, Huntly AB54 7NE	01466 711334	35
Cuthbertson, Valerie DipTMus DCS	2003	1997	105 Bellshill Road, Motherwell ML1 3SJ [E-mail: vcuthbertson@tiscali.co.uk]	01698 259001	22

Name			Address		Tel	No.
Deans, Raymond (Mr) DCS	1994	1998	60 Ardmory Road, Rothesay, Isle of Bute PA20 0PG [E-mail: deans@fish.co.uk]		01700 504893	19
Dickson, Carol (Miss) DCS	1991	1996	Madras House, 29 Madras Road, Auchtermuchty, Cupar KY14 7BW		01337 828874	25
Douglas, Marilyn (Miss) DCS	1988	1987	Heimdal, Quarff, Shetland ZE2 9EZ [E-mail: dickson@fish.co.uk]		01950 477584	46
Dunnett, Linca (Mrs)	1976	2000	17 Munro Road, Glasgow G13 1SQ	(Office)	0141-959 3732 / 0141-552 4040	[16]
Erskine, Morag (Miss) DCS	1979	1986	111 Mains Drive, Park Mains, Erskine PA8 7JJ		0141-812 6096	14
Evans, Mark (Mr) RGN DCS	1988	2000	13 Easter Drylaw Drive, Edinburgh EH4 2QA [E-mail: mevansdcs@aol.com]		0131-343 3089	1
Gargrave, Mary (Mrs) DCS	1989	1998	229/2 Calder Road, Edinburgh EH11 4RG	(Office)	0131-476 3493 / 0131-443 9452	1
Gordon, Margaret (Mrs) DCS	1998	2001	92 Lanark Road West, Currie EH14 5LA		0131-449 2554	1
Gray, Greta (Miss) DCS	1992	1998	67 Crags Avenue, Paisley PA2 6SG		0141-884 6178	14
Hamilton, James (Mr) DCS	1997	2000	6 Beckfield Gate, Glasgow G33 1SW [E-mail: kg@hamilton692.freeserve.co.uk]		0141-558 3195	16
Hamilton, Karen (Mrs) DCS	1995	1998	6 Beckfield Gate, Glasgow G33 1SW		0141-558 3195	16
Hughes, Helen (Miss) DCS	1977	1980	2/2, 43 Burnbank Terrace, Glasgow G20 6UQ [E-mail: helenhughes@fish.co.uk]		0141-333 9459	16
King, Chris (Mrs) DCS	2002		28 Kilnford, Dundonald, Kilmarnock KA2 9ET [E-mail: chrisking99@onetel.net.uk]		01563 851197	10
King, Margaret (Miss) DCS	2002		56 Murrayfield, Fochabers IV32 7EZ		01343 820937	35
Love, Joanna (Ms) BSc DCS	1992	2000	92 Everard Drive, Glasgow G21 1XQ [E-mail: jolove14@hotmail.com]		0141-563 5859	16
Lundie, Ann V. (Miss) DCS	1972	1992	20 Langdykes Drive, Cove, Aberdeen AB12 3HW		01224 898416	31
Lyall, Ann (Miss) DCS	1980	1979	117 Barlia Drive, Glasgow G45 0AY [E-mail: amlyall@btinternet.com]		0141-631 3643	16
MacDonald, Anne (Miss) BA	1980	1998	62 Berwick Drive, Glasgow G52 3JA	(Mbl)	0141-883 5618 / 07976 786174	16
McDowall, Sarah (Mrs) DCS	1991	1990	116 Scott Road, Glenrothes KY6 1AE		01592 562386	25
McIntosh, Kay (Mrs) DCS	1990		4 Jacklin Green, Livingston EH54 8PZ		01506 495472	2
McKay, Kenneth (Mr) DCS	1996	1995	11F Balgowan Road, Letham, Perth PH1 2JG	(Mbl)	01738 621169 / 07952 076331	28
MacKinnon, Ronald (Mr) DCS	1996	1995	71 Cromarty Road, Cairnhill, Airdrie ML6 9RL [E-mail: kennydands@hotmail.com]		01236 762024	22
McLellan, Margaret (Mrs)	1986	1997	18 Broom Road East, Newton Mearns, Glasgow G77 5SD		0141-639 6853	16
McNaughton, Jenette (Miss) DCS	1982	1997	4 Dunellan Avenue, Moodiesburn, Glasgow G69 0GB		01236 870180	22
McPheat, Elspeth (Miss)	1985	1997	11/5 New Orchardfield, Edinburgh EH6 5ET		0131-554 4143/01224 486240	1
Martin, Jane (Miss) DCS	1979	1979	12A Carnoustie Court, Ardler, Dundee DD2 3RB [E-mail: janimar@aol.com]		01382 813786	29
Merrilees, Ann (Mrs) DCS	1994	2000	0/1, 15 Crookston Grove, Glasgow G52 3PN [E-mail: ann@merrilees.freeserve.co.uk]		0141-883 2488	16
Mitchell, Joyce (Mrs) DCS	1994	1993	16/4 Murrayburn Place, Edinburgh EH14 2RR [E-mail: joyce@mitchell71.freeserve.co.uk]		0131-453 6548	1

NAME	COM		ADDRESS	TEL	PRES
Mulligan, Anne (Miss) MA DCS	1974	1986	27A Craigour Avenue, Edinburgh EH17 7NH [E-mail: mulliganne@aol.com]	0131-664 3426 / 0131-242 1996 (Office)	1
Munro, Patricia (Miss) BSc DCS	1986	2002	11 Hurlingham Square, Peterborough Road, London SW6 3DZ [E-mail: patm@totalise.co.uk]	020 7610 6994	47
Nicholson, David (Mr) DCS	1994	1993	2D Doonside, Kildrum, Cumbernauld, Glasgow G67 2HX	01236 732260 / 07703 332270 (Mbl)	22
Nicol, Joyce (Mrs) BA DCS	1974	1998	93 Brisbane Street, Greenock PA16 8NY	01475 723235 / 07957 642709 (Mbl)	14
Nicol, Senga (Miss) DCS	1993	2000	0/2, 367 Wellshot Road, Glasgow G32 9QP	0141-778 2667	16
Ogilvie, Colin (Mr) DCS	1998	1998	32 Upper Bairtree Court, Glasgow G67 2HX	01592 882820	16
Palmer, Christine (Ms) DCS			71 Pitlochie Terrace, Kinglassie, Lochgelly KY5 0XX [E-mail: chris@bizilitulhoos.freeserve.co.uk]		25
Rennie, Agnes M. (Miss) DCS	1974	1979	3/1 Craigmillar Court, Edinburgh EH16 4AD	0131-661 8475	1
Rose, Lewis (Mr) DCS	1993	1998	16 Gean Drive, Blackburn, Aberdeen AB21 0YN [E-mail: scimnorth@uk.uumail.com]	01224 790145 / 07811 808498 (Mbl)	31
Ross, Duncan (Mr) DCS	1996	1996	64 Stewart Crescent, Aberdeen AB15 5SR [E-mail: dross@fish.co.uk]	01224 692519	31
Rycroft, Pauline (Miss) DCS	2003		5 Thornville Terrace, Edinburgh EH6 8DB	0131-554 6564	1
Steele, Marilynn J. (Mrs) BD DCS			2 Northfield Gardens, Prestonpans EH32 9LQ	01875 811497	1
Steven, Gordon BD DCS	1997	1997	51 Nantwich Drive, Edinburgh EH7 6RB	0131-669 2054 / 07904 385256 (Mbl)	3
Stewart, Marion (Miss) DCS	1991	1994	Kirk Cottage, Kirkton of Skene, Westhill, Skene AB32 6XE	01224 743407	33
Tait, Agnes (Mrs) DCS	1995	1994	2 Lennox Drive, Faifley, Clydebank G81 5JU	01389 873196	18
Thomson, Phyllis (Miss) DCS	1986		63 Caroline Park, Mid Calder, Livingston EH53 0SJ	01506 883207	11
Urquhart, Barbara (Mrs) DCS	1986	1994	9 Standalane, Kilmaurs, Kilmarnock KA3 2NB	01563 538289	2
Wilson, Glenda (Mrs) DCS	1990	2000	88 Seafield Rows, Seafield, Bathgate EH47 7AW	01506 655298	10
Wilson, Muriel (Miss) MA BD DCS			23 Jellieston Terrace, Patna, Ayr KA6 7IZ	01292 532492	
Wishart, William (Mr) DCS	1994	1993	10 Stanley Drive, Paisley PA2 6HE	0141-884 4177 / 07971 422201 (Mbl)	14
Wright, Lynda (Miss) BEd DCS	1979	1992	6 Key Cottage, High Street, Falkland, Cupar KY15 7BD	01337 857705	26

THE DIACONATE (Retired List)

NAME	COM	ADDRESS	TEL	PRES
Anderson, Catherine B. (Mrs) DCS	1975	13 Mosshill Road, Bellshill, Motherwell ML4 1NQ	01698 745907	17
Anderson, Mary (Miss) DCS	1955	33 Ryehill Terrace, Edinburgh EH6 8EN	0131-553 2818	1

Name	Year	Address	Telephone	No.
Bayes, Muriel C. (Mrs) DCS	1963	Flat 6, Carleton Court, 10 Fenwick Road, Glasgow G46 4AN	0141-633 0865	16
Beaton, Jamesina (Miss) DCS	1953	Fairhills, Fort Augustus PH32 4DS	01320 366252	38
Bryden, Agnes Y. (Mrs) DCS	1963	9 Rosewell Place, Aberdeen AB15 6HN	01224 315042	31
Cameron, Margaret (Miss) DCS	1961	2 Rowans Gate, Paisley PA2 6RD	0141-840 2479	14
Campbell, Margaret M.M. (Miss) DCS	1958	Kirkcare, 11 Leodamus Place, Port Ellen, Isle of Islay PA42 7EL		19
Copland, Agnes M. (Mrs) MBE DCS	1950	3 Craigmuschat Road, Gourock PA19 1SE	01475 631870	14
Cunningham, Alison G. (Miss) DCS	1961	23 Strathblane Road, Milngavie, Glasgow G62 8DL	0141-563 9232	18
Drummond, Rhoda (Miss) DCS	1960	23 Grange Loan, Edinburgh EH9 2ER	0131-668 3631	1
Finlayson, Ellena B. (Miss) DCS	1963	16E Denwood, Summerhill, Aberdeen AB15 6JF	01224 321147	31
Flockhart, Andrew (Mr) DCS	1988	31 Castle Street, Rutherglen, Glasgow G73 1DY	0141-569 0716	16
Gillespie, Ann M. (Miss) DCS	1969	Barlochan House, Palnackie, Castle Douglas DG7 1PF	01556 600378	8
Gillon, Phyllis (Miss) DCS	1957	The Hermitage Home, 15 Hermitage Drive, Edinburgh EH10 6BX	0131-447 0664	1
Gordon, Fiona S. (Mrs) MA DCS	1958	Machrie, 3 Cupar Road, Cuparmuir, Cupar KY15 5RH [E-mail: machrie@madasafish.com]	01334 652341	26
Gray, Catherine (Miss) DCS	1969	10C Eastern View, Gourock PA19 1RJ	01475 637479	14
Gray, Christine (Mrs) DCS	1969	11 Woodside Avenue, Thorniebank, Glasgow G46 7HR	0141-571 1008	16
Howden, Margaret (Miss) DCS	1954	38 Munro Street, Kirkcaldy KY1 1PY	01592 205913	25
Hutchison, Alan E.W. (Mr) DCS	1988	132 Lochbridge Road, North Berwick EH39 4DR	01620 894077	3
Hutchison, Maureen (Mrs) DCS	1961	23 Drylaw Crescent, Edinburgh EH4 2AU	0131-332 8020	1
Johnston, Mary (Miss) DCS	1987	19 Lounsdale Drive, Paisley PA2 9ED	0141-849 1615	14
McBain, Margaret (Miss) DCS	1974	33 Quarry Road, Paisley PA2 7RD	0141-884 2920	14
McCallum, Moyra (Miss) MA BD DCS	1965	176 Hilton Drive, Aberdeen AB24 4LT [E-mail: moymac@aol.com]	01224 486240	31
McCully, M. Isobel (Miss) DCS	1974	10 Broadstone Avenue, Port Glasgow PA14 5BB	01475 742240	14
McGarva, Sadie (Miss) DCS	1954	87 Hunter Drive, Irvine KA12 9BS	01294 271257	11
MacLean, Donald A. (Mr) DCS	1988	8 Upper Barvas, Isle of Lewis HS2 0QX	01851 840454	44
MacPherson, James B. (Mr) DCS	1988	104 Cartside Street, Glasgow G42 9TQ	0141-616 6468	16
MacQuien, Duncan (Mr) DCS	1988	2 Manor Crescent, Gourock PA19 1VY	01475 633407	14
Macrae, William (Mr) DCS	1988	6 Park View Terrace, Isle of Scalpay, Isle of Harris HS4 3XX	01859 540288	43
Malvenan, Dorothy (Miss) DCS	1955	Flat 19, 6 Craigie Street, Dundee DD4 6PF	01382 462495	29
Martin, Neil (Mr) DCS	1988	3 Strathmiglo Place, Stenhousemuir, Larbert FK5 4UQ	01324 551362	22
Miller, Elsie M. (Miss) DCS	1974	30 Swinton Avenue, Rowanbank, Baillieston, Glasgow G69 6JR	0141-771 0857	22
Morrison, Dr Jean	1964	45 Corslet Road, Currie EH14 5LZ [E-mail: jean.morrison@blueyonder.co.uk]	0131-449 6859	1
Mortimer, Aileen (Miss) DCS	1976	38 Sinclair Way, Knightsridge, Livingston EH54 8HW	01506 430504	2
Moyes, Sheila (Miss) DCS	1957	158 Pilton Avenue, Edinburgh EH5 2JZ	0131-551 1731	1
Potts, Jean M. (Miss) DCS	1973	28B East Claremont Street, Edinburgh EH7 4JP	0131-557 2144	1
Ramsay, Katherine (Miss) MA DCS	1958	25 Homeroyal House, 2 Chalmers Crescent, Edinburgh EH9 1TP	0131-667 4791	1

Name		Address	Phone	No.
Ronald, Norma A. (Miss) MBE DCS	1961	43/26 Gillespie Crescent, Edinburgh EH10 4HY	0131-228 1008	1
Rutherford, Ellen B. (Miss) MBE DCS	1962	41 Duncanston, Conon Bridge, Dingwall IV7 8JB	01349 877439	39
Scrimgeour, Alice M. (Miss) DCS	1950	265 Golfhill Drive, Glasgow G31 2PB	0141-564 9602	16
Smith, Catherine (Mrs) DCS	1964	21 Lingaro, Bixter, Shetland ZE2 9NN	01595 810207	46
Smith, Lillian (Miss) MA DCS	1977	6 Fintry Mains, Dundee DD4 9HF	01382 500052	29
Steele, Jean (Miss) DCS	1952	93 George Street, Paisley PA1 2JX	0141-889 9512	14
Stuart, Anne (Miss) DCS	1966	19 St Colme Crescent, Aberdour, Burntisland KY3 0ST	01383 860049	24
Teague, Yvonne (Mrs) DCS	1965	46 Craigcrook Avenue, Edinburgh EH4 3PX	0131-336 3113	1
Thom, Helen (Miss) BA DipEd MA DCS	1959	84 Great King Street, Edinburgh EH3 6QU	0131-556 5687	1
Trimble, Robert DCS	1988	5 Templar Rise, Livingston EH54 6PJ	01506 412504	2
Webster, Elspeth H. (Miss) DCS	1950	82 Broomhill Avenue, Burntisland KY3 0BP	01592 873616	25
Weir, Minnie Mullo (Miss) MA DCS	1934	37 Strathearn Court, Strathearn Terrace, Crieff PH7 3DS	01764 654189	
White, Elizabeth (Miss) DCS	1950	Rodger Park Nursing Home, Rutherglen, Glasgow G73 3QZ		16

SUPPLEMENTARY LIST

Forrest, Janice (Mrs)	1990	The Manse, Southend, Campbeltown, Argyll PA28 6RQ	01586 830274
Gilroy, Lorraine (Mrs)	1988	5 Bluebell Drive, Cheverel Court, Bedward CV12 0GE	02476 366031
Guthrie, Jennifer (Miss) DCS	1993	14 Eskview Terrace, Ferryden, Montrose DD10 9RD	01674 674413
Harris, Judith (Mrs)	1988	243 Western Avenue, Sandfields, Port Talbot, West Glamorgan SA12 7NF	01639 884855
Hood, Katrina (Mrs)	1982	67C Farquhar Road, Edgbaston, Birmingham B18 2QP	
Hudson, Sandra (Mrs)	1969	10 Albany Drive, Rutherglen, Glasgow G73 3QN	
Muir, Alison M. (Mrs)		77 Arthur Street, Dunfermline KY12 0JJ	
Ramsden, Christine (Miss)	1978	52 Noel Street, Nottingham NG7 6AW	
Walker, Wikje (Mrs)	1970	24 Brodie's Yard, Queen Street, Coupar Angus PH13 9RA	01159 789313
Wallace, Catherine (Mrs)		4 Thornwood Court, Setauket, NY 11733, USA	01828 628251

LIST H – MINISTERS HAVING RESIGNED MEMBERSHIP OF PRESBYTERY

(in Terms of Act III 1992)

(Resignation of Presbytery membership does not imply the lack of a practising certificate.)

NAME	ORD	ADDRESS	TEL	PRES
Bailey, W. Grahame MA BD	1939	148 Craiglea Drive, Edinburgh EH10 5PU	0131-447 1663	1
Balfour, Thomas MA BD	1945	1 Dean Court, Longniddry EH32 0QT	01875 852694	3
Beck, John C. BD	1975	43A Balvenie Street, Dufftown, Keith AB55 4AS		35
Bogle, Michael M. MA	1936	30 Woodburn Terrace, Edinburgh EH10 4SS	0131-447 3231	1
Cattanach, W.D. DD	1951	412 Carlyle Court, 173 Comely Bank Road, Edinburgh EH4 1DJ	0131-332 4503	1
Cooper, George MA BD	1943	8 Leighton Square, Alyth PH11 8AQ	01828 633746	1
Craig, Eric MA BD BA	1959	5 West Relugas Road, Edinburgh EH9 2PW	0131-667 8210	1
Craig, John W. MA BD	1951	83 Milton Road East, Edinburgh EH15 2NL	0131-657 2309	1
Crawford, S.G. Victor	1980	Crofton, 65 Main Road, East Wemyss, Kirkcaldy KY1 4RL	01592 712325	25
Drummond, R. Hugh	1953	19 Winton Park, Edinburgh EH10 7EX	0131-445 3634	1
Ferguson, Ronald MA BD ThM	1972	Vinbreck, Orphir, Orkney KW17 2RE	01856 811378	45
		[E-mail: ronblueyonder@aol.com]		
Finlayson, Duncan MA	1943	Flat 3, Nicholson Court, Kinnettas Road, Strathpeffer IV14 9BG	01997 420014	39
Gordon, Alasdair B. BD LLB	1970	31 Binghill Park, Milltimber, Aberdeen AB13 0EE	01224 571633	31
Greig, James C.G. MA BD STM	1955	Block 2, Flat 2, Station Lofts, Strathblane, Glasgow G63 9BD	01360 771915	16
		[E-mail: jgreig@netcomuk.co.uk]		
Grubb, George D.W.	1962	10 Wellhead Close, South Queensferry EH30 9WA	0131-331 2072	1
BA BD BPhil DMin				
Hosie, James MA BD MTh	1959	Hilbre, Strachur, Cairndow, Dunoon PA27 8BY	01369 860634	19
Howie, William MA BD STM	1964	26 Morgan Road, Aberdeen AB2 5IY	01224 483669	31
Hurst, Frederick R. MA	1965	Apartment 10, 20 Abbey Drive, Glasgow G14 9JX	0141-959 2604	40
Lambie, Andrew BD	1957	1 Mercat Loan, Biggar ML12 6DG	01899 221352	13
Levison, Mary I. (Mrs) BA BD DD	1978	2 Gillsland Road, Edinburgh EH10 5BW	0131-228 3118	1
Lynn, Joyce (Mrs) MIPM BD	1995	Grunavi, Sanday, Orkney KW17 2BA	01857 600349	45
McCaskill, George I.L. MA BD	1953	19 Tyler's Acre Road, Edinburgh EH12 7HY	0131-334 7451	1
Macfarlane, Alwyn J.C. MA	1957	Flat 12, Homeburn House, 177 Fenwick Road, Giffnock, Glasgow G46 6JD	0141-620 3235	1
Macfarlane, Donald MA	1940	8 Muirfield Gardens, Inverness IV2 4HF	01463 231977	37
Macfarlane, Kenneth	1963	9 Bonnington Road, Peebles EH45 9HF	01721 723609	4
MacLeod, Ian I.S. MA BD	1954	48 Wellside Court, 6 Wellside Place, Falkirk FK1 6RG	01324 610158	22
Mackie, Steven G. MA BD	1956	38 Grange Loan, Edinburgh EH9 2NR	0131-667 9532	1
McLuskey, J. Fraser MC DD	1938	54/5 Eildon Terrace, Edinburgh EH3 5LU	0131-652 3950	47
Mair, John BSc	1965	21 Kenilworth Avenue, Helensburgh G84 7JR	01436 671744	18
Malcolm, John W. MA BD PhD	1939	16 Abbotsford Court, Edinburgh EH10 5EH	0131-447 0326	1
Marshall, James S. MA PhD	1939	25 St Mary's Street, St Andrews KY16 8AZ	01334 476136	26

NAME	ORD	ADDRESS	TEL	PRES
Millar, Jennifer M. (Mrs) BD DipMin	1986	17 Mapledene Road, Scone, Perth PH2 6NX	01738 550270	28
Miller, Irene B. (Mrs) MA BD	1984	5 Braeside Park, Aberfeldy PH15 2DT	01887 829396	27
Monro, George D. TD MA	1935	c/o Mrs E.A. Searle, 28 Redwood Drive, Aylesbury, Bucks HP21 7TN		1
Morris, Gordon C. MA BD	1941	Belleville Lodge, 5 Blacket Avenue, Edinburgh EH9 1RR		1
Nelson, John MA BD	1941	7 Manse Road, Roslin EH25 9LF	0131-440 3321	3
Ogilvie, Kenneth G. MA	1953	124 Comiston Drive, Edinburgh EH10 5QU	0131-447 8909	1
Petty, P.W.P.	1962	7 Marchbank Place, Balerno EH14 7EU	0131-449 2123	26
Robertson, Crichton MA	1938	Robin Hill, Ludlow Road, Church Stretton SY6 6AD	01694 722046	3
Ross, John H.G. OBE MA BD	1940	43 Arden Street, Edinburgh EH9 1BS	0131-447 2027	1
Shaw of Chapelverna, Duncan *Bundesverdienstkreuz* PhD ThDr Drhc JP	1951	4 Sydney Terrace, Edinburgh EH7 6SL	0131-669 1089	19
Shaw, D.W.D. BA BD LLB WS DD	1960	4/13 Succoth Court, Edinburgh EH12 6BZ	0131-337 2130	26
Smith, Ralph C.P. MA STM	1960	2A Waverley Road, Eskbank, Dalkeith EH22 3DJ	0131-663 1234	3
Spowart, Mary G. (Mrs)	1978	Aldersyde, St Abbs Road, Coldingham, Eyemouth TD14 5NR	01890 771697	26
Stobie, Charles I.G.	1942	Ingham Court, 23/3 Salisbury Road, Edinburgh EH16 5AA		26
Swan, Andrew MA	1941	11 The Terrace, Ardbeg, Rothesay, Isle of Bute PA20 0NP	01700 502138	14
Taylor, Alexander T.H. MA BD	1938	4 The Pleasance, Strathkinness, St Andrews KY16 9SD	01334 850585	26
Webster, John G. BSc	1964	Plane Tree, King's Cross, Brodick, Isle of Arran KA27 8RG	01770 700747	16
Westmarland, Colin A.	1971	PO Box 5, Cospicua, CSPOI, Malta	00356 216 923552	48
Wilkie, George D. OBE BL	1948	2/37 Barnton Avenue West, Edinburgh EH4 6EB	0131-339 3973	1
Wylie, W. Andrew	1953	Well Rose Cottage, Peat Inn, Cupar KY15 5LH	01334 840600	26

LIST I – MINISTERS HOLDING PRACTISING CERTIFICATES (under Act II, as amended by Act VIII 2000)

NAME	ORD	ADDRESS	TEL	PRES
Aitken, Ewan R. BA BD	1992	159 Restalrig Avenue, Edinburgh EH7 6PJ	0131-228 1539	1
Aitken, James BD	2002	26 Gardner's Crescent, Edinburgh EH3 8DF	0131-346 0685	1
Alexander, Helen J.R. (Miss) BD	1981	7 Polwarth Place, Edinburgh EH11 1LG		1
Anderson, David MA BD	1975	Rowan Cottage, Aberlour Gardens, Aberlour AB38 9LD	01340 871906	35
Arbuthnott, Joan (Mrs) MA BD	1993	139/1 New Street, Musselburgh EH21 6DH	0131-665 6736	3
Archer, Nicholas D.C. BA BD	1971	Hillview, Edderton, Tain IV19 4AJ	01862 821494	47
Atkins, Yvonne E.S. (Mrs) BD	1997	13 Grange Crescent East, Prestonpans EH32 9LS	01875 815137	3
Bardgett, Frank D. MA BD PhD	1987	6 Inchcolm Drive, North Queensferry, Inverkeithing KY11 1LD	01383 416863	36
Beattie, Warren R. BSc BD	1991	33A Chancery Lane, Singapore 908554	0065 256 3208	1

Name	Year	Address	Phone	No.
Black, James S. BD DPS	1976	7 Breck Terrace, Penicuik EH26 0RJ	01968 677559	3
Black, W. Graham MA BD	1983	72 Linksview, Linksfield Road, Aberdeen AB24 5RG	01224 492227	31
Blakey, Stephen A. BSc BD	1977	49 Ashgrove Street, Ayr KA7 3BG	01292 294881	10
Blane, Quintin A. BSc BD MSc	1979	18D Kirkhill Road, Penicuik EH26 8HZ	01968 670017	3
Blythe, Scott C. BSc BD	1997	45 Stewart House, St Peter Street, Colchester CO1 1BQ	01206 515672	31
Boyd, Ian R. MA BD PhD	1989	33 Castleton Drive, Newton Mearns, Glasgow G77 3LE		16
Boyd, Kenneth M. MA BD PhD	1970	1 Doune Terrace, Edinburgh EH3 6DY	0131-225 6485	1
Buchan, Isabel C. (Mrs) BSc BD	1975	26 Allan Robertson Drive, St Andrews KY16 8EY	01334 473875	26
Buchanan-Smith, Robin D. BA ThM	1962	Isle of Eriska, Ledaig, Oban, Argyll PA37 1SD		19
Campbell, Thomas R. MA BD	1986	Craigleith, Bowfield Road, Howwood, Johnstone PA9 1BS	01506 842722	14
Currie, Gordon C.M. MA BD	1975	43 Deanburn Park, Linlithgow EH49 6HA		2
Davidson, John F. BSc	1970	49 Craigmill Gardens, Carnoustie DD7 6HX [E-mail: jfdavid@breathemail.net]	01241 855412	30
Davies, Gareth W. BA BD	1979	Pitadro House, Fordell Gardens, Dunfermline KY11 7EY	01383 417634	24
Drummond, Norman W. MA BD	1976	c/o Columba 1400 Ltd, Staffin, Isle of Skye IV51 9JY	01478 611400	42
Ellis, David W. GIMechE GIProdE	1962	4 Wester Tarsappie, Rhynd Road, Perth PH2 8PT	01738 449618	16
Ferguson, Sinclair B. MA BD PhD	1971	Westminster Seminary, 3878 Oak Lawn Avenue, Dallas, TX 75219, USA		16
Finlay, Joanne G. (Mrs) DipMusEd	1996	6 Herd Green, Livingston EH54 8PU	01506 200132	2
Fleming, Thomas G.	1961	5 Glenbervie Drive, Larbert FK5 4NP	01324 552004	22
Flockhart, D. Ross OBE MA BD DUniv	1955	Longwood, Humbie EH36 5PN	01875 833208	3
Fowler, Richard C.A. BSc MSc BD	1978	4 Gardentown, Whalsay, Shetland ZE2 9AB	01806 566538	46
Fraser, Ian M. MA BD PhD	1946	Ferndale, Gargunnock, Stirling FK8 3BW	01786 860612	23
Frew, John M. MA BD	1946	17 The Furrows, Walton-on-Thames KT12 3JQ		16
Gilmour, Robert M. MA BD	1942	'Bellevue', Station Road, Watten, Wick KW1 5YN	01955 621317	37
Grubb, George D.W. BA BD BPhil DMin	1962	10 Wellhead Close, South Queensferry EH30 9WA	0131-331 2072	1
Gunn, F. Derek BD	1986	6 Yardley Place, Falkirk FK2 7FH	01324 624938	22
Hendrie, Yvonne (Mrs)	1995	98 Duncansby Way, Perth PH1 5XF	01738 441029	28
Higgins, G.K.	1957	150 Broughty Ferry Road, Dundee DD4 6JJ	01382 461288	29
Howitt, Jane M. (Miss) MA BD	1996	PO Box 476, LV-1050 Riga 50, Latvia		16
Ireland, Andrew BA BTh DipRD	1963	48 Jubilee Court, St Margaret's Street, Dunfermline KY12 7PE	01383 732223	24
Jack, Alison M. (Mrs) MA BD PhD	1998	Glenallan, Doune Road, Dunblane FK15 9AT	01786 823241	23
Jamieson, Esther M.M. (Mrs) BD	1984	1 Redbarn, Bayview, Stornoway HS1 2UV	01851 704789	44
Johnstone, Donald B.	1969	22 Glenhove Road, Cumbernauld, Glasgow G67 2JZ	01236 612479	22
Johnstone, Robert MTheol	1973	59 Cliffburn Road, Arbroath DD11 5BA	01241 439292	32
Kenny, Celia G. (Mrs) BA MTh		98/17 East London Street, Edinburgh	0131-556 6647	5
Lawrie, Robert M. BD MSc DipMin LLCM(TD)	1994	West Benview, Main Road, Langbank, Port Glasgow PA14 6XP	01475 540240	14
Liddiard, F.G.B. MA	1957	34 Trinity Fields Crescent, Brechin DD9 6YF	01356 622966	30
Logan, Thomas M. LTh	1971	3 Duncan Court, Kilmarnock KA3 7TF	01563 524398	11
MacArthur, Alexander MA	1946	Luath, St Barchan's Road, Kilbarchan, Johnstone PA10 2AR	01505 702598	14
Macaskill, Donald MA BD PhD	1994	44 Forfar Avenue, Glasgow G52 3JQ	0141-883 5956	16

Name	Year	Address	Telephone	No.
McDonald, Ross J. BA BD ThM	1998	14 Crosbie Street, Glasgow G20 0BD	01721 723609	16
Macfarlane, Kenneth	1963	9 Bonnington Road, Peebles EH45 9HF		4
McKean, Martin J. BD DipMin	1984	56 Kingsknowe Drive, Edinburgh EH14 2JX		1
McKinnon, Lily F. (Mrs) MA BD	1993	12 Carleton Gate, Giffnock, Glasgow G46 6NU	0141-637 8399	16
McLean-Foreman, Anthony	1995			
McLellan, Andrew R.C. MA BD STM DD	1970	4 Liggars Place, Dunfermline KY12 7XZ	01383 725959	1
MacPherson, Gordon C.	1963	203 Capelrig Road, Patterton, Newton Mearns, Glasgow G77 6ND	0141-616 2107	16
McPherson, William BD DipEd	1993	83 Laburnum Avenue, Port Seton, Prestonpans EH32 0UD	01875 812252	22
Mackie, Steven G. MA BD	1956	38 Grange Loan, Edinburgh EH9 2NR	0131-667 9532	1
Mailer, Colin (Aux)	1996	Innis Chonain, Back Row, Polmont, Falkirk FK2 0RD	01324 712401	
Main, Arthur W.A. BD	1954	13/3 Eildon Terrace, Edinburgh EH3 5NL	0131-556 1344	16
Manners, Stephen MA BD	1989	124 Fernieside Crescent, Edinburgh EH17 7DH		1
Marr, Ian MA BD	1984	116 Jeanfield Road, Perth PH1 1LP	01738 632530	28
Masson, John D.	1984	2 Beechgrove, Craw Hall, Brampton CA8 1TS	ex-directory	7
Matheson, Iain G. BD BMus	1985	16 New Street, Musselburgh EH21 6JP	0131-665 2128	3
Middleton, Paul BMus BDThM	2000	7/1 Atholl Crescent Lane, Edinburgh EH3 8ET	0777 9909801	
Mill, John Stuart MA BD MBA DipEd	1974	13 Succoth Park, Edinburgh EH12 6BX	0131-346 4124	1
Millar, Peter W. MA BD PhD	1971	Iona Cottage, Laggan, Newtonmore PH20 1AN [E-mail: ionacottage@hotmail.com]	01528 544337	36
Miller, Irene B. (Mrs) MA BD	1984	5 Braeside Park, Aberfeldy PH15 2DT	01887 829396	27
Mills, Archibald MA PhD	1953	32 High Street, South Queensferry EH30 9PP	0131-331 3906	1
Moodie, Alastair R. MA BD	1978	5 Buckingham Terrace, Glasgow G12 8EB		16
Munro, Alexander W. MA BD	1978	Gilldrive, Gill Bank Road, Ilkley, West Yorks LS29 0AV		47
Newell, Alison M. (Mrs) BD	1986	1A Inverleith Terrace, Edinburgh EH3 5NS		1
Newell, J. Philip	1982	1A Inverleith Terrace, Edinburgh EH3 5NS		1
Ostler, John H. MA LTh	1975	52E Middleshot Square, Prestonpans EH32 9RJ	01875 814358	3
Picken, Stuart D.B. MA BD PhD	1967	19 Millhill Drive, Greenloaning, Dunblane FK15 0SL	01786 880545	23
Provan, Iain W. MA BA PhD	1991	Regent College, 5800 University Boulevard, Vancouver BC V6T 2E4, Canada	001 604 224 3245	1
Quigley, Barbara D. (Mrs) MTheol ThM DPS	1979	7 Albany Terrace, Dundee DD3 6HQ	01382 223059	29
Rodwell, Anna J. (Mrs) BD DipMin	1998			6
Ross, Alison J. (Mrs) BD	1995			19
Sawers, Hugh BA	1968	2 Rosemount Meadows, Castlepark, Bothwell, Glasgow G71 8EL	01698 853960	17
Scouller, Hugh BSc BD	1985	39 Melbourne Place, North Berwick EH39 4JS	01620 893021	3
Squires, J. Finlay R. MA BD	1964	16 Bath Street, Stonehaven AB39 2DH	01569 762458	32
Steenbergen, Pauline (Ms) MA BD		1 Landale Road, Peterhead AB42 1QN	01779 472141	34
Stewart, Anne S. (Mrs) BD	1998	35 Rose Crescent, Perth PH1 1NT	01738 624167	28
Stewart, Margaret L. (Mrs) BSc MB ChB BD	1985	28 Inch Crescent, Bathgate EH48 1EU	01506 653428	2
Strachan, David G. BD DPS	1978	1 Deeside Park, Aberdeen AB15 7PQ	01224 324101	31
Strachan, Gordon MA BD PhD	1963	59 Merchiston Crescent, Edinburgh EH10 5AH	0131-229 3654	1

Name	Year	Address	Telephone	
Thomas, W. Colville BTh BPhil DPS DSc	1964	11 Muirfield Crescent, Gullane EH31 2HN	01620 842415	3
Tollick, Frank BSc DipEd	1958	3 Bellhouse Road, Aberdour, Burntisland KY3 0TL	01383 860559	24
Torrance, Iain R. TD MA BD DPhil	1982	64 Mercer Street, Princeton, NJ 08542-0808, USA	(Tel) 001 609 497 7800	31
Turnbull, Julian S. BSc BD MSc CEng MBCS	1980	25 Hamilton Road, Gullane EH31 2HP [E-mail: jules-turnbull@zetnet.co.uk]	01620 842958	3
Ward, Michael J. BSc BD PhD	1983	Chaplain's Lodge, 19 Devonshire Avenue, Grimsby DN32 0BW	01546 602143	45
Watt, John H.I. MA BD	1960	Lyndale, 24 Bank Street, Wigtown DG8 9HP	001 604 947 0636	19
Weir, Mary K. (Mrs) BD PhD	1968	1249 Millar Road RR1, SITEH-46, BC V0N 1G0, Canada	01461 500378	1
Williams, Linda J. (Mrs) BD	1993	The Manse, Kirtlebridge, Lockerbie DG11 3LY [E-mail: ljpwilliams@btopenworld.com]		7
Wilson, Thomas F. BD	1984	55 Allison Close, Cove, Aberdeen AB12 3WG	01224 873501	31
Winn, Fiona M.M. MA BD RGN	1994	35 Ashwood Avenue, Melbourne 3190, Australia	0061 3 9555 2038	1
Wood, Peter J. MA BD	1993	97 Broad Street, Camborne, Cambridgeshire CB3 6DH	01954 715558	47

LIST J – MISSION AND EVANGELISM ADVISERS

SENIOR ADVISER with South Region	Rev. David E.P. Currie BSc BD	21 Rosa Burn Avenue, Lindsayfield, East Kilbride, Glasgow G75 9DE [E-mail: nmsenioradviser@uk.uumail.com] Office: contact via the Church of Scotland Offices	01355 248510 07775 515594	(Tel) (Mbl)
CONGREGATIONAL DEVELOPMENT ADVISER	Mr Brian Burden	'Edinbane', Mid Road, Northmuir, Kirriemuir DD8 4QX [E-mail: nmadvisercd@uk.uumail.com]	01575 575280 07899 790466	(Tel/Fax) (Mbl)
MISSIONS CO-ORDINATOR	Mr Philip Wray BSc Msc	59 Elmbank Street, Glasgow G2 4PQ (Office) [E-mail: missionco-ordinator@uk.uumail.com]	0141-352 6946 07900 900776	(Tel) (Mbl)
REGIONAL ADVISER (EAST)	Rev. Robin J. McAlpine BDS BD	10 Seton Place, Kirkcaldy KY2 6UX [E-mail: nmadvisereast@uk.uumail.com] St Bryce Kirk Centre, St Brycedale Avenue, Kirkcaldy KY1 1ET (Office) [E-mail: nmkirkcaldy@uk.uumail.com]	01592 643518 01592 646406	(Tel) (Tel/Fax)
REGIONAL ADVISER (NORTH)	Rev. Richard Gibbons	3 Holm Burn Place, Inverness IV2 6WT [E-mail: nmadvisernorth@uk.uumail.com] National Mission Highland Office, Main Street, North Kessock, Inverness IV1 3XN [E-mail: nminverness@uk.uumail.com]	01463 226889 01463 731712	

PRIORITY AREAS SUPPORT WORKER	Rev. Martin J. Johnstone MA BD	3 Herries Road, Glasgow G41 4DE [E-mail: upaadviser@uk.uumail.com]	0141-423 3760 (Tel)
		59 Elmbank Street, Glasgow G2 4PQ (Office) [E-mail: nmglasgow@uk.uumail.com]	0141-333 1948 (Tel/Fax)
ANGUS PRESBYTERY CONGREGATIONAL DEVELOPMENT ADVISER	Mr Gordon Anderson	33 Grampian View, Ferryden, Montrose DD10 9SU	01674 674915
GLASGOW PRESBYTERY CONGREGATIONAL FACILITATOR	Rev. John K. Collard MA BD	1 Nelson Terrace, East Kilbride, Glasgow G74 2EY	01355 520093
HAMILTON PRESBYTERY CONGREGATIONAL DEVELOPMENT OFFICER	Mr David Geddes	108 Maxwelton Avenue, East Kilbride, Glasgow G74 3DU	01355 235998

LIST K – OVERSEAS LOCATIONS

EUROPE

AMSTERDAM
Rev. John A. Cowie (1990) and Mrs Gillian Cowie
Jan Willem Brouwersstraat 9, NL-1071 LH Amsterdam, The Netherlands   (Tel) 0031 20 672 2288
[E-mail: j.cowie2@chello.nl; Website: http://www.ercadam.nl]   (Fax) 0031 20 676 4895
The English Reformed Church, The Begijnhof (off the Spui). Service each Sunday at 10:30am.

BRUSSELS
Vacant
23 Square des Nations, B-1000 Brussels, Belgium   (Tel/Fax) 0032 2 672 40 56
[Website: http://www.welcome.to/st-andrews]
St Andrew's Church, Chaussée de Vleurgat 181 (off Ave. Louise). Service each Sunday at 11:00am.
[E-mail: st-andrews@welcome.to]

BUDAPEST
Rev. Kenneth I. Mackenzie (1999) and Mrs Jayne Mackenzie, Oltvany Arok 25, XI Budapest   (Tel/Fax) 0036 1 246 2258
St Columba's Scottish Mission, Vorosmarty utca 51, H-1064 Budapest, Hungary   (Church Tel) 0036 1 343 8479
[E-mail: mackenzie@mail.datanet.hu]
Service in English and Sunday School each Sunday at 11:00am.
Rev. Bertalan Tamas (1976, held previous appointment) and Mrs Elizabeth Tamas
The General Synod of the Reformed Church in Hungary, 1440 Budapest, PF15, Hungary   (Tel/Fax) 0036 1 460 0708
[E-mail: zsinatko@axelero.hu]

COSTA DEL SOL

(Tel) 0034 95 247 8077

Vacant
Astighi 2, 5th Floor, No. 4, E-29640 Malaga, Spain
Services at Lux Mundi Ecumenical Centre, Calle Nueva 7, Fuengirola.   Service each Sunday at 10:30am.

GENEVA

(Tel/Fax) 0041 22 798 29 09

Rev. Ian A. Manson (2001) and Mrs Roberta Manson
[E-mail: cofsg@pingnet.ch; Website: http://www.welcome.to/cofsgeneva]
6 Chemin Tavernay, CH-1218 Grand Saconnex, Geneva, Switzerland
The Calvin Auditoire, Place de la Taconnerie (beside Cathedral of St Pierre).   Service each Sunday at 11:00am.

GIBRALTAR

(Tel) 00350 77040
(Fax) 00350 40852

Rev. Stewart J. Lamont (2003) and Mrs Lara Lamont
St Andrew's Manse, 29 Scud Hill, Gibraltar
St Andrew's Church, Governor's Parade.   Service each Sunday at 10:30am.
[E-mail: billsmth@gibnet.gi]

LAUSANNE

(Tel/Fax) 0041 21 323 98 28

Vacant
26 Avenue de Rumine, CH-1005 Lausanne, Switzerland
[E-mail: scotskirklausanne@bluewin.ch]
Service each Sunday at 10:30am.

LISBON

(Tel/Fax) 00351 21 395 7677

Vacant
The Manse, Rua da Arriaga 11, 1200-608, Lisbon, Portugal
[E-mail: st.andrewschurch@clix.pt]
St Andrew's Church, Rua da Arriaga 13–15, Lisbon.   Service each Sunday at 11:00am.

MALTA

(Tel/Fax) 00356 222 643

Rev. David Morris (2003) and Mrs Jacky Morris (not Church of Scotland)
[E-mail: davidmorris486@hotmail.com]
La Romagnola, 13 Triq is-Sieqjamisrah Eola, Attard BZN 05
St Andrew's Church, 210 Old Bakery Street, Valletta.   Service each Sunday at 10:30am.

PARIS

(Tel/Fax) 0033 1 48 78 47 94

Rev. William M. Reid (1993) and Mrs Esther Reid
10 Rue Thimonnier, F-75009 Paris, France
[E-mail: scotskirk@wanadoo.fr; Website: http://www.scotskirkparis.com]
The Scots Kirk, 17 Rue Bayard, F-75008 Paris (Metro: Roosvelt)
Service each Sunday at 10:30am.

ROME

(Tel) 0039 06 482 7627
(Fax) 0039 06 487 4370

Rev. William B. McCulloch (2001) and Mrs Jean McCulloch
[E-mail: revwbmcculloch@hotmail.com]
Via XX Settembre 7, 00187 Rome, Italy.   Service each Sunday at 11:00am.

ROTTERDAM

(Tel/Fax) 0031 10 220 4199
(Tel) 0031 10 412 4779

Rev. Robert A. Calvert (1995) and Mrs Lesley-Ann Calvert
Gelebrem 59, NL-3068 TJ Rotterdam, The Netherlands
[E-mail: scotsintchurch@cs.com; Website: http://www.scotsintchurch.com]
The Scots Kirk, Schiedamsevest 121, Rotterdam.   Service each Sunday at 10:30am.
Informal service at 9:15am.

TURIN

Rev. Robert A. Mackenzie (2001) and Mrs Anne Mackenzie
Via Sante Anselmo 6, 10125 Turin, Italy
[E-mail: valdese.english@arpnet.it; Website: http://www.englishspeakingchurchturin.com]
The English-Speaking Church in Turin: service each Sunday at 10:30am.
Casa Valdese, Corbo Vittoro Emanuele 25, 10125 Turin, Italy

(Church office Tel) 0039 11 650 9467

AFRICA

KENYA

Presbyterian Church of East Africa
Dr Elizabeth Borlase (1992) and Kevin Borlase
Rev. Elaine W. McKinnon (1992)
Dr Alison Wilkinson (1992)

PCEA Kikuyu Hospital, PO Box 45, Kikuyu, Kenya   (Fax) 00254 665 01626
Presbyterian College, PO Box 387, Kikuyu, Kenya
PCEA Chogoria Hospital, PO Box 35, Chogoria, Kenya   (Fax) 00254 166 22122
[E-mail: alisonjwilkinson@swiftkenya.com]

MALAWI

Church of Central Africa Presbyterian
Synod of Blantyre
Rev. Bruce Ritchie (2001)

Zomba Theological College, PO Box 130, Zomba, Malawi

Synod of Livingstonia
Dr Andrew and Mrs Felicity Gaston (1997)
Miss Helen Scott (2000, held previous appointment)
Dr Alex Maclean (2001) and Mrs Carolyn Maclean

LISAP, PO Box 279, Ekwendeni, Malawi
CCAP Girls' Secondary School, PO Box 2, Ekwendeni, Malawi
Embangweni Hospital, PO Box 7, Embangweni,
 Mzimba District, Malawi

Mrs Dorothy Halliday (2003)

David Gordon Memorial Hospital, PO Box 5, Livingstonia, Rumpi, Malawi

SOUTH AFRICA

Rev. Graham Duncan (1998, held previous appointment)
and Mrs Sandra Duncan (1998)

56 Daphne Road, Maroelana 00081, Pretoria, South Africa

ZAMBIA

United Church of Zambia
Rev. Colin D. Johnston (1994)

Trinity UCZ, PO Box 30079, Lusaka, Zambia
[E-mail: trinity@zammet.zm]

Ms Jane Petty (2000)
Mr Brian Payne (2002) and Mrs Georgina Payne (2002)

Mwandi Mission Hospital, PO Box 60693, Livingstone, Zambia
United Church of Zambia Synod Office, Lusaka,
 Zambia
[E-mail: uczsynod@zammet.zm]

(Tel) 00260 1 250 641
(Fax) 00260 1 252 198

THE CARIBBEAN, CENTRAL AND SOUTH AMERICA

BAHAMAS

Rev. John Fraser (2002) and Mrs Jillian Fraser — St Andrew's Manse, PO Box N1099, Nassau — (Tel) 001 242 322 5475 / (Fax) 001 242 323 1960

Alastair H. Gray (2003) and Mrs Nina Gray — Lucaya Presbyterian Kirk, PO Box F-40777, Freeport [E-mail: a.gray@tinyworld.co.uk] — (Tel) 001 242 373 2568 / (Fax) 001 242 373 4961

BERMUDA

Rev. T. Alan W. Garrity (1999) and Mrs Elizabeth Garrity — The Manse, PO Box PG88, Paget PGBX, Bermuda [E-mail: revtawg@logic.bm *and* christchurch@logic.bm] [Church website: www.christchurch.bm] — (Tel) 001 441 236 0400 and (Tel) 001 441 236 1882 / (Fax) 001 441 232 0552

JAMAICA

United Church of Jamaica and Grand Cayman

Rev. Roy A. Dodman and Mrs Jane Dodman (1983) — PO Box 64, Stony Hill, Kingston 9, Jamaica [E-mail: rdodman@cwjamaica.com] — (Tel) 001 876 756 3331

Rev. Margaret Fowler (1988) — PO Box 3097, Negril, Westmoreland, Jamaica [E-mail: revm@cwjamaica.com] — (Tel) 001 876 640 0846

TRINIDAD

Vacant — Church of Scotland Greyfriars St Ann's, 50 Frederick Street, Port of Spain, Trinidad — (Tel/Fax) 001 868 622 1757

ASIA

Ecumenical Appointments

BANGLADESH

Church of Bangladesh

Ms Gillian Rose (1996) — Bollobhpur Hospital, PC Kedargonj, DR Meherpur, Bangladesh

Mr Andrew and Mrs Rosemary Symonds (1999) — St Andrew's College, Dhaka, Bangladesh [E-mail: ajsymond@bd.drik.net]

Ms Ann Tuesley (2000) — Rajshahi Hospital, Kushtia, Bangladesh

CHINA

Together with Scottish Churches China Group

Mr Ian Groves (1996) — Amity Foundation, Overseas Office, 4 Jordan Road, Kowloon, Hong Kong

Mr Mick and Mrs Anne Kavanagh (1997) — Nanping Teachers' College, 45 Guanshatian, Nanping, Fujian 353000, China

Mr Richard Brunt (1998) — Tai'an Teachers' College, 56 Wenhua Road, Tai'an, Shandong 271000, China

Michelle and Jody Marshall (2002) — Yichun Teachers' College, Jiangxi Province, China

Janet Dickinson, Joanna White, Matthew Syddall and Alan Moss (all 2003) have no placements at present because of the SARS situation.

NEPAL

United Mission to Nepal

Mrs Marianne Karsgaard (2001) — PO Box 126, Kathmandu, Nepal [E-mail: marianne@wlink.com.np] — (Fax) 00977 1 225 559

Miss Christine Stone — UMN, PO Box 126, Kathmandu, Nepal

SRI LANKA   **Presbytery of Lanka**
            Rev. John P.S. Purves BSc BD (2003)

            St Andrew's Scots Kirk, Colombo
            St Andrew's Church Manse. 73 Galle Road, Colombo 3,   (Tel) 94 1386 774
            Sri Lanka
            [E-mail: reverend@sltnet.lk]

THAILAND   **Church of Christ in Thailand**
            Mr Michael D. Fucella and Mrs E. Jane Fucella (1990)

            2, MU3, Tambon Nongloo, Sangklaburi, Kanchanaburi 71240, Thailand
            [E-mail: jfucella@loxinfo.co.th]

MIDDLE EAST AND NORTH AFRICA

EGYPT   Dr Keith Russell (2000) and Mrs Lai Fun Russell

            The Joint Relief Ministry of All Saints' Anglican   (Tel) 00202 738 0821
            Cathedral, Michel Lutfallah Street, Zamalek 11211,   (Fax) 00202 735 8941
            Cairo, Egypt
            [E-mail: russell@link.net]

ISRAEL   [Note: Church Services are held in St Andrew's Scots Memorial Church, Jerusalem, each Sunday at 10.00am, and at St Andrew's, Galilee (contact minister for worship time)]

            Jerusalem
            Rev. Clarence W. Musgrave (2000)
            and Mrs Joan Musgrave

            St Andrew's, Jerusalem, PO Box 8619, Jerusalem 91086, Israel
            (Tel: 00972 2 6732401; Fax: 00972 2 673 1711)
            [E-mail: standjer@netvision.net.il] [Private E-mail: stachjer@netvision.net.il;
            Website: http://www.scothotels.co.il]

            Tiberias
            Rev. Fred Hibbert (1996)
            and Mrs Diane Hibbert

            St Andrew's, Galilee, PO Box 104, Tiberias, Israel
            [E-mail: scottie@netvision.net.il] (Tel: 00972 4 6721165; Fax: 00972 4 6790145)
            [Private e-mail: scotdir@netvision.net.il]
            [Website: http://www.scothotels.co.il]

            Jaffa
            Mr Christopher Mottershead (2000)
            and Mrs Sue Mottershead

            Tabeetha School, PO Box 8170, 21 Yefet Street, Jaffa, Israel
            (Tel: 00972 3 6821581; Fax: 00972 3 6819357)
            [E-mail: costab@netvision.net.il;
            Website: http://www.tabeetha.htmlplant.com]
            Tabeetha School

            Mrs Karen Anderson (1992)

LEBANON   Mr David Kerry (1999)

            Near East School of Theology, Sourati Street,   (Tel) 00961 1346 708
            PO Box 13-5780, Chouran, Beirut, Lebanon   (Fax) 00961 1347 129
            [E-mail: nest.lib@inco.com.lb]

LIST L – OVERSEAS RESIGNED AND RETIRED MISSION PARTNERS (ten or more years' service)

NAME	APP	RET	AREA	ADDRESS
Aitken, Faith (Mrs)	1957	1968	Nigeria	High West, Urlar Road, Aberfeldy PH15 2ET
	1987	1990	Zambia	
Anderson, Kathleen (Mrs)	1955	1968	Pakistan	1A Elms Avenue, Great Shelford, Cambridge CB2 5LN
Archibald, Mary L. (Miss)	1964	1982	Nigeria/Ghana	490 Low Main Street, Wishaw ML2 7PL
Bailey, Winifred (Miss)	1949	1979	Kolhapur	Marian House, Room 10, 7/10 Oswald Road, Edinburgh EH9 2HE
Barbour, Edith R. (Miss)	1952	1983	North India	13/11 Pratik Nagar, Yerwada, Pune 411006, Maharashtra, India
Baxter, Rev. Richard and Mrs Ray	1954	1969	Malawi	138 Braid Road, Edinburgh EH10 6JB
Berkeley, Dr John and Dr Muriel	1967	1977	Bhutan	Drumbeg, Coylumbridge, Aviemore PH22 1QU
Bogle, Rev. Michael M.	1995	1998	Yemen	30 Woodburn Terrace, Edinburgh EH10 4SS
Boyle, Lexa (Miss)	1936	1961	Lovedale	7 Maxwell Grove, Glasgow G41 5JP
Bone, Mr David and Mrs Isobel	1959	1992	Aden/Yemen/Sudan	315 Blackness Road, Dundee DD2 1SH
	1977	1988	Malawi	
Bone, Elizabeth (Mrs)	1950	1964	Malawi	2A Elm Street, Dundee DD2 2AY
Brodie, Rev. Jim	1980	1984	North India	25A Keptie Road, Arbroath DD11 3ED
	1955	1974	Nepal	
	1996	1998	Pakistan	
	1967	1980	Pakistan	
Brown, Janet H. (Miss)	1988	1998	Zambia	6 Baxter Park Terrace, Dundee DD4 6NL
Burnett, Dr Fiona	1964	1967	Nigeria	The Glenholm Centre, Broughton, Biggar ML12 6JF
Burnett, Dr Robin and Mrs Storm	1968	1977	South Africa	79 Bank Street, Irvine KA12 0LL
Burt, M.R.C. (Miss)	1940	1975	Kenya	22 The Loaning, Chirnside, Duns TD11 3YE
Byers, Rev. Alan and Rev. Mairi	1960	1971	Ghana	Meadowbank, Plumdon Road, Annan DG12 6SJ
Campbell, George H.	1957	1971	Livingstonia	27 Avenue Street, Stewarton, Kilmarnock KA3 5AP
Coltart, Rev. Ian O.	1967	1985	North India	The Manse, Arbirlot, Arbroath DD11 2NX
Conacher, Marion (Miss)	1963	1993	India	41 Magdalene Drive, Edinburgh EH15 3BG
Conn, A. (Mr)	1937	1960	Blantyre	90 Endbutt Lane, Great Crosby, Liverpool L23
Cooper, Rev. George	1966	1986	Kenya	69 Montpelier Park, Edinburgh EH10 4WD
Cowan, Dr Betty	1969	1988	North India	2 Sunningdale Square, Kilwinning KA13 6PH
Crosbie, Ann R (Miss)	1955	1967	Nigeria	21 Fieldhead Square, Glasgow G43 1HL
Dabb, Dr R. Gwen	1943	1971	Blantyre	14/44 Ethel Terrace, Edinburgh EH10 5NA
Dawson, Miss Anne	1976	2000	Malawi	5 Cattle Market, Clackmannan FK10 4EH
Dick, Dr James and Mrs Anne	1954	1957	North India	1 Tummel Place, Comrie, Crieff PH6 2PG
	1957	1968	Nepal	

Dougall, Ian C.	1960	1990	Kenya	60B Craigmillar Park, Edinburgh EH16 5PU
Drever, Dr Bryan	1962	1982	Aden/Yemen/Pakistan	188 Addison Road, King's Head, Birmingham
Duncan, Mr David and Mrs Allison	1952	1969	Nigeria	7 Newhailes Avenue, Musselburgh EH21 6DW
Dunlop, Mr. Walter T. and Mrs Jennifer	1979	1994	Malawi/Israel	50 Oxgangs Road, Edinburgh EH13 9DR
Fauchelle, Rev. Don and Mrs Margaret	1971 / 1991	1979 / 1999	Zambia, Malawi, Zimbabwe	Flat 3, 22 North Avenue, Devonport, Auckland 1309, New Zealand
Ferguson, Mr John K.P. and Mrs Margaret	1977	1989	Pakistan	12 Bencleuch Place, Bourtreehill South, Irvine KA11 1EL
Finlay, Carol (Ms)	1990	2001	Malawi	96 Broomfield Crescent, Edinburgh EH12 7LX
Fischbacher, Dr Colin M. and Mrs Sally	1986	1998	Malawi	11 Barclay Square, Gosforth, Newcastle-upon-Tyne NE3 2JB
Foster, Joyce (Miss)	1968	1972	Kenya	99 Sixth Street, Newtongrange EH22 4LA
	1972	1981	Malawi	
Gall, E.G. (Miss)	1940	1962	Blantyre	151 Raeburn Heights, Glenrothes KY16 1BW
Hutchison, C.M. (Mr)	1951	1972	Calabar	75 Grampian Road, Torry, Aberdeen AB11 8ED
Irvine, Mr Clive and Mrs Su	1984	1999	Nepal	McGregor Flat, 92 Blackford Avenue, Edinburgh EH9 3ES
Irvine, Elsabe (Mrs)	1951	1987	Malawi	60 Thirlestane Road, Edinburgh EH9 1AR
Irvine, Dr Geoffrey C. and Mrs Dorothy	1952	1989	Kenya	Lakeside, PO Box 1356 Naivasha, Kenya
Karam, Ishbel (Mrs)	1968	1985	Pakistan	Hillsgarth, Baltasound, Unst, Shetland ZE2 9DY
King, Dr Alistair and Mrs Betty	1955	1971	North India	23 Main Street, Newstead, Melrose TD6 9DX
Knowles, Dr John K. and Mrs Heather	1976	1992	Malawi	Trollopes Hill, Monton Combe, Bath BA2 7HX
Laidlay, Dr Rorie and Mrs Una	1961	1968	Yemen	Isles View, 5 Bell's Road, Lerwick, Shetland ZE1 0QB
	1968	1971	Pakistan	
	1971	1978	Yemen	
Lamont, Rev. A. Donald	1941	1975	Kenya	36 St Clair Terrace, Edinburgh EH10 5PS
Liddell, Margaret (Miss)	1964	1980	Zambia	20 Wyvis Crescent, Conon Bridge, Dingwall IV7 8BZ
Logie, Robina (Mrs)	1950	1960	North India	23 Stonefield Drive, Inverurie AB5 9DZ
Lyon, Rev. D.H.S.	1952	1972	Nagpur	30 Mansfield Road, Balerno EH14 7JZ
MacDonald, Dr Alistair and Mrs Freda	1949	1962	Nigeria	10 Millside, Morpeth, Northumberland NE61 1PN
McArthur, G. (Mr)	1956	1972	South Africa	3 Craigcrook Road, Edinburgh EH4 3NQ
McCulloch, Lesley (Mrs)	1982	1992	Malawi/Pakistan	c/o 19 North Approach Road, Kincardine, Alloa FK10 4NW
McCutcheon, Agnes W.F. (Miss)	1957	1989	India	10A Hugh Murray Grove, Cambuslang, Glasgow G72 7NG
McDougall, Rev. John N.	1935	1960	West Pakistan	2/58 Allendale Road, Mount Albert, Auckland 3, New Zealand
McGoff, A.W. (Miss)	1954	1974	Kolhapur	6 Mossvale Walk, Craigend, Glasgow G33 5PF

McMahon, Rev. Robert and Mrs Jessie	1959	1976	North India	7 Ridgepark Drive, Lanark ML11 7PG
MacGregor, Rev. Margaret	1959	1994	India	Gordon Flat, 16 Learmonth Court, Edinburgh EH4 1PB
McKenzie, Rev. Robert	1938	1951	India	23 Foulis Crescent, Edinburgh EH14 5BN
McKenzie, Rev. W.M.	1958	1974	Zambia	Troqueer Road, Dumfries DG2 7DF
McMillan, Helen (Miss)	1981	2003	Pakistan	17/1 New Orchardfield, Edinburgh EH6 5ET
Macrae, Rev. Norman and Mrs Claire	1943	1960	Nigeria	49 Lixmount Avenue, Edinburgh EH5 3EW
MacKinnon, E.L. (Miss)	1952	1972	Nigeria	142 Glencairn Street, Stevenson KA20 3BU
Malley, Beryl Stevenson (Miss)	1982	1992	Malawi	272/2 Craigcrook Road, Edinburgh EH4 7TF
Marshall, Rev. Fred J.	1946	1992	Bermuda	Flat 3, 31 Oswald Road, Edinburgh EH9 2HT
Millar, Rev. Margaret R.M.	1967	1996	Malawi/Zambia	The Manse, Taynuilt, Argyll PA35 1HW
Millar, Rev. Peter	1976	1989	South India	
Moir, Rev. Ian and Mrs Elsie	1962	1973	South Africa	28/6 Comely Bank Avenue, Edinburgh EH4 1EL
Moore, Rev. J. Wilfred and Mrs Lillian	1943	1957	Ghana	31 Lennox Gardens, Linlithgow EH49 7PZ
Morrice, Rev. Dr Charles and Mrs Margaret	1971	1998	Buenos Aires/Kenya	104 Baron's Hill Avenue, Linlithgow EH49 7JG
Morris, Rev. Gordon C.	1948	1983	Zambia, Argentina	42 Regent Street, Edinburgh EH5 2AY
Morton, Rev. Alasdair J.	1960	1973	Zambia	8 Ormiston Grove, Melrose TD6 9SR
Morton, Rev. Colin	1988	1998	Israel	313 Lanark Road West, Currie EH14 5RS
Munro, Harriet (Miss)	1959	1969	Malawi	26 The Forge, Braidpark Drive, Glasgow G46 6LB
Murison, Rev. W.G.	1951	1971	Santalia	21 Hailes Gardens, Edinburgh EH13 0JL
Murray, Rev. Douglas and Mrs. Sheila	1994	2004	Switzerland	Flat 9, 4 Bonnington Gait, Edinburgh EH6 5NZ
Murray, Mr Ian and Mrs Isabel	1962	2000	Pakistan	17 Piershill Terrace, Edinburgh EH8 7EY
Musk, Dr Chad and Mrs Lily	1959	1959	Malawi	1 Tulloch Place, St Andrews KY16 8XJ
	1959	1959	Zambia	
Nelson, Rev. John and Mrs Anne	1974	1974	Pakistan	7 Manse Road, Roslin EH25 9LF
	1947	1952	North India	
	1970	1973	North India	
Nicholson, Rev. Thomas S.	1981	1995	Taiwan	Todholes, Greenlaw, Duns TD10 6XD
Nicol, Catherine (Miss)	1960	2000	Pakistan	St Columba Christian Girls' RTC, Barah Patthar, Sialkot 2, Pakistan
Nutter, Margaret (Miss)	1966	1979	Pakistan	Kilmorich, 14 Balloch Road, Balloch, Alexandria G83 8SR
Pacitti, Rev. Stephen A.	1977	1996	Taiwan	157 Nithsdale Road, Pollokshields, Glasgow G41 5RD
Pattison, Rev. Kenneth and Mrs Susan	1966	1977	Malawi	The Manse, Delny, Invergordon IV18 0NW
Petty, Rev. Phil	1952	1962	Malawi	7 Marchbank Place, Balerno EH14 7EU
Philip, Rev. David Stuart	1978	1991	Gibraltar	6 St Bernard's Crescent, Edinburgh EH4 1NP
Philip, Dr J. Murray and Mrs Margaret	1951	1968	Nigeria	Penlan, Holm Farm Road, Catrine, Mauchline KA5 6TA
Philp, Rev. Robert and Mrs Jeane	1937	1961	Kenya	2 Hockley Court, Weston Park West, Bath BA1 4AR

Philpot, Rev. David	WCC Geneva	1981	1995	2/27 Pentland Drive, Edinburgh EH10 6PX
Rae, Rev. David	India	1953	1989	29 Falcon Avenue, Edinburgh EH10 4AL
Reid, Ann (Miss)	Ghana	1988	1996	19 Cloughwood Crescent, Shevington, Lancs WN6 8EP
Reid, Margaret I. (Miss)	Malawi	1964	1982	26A Angle Park Terrace, Edinburgh EH11 2JT
Rennie, Rev. Alistair M.	Malawi	1939	1976	13 Tullich Terrace, Tillicoultry FK13 6RD
Rhodes, Rev. William S.	North India	1954	1981	22 Hamilton Place, Edinburgh EH3 5AU
Ritchie, Ishbel M. (Miss)	Eastern Himalaya	1955	1996	8 Ross Street, Dunfermline KY12 0AN
Ritchie, Rev. J.M.	Yemen	1974	1977	46 St James' Gardens, Penicuik EH26 9DU
Ritchie, Margaret (Miss)	Zambia	1968	1978	1 Afton Bridgend, New Cumnock KA18 4AX
Ritchie, Mary Scott (Miss)	Malawi/Israel	1968	1991	Afton Villa, 1 Afton Bridgend, New Cumnock KA18 4AX
Ross, Rev. Prof. Kenneth and Mrs Hester	Malawi	1988	1998	35 Madeira Street, Edinburgh EH6 4AJ
Rough, Rev. Margaret E. (Miss)	Blantyre	1966	1987	6 Glebe Street, Dumfries DG1 2LF
Roy, Rev. Alan J.	Zambia	1960	1972	14 Comerton Place, Drumoig, St Andrews KY16 0NQ
Russell, M.M. (Miss)	Nigeria	1946	1969	14 Hozier Street, Carluke ML8 5DW
Samuel, Lynda (Mrs)	Madras	1974	1990	c/o Balgownie, 1 Argyll Street, Brechin DD9 6JL
Shepherd, Dr Clyne and Mrs Anne	Nigeria	1956	1968	8 St Clair Terrace, Edinburgh EH10 5NW
Smith, Mr Harry and Mrs Margaret	Nigeria	1959	1967	31 Woodville Crescent, Sunderland SR4 8RE
Smith, M.L. (Miss)	Malawi	1968	1970	6 Fintry Mains, Dundee DD4 9HF
Smith, Rev. W. Ewing	Madras	1962	1973	8 Hardy Gardens, Bathgate EH48 1NH
Sneddon, Mr Sandy and Mrs Marie	Delhi	1986	1978	84 Greenend Gardens, Edinburgh EH17 7QH
Steedman, Martha (Mrs) (nee Hamilton)	Pakistan	1955	2003	Muir of Blebo, Blebo Craigs, Cupar KY15 5TZ
Stewart, Marion G. (Miss)	North India	1976	1966	Kirk Cottage, Kirkton of Skene, Westhill, Skene AB32 6XX
Stiven, Rev. Iain	Malawi/Israel	1959	1989	7 Gloucester Place, Edinburgh EH3 6EE
Stone, W. Vernon MA BD	Pakistan	1949	1969	36 Woodrow Court, Port Glasgow Road, Kilmacolm PA13 4QA
Taylor, Rev. A.T.H.	Zambia	1938	1966	4 The Pleasance, Strathkinness, St Andrews KY16 9SD
Tennant, Frances (Miss)	Nigeria/Jamaica	1965	1972	101 St John's Road, Edinburgh EH12 6NN
Wallace, A. Dorothy (Miss)	Pakistan	1953	1977	7 Bynack Place, Nethy Bridge PH25 3DU
Walker, Rev. Donald and Mrs Judith	North India	1981	1991	2 Wilson Road, Banchory AB31 3UY
Westmarland, Rev. Colin	Zambia	1975	1994	PO Box 5, Cospicua, CSPOI, Malta
Wilkie, Rev. James L.	Malta	1959	2001	7 Comely Bank Avenue, Edinburgh EH4 1EW
Wilkinson, Rev. John	Zambia	1946	1976	70 Craigleith Hill Gardens, Edinburgh EH4 2JH
Wilson, Irene (Ms)	Kenya	1993	1975	
Wilson, M.H. (Miss)	Israel	1946	2004	7 Lady's Well, Moat Road, Annan DG12 5AD
Wilson, Rev. Mark	Nasik	1953	1977	37 Kings Avenue, Longniddry EH32 0QN

LIST M – PARISH ASSISTANTS and PROJECT WORKERS

NAME	APP	ADDRESS	APPOINTMENT	TEL	PRES
Adam, Dougie	2001	175 Fairview Drive, Danestone, Aberdeen AB22 8ZZ	Aberdeen: Bridge of Don	07729 781634	31
Bauer, Alex (Mrs)	2001	26 Netherhouse Avenue, Lenzie, Glasgow G66 5NG	Linwood	07900 531196	14
Black, Colm	2001	2B Mason Road, Inverness IV2 3SZ	Inverness: Hilton	01463 717208	37
Brown, Sarah (Miss)	2003	2/1, 3 Bathgate Street, Glasgow G31 1DZ	Govan Old, Linthouse St Kenneth's and New Govan	0141-556 2959	16
Campbell, Alasdair	2000	3 Gellatly Road, Dunfermline KY11 4BH	Dunfermline: Dalgety	01383 726238	24
Close, David	2001	5 Shortroods Road, Paisley PA3 2NT	The Star Project: Paisley North	0141-889 5850	14
Conlin, Melodie	2000	Bridgeton Business Centre, Suite 313, 285 Abercromby Street, Glasgow G40 2DD	Glasgow East End	0141-554 0997	16
Cowie, Marjorie	2002	35 Balbirnie Avenue, Markinch, Glenrothes KY7 6BS	Glenrothes: St Margaret's	01592 758402	25
Dawson, Mike (Rev.)	2003	12 Sighthill Crescent, Edinburgh EH11 4QE	Edinburgh: Holy Trinity	0131-453 6279	1
Douglas, Jessie (Mrs)	1999	24 Niddrie Marischal Crescent, Edinburgh EH16 4LA	Edinburgh: Richmond Craigmillar	0131-669 6848	1
Falconer, Alexander J.	1996	59 Waldegrave Road, Carlisle CA2 6EW	The Border Kirk	01228 544757	7
Finch, John	2002	71 Maxwell Avenue, Glasgow G61 8NZ	Glasgow: St Francis in the East	0141-587 7390	16
Govan, Alec	1999	Braeside Cottage, 1 School Road, Sandford, Strathaven ML10 6BF	Hamilton: Trinity	01357 523815	17
Haringman, Paul	2003	71/13 Harrison Road, Edinburgh EH11 1EQ	Newbattle	0131-466 1403	3
Hutchison, John BA	2001	30/4 West Pilton Gardens, Edinburgh EH4 4EG	Edinburgh: The Old Kirk	0131-538 1622	1
Johnston, Mark (Rev.)	2003	5 Bruce Walk, Redmoss, Nigg, Aberdeen AB12 3LX	Cove New Charge Development	01224 874269	31
McBean, Archie	1999	28 Taransay Crescent, Aberdeen AB16 6UG	Aberdeen: Mastrick	01224 789784	31
McLauchlan, Dorothy Jean	2001	114 Brownside Road, Glasgow G72 8AF	Glasgow: Cranhill	0141-641 3171	16
Muir, Graeme	2001	2 Nithsdale Place, Noblehill, Dumfries DG1 3HT	Dumfries: St George's	01387 267470	8
Philip, Elizabeth MA BA	2001	43 Smithycroft Road, Glasgow G33 2RH [E-mail: elizabethphilip@cheerful.com]	Glasgow: Garthamlock/Craigend East	0141-770 7593	16
Reford, Susan	2001	32 Jedburgh Street, Blantyre, Glasgow G72 0SU	East Kilbride: Moncreiff	01698 820122	17
Rose, Jo (Miss)	2003	3 Millerfield Place, Edinburgh EH9 1LW	Kaimes Lockhart Memorial	0131-667 1568	1
Smith, David	2003	Parkview, Troustrie, Crail, Anstruther KY10 3XD	Benarty and Lochgelly	01333 450796	24
Young, Neil James	2001	1/2, 33 Alexandra Park Street, Glasgow G31 2UB	Glasgow: St Paul's	07748 808488	16

LIST N – READERS

1. EDINBURGH

Beasley, Ronald E. — 37 Warrender Park Terrace, Edinburgh EH9 1EB — 0131-229 8383
Davies, Ruth (Mrs) (attached to Liberton) — 4 Hawkhead Grove, Edinburgh EH16 6LS — 0131-664 3608
Farrant, Yvonne (Mrs) — Flat 7, 14 Duddingston Mills, Edinburgh EH8 7NF
Farrell, William J. — 50 Ulster Crescent, Edinburgh EH8 7JS — 0131-661 1026
Farrow, Edmund — 14 Brunswick Terrace, Edinburgh EH7 5PG — 0131-558 8210
Kerrigan, Herbert A. MA LLB QC — Airdene, 20 Edinburgh Road, Dalkeith EH22 1JY — 0131-660 3007
Kinnear, M.A. — 25 Thorburn Road, Edinburgh EH13 0BH — 0131-441 3150
Morrison, Peter K. — 65 Balgreen Road, Edinburgh EH12 5UA — 0131-337 7711
Pearce, Martin — 4 Corbiehill Avenue, Edinburgh EH4 5DR — 0131-336 4864
Wyllie, Anne (Miss) — 46 Jordan Lane, Edinburgh EH10 4QX — 0131-447 9035

2. WEST LOTHIAN

Blackwood, Michael — Inshaig Cottage, Hatton, Kirknewton EH27 8DZ — 0131-333 1448
Coyle, Charlotte (Mrs) — 28 The Avenue, Whitburn EH47 0DA — 01501 740687
Elliott, Sarah (Miss) — 105 Seafield, Bathgate EH47 7AW — 01506 654950
Notman, Jean G.S. (Miss) — 31 South Loch Park, Bathgate EH48 2QZ — 01506 633820
Rankin, Stuart A.D. — 7 Watson Green, Deer Park, Livingston EH54 8RP — 01506 439911
[E-mail: stuart@sadrankin.com]

3. LOTHIAN

Booth, Sidney J. IEng CCME — 6 Winton Court, Cockenzie, Prestonpans EH32 0JW — 01875 813978
Cannon, S. Christopher MA — Briarwood, Winterfield Place, Belhaven, Dunbar EH42 1QQ — 01368 864991
Evans, W. John IEng MIIE(Elec) — Edenwood, 29 Smileyknowes Court, North Berwick EH39 4RG — 01620 894309
[E-mail: jevans7is@hotmail.com]
Gibson, C.B. Stewart — 27 King's Avenue, Longniddry EH32 0QN — 01875 853464
[E-mail: stewartgibson@waitrose.com]
Hogg, David MA — 82 Eskhill, Penicuik EH26 8DQ — 01968 676350
Lyall, George JP — Mossgiel, 13 Park Road, Bonnyrigg EH19 2AW — 0131-663 9343
[E-mail: george.lyall@bigfoot.com]
Trevor, A. Hugh MA — 29A Fidra Road, North Berwick EH39 4NE — 01620 894924
[E-mail: htrevor@onetel.net.uk]
Yeoman, Edward T.N. FSA(Scot) — 75 Newhailes Crescent, Musselburgh EH21 6ES — 0131-653 2291

4. MELROSE AND PEEBLES

Butcher, John W. — 'Sandal', 13 Ormiston Grove, Melrose TD6 9SR — 01896 822339
Cashman, Margaret D. (Mrs) — 38 Abbotsford Road, Galashiels TD1 3HR — 01896 752711

5. DUNS

Deans, M. (Mrs) BA	The Lodge, Edrington House, Mordington, Berwick-on-Tweed TD15 1UF	01289 386222
Elphinston, Enid (Mrs)	Edrington House, Berwick-on-Tweed TD15 1UF	01289 386359
Landale, William	Cranshaws House, Cranshaws, Duns TD11 3SJ	01361 890242

6. JEDBURGH

Finlay, Elizabeth (Mrs)	10 Inch Park, Kelso TD5 7EQ	01573 226641
Knox, Dagmar (Mrs)	3 Stichill Road, Ednam, Kelso TD5 7QQ	01573 224883
Thomson, Robert R.	34/36 Fisher Avenue, Hawick TD9 9NB	01450 373851

7. ANNANDALE AND ESKDALE

Boncey, David	Redbrae, Beattock, Moffat DG10 9RF	01683 300613
	[E-mail: bonceyofredbrae@yahoo.co.uk]	
Brown, Martin J.	Lochouse Farm, Beattock, Moffat DG10 9SG	01683 300451
Brown, S. Jeffrey BA	Skara Brae, 8 Ballplay Road, Moffat DG10 9AR	01683 220475
Chisholm, Dennis A.G. MA BSc	Moss-side, Hightae, Lockerbie DG11 1JR	01387 811803
Dodds, Alan	Trinco, Battlehill, Annan DG12 6SN	01461 201235
Jackson, Susan (Mrs)	48 Springbells Road, Annan DG12 6LQ	01461 204159
	[E-mail: shjackson@supanet.com]	
Morton, Andrew A. BSc	19 Sherwood Park, Lockerbie DG11 2DX	01576 203164
	[E-mail: thecroft@macunlimited.net]	

8. DUMFRIES AND KIRKCUDBRIGHT

Archer, Morven (Mrs)	1 Grilloch Drive, Dumfries DG1 4DP	01387 263946
Carroll, J. Scott	17 Downs Place, Heathhall, Dumfries DG1 3RF	01387 265350
Greer, Kathleen (Mrs) MEd	10 Watling Street, Dumfries DG1 1HF	01387 256113
Marsh, Sally (Mrs) BTh	32 Queen Street, Castle Douglas DG7 1HS	01556 503706
Ogilvie, D.W. MA FSAScot	Lingerwood, 2 Nelson Street, Dumfries DG2 9AY	01387 264267
Paterson, Ronald M. (Dr)	Mirkwood, Ringford, Castle Douglas DG7 2AL	01557 820202
Piggins, Janette (Mrs)	Cleugh Wood, Dalbeattie DG5 4PF	01387 780655

9. WIGTOWN AND STRANRAER

Clough, Alan	Dowiesbank, Whauphill, Newton Stewart DG8 9PN	01988 700824
Connery, Graham	Skellies Knowe, West Ervie, Stranraer DG9	01776 854277
Robinson, J.J.	Kirwaugh, Wigtown, Newton Stewart DG8 9AY	01988 403244
Williams, Roy	120 Belmont Road, Stranraer DG9 7BG	

10. AYR

Fleming, William H.	35 Briar Grove, Ayr KA7 3PD	01292 268599
Jamieson, I.	2 Whinfield Avenue, Prestwick KA9 2BH	01242 476898
McNally, David BEd MEd PhD ACP	50 Kenmore, Troon, KA10 6PF	01292 312015
Morrison, James	27 Monkton Road, Prestwick KA9 1AP	01292 479313
Murphy, I.	56 Lamont Crescent, Cumnock, KA18 3DU	01290 423675
Riome, Elizabeth (Mrs)	Monkwood Mains, Minishant, Maybole KA19 8EY	01292 443440
Todd, Joy M. (Mrs) BD	15 Firth Road, Troon KA10 6TF	01292 312995
Wilson, Fiona (Mrs)	12 Main Street, Barrhill KA26 0PP	01465 821316

11. IRVINE AND KILMARNOCK

Bircham, James	8 Holmlea Place, Kilmarnock KA1 1UU	01563 532287
Cuthbert, Helen (Miss) MA MSc	63 Haining Avenue, Kilmarnock KA1 3QN	01563 550403
Crosbie, Shona (Mrs)	4 Campbell Street, Darvel KA17 0PA	01560 322229
Findlay, Elizabeth (Mrs)	19 Keith Place, Kilmarnock KA3 7NS	01563 528084
Hamilton, Margaret A. (Mrs)	59 South Hamilton Street, Kilmarnock KA1 2DT	01563 534431
Jamieson, John BSc(Hons) DEP AFBPSS	22 Moorfield Avenue, Kilmarnock KA1 1TS	01563 534065
Lightbody, Hunter B.	36 Rannoch Place, Irvine KA12 9NQ	01294 273955
McAllister, Anne C. (Mrs)	39 Bowes Rigg, Stewarton KA3 5EN	01560 483191
McLean, Donald	1 Four Acres Drive, Kilmaurs, Kilmarnock KA3 2ND	01563 381475
MacTaggart, Elspeth (Miss)	21 Scargie Road, Kilmarnock KA3 1QR	01563 527713
Mills, Catherine (Mrs)	59 Crossdene Road, Crosshouse, Kilmarnock KA2 0JU	01563 535305
Scott, William BA DipEd	6 Elgin Avenue, Stewarton, Kilmarnock KA3 3HJ	01560 484273
Storm, Iain	17 Kilwinning Road, Irvine KA12 8RR	01294 277647
Wilson, Robert L.S. MA BD	57 Woodstock Street, Kilmarnock KA1 2JH	01563 526658

12. ARDROSSAN

Allan, J.H.	Creag Dhubh, Golf Course Road, Whiting Bay, Brodick, Isle of Arran KA27 8RE	01770 700462
Barclay, Elizabeth (Mrs)	2 Jacks Road, Saltcoats KA21 5NT	01294 471855
Hunter, Jean C.Q. (Mrs)	The Manse, Shiskine, Isle of Arran KA27 8EP	01770 860380
Mackay, Brenda H. (Mrs)	19 Eglinton Square, Ardrossan KA22 8LN	01294 464491
Mills, Colin J.	Roadend Christian Guesthouse, Shiskine, Brodick, Isle of Arran KA27 8EW	01770 860448

13. LANARK

Allan, Robert	59 Jennie Lee Drive, Overtown, Wishaw ML2 0EE	01698 376738
Grant, Alan	25 Moss-side Avenue, Carluke ML8 5UG	01555 771419
Kerr, Sheilagh I. (Mrs)	Dunvegan, 29 Wilsontown Road, Forth, Lanark ML11 8ER	01555 812214

14. GREENOCK AND PAISLEY

Banks, Russell	18 Aboyne Drive, Paisley PA2 7SJ	0141-884 6925
	[E-mail: cbanks25@aol.com]	
Campbell, Tom BA DipCPC	100 Craigielea Road, Renfrew PA4 8NJ	0141-886 2503
	[E-mail: thomas.campbell1180@ntlworld.co.uk]	
Davey, Charles L.	16 Divert Road, Gourock PA19 1DT	01475 631544
	[E-mail: charles@davey2.freeserve.co.uk]	
Glenny, John C.	49 Cloch Road, Gourock PA19 1AT	01475 636415
	[E-mail: jacklizg@aol.com]	
Jamieson, J.A.	148 Finnart Street, Greenock PA16 8HY	01475 729531
McFarlan, Elizabeth (Miss)	20 Fauldswood Crescent, Paisley PA2 9PA	01505 358411
	[E-mail: elizabeth.mcfarlan@ntlworld.com]	
McHugh, Jack	'Earlshaugh', Earl Place, Bridge of Weir PA11 3HA	01505 612789
	[E-mail: jrmchugh@btinternet.com]	

Marshall, Leon M.	Glenisla, Gryffe Road, Kilmacolm PA13 4BA [E-mail: lm@stevenson-kyles.co.uk]	01505 872417
Maxwell, Margaret (Mrs) BD	2 Grants Avenue, Paisley PA2 6AZ [E-mail: sandra1.maxwell@virgin.net]	0141-884 3710
Orry, Geoff	'Rhu Ellan', 4 Seaforth Crescent, Barrhead Glasgow G78 1PL	0141-881 9748

16. GLASGOW

Armstrong, J.	44 Eckford Street, Glasgow G32 7AJ	0141-778 4745
Birchall, Edwin R.	11 Sunnybank Grove, Clarkston, Glasgow G76 7SU	0141-638 4332
Calder, William	111 Muirside Avenue, Kirkintilloch, Glasgow G66 3PP	0141-776 5495
Callander, Thomas M.S.	31 Dalkeith Avenue, Bishopbriggs, Glasgow G64 2HQ	0141-563 6955
Campbell, Jack T. BD BEd	27 Springfield Road, Bishopbriggs, Glasgow G64 1PJ	0141-563 5837
Clark, J. Michael	1/2, 7 Grandtully Drive, Glasgow G12 0DP	
Clarke, Samuel	'Gola', 142 Shelley Road, Glasgow G12 0XN	0141-337 2238
Dickson, Hector	'Guito', 61 Whitton Drive, Giffnock, Glasgow G46 6EF	0141-637 0080
Findlay, William	36 Firpark Road, Bishopbriggs, Glasgow G64 1SP	0141-772 7253
Galbraith, Iain B.	Beechwood, Overton Road, Alexandria G83 0LJ	01389 753563
Gibson, James N.	153 Peveril Avenue, Glasgow G41 3SF	0141-632 4162
Horner, David J.	32 Burnside Road, Rutherglen, Glasgow G73 4RS	0141-634 2178
Hunt, Roland	4 Flora Gardens, Bishopbriggs, Glasgow G64 1DS	0141-563 3257
Lennie, Henry	14 Clyde Place, Cambuslang, Glasgow G72 7QT	0141-641 1410
Lockhart, James C.	56 Springfield Road, Bishopbriggs, Glasgow G64 1PN	0141-772 1852
MacColl, Duncan N.	14 Mosspark Avenue, Glasgow G52 1JX	0141-427 2395
McFarlane, Robert	25 Avenel Road, Glasgow G13 2PB	0141-954 5540
McLaughlin, C.	8 Lamlash Place, Glasgow G33 3XH	0141-774 2483
McLellan, Duncan	138 King's Park Avenue, Glasgow G44 4HS	0141-632 8433
Middleton, W.G.	20 Rannoch Avenue, Bishopbriggs, Glasgow G64 1BU	0141-772 6240
Montgomery, Hamish	13 Avon Avenue, Kessington, Bearsden, Glasgow G61 2PS	0141-942 3640
Nairne, Elizabeth (Mrs)	229 Southbrae Drive, Glasgow G13 1TT	0141-959 5066
Philips, John B.	2/3, 30 Handel Place, Glasgow G5 0TP	0141-429 7716
Robertson, Adam	423 Amulree Street, Glasgow G32 7SS	0141-573 6662
Shirlaw, William	77 Southpark Avenue, Glasgow G12 8LE	0141-339 0454
Stuart, Alex	107 Baldorran Crescent, Cumbernauld, Glasgow G68 9EX	01236 727710
Tindall, Margaret (Mrs)	23 Ashcroft Avenue, Lennoxtown, Glasgow G65 7EN	01360 310911
Williamson, John G.	34 King Edward Road, Glasgow G13 1QW	0141-959 1300
Wilson, George A.	46 Maxwell Drive, Garrowhill, Baillieston, Glasgow G69 6LS	0141-771 3862

17. HAMILTON

Beattie, Richard	4 Bent Road, Hamilton ML3 6QB	01698 420806
Bell, Sheena	2 Langdale, East Kilbride, Glasgow G74 4RP	01355 248217
Black, Gavin	11 Torrance Road, West Mains, East Kilbride, Glasgow G74 1AR	01355 224600
Clemenson, Anne	25 Dempsey Road, Lochview, Bellshill ML4 2UF	01698 291019
Cruickshanks, William	63 Progress Drive, Caldercruix, Airdrie ML6 7PU	01236 843352
Falconer, Leslie D.	48 Fraser River Tower, East Kilbride, Glasgow G75 8AD	01355 230133

Name	Address	Telephone
Haggarty, Frank	46 Glen Road, Caldercruix, Airdrie ML6 7PZ	01236 842182
Hawthorne, William G. MBE	172 Main Street, Plains, Airdrie ML6 7JH	01236 842230
Hewitt, Samuel	3 Corrie Court, Earnock, Hamilton ML3 9XE	01698 457403
Hislop, Eric	1 Castlegait, Strathaven ML10 6FF	01357 520003
Leckie, Elizabeth	41 Church Street, Larkhall ML9 1EZ	01698 308933
McCleary, Isaac	719 Coatbridge Road, Bargeddie, Glasgow G69 7PH	0141-236 0158
McMillan, Georgina	1 Damgaber Gardens, Quarter, Hamilton ML3 7XX	01698 424040
McRae, James	36 Crosshill Road, Strathaven ML10 6DS	01357 520053
Queen, Leslie	60 Loch Assynt, East Kilbride, Glasgow G74 2DW	01355 233932
Robertson, Rowan	68 Townhead Road, Coatbridge ML5 2HU	01236 425703
Smith, Alexander	6 Coronation Street, Wishaw ML2 8LF	01698 385797
Stevenson, Thomas	34 Castle Wynd, Quarter, Hamilton ML3 7XD	01698 282263
White, Ian	21 Muirhead, Stonehouse, Larkhall ML9 3HG	01698 792772
Wilson, William	115 Chatelherault Crescent, Low Waters Estate, Hamilton ML3 9PL	01698 421856

18. DUMBARTON

Name	Address	Telephone
Hart, R.J.M. BSc	7 Kidston Drive, Helensburgh G84 8QA	01436 672039

19. ARGYLL

Binner, Aileen	'Ailand', Connel, Oban PA37 1QX	01631 710264
Challis, John O.	Bay Villa, Strachur, Cairndow PA27 8DE	01369 860436
Elwis, Michael	Erray Farm Cottage, Tobermory, Mull PA75 6PS	01688 302331
Holden, Robert	Orsay, West Bank Road, Ardrishaig, Lochgilphead PA30 8HG	01546 603211
Logue, David	3 Braeface, Tayvallich, Lochgilphead PA31 8PN	01546 870647
Mitchell, James S.	4 Main Street, Port Charlotte, Isle of Islay PA48 7TX	01496 850650
Morrison, John	Tigh na Barnashaig, Tayvallich, Lochgilphead PA31 8PN	01546 870637
Ramsay, Matthew M.	Portnastorm, Carradale, Campbeltown PA28 6SB	01583 431381
Roberts, John V.	20 Toberonochy, Isle of Luing, Oban PA34 4UE	01852 314301

(Prefix 18001 Text, prefix 18002 Voice)

Name	Address	Telephone
Simpson, J.	Ardmhullean, Longsdale Road, Oban PA34 5JW	01631 562022
Sinclair, Margaret (Mrs)	2 Quarry Place, Furnace, Inveraray PA32 8XW	01499 500633
Stewart, Agnes	Creagdhu Mansions, New Quay Street, Campbeltown PA28 6BB	01586 552805
Stewart, John Y.S.	9 Foulis Road, Inveraray PA32 8UW	01499 302077
Strather, Angela (Mrs)	9 Gartness Cottages, Ballygrant, Isle of Islay PA45 7QN	01496 840527
Zielinski, Jen (Mrs)	26 Cromwell Street, Dunoon PA23 7AX	01369 706136

22. FALKIRK

Duncan, Lorna (Mrs) BA	Richmond, 28 Solway Drive, Head of Muir, Denny FK5 5NS	01324 813020
O'Rourke, Edith (Mrs)	16 Achray Road, Cumbernauld, Glasgow G67 4JH	01236 732813
Sarle, Andrew BSc BD	114 High Station Road, Falkirk FK1 5LN	01324 621648
Stewart, Arthur MA	51 Bonnymuir Crescent, Bonnybridge, Falkirk FK4 1GD	01324 812667
Struthers, I.	169 The Auld Road, Cumbernauld, Glasgow G67 2RQ	01236 733879

23. STIRLING

Brown, Kathryn (Mrs)	The Manse, Tullibody, Alloa FK10 2RG	01259 213236
Durie, Alastair	25 Forth Place, Stirling FK8 1UD	01786 451029
Kimmitt, Alan	111 Glasgow Road, Bannockburn, Stirling FK7 0PF	01786 817014
Lamont, John	Middleton Cottage, Muckhart Road, Dollar FK14 7PQ	01259 742800
Tilly, Patricia	4 Imerdownie Place, Dollar FK14 7BY	01259 742094

24. DUNFERMLINE

Adams, William	24 Foulford Street, Cowdenbeath KY4 0EQ	01383 822293
Arnott, Robert G.K.	25 Sealstrand, Dalgety Bay, Dunfermline KY11 5GH	01383 830442
Conway, Bernard	4 Centre Street, Kelty KY4 0DU	ex-directory
Grant, Allan	6 Normandy Place, Rosyth KY11 2HJ	
McCaffery, Joyce (Mrs)	79 Union Street, Cowdenbeath KY4 9SA	

25. KIRKCALDY

Biernat, Ian	2 Formonthills Road, Glenrothes KY6 3EF	01592 741487
Weatherston, Catriona M.A. (Miss) BSc	'Cruachan', Church Road, Leven KY8 4JB	01333 424636

26. ST ANDREWS

Allan, Angus J.	Craigmore, The Barony, Cupar KY15 5ER	01334 653369
Browning, Margaret (Miss)	20 Albert Crescent, Newport-on-Tay DD6 8DT	01382 542140
Elder, Morag (Mrs)	5 Provost Road, Tayport DD6 9JE	01382 552218
King, C.M. (Mrs)	8 Bankwell Road, Anstruther KY10 3DA	01333 310017
Kinnis, W.K.B. (Dr)	4 Dempster Court, St Andrews KY16 9EU	01334 476959
Sherriffs, Irene (Mrs)	Cragganmhor, 79 Tay Street, Newport-on-Tay DD1 8AQ	01382 542193
Smith, Elspeth (Mrs)	Whinstead, Dalgairn, Cupar KY15 4PH	01334 653269

27. DUNKELD AND MEIGLE

Carr, Graham	St Helen's, Meigle Road, Alyth PH11 8EU	01828 632474
Howat, David	Lilybank Cottage, Newton Street, Blairgowrie PH10 6MZ	01250 874715
Macmartin, Duncan M.	Teallach, Old Crieff Road, Aberfeldy PH15 2DG	01887 820693
Saunders, Grace (Ms)	40 Perth Street, Blairgowrie PH10 6DQ	01250 873981
Templeton, Elizabeth (Mrs)	Tenandry Manse, Killiecrankie, Pitlochry PH16 5LH	01796 472360

28. PERTH

Begg, James	Benholm, 12 Commissioner Street, Crieff PH7 3AY [E-mail: beggjlcrieff@tinyworld.co.uk]	01764 655907
Brown, Stanley	14 Buchan Drive, Perth PH1 1NQ	01738 628818
Buchan, James S.	47 Dunkeld Road, Perth PH1 5RP	01738 621814
Chappell, E. (Mrs)	Fiscal's House, Flat B, 1 South Street, Perth PH2 8NJ [E-mail: chappell@fish.co.uk]	01738 587808
Coulter, Hamish	95 Cedar Drive, Perth PH1 1RW [E-mail: hamish@coulter9530.freeserve.co.uk]	01738 636761
Hastings, W.P.	5 Craigroyston Road, Scone, Perth PH2 6NB	01738 560498
Johnstone, David	92 Duncansby Way, Perth PH1 5XF [E-mail: dcmj@fish.co.uk]	01738 442051
Laing, John	10 Graybank Road, Perth PH2 0GZ [E-mail: laing_middlechurch@hotmail.com]	
Livingstone, Alan	Strathmore House, 6 Lauder Crescent, Perth PH1 1SU	01738 623888

Michie, Margaret (Mrs)	3 Loch Leven Court, Wester Balgedie, Kinross KY13 7NE [E-mail: margaretmichie@balgedie.freeserve.co.uk]	01592 840602
Ogilvie, Brian	67 Whitecraigs, Kinnesswood, Kinross KY13 9TN [E-mail: brianj.ogilvie1@btopenworld.com]	01592 840823
Packer, Joan (Miss)	11 Moredun Terrace, Perth PH2 0DA	01738 623873
Thorburn, Susan (Mrs)	3 Dalealty Cottages, St Madoes Road, Errol, Perth PH2 7TJ [E-mail: s_thor2@yahoo.com]	01821 642681
Wilkie, Robert	24 Huntingtower Road, Perth PH1 2JS	01738 628301
Yellowlees, Deirdre (Mrs)	Ringmill House, Gannochy Farm, Perth PH2 7IH [E-mail: d.yellowlees@btinternet.com]	01738 633773

29. DUNDEE

Baxter, John T.G.	2 Garten Street, Broughty Ferry, Dundee DD5 3HH	01382 739997
Bell, S. (Dr)	10 Victoria Street, Newport-on-Tay DD6 8DJ	01382 542315
Brown, Isobel (Mrs)	10 School Wynd, Muirhead, Dundee DD2 5LW	01382 580545
Doig, Andrew	6 Lyndhurst Terrace, Dundee DD2 3HP	01382 610596
Johnston, William (Emeritus)	62 Forthill Road, Broughty Ferry, Dundee DD5 3TJ	01382 739704
Owler, Harry G. (Emeritus)	43 Brownhill Road, Dundee DD2 4LH	01382 622902
Ramsay, Thomas A.	Inchcape Place, Broughty Ferry, Dundee DD5 2LP	01382 778915
Rodgers, Mary (Mrs)	12 Balmerino Road, Dundee DD4 8RN	01382 500291
Shepherd, E.	34 Dalmahoy Drive, Dundee DD2 3UT	01382 815825
Simpson, Webster	51 Wemyss Crescent, Monifieth, Dundee DD5 4RA	01382 535218
Webster, Charles A.	16 Bath Street, Broughty Ferry, Dundee DD5 2BY	01382 739520
Woodley, A.G. (Dr)	67 Marlee Road, Broughty Ferry, Dundee DD5 3EU	01382 739820

30. ANGUS

Anderson, Gordon	33 Grampian View, Ferryden, Montrose DD10 9SU	01674 674915
Beedie, A.W.	62 Newton Crescent, Arbroath DD11 3JZ	01241 875001
Davidson, P.I.	95 Bridge Street, Montrose DD10 8AF	01674 674098
Edwards, Dougal	25 Mackenzie Street, Carnoustie DD7 6HD	01241 852666
Gray, Ian	15 Rossie Island Road, Montrose DD10 9NH	01674 677126
Gray, Linda (Mrs)	8 Inchgarth Street, Forfar DD8 3LY	01307 464039
Leslie Melville, Ruth (Hon. Mrs)	Little Deuchar, Fern, Forfar DD8 3RA	01356 650279
Nicol, Douglas C.	Edenbank, 16 New Road, Forfar DD8 2AE	01307 463264
Stevens, Peter J. BSc BA	7 Union Street, Montrose DD10 8PZ	01674 673710
Thompson, Anne	22 Braehead Drive, Carnoustie DD7 7SX	01241 852084
Wheat, M.	16A South Esk Street, Montrose DD10 8BJ	01674 676083

31. ABERDEEN

Forrester, Arthur A.	158 Lee Crescent North, Bridge of Don AB22 8FR	01224 822783
Gray, Peter PhD	165 Countesswells Road, Aberdeen AB15 7RA	01224 318172
Sinton, George P. FIMLS	12 North Donside Road, Bridge of Don, Aberdeen AB23 8PA	01224 702273

32. KINCARDINE AND DEESIDE

Atkins, Sally (Mrs)   9 Feugh View, Strachan, Banchory AB31 6NF   01330 850434
Bell, Peter D. BA   63 St Nicholas Drive, Banchory AB31 5YE   01330 823661
Cameron, Ann (Mrs)   30 Wilson Road, Banchory AB31 5UY   01330 825953
Coles, Stephen   205 High Street, Laurencekirk AB30 1BQ   01561 378400
Grant, Prof. Raymond MA PhD Ballochbrock, Braemar, Ballater AB35 5YQ   01339 741340
Harris, Michael   The Gables, Netherley Park, Netherley, Stonehaven AB39 3QM   01569 731091
McCafferty, W. John   Lynwood, Cammachmore, Stonehaven AB39 3NR   01569 730281
                             [E-mail: john.mccafferty@oopuscompany.com]
McLuckie, John   Kedron, Netherley Place, Ballater AB35 5QN   01339 755489
                             [E-mail: j-r-mcluckie@supanet.com]
Middleton, Robbie (Capt.)   7 St Ternan's Road, Newtonhill, Stonehaven AB39 2PF   01569 730852
Platt, David   2 St Michael's Road, Newtonhill, Stonehaven AB39 3RW   01569 730465
Sedgwick, Sheila (Dr) BA BD MEd PhD   Girnock Shiel, Glengirnock, Ballater AB35 5SS   01339 755292
Simpson, E. Elizabeth (Mrs) 33 Golf Road, Ballater AB35 5QX   01339 755597
                             [E-mail: connemara33@yahoo.com]
Woods, Julie (Mrs)   23 St Aidan Crescent, Banchory AB31 5YX   01330 824184

33. GORDON

Findlay, Patricia (Mrs)   Douglas View, Tullynessle, Alford AB33 8QR   01975 562379
Hart, Elsie (Mrs)   The Knoll, Craigearn, Kemnay AB51 9LN   01467 642105
Mitchell, Jean (Mrs)   6 Cowgate, Oldmeldrum, Inverurie AB51 0EN   01651 872745
Rennie, Lyall   Dunisla, Oyne, Insch AB52 6QU   01464 851587
Robb, Margaret (Mrs)   Chrislouan, Keithhall, Inverurie AB51 0LN   01651 882310
Robertson, James Y.   1 Nicol Road, Kintore, Inverurie AB51 0QA   01467 633001
Sutherland, Susan (Mrs)   53 Westhill Grange, Westhill AB32 6QJ   01224 741889

34. BUCHAN

Brown, Lillian (Mrs)   Bank House, 45 Main Street, Aberchirder, Huntly AB54 7ST   01466 780330
Davidson, James   19 Great Stuart Street, Peterhead AB42 1JX   01779 470242
Lumsden, Vera (Mrs)   8 Queen's Crescent, Portsoy, Banff AB45 2PX   01261 842712
McColl, John   East Cairnchina, Lonmay, Fraserburgh AB43 8RH   01346 532558
Mair, Dorothy (Miss)   53 Dennyduff Road, Fraserburgh AB43 9LY   01346 513879
Michie, William   34 Seafield Street, Whitehills, Banff AB45 2NR   01261 861439
Noble, John   44 Henderson Park, Peterhead AB42 2WR   01779 472522
Ogston, Norman   Rowandale, 6 Rectory Road, Turriff AB53 4SU   01888 560342
Simpson, Andrew C.   10 Wood Street, Banff AB45 1JX   01261 812538
Smith, Ian M.G. MA   Chomriach, 2 Hill Street, Cruden Bay, Peterhead AB42 0HF   01779 812698
Smith, Jenny (Mrs)   5 Seatown Place, Cairnbulg, Fraserburgh AB43 8WP   01346 582980
Sneddon, Richard   8 School Road, Peterhead AB42 2BE   01779 474492

35. MORAY

Benson, F. Stuart   8 Springfield Court, Forres IV36 3WY   01309 671525
Carson, John   2 Woodside Drive, Forres IV36 2UF   01309 674541
Forbes, Jean (Mrs)   Greenmoss, Drybridge, Buckie AB56 5JB   01542 831646

MacKenzie, Stuart G. MA — Woodend Cottage, Blackburn, Fochabers IV32 7LN — 01343 843248
Middleton, Alex — Coral Cottage, Pilmuir Road, Forres IV36 2HU — 01309 676912

36. ABERNETHY
Berkeley, John S. (Dr) — Drumbeg, Coylumbridge, Aviemore PH22 1QU — 01479 811055
Duncanson, Mary (Mrs) — Falas-an-Duin, Catlodge, Laggan, Newtonmore PH20 1BS — 01528 544399

37. INVERNESS
Barry, Dennis — 50 Holm Park, Inverness IV2 4XU — 01463 225883
Cook, Arnett D. — 128 Laurel Avenue, Inverness IV3 5RS — 01463 242586
Maclean, Hamish — 63 Ashton Road, Inverness IV2 3UY — 01463 239030
Robertson, Hendry — 'Park House', 51 Glenurquhart Road, Inverness IV3 5PB — 01463 231858

38. LOCHABER
Chalkley, Andrew — 2 Telford Place, Claggan, Fort William PH33 6QG [E-mail: andrew.chalkley@btinternet.com] — 01397 700271
Dick, Robert — 8 Lanark Place, Fort William PH33 6UD — 01397 704833
Fraser, John A. — 26 Clunes Avenue, Caol, Fort William PH33 7BJ [E-mail: john.afraser@btopenworld.com] — 01397 703467
Maitland, John — St Monance, Ardgour, Fort William PH33 7AA — 01855 841267
Thomas, Geoff — Drumcannach, Station Road, Arisaig PH39 4NJ — 01687 450230

39. ROSS
Finlayson, Michael R. — Amberlea, Evanton IV16 9UY — 01349 830598
Gilbertson, Ian — Firth View, Craigrory, North Kessock, Inverness IV1 1XH — 01463 731538
Galbraith, Hamish — Kinnettas House, Strathpeffer IV14 9AJ — 01997 421832
McCredie, Frederick — Highfield Park, Conon Bridge, Inverness IV7 8AP — 01349 862171
Robertson, John (Dr) — East Wing, Kincurdie House, Rosemarkie IV10 8SJ — 01381 621388
Woodham, Maisey F. (Mrs) — Scardroy, Greenhill, Dingwall IV15 9JQ — 01349 862116

40. SUTHERLAND
Mackay, Donald F. — The Retreat, Lillieshall Street, Helmsdale KW8 6JF — 01431 821469
Stobo, Mary (Mrs) — Druim-an-Sgairnich, Lower Gledfield, Ardgay IV24 3BG — 01863 766529
Weidner, Karl — St Vincent Road, Tain IV19 1JR — 01862 892090

41. CAITHNESS
Clarkson, David — 22 Ola Drive, Scrabster, Thurso KW14 7VE — 01847 892109
Duncan, Esme (Miss) — Avalon, Upper Warse, Canisbay, Wick KW1 4YD — 01955 611455
Macnee, Anthea (Mrs) — The Manse, Canisbay, Wick KW1 4YH — 01955 611309

42. LOCHCARRON – SKYE
Mackenzie, Hector — 53 Strath, Gairloch IV21 2DB — 01445 712433
Macrae, D.E. — Nethania, 52 Strath, Gairloch IV21 2DB — 01445 712235

Murray, John W. — Totescore, Kilmuir, Portree, Skye IV51 9YW — 01470 522297
Ross, R. Ian — St Conal's, Inverinate, Kyle of Lochalsh IV40 8HB — 01599 511371

43. UIST
Lines, Charles — 240 Ullswater Road, Southmead, Bristol BS10 6EQ — 01779 508978
MacAulay, John — Fernhaven, Flodabay, Isle of Harris HS3 3HA — 01859 530340
MacNab, Ann (Mrs) — Druim Skillivat, Scolpaig, Lochmaddy, Isle of North Uist HS6 5DH — 01876 510701
MacSween, John — 5 Scott Road, Tarbert, Isle of Harris HS3 3DL — 01859 502338
Taylor, Hamish — Tigh na Tobair, Flodabay, Isle of Harris HS3 3HA — 01859 530310

44. LEWIS
Forsyth, William — 1 Berisay Place, Stornoway, Isle of Lewis HS1 2TF — 01851 702332
McAlpin, Robert J.G. MA FEIS — 42A Upper Coll, Back, Isle of Lewis HS2 0LS — 01851 820288
Murray, Angus — 4 Ceann Chilleagraidh, Stornoway, Isle of Lewis HS1 2UJ — 01851 703550

45. ORKNEY
Robertson, Johan (Mrs) — Old Manse, Eday, Orkney KW17 2AA — 01857 622251
Steer, John — Beckington, Hillside Road, Stromness, Orkney KW16 3AH — 01856 850815

46. SHETLAND
Christie, William C. — 11 Fullaburn, Bressay, Shetland ZE2 9ET — 01595 820244
Greig, Diane (Mrs) MA — The Manse, Sandwick, Shetland ZE2 9HW — 01950 431244
Jamieson, Ian MA — Linksview, Ringsta, Quendale, Shetland ZE2 9JD — 01950 460477
Laidlay, Una (Mrs) — 5 Bells Road, Lerwick, Shetland ZE1 0QB — 01595 695147
MacGregor, Robert — Olna Cottage, Brae, Shetland ZE2 9QS — 01806 522773

47. ENGLAND
Green, Peter (Dr) — Samburu Cottage, Russells Green Road, Ninfield, East Sussex — 01424 892033
Mackay, Donald (Reader Emeritus) — 90 Hallgarth Street, Elvet, Durham DH1 3AS — 0191-383 2110
Goodbourne, David (Dr) — 145 Westcombe Hill, Blackheath, London SE3 7DP — 020 8305 0126

48. EUROPE
Ross, David — URB EL Campanario, EDF Granada, Esc 14, Baja B, Ctra Cadiz N-340, Km 168, 29680 Estepona, Malaga, Spain — Tel/Fax +34 952 88 26 34
[E-mail:rosselcampanario@yahoo.co.uk]
Sharp, James — 102 Rue des Eaux-Vives, CH-1207 Geneva, Switzerland — 0041 22 786 48 47
[E-mail: jsharp@world.scout.org]

LIST O – REPRESENTATIVES ON COUNCIL EDUCATION COMMITTEES

COUNCIL	NAME	ADDRESS
ABERDEEN CITY	Mr Ronald Riddell	66 Hammersmith Road, Aberdeen AB10 6ND
ABERDEENSHIRE	Mr William Michie	34 Seafield Street, Whitehills, Banff AB45 2NR
ANGUS	Rev. Allan Webster	7 Braehead Road, Letham, Forfar DD8 2PG
ARGYLL and BUTE	Miss Fiona Fisher	2 Nursery Cottages, Kilmun, Dunoon PA23 8SE
BORDERS	Professor George O.B. Thomson	Rathmore, Springhill Road, Peebles EH45 9ER
CLACKMANNAN	Rev. T. John Brown	The Manse, 16 Menstrie Road, Tullibody, Alloa FK10 2RG
DUMFRIES and GALLOWAY	Mr Robert McQuistan	Kirkdale Schoolhouse, Carsluith, Newton Stewart DG8 7DT
DUNDEE	Rev. James L. Wilson	53 Old Craigie Road, Dundee DD4 7JD
EAST AYRSHIRE	Rev. John Taylor	62 Woodlands Grove, Kilmarnock KA3 1TZ
EAST DUNBARTONSHIRE	Mrs Barbara Jarvie	18 Camerton Crescent, Milton of Campsie, Glasgow G66 8DR
EAST LOTHIAN	Rev. Cameron Mackenzie	15 West Road, Haddington EH41 3RD
EAST RENFREWSHIRE	Rev. Maureen Leitch	14 Maxton Avenue, Barrhead, Glasgow G78 1DY
EDINBURGH CITY	Mr A. Craig Duncan	2 East Barnton Gardens, Edinburgh EH4 6AR
EDINBURGH CITY	Rev. William Armitage	26 Inchview Terrace, Edinburgh EH7 6TQ
FALKIRK	Mrs Margaret Coutts	34 Pirleyhill Gardens, Falkirk FK1 5NB
FIFE	Rev. Alistair McLeod	40 Liberton Drive, Glenrothes KY6 3PB
GLASGOW CITY	Rev. Andrew J. Philip	The Manse, 43 Smithycroft Road, Riddrie, Glasgow G33 2RH
HIGHLAND	Rev. Alexander Glass	Craigton, Tulloch Avenue, Dingwall IV15 9LH
INVERCLYDE	Rev. William Armstrong	3A Montgomerie Terrace, Skelmorlie PA17 5TD
MIDLOTHIAN	Rev. Mrs Jan Gillies	The Manse, Newton Church Road, Danderhall, Dalkeith EH22 1SR
MORAY	Mrs Mary Nelson	Skeoberry, Mosstowie, Elgin IV30 8TX
NORTH AYRSHIRE	Miss Elspeth McTaggart	21 Scargie Road, Kilmarnock KA1 4UR
NORTH LANARKSHIRE	Rev. Dr Andrew Gardner	31 Victoria Place, Airdrie ML6 8BX
ORKNEY	Mrs Carole Macnaughton	The Cathedral Manse, Berstane Road, Kirkwall, Orkney KW15 1NA
PERTH and KINROSS	Mr Alex Dunlop	3 Auchmore Drive, Rosemount, Blairgowrie PH10 6LZ
RENFREWSHIRE	Mr George Hamilton	33 St Ninian's Road, Paisley PA2 6TP
SHETLAND	Rev. Winnie Munson	The Manse, Grindwell, Brae, Shetland ZE2 9QJ
SOUTH AYRSHIRE	Rev. Dr John Lochrie	Manse Road, Colmonell, Girvan KA26 0SA
SOUTH LANARKSHIRE	Mrs Marion Dickie	2 Murchison Drive, East Kilbride, Glasgow G75 8HF
STIRLING	Mr George Bennie	3 Baron Court, Buchlyvie, Stirling FK8 3NJ
WEST DUNBARTONSHIRE	Miss Sheila Rennie	128 Dumbuie Avenue, Dumbarton G82 2JW
WEST LOTHIAN	Rev. John Povey	The Manse, 19 Maryfield Park, Mid Calder, Livingston EH53 0SB
WESTERN ISLES	Rev. Andrew W.F. Coghill	Leurbost, Lochs, Isle of Lewis HS2 9NS

LIST P – RETIRED LAY AGENTS

Forrester, Arthur A.	158 Lee Crescent North, Bridge of Don, Aberdeen AB22 8FR
Lamont, Donald	Staffin House Nursing Home, Portree, Isle of Skye IV51 9JS
Scott, John W.	15 Manor Court, Forfar DD8 1BR
Shepherd, Dennis	Mission House, Norby, Sandness, Shetland ZE2 9PL

LIST Q – MINISTERS ORDAINED FOR SIXTY YEARS AND UPWARDS

Until 1992, the *Year Book* contained each year a list of those ministers who had been ordained 'for fifty years and upwards'. For a number of reasons, that list was thereafter discontinued. The current Editor was encouraged to reinstate such a list, and the edition for 2002 included the names of those ordained for sixty years and upwards. With ministers, no less than the rest of society, living longer, it was felt reasonable to proceed on that basis. Correspondence made it clear that this list was welcomed, and it was continued in an appropriately updated form last year. Again this year, an updated version is offered following the best enquiries that could be made. The date of ordination is given in full where it is known.

1930	4 June	James Clarence Finlayson (Edinburgh:Grange)
1931	18 December	Robert Law Kinnis (Baillieston: Mure Memorial)
1932	14 August	Thomas Mackenzie Donn (Duthil)
1933	20 October	The Very Rev. William Roy Sanderson (Stenton with Whittingehame)
1934	10 July	Walter Macfarlane Calderwood (Leven: Forman)
	31 July	Thomas Roberts Robertson (Broughton, Glenholm and Kilbucho with Skirling)
	3 November	Owain Tudor Hughes (Guernsey: St Andrew's in the Grange)
1935	10 April	George Douglas Monro (Yester)
	30 October	David Stevens (Glenesk)
	6 November	Joseph Blair Gillon (Borthwick with Heriot)

1936	5 April	George Thomas Jamieson (Stirling: Viewfield)
	29 April	Robert Paterson Mackenzie (Dunfermline: St Leonard's)
	13 May	Norman Birnie (Monquhitter)
	12 July	Michael McCulloch Bogle (Banton)
	25 August	Ronald Stewart Wallace (Edinburgh: Lothian Road)
	September	The Very Rev. James Gunn Matheson (Portree)
1937	14 February	Robert Allan Howieson (Newport-on-Tay: St Thomas's)
	31 March	James Brown Mirrlees (Aberdeen: High Hilton)
	14 April	Anthony James Grubb (Deer)
	15 October	Robert Anderson Philp (Stepps: St Andrew's)
1938	26 February	John Macgregor MacKechnie (Kilchrenan and Dalavich)
	8 June	Crichton Robertson (Cockpen and Carrington with Lasswade)
	29 June	George Alestair Alison Bennett (Strathkinness)
	1 July	Alexander Thomas Hain Taylor (Dunoon Old and St Cuthbert's)
	13 October	Robert Hamilton (Kelso Old)
	8 November	Archibald Alexander Orrock (Teacher: Religious Instruction)
	15 November	The Very Rev. James Fraser McLuskey (London St Columba's with Newcastle)
1939	23 February	William Uist Macdonald (Aberdalgie and Dupplin with Forteviot)
	2 June	David Noel Fisher (Glasgow: Sherbrooke St Gilbert's)
	7 July	John Welsh Malcolm (Uddingston: Park)
	27 October	James Scott Marshall (Associate Minister: Leith South)
	12 November	Alexander McRae Houston (Tibbermore)
	18 November	David Sloan Walker (Makerstoun with Smailholm with Stichill, Hume and Nethorn)
	10 December	Wellesley Grahame Bailey (Ladykirk with Whitsome)
	22 December	Alastair McRae Rennie (Kincardine Croick and Edderton)
1940	24 February	James Johnstone Turnbull (Arbirlot with Colliston)
	20 March	The Very Rev. Thomas Forsyth Torrance (Professor of Christian Dogmatics: Edinburgh University)
	22 March	Donald MacKellar Leitch Urie (Kincardine O'Neil)
	25 April	Angus MacDougall (Sleat)
	29 May	Norman McGathan Bowman (Edinburgh: St Mary's)
	23 June	Andrew Montgomery Russell (Aberdeen: Woodside North)
	14 July	Nigel Ross MacLean (Perth: St Paul's)
	21 August	Donald MacFarlane (Inverness: East)

	3 September	Arthur Thomas Hill (Ormiston with Prestonpans: Grange)
	6 September	Peter McPhail (Creich, Flisk and Kilmany)
	29 September	John Hugh Gunn Ross (Dundurn)
	18 December	Colin Campbell (Glasgow: Williamwood)
1941	26 January	Samuel Ballantyne (Aberdeen: Rutherford)
	29 May	Harry Galbraith Miller (Iona and Ross of Mull)
	1 June	The Very Rev. John McIntyre (Professor of Divinity: Edinburgh University)
	1 June	Robert Bernard William Walker (Lesmahagow: Abbeygreen)
	6 June	Thomas Williamson (Dyke with Edinkillie)
	3 July	Donald William MacKenzie (Auchterarder: The Barony)
	20 July	Allan Donald Lamont (Nakuru)
	21 September	Silvester Skinner (Lumphanan)
	21 September	Andrew Swan (Greenock: St Margaret's)
	31 October	Gordon Cumming Morris (Buenos Aires)
	9 December	John Nelson (Crawford and Elvanfoot with Leadhills and Wanlockhead)
1942	2 January	James Gilbert Morrison (Rotterdam)
	4 February	Robert Macbean Gilmour (Kiltarlity)
	15 April	Frank Haughton (Kirkintilloch: St Mary's)
	5 July	Norman Christopher Macrae (Loanhead)
	26 August	Arthur William Bruce (Fortingall and Glenlyon)
	3 September	James Robert Moffett (Paisley: St Matthew's)
	19 November	Donald Angus MacRae (Tarbert)
	22 November	Robert Gray (Stonehaven: Fetteresso)
	23 November	Frederick Haslehurst Fulton (Clunie, Lethendy and Kinloch)
	25 November	Charles Ian Graham Stobie (Fyvie)
	24 December	James Bews (Dundee: Craigiebank)
1943	11 May	Leon David Levison (Ormiston with Pencaitland)
	2 June	Duncan Finlayson (Morvern)
	22 June	William Cadzow McCormick (Glasgow: Maryhill Old)
	24 June	James Murray Hutcheson (Glasgow: Possilpark)
	3 September	George Cooper (Delting with Nesting and Lumnasting)
	21 September	John Campbell (Urquhart)
	1 October	Alick Hugh McAulay (Bellie with Speymouth)
	7 October	Hugh Talman (Polmont Old)
	28 November	David Hutchison Whiteford (Gullane)
		William Finlayson Young (Kinglassie)

LIST R – DECEASED MINISTERS

The Editor has been made aware of the following ministers who have died since the publication of the previous volume of the *Year Book*.

Allan, James Brown	(Motherwell: South Dalziel)
Armour, Charles	(St Andrews: Holy Trinity)
Bird, John William	(Bathgate: High)
Broster, David	(Kilbirnie: St Columba's)
Brown, Robert Russell	(Perth: Kinnoull)
Chirnside, Charles	(Tullibody: St Serf's)
Crawford, Robert	(Annan: Erskine)
Davidson, David Wallace	Auxiliary Minister: Moderator's Chaplain: Presbytery of South Argyll
Davison, Charles Fyfe	(Guernsey: St Andrew's in the Grange)
Douglas, James Dixon	(Rothesay: St John's)
Forrester-Paton, Colin	(Hawick Burnfoot)
Gibson, Alexander Cameron	(Eskdalemuir with Hutton and Corrie with Tundergarth)
Goudie, Stuart Maclean	(Perceton and Dreghorn)
Grant, James	(Penpont, Keir and Tynron)
Grieve, David Shepherd Alan	(Arbirlot with Carmyllie with Colliston)
Hamilton, James	(Auchterhouse)
Henderson, David Cecil	(Glamis)
Hepburn, James Lamb	(Ardoch with Blackford)
Howe, Andrew Youngson	(Rosskeen)
Jamieson, John	(Balfron)
Jamieson, Robert Cummings	(Galston Old)
Johnston, John	(Hospital Chaplain)
Law, Arthur	(Kincardine in Menteith with Norrieston)
Macdonald, James Ferguson	(Bendochy with Kinclaven)
Macdonald, Murdo Ewen	(University of Glasgow)
McDonald, James Ian Hamilton	(University of Edinburgh)
Mackenzie, George Ramsay Rattray	(Dundee: Logie and St John's Cross)
MacKinnon, Alexander Wallace	(Fern, Careston and Menmuir with Oathlaw Tannadice)
Mackinnon, Duncan	(Plockton and Kyle)
MacLean, Hector Angus Macintosh	(Duror with Glencoe)
McLean, Margaret Gilchrist	(Community Minister: Presbytery of Annandale and Eskdale)
McLeish, David Nairn	(Fisherton)
McMillan, Hector Grant	(Associate: Dundee Whitfield)

Macpherson, Norman John	(Blairgowrie: St Mary's South)
Marr, Edward Rankine	(Buittle)
Marshall, James Scott	(Lochgoilhead and Kilmorich)
Martin, Francis	(Pitlochry East)
Martin, Robert Alexander Kyle	(Kilmarnock: St Andrew's Glencairn)
Morrison, Alexander	(Barvas)
Moyes, Andrew	(Broxburn)
Murray, Duncan	(Lossiemouth: St Gerardine's High)
Patience, Donald	(Kilmaurs)
Porteous, Norman Walker	(University of Edinburgh)
Porter, John Clarke	(Forres: St Leonard's)
Russell, Arthur Colin	(Aberlemno)
Samuel, Robert Ronald	(Rothesay: Trinity)
Sandilands, Ian Smeaton	(Black Mount)
Scott, Gideon George	(Dundee: Albany-Butterburn with St David's North)
Scott, William Derek	(Maud with Savoch)
Slack, John Watson	(Ashkirk with Selkirk: Lawson Memorial)
Smith, Myra Daphne Walker	(Kirkmahoe)
Stewart, Donald	(Fenwick)
Stewart, Matthew Smith	(Boat of Garten and Kincardine with Duthil)
Stuart, John Thomson	(Duffus, Spynie and Hopeman)
Sutherland, Alexander Smart	(Symington with Craigie)
Swinton, Alan Christie	(Hospital Chaplain)
Thomson, James Grant-Suttie Stewart	(Wigtown)
Torrance, James Bruce	(University of Aberdeen)
Wilson, Robert (Roy)	Auxiliary Minister with the Clerk of Dumbarton Presbytery

SECTION 7

Congregational
Statistics
2003

CHURCH OF SCOTLAND STATISTICS
FOR 2003

Congregations 1,546
Communicants 553,248
Elders 42,071
Charges 1,229
Ministers serving charges 1,042
Chaplains to HM Forces 32
Students completing their courses 17

NOTES ON CONGREGATIONAL STATISTICS

Com   Number of communicants at 31 December 2003.

Eld   Number of elders at 31 December 2003.

G   Membership of the Guild including Young Woman's Group. The letter 'j' beside a figure indicates that the figure is a joint figure for all the congregations making up the charge.

In 03   Ordinary General Income for 2003. Ordinary General Income consists of members' offerings, contributions from congregational organisations, regular fund-raising events, income from investments, deposits and so on. This figure does not include extraordinary or special income, or income from special collections and fund-raising for other charities.

Ass   Amount allocated to congregations for the Mission and Aid Fund in 2003.

Gvn   Amount contributed by congregations to the Mission and Aid Fund in 2003. The amount shown includes contributions to allocation and voluntary extra contributions. The figures do not take into account late payments made in 2004 for 2003 but may contain late payments made in 2003 for 2002 and prior years.

–18   This figure shows 'the number of children and young people aged 17 years and under who are involved in the life of the congregation'.

(NB Figures may not be available for new charges created or for congregations which have entered into readjustment late in 2003 or during 2004.)

Congregation	Com	Eld	G	In 03	Ass	Gvn	–18
1. Edinburgh							
Albany Deaf Church of Edinburgh	131	12	–	–	–	–	–
Balerno	842	71	57	115915	24490	26901	60
Barclay	328	35	–	98856	19338	19338	60
Blackhall St Columba	1118	88	48	144271	44990	45737	107
Bristo Memorial Craigmillar	193	7	26	–	–	–	49
Broughton St Mary's	298	33	33	49375	7920	7920	102
Canongate	456	52	–	69606	13490	13490	20
Carrick Knowe	554	43	85	62246	12400	12705	40
Colinton	1085	81	–	185079	42746	43442	342
Colinton Mains	235	16	22	44688	3608	3950	35
Corstorphine Craigsbank	670	33	–	95049	20100	20100	121
Corstorphine Old	597	55	60	77325	17160	17160	15
Corstorphine St Anne's	482	48	52	70487	15410	20410	50
Corstorphine St Ninian's	1077	75	65	158902	36040	39540	110
Craigentinny St Christopher's	168	16	–	32445	–	–	80
Craiglockhart	564	56	40	118662	29300	29300	261
Craigmillar Park	315	23	31	82322	18710	18710	23
Cramond	1334	109	25	202891	49100	66100	104
Currie	825	61	88	156471	42250	42250	187
Dalmeny	137	9	9	12395	660	660	–
Davidson's Mains	826	73	56	154276	40800	40800	160
Dean	246	29	20	61368	12694	12694	15
Drylaw	233	16	–	22923	–	–	–
Duddingston	866	64	44	84087	17787	18132	174
Fairmilehead	1017	71	33	94109	24480	24480	65
Gilmerton	–	–	–	–	–	–	–
Gorgie	345	39	–	66258	12900	13000	60
Granton	367	33	–	36789	4600	4560	45
Greenbank	984	92	80	169465	55000	55000	–
Greenside	242	32	–	36458	8710	8710	12
Greyfriars Tolbooth and Highland	399	44	16	97423	21480	21480	10
High (St Giles')	691	45	–	154124	39870	44469	–
Holyrood Abbey	275	34	20	140764	38000	38000	192
Holy Trinity	173	33	–	70274	6600	6600	117
Inverleith	381	43	–	72487	17220	17220	49
Juniper Green	430	35	–	79111	16164	16164	56
Kaimes Lockhart Memorial	100	8	12	–	–	–	–
Kirkliston	368	40	51	62727	5990	5990	–
Kirk o' Field	228	28	–	37705	7909	7909	2
Leith North	486	47	–	67369	13170	13170	150
Leith St Andrew's	313	32	–	51264	7550	7550	169
Leith St Serf's	317	33	23	48700	7540	7950	185
Leith St Thomas' Junction Road	301	24	–	48563	7346	7346	9
Leith South	593	82	–	93188	24512	24512	125
Leith Wardie	602	80	65	110929	26490	27083	130
Liberton	909	72	73	128662	26120	26120	70

Congregation	Com	Eld	G	In 03	Ass	Gvn	–18
Liberton Northfield	297	9	33	49550	–	227	30
London Road	401	30	23	51305	7710	7710	74
Marchmont St Giles'	326	45	26	62049	15160	15263	52
Mayfield Salisbury	779	71	32	193426	57500	62260	45
Morningside	799	102	20	76181	28660	28855	29
Morningside United	228	32	–	74472	7152	11109	43
Muirhouse St Andrew's	129	10	–	9043	–	–	67
Murrayfield	601	68	–	125046	32810	32810	45
Newhaven	261	17	42	70430	11530	11530	78
New Restalrig	307	19	24	119781	18128	18128	31
Old Kirk	199	10	–	21196	–	139	12
Palmerston Place	505	75	–	137418	39750	39750	60
Pilrig St Paul's	363	30	36	49803	1500	1500	70
Polwarth	351	25	20	60305	13160	13160	25
Portobello Old	414	43	42	42571	8272	9542	132
Portobello St James'	412	39	–	58931	8620	8620	34
Portobello St Philip's Joppa	699	71	91	119062	29000	29000	106
Priestfield	248	25	28	65732	8657	8270	20
Queensferry	822	49	79	78003	11240	11361	150
Ratho	251	23	18	30179	–	–	27
Reid Memorial	453	25	–	82636	20570	20995	28
Richmond Craigmillar	117	8	–	14284	–	–	50
St Andrew's and St George's	386	49	16	156497	36460	36960	40
St Andrew's Clermiston	345	22	–	41332	–	–	157
St Catherine's Argyle	298	30	26	118111	29500	29500	78
St Colm's	190	21	31	28473	3333	3333	15
St Cuthbert's	528	66	–	99018	40650	40650	38
St David's Broomhouse	198	13	–	45457	4820	4820	25
St George's West	189	42	–	69154	22694	22730	26
St John's Oxgangs	304	25	38	24916	–	593	14
St Margaret's	451	42	26	42496	8040	8040	25
St Martin's	262	13	–	18638	–	–	98
St Michael's	511	31	–	55614	11960	11960	30
St Nicholas' Sighthill	571	33	21	52064	7920	8020	65
St Stephen's Comely Bank	507	27	40	119742	25900	25900	150
Slateford Longstone	325	27	44	–	7790	7790	30
Stenhouse St Aidan's	247	21	–	26511	–	301	40
Stockbridge	374	40	32	49402	7660	7660	21
Tron Moredun	154	14	–	–	–	–	10
Viewforth	248	26	19	55768	11000	11000	25

2. West Lothian

Abercorn	93	9	9	9582	715	715	–
Pardovan, Kingscavil and Winchburgh	311	23	18	42137	2145	2145	27
Armadale	693	40	32	50702	10650	8520	114
Avonbridge	92	10	11	13234	440	840	11
Torphichen	287	19	–	38324	3399	3090	52
Bathgate: Boghall	296	36	20	57896	10140	10140	101

Congregation	Com	Eld	G	In 03	Ass	Gvn	–18
Bathgate: High	633	43	37	77375	12810	12810	93
Bathgate: St David's	297	13	17	43027	7678	5100	20
Bathgate: St John's	391	22	35	57927	7100	7100	127
Blackburn and Seafield	552	34	–	51985	6237	6237	90
Blackridge	119	7	–	15772	1940	1940	–
Harthill: St Andrew's	264	21	34	51666	6620	6620	108
Breich Valley	226	10	26	26844	–	–	7
Broxburn	539	31	45	54978	7790	7790	110
Fauldhouse: St Andrew's	288	16	20	42251	4070	4070	8
Kirknewton and East Calder	552	38	28	70312	12440	12440	96
Kirk of Calder	712	43	27	63722	11750	15623	80
Linlithgow: St Michael's	1550	102	66	247752	55900	61076	352
Linlithgow: St Ninian's Craigmailen	558	58	76	66064	10120	10120	140
Livingston Ecumenical	827	50	–	–	–	–	495
Livingston: Old	497	36	25	58868	10230	10394	61
Polbeth Harwood	256	36	–	29450	400	400	5
West Kirk of Calder	344	29	36	38314	7106	7706	25
Strathbrock	381	45	25	93667	15340	15340	38
Uphall South	241	18	–	44667	500	500	58
Whitburn: Brucefield	462	30	27	59816	9890	9890	15
Whitburn: South	409	32	38	47040	11970	11970	109

3. Lothian

Congregation	Com	Eld	G	In 03	Ass	Gvn	–18
Aberlady	310	32	–	31609	6765	6765	30
Gullane	494	41	52	52066	9840	9840	40
Athelstaneford	227	18	–	19660	2760	1000	20
Whitekirk and Tyninghame	158	19	–	–	5660	5660	18
Belhaven	777	34	67	57372	10540	10640	140
Spott	105	7	–	10334	1221	1221	12
Bolton and Saltoun	211	18	18	19762	3700	3700	15
Humbie	93	10	12	13667	3350	3350	12
Yester	310	22	21	23499	2930	2930	14
Bonnyrigg	881	73	72	80307	16550	4259	56
Borthwick	86	5	11	18464	160	1000	8
Cranstoun, Crichton and Ford	279	19	–	33807	4380	4380	20
Fala and Soutra	77	6	12	8036	1546	1606	5
Cockenzie and Port Seton: Chalmers M'r'l	306	29	50	57272	9185	9185	60
Cockenzie and Port Seton: Old	448	12	25	25582	–	2000	–
Cockpen and Carrington	359	24	37	23141	2684	–	36
Lasswade	351	24	22	26256	3773	3773	18
Rosewell	147	11	–	11905	1560	3280	5
Dalkeith: St John's and King's Park	582	47	22	68068	12440	12440	55
Dalkeith: St Nicholas Buccleuch	546	20	29	37071	7890	7890	25
Dirleton	269	19	20	28167	5599	5599	14
North Berwick: Abbey	339	30	47	59073	13288	13288	46
Dunbar	863	28	48	69958	10153	10153	60
Dunglass	360	20	19	25035	–	–	3
Garvald and Morham	48	9	–	12573	1881	1881	31

Congregation	Com	Eld	G	In 03	Ass	Gvn	–18
Haddington: West	492	39	53	61550	10373	10373	62
Gladsmuir	231	12	14	17828	2790	2790	–
Longniddry	470	37	50	66619	17100	17100	57
Glencorse	367	14	–	26132	4240	4240	17
Roslin	401	10	–	28638	3140	3140	–
Gorebridge	495	24	44	59546	4389	4442	40
Haddington: St Mary's	772	63	–	96425	22670	22670	35
Howgate	45	5	8	15432	2200	2200	2
Penicuik: South	255	15	–	82180	20878	20953	75
Loanhead	442	27	44	49115	3950	4069	98
Musselburgh: Northesk	445	36	19	58607	10549	10549	104
Musselburgh: St Andrew's High	460	38	34	52383	5250	5250	12
Musselburgh: St Clement's and St Ninian's	384	46	9	33112	–	–	20
Musselburgh: St Michael's Inveresk	546	40	32	62206	9600	9600	25
Newbattle	715	48	59	52818	5750	5750	44
Newton	304	9	16	15276	–	–	–
North Berwick: St Andrew Blackadder	762	57	33	83879	16890	16890	100
Ormiston	193	13	39	26251	3916	3981	–
Pencaitland	275	13	12	44941	8660	8660	60
Penicuik: North	646	40	–	76109	13310	13582	100
Penicuik: St Mungo's	503	24	28	49619	8050	13200	10
Prestonpans: Prestongrange	409	51	28	41706	5190	5190	37
Tranent	379	17	32	46746	5750	5750	–
Traprain	553	36	34	52175	11220	11220	5

4. Melrose and Peebles

Ashkirk	75	4	11	10679	1584	2084	8
Selkirk	629	28	36	58216	10120	10352	23
Bowden	101	14	12	19278	2570	2570	–
Newtown	205	13	–	15349	2853	2853	–
Broughton, Glenholm and Kilbucho	169	15	28j	14070	–	960	–
Skirling	93	8	j	8548	–	360	12
Stobo and Drumelzier	105	7	j	13036	–	720	–
Tweedsmuir	46	7	j	7997	–	–	10
Caddonfoot	223	17	–	18276	1560	1560	21
Galashiels: St Ninian's	571	48	45	50756	9340	10285	12
Carlops	73	12	–	13108	1617	1617	10
Kirkurd and Newlands	112	8	10	15775	2030	2030	–
West Linton: St Andrew's	258	20	33	31396	5519	5588	35
Channelkirk	83	6	6	7694	770	770	24
Lauder: Old	352	19	18	33561	2400	2400	33
Earlston	586	16	16	36544	4048	4048	15
Eddleston	119	7	12	9811	720	1380	–
Peebles: Old	702	45	–	90764	13120	13120	140
Ettrick and Yarrow	215	18	8	33935	–	250	27
Galashiels: Old and St Paul's	430	24	34	59506	8085	8085	112
Galashiels: St Aidan's	485	24	22	35105	4490	4644	61
Galashiels: St John's	274	16	–	39294	–	800	82

Congregation . . . . Com	Eld	G	In 03	Ass	Gvn	–18
Innerleithen, Traquair and Walkerburn 500	36	68	55655	10210	10210	90
Lyne and Manor 109	11	–	22201	200	200	28
Maxton and Mertoun 154	17	15	15100	3250	3250	7
St Boswells 337	25	29	32766	4660	4660	45
Melrose 906	54	49	99518	16850	17569	50
Peebles: St Andrew's Leckie 704	43	–	77963	15411	16292	57
Stow: St Mary of Wedale and Heriot 196	15	–	37177	–	–	31

5. Duns

Ayton and Burnmouth 207	9	–	14421	–	–	6
Grantshouse and Houndwood and Reston . . 136	5	13	9595	–	–	–
Berwick-on-Tweed: St Andrew's						
Wallace Green and Lowick 509	27	37	46418	3209	3454	13
Bonkyl and Preston 88	7	–	7578	1078	1078	–
Chirnside 409	23	–	19584	2410	1446	–
Edrom: Allanton 83	11	–	5448	704	704	–
Coldingham and St Abb's 118	7	13	24808	1679	1679	15
Eyemouth 282	24	55	35297	4800	5243	36
Coldstream 427	27	24	43168	3950	3950	72
Eccles 103	10	19	7444	830	830	6
Duns 568	22	45	42836	3148	3148	30
Fogo and Swinton 142	4	–	9168	–	–	4
Ladykirk 36	7	12	7326	–	–	–
Leitholm 102	9	–	11599	–	–	1
Whitsome 48	4	11	4731	–	–	–
Foulden and Mordington 94	11	10	7923	–	–	–
Hutton and Fishwick and Paxton 99	9	13	12019	–	–	–
Gordon: St Michael's 73	5	14j	8785	760	760	10
Greenlaw 162	12	24	17417	2511	2511	13
Legerwood 68	8	–	5954	590	590	3
Westruther 51	6	j	6343	715	715	6
Kirk of Lammermuir 77	9	–	15368	–	–	8
Langton and Polwarth 92	6	22	13525	–	–	–

6. Jedburgh

Ancrum 226	16	16	19995	400	660	22
Crailing and Eckford 104	11	–	5382	350	1050	–
Lilliesleaf 167	10	16	12703	400	436	10
Cavers and Kirkton 158	11	–	9774	1073	1073	–
Hawick: St Mary's and Old 646	31	51	49161	7953	7953	108
Hawick: Burnfoot 215	14	15	26913	–	1500	89
Hawick: Teviot and Roberton 405	12	8	44538	5490	5490	33
Hawick: Trinity 903	31	52	52689	8110	9152	88
Hawick: Wilton 440	27	36	34120	1920	1920	24
Teviothead 81	4	11	5990	1397	1457	–
Hobkirk and Southdean 182	13	10	11449	750	834	17
Ruberslaw 337	–	25	29087	1200	1200	–
Jedburgh: Old and Edgerston 776	24	25	43686	8130	9580	28

Congregation . . . . Com	Eld	G	In 03	Ass	Gvn	–18
Jedburgh: Trinity 255	13	31	41889	4180	4180	4
Kelso: North and Ednam 1533	74	66	100584	19910	19910	33
Kelso: Old and Sprouston 666	42	35	49093	7320	7619	11
Linton 85	5	–	10209	946	946	3
Morebattle and Hownam 210	12	39	21597	2354	2354	15
Yetholm. 208	12	20	21911	2730	2730	6
Makerstoun and Smailholm 79	7	–	7616	–	–	10
Roxburgh 68	6	–	6794	–	–	2
Stichill, Hume and Nenthorn 85	7	16	9924	–	–	5
Oxnam 99	6	–	6608	525	525	–

7. Annandale and Eskdale

Annan: Old 448	40	55	54924	11020	11020	72
Annan: St Andrew's. 815	45	81	59478	8041	9851	100
Applegarth and Sibbaldbie. 180	8	17	8627	846	846	3
Johnstone 129	7	–	4287	200	200	–
Lochmaben 568	24	46	48871	4820	5320	20
Brydekirk 59	6	–	6292	–	–	–
Hoddam. 147	8	–	10978	–	–	–
Canonbie. 187	12	–	17725	200	200	15
Liddesdale. 167	8	19	39263	400	604	38
Carlisle: Chapel Street. 395	39	43	56053	9440	9440	26
Longtown: St Andrew's. 45	9	19	5062	500	500	–
Dalton 126	8	5	16828	1305	1305	12
Hightae 102	6	16	10507	791	881	20
St Mungo 144	8	14	14632	851	851	7
Dornock 195	12	–	14125	–	–	50
Eskdalemuir 35	2	–	3191	–	–	–
Hutton and Corrie 82	6	–	8309	–	65	–
Tundergarth. 76	8	9	6432	–	–	–
Gretna: Old, Gretna: St Andrew's and						
Half Morton and Kirkpatrick Fleming . . . 421	31	14	29192	1134	–	85
Kirkpatrick Juxta. 155	7	–	–	350	300	–
Moffat: St Andrew's 540	41	42	71891	9372	9372	45
Wamphray. 58	7	–	6067	1030	1030	–
Kirtle-Eaglesfield 126	10	18	15510	630	–	–
Middlebie 105	9	13	6911	160	–	6
Waterbeck 71	6	–	2277	160	–	–
Langholm, Ewes and Westerkirk 571	36	61	38287	5300	5300	36
Lockerbie: Dryfesdale 899	47	47	47965	4790	4790	28

8. Dumfries and Kirkcudbright

Anwoth and Girthon 357	24	34	45416	10050	10510	12
Borgue 63	7	7	6610	230	230	14
Auchencairn and Rerrick 141	11	–	8958	1338	1636	6
Buittle and Kelton 233	18	25	23650	2060	2060	8
Balmaclellan and Kells 154	13	16	12886	–	–	15
Carsphairn. 112	8	10	8543	–	600	9

Congregation	Com	Eld	G	In 03	Ass	Gvn	–18
Dalry	198	12	21	11177	–	–	17
Balmaghie	165	6	14	12190	1116	905	6
Tarff and Twynholm	206	16	33	24407	4037	4037	14
Caerlaverock	172	8	–	6701	–	200	20
Castle Douglas	600	37	60	56227	3830	3830	30
Closeburn	265	10	–	19593	1823	1823	–
Durisdeer	181	7	27	17053	1485	1485	20
Colvend, Southwick and Kirkbean	388	28	37	46666	11811	11967	12
Corsock and Kirkpatrick Durham	144	16	26	18583	1716	1716	38
Crossmichael and Parton	201	14	17	20296	3069	3070	22
Cummertrees	55	5	8	6572	450	500	–
Mouswald	84	7	15	7101	378	798	–
Ruthwell	103	8	17	9750	1144	758	15
Dalbeattie	690	39	58j	49549	7820	7970	50
Urr	228	15	j	15144	1850	1850	22
Dumfries: Greyfriars	253	12	23	–	10400	10400	–
Dumfries: Lincluden	138	12	–	16388	–	102	22
Holywood	184	14	–	17622	–	127	10
Dumfries: Lochside	402	16	32	–	–	–	12
Dumfries: Maxwelltown West	752	49	50	64727	10010	10010	123
Dumfries: St George's	550	47	49	69657	12210	12210	58
Dumfries: St Mary's	666	45	41	51134	8150	8172	11
Dumfries: St Michael's and South	959	52	36	71458	8866	8866	60
Dumfries: Troqueer	455	32	25	75898	9860	9860	40
Dunscore	263	18	10	30106	3100	3100	19
Glencairn and Moniaive	221	14	–	25983	2590	2590	10
Irongray, Lochrutton and Terregles	535	34	27	28371	3157	3157	24
Kirkconnel	386	11	16	45503	5460	5560	8
Kirkcudbright	740	44	–	63620	12050	12050	40
Kirkgunzeon	60	10	–	6860	–	68	–
Kirkmahoe	408	19	31	28658	801	801	42
Kirkmichael, Tinwald and Torthorwald	584	40	34	45918	7100	7100	40
Lochend	56	4	8	3357	–	–	–
New Abbey	233	12	11	20907	–	–	110
Penpont, Keir and Tynron	197	12	–	16242	250	250	10
Thornhill	314	13	21	21835	990	990	–
Sanquhar: St Bride's	534	27	38	42859	5120	5120	48

9. Wigtown and Stranraer

Congregation	Com	Eld	G	In 03	Ass	Gvn	–18
Ervie Kirkcolm	258	18	–	18213	1385	1385	27
Leswalt	299	15	19	24293	2460	3590	15
Glasserton and Isle of Whithorn	120	8	–	12002	1540	1631	–
Whithorn: St Ninian's Priory	329	11	26	24581	2370	2370	34
Inch	268	18	13	15427	1770	1786	27
Stranraer: St Andrew's	490	30	–	40656	6400	6400	105
Kirkcowan	213	11	14	23309	2618	2698	–
Wigtown	254	14	17	34271	4650	4650	20

Congregation . . . . Com	Eld	G	In 03	Ass	Gvn	–18
Kirkinner. 175	7	16	13828	–	–	–
Sorbie 173	8	11	15417	–	–	–
Kirkmabreck 195	12	28	18042	2260	2260	12
Monigaff 459	28	–	34946	5100	5100	20
Kirkmaiden 248	19	24	22446	3230	3338	28
Stoneykirk. 415	25	–	27017	3531	3531	44
Mochrum. 303	20	42	26434	–	–	41
New Luce 114	10	35j	9137	1810	1810	14
Old Luce 332	23	j	34088	4540	4681	–
Penninghame. 638	48	27	56382	15020	12098	10
Portpatrick. 264	11	30	17581	2300	2300	12
Stranraer: St Ninian's 474	25	27	37401	7360	7360	40
Stranraer: High Kirk 629	36	21	54726	6920	6920	105
Stranraer: Old 352	22	34	44499	6990	6990	3

10. Ayr

Alloway. 1316	–	47	171240	48000	56000	–
Annbank 307	15	23	24374	3300	3500	15
Tarbolton. 554	34	31	34094	6590	6590	18
Arnsheen Barrhill 103	3	–	8964	–	–	1
Colmonell 215	17	–	20053	–	–	7
Auchinleck 398	25	42	–	5171	5171	30
Catrine 131	17	31	22600	2791	2791	–
Ayr: Auld Kirk of Ayr						
(St John the Baptist). 705	83	51	77478	25201	25373	35
Ayr: Castlehill 856	48	76	76416	16760	16760	30
Ayr: Newton on Ayr. 442	39	49	82111	18139	18139	380
Ayr: St Andrew's 598	67	32	81863	16160	16760	17
Ayr: St Columba 1730	132	68	164088	42000	42000	150
Ayr: St James' 553	34	51	58115	7890	7890	129
Ayr: St Leonard's. 647	55	40	72145	15360	15360	44
Ayr: St Quivox 406	38	21	50172	6070	6070	23
Ayr: Wallacetown 403	24	43	41500	8020	8167	12
Ballantrae 285	21	49	35641	2720	2720	25
Barr. 74	6	11	5464	247	247	–
Dailly 184	14	19	15440	260	260	26
Girvan: South 336	21	34	34393	1760	1760	–
Coylton 364	19	–	23362	–	–	120
Drongan: The Schaw Kirk 292	25	18	19434	–	–	104
Craigie 126	7	–	15286	1889	1889	21
Symington. 402	22	25	48572	12288	12288	25
Crosshill 195	12	28	16036	840	840	9
Dalrymple 360	16	–	27434	2210	2210	–
Dalmellington 349	25	87	44613	3113	3113	102
Dundonald. 579	47	64	–	9500	11881	41
Fisherton 160	11	10	11993	120	120	–
Kirkoswald 273	20	16	36074	2607	2607	6
Girvan: North (Old and St Andrew's) 1077	70	42	68859	13600	13600	120

Congregation	Com	Eld	G	In 03	Ass	Gvn	–18
Kirkmichael	239	22	22	22514	–	–	9
Straiton: St Cuthbert's	167	15	16	11189	–	–	13
Lugar	179	7	21	–	2310	2360	5
Old Cumnock: Old	429	19	50	51062	8510	8510	27
Mauchline	600	24	70	62014	11560	11560	85
Maybole	689	32	44	58460	5770	5770	15
Monkton and Prestwick: North	534	44	51	102240	12060	12146	109
Muirkirk	245	17	27	20954	2000	2000	10
Sorn	185	15	23	22618	2904	2904	22
New Cumnock	611	40	55	56760	5810	5810	49
Ochiltree	289	23	23	20692	3440	3640	36
Stair	224	16	28	23026	4862	5062	50
Old Cumnock: Crichton West and St Ninian's	437	30	58	44822	4700	4700	33
Patna: Waterside	168	12	18	15588	–	–	48
Prestwick: Kingcase	1110	100	55	95326	19500	19500	260
Prestwick: St Nicholas'	859	73	72	93903	20150	20350	–
Prestwick: South	402	35	56	75695	14950	14950	100
Troon: Old	1267	80	–	133866	33570	33815	100
Troon: Portland	778	53	52	102439	21520	21520	42
Troon: St Meddan's	1162	136	88	143642	33590	33590	95

11. Irvine and Kilmarnock

Congregation	Com	Eld	G	In 03	Ass	Gvn	–18
Crosshouse	364	28	31	34324	1563	1563	25
Darvel	636	33	59	39888	5030	5166	20
Dreghorn and Springside	680	59	40	65499	16780	17087	45
Dunlop	437	36	42	55946	9000	9300	45
Fenwick	443	25	32	–	8150	8150	30
Galston	803	70	87	109689	17260	17476	154
Hurlford	609	26	45	63166	4180	4180	33
Irvine: Fullarton	526	40	50	91599	19000	19250	153
Irvine: Girdle Toll	223	19	23	38455	–	–	200
Irvine: Mure	463	28	34	74650	12460	12460	66
Irvine: Old	577	36	30	83743	19900	19900	15
Irvine: Relief Bourtreehill	410	36	31	39531	2234	2234	50
Irvine: St Andrew's	378	19	54	–	5203	5356	180
Kilmarnock: Grange	461	31	54	58829	10280	10280	39
Kilmarnock: Henderson	807	82	67	107534	20350	20350	42
Kilmarnock: Howard St Andrew's	455	39	45	69861	13570	13570	6
Kilmarnock: Laigh West High	956	69	58	136677	35000	35000	203
Kilmarnock: Old High Kirk	325	18	20	–	4610	4610	26
Kilmarnock: Riccarton	381	34	36	66095	8990	8990	145
Kilmarnock: St John's Onthank	316	24	26	37498	4345	4345	115
Kilmarnock: St Kentigern's	291	28	–	48958	5190	5190	150
Kilmarnock: St Marnock's	756	82	–	100279	16302	16302	319
Kilmarnock: St Ninian's Bellfield	237	20	21	28639	1597	1597	30
Kilmarnock: Shortlees	129	13	22	29173	2167	2167	52
Kilmaurs: St Maur's Glencairn	372	22	22	56024	7460	7460	27

Congregation . . . . Com	Eld	G	In 03	Ass	Gvn	–18
Newmilns: Loudoun 414	12	–	67607	10736	10736	30
Stewarton: John Knox 398	38	29	71468	12520	13520	120
Stewarton: St Columba's 560	41	67	61168	12320	12985	74
12. Ardrossan						
Ardrossan: Barony St John's 361	25	42	44977	6160	6160	25
Ardrossan: Park 512	35	44	55711	7216	7246	115
Beith: High 928	83	39	64880	12480	12879	123
Beith: Trinity 257	35	37	45482	8162	8162	52
Brodick 215	20	–	34746	–	689	12
Corrie 72	8	–	14877	–	216	–
Cumbrae 353	22	56	38176	–	400	43
Dalry: St Margaret's 1084	61	46	68624	22240	22240	132
Dalry: Trinity 333	23	38	68602	14900	15443	68
Fairlie 274	28	41	52460	7403	7403	26
Fergushill 52	5	–	6786	–	–	12
Kilwinning: Erskine 125	13	19	23215	–	2100	3
Kilbirnie: Auld Kirk 539	37	18	50570	3460	3460	67
Kilbirnie: St Columba's 610	35	32	60082	6240	9240	96
Kilmory 41	4	–	9336	–	–	6
Kilwinning: Abbey 895	58	65	89133	16620	16840	102
Kilwinning: Mansefield Trinity 234	16	55	37735	–	–	–
Lamlash 150	13	38	30535	–	100	15
Lochranza and Pirnmill 73	6	24	11543	–	–	–
Shiskine 68	6	14	15473	–	–	9
Largs: Clark Memorial 1010	90	70	101611	23560	23560	68
Largs: St Columba's 619	52	57	64725	13030	13030	60
Largs: St John's 928	52	88	114057	25784	28784	92
Saltcoats: New Trinity 390	49	34	55383	8210	8210	22
Saltcoats: North 405	19	22	44185	5900	6500	78
Saltcoats: St Cuthbert's 539	52	39	79677	18590	18590	120
Stevenston: Ardeer 361	23	35	39470	5340	7524	110
Stevenston: Livingstone 398	32	35	47622	7128	7128	19
Stevenston: High 272	29	56	58111	11080	11080	27
West Kilbride: Overton 371	32	28	51906	7060	7065	25
West Kilbride: St Andrew's 724	50	42	82037	14550	14550	154
Whiting Bay and Kildonan 134	15	–	37382	–	1334	15
13. Lanark						
Biggar 704	45	72	61631	14820	14820	30
Black Mount 107	7	15	10480	–	29	–
Culter 99	7	–	–	–	–	–
Libberton and Quothquan 93	9	–	16265	–	200	6
Cairngryffe 276	18	19	24024	3482	3482	17
Symington 260	18	27	22723	4600	4140	18
Carluke: Kirkton 848	60	27	91329	19240	19240	385
Carluke: St Andrew's 403	17	24	47512	4500	4152	30
Carluke: St John's 859	65	50	88778	15430	15430	106

Congregation . . . . Com	Eld	G	In 03	Ass	Gvn	–18
Carnwath. 412	18	25	40945	2475	4725	24
Carstairs 229	12	28	24896	1990	2255	60
Carstairs Junction 123	5	20	15196	2169	193	–
Coalburn 177	6	17	12652	1000	1050	5
Lesmahagow: Old 700	35	30	–	8043	8681	108
Crossford. 202	7	11	27870	3210	3210	23
Kirkfieldbank 138	8	14	15856	1122	1122	17
Douglas: St Bride's 352	30	23	36319	3190	3190	21
Douglas: Water and Rigside. 95	12	16	17314	2010	2010	12
Forth: St Paul's 430	26	60	47364	2610	2610	60
Glencaple 266	21	18	23395	1106	1106	17
Lowther. 47	5	–	7422	567	567	5
Kirkmuirhill 300	19	61	76155	19350	20400	80
Lanark: Greyfriars 907	54	39	66856	13520	13520	96
Lanark: St Nicholas' 661	48	44	76540	14710	14710	80
Law. 167	22	36	36017	–	338	168
Lesmahagow: Abbeygreen. 234	18	17	73941	11430	11430	25

14. Greenock and Paisley

Barrhead: Arthurlie 373	26	26	75973	14080	14080	110
Barrhead: Bourock 559	53	70	73779	13170	13170	226
Barrhead: South and Levern 478	42	32	69688	13280	13280	24
Bishopton 887	51	–	77721	15570	15570	144
Bridge of Weir: Freeland 457	51	–	98219	20627	20627	85
Bridge of Weir: St Machar's Ranfurly 540	46	43	73985	16540	16540	45
Caldwell 272	19	–	54976	8250	8250	90
Elderslie Kirk 645	65	59	88483	22150	22703	200
Erskine 470	37	60	100139	16184	16184	233
Gourock: Old Gourock and Ashton 1065	70	75	115755	29000	27200	300
Gourock: St John's 722	77	30	92471	20100	20100	310
Greenock: Ardgowan. 493	50	42	79363	10980	10980	221
Greenock: Eastend . . . . –	–	–	8739	–	–	–
Greenock: Finnart St Paul's 382	36	–	73686	15640	15640	95
Greenock: Mount Kirk. 379	44	25	56756	10400	10400	175
Greenock: Old West Kirk. 362	31	30	67320	14800	14800	25
Greenock: St George's North. 366	39	–	–	13050	1228	117
Greenock: St Luke's 765	74	50	107367	27930	27930	222
Greenock: St Margaret's 229	24	28	28655	–	–	104
Greenock: St Ninian's 274	21	–	21792	–	–	45
Greenock: Wellpark Mid Kirk 695	57	30	72999	11960	11974	100
Houston and Killellan 756	61	52	108212	24037	24037	220
Howwood 228	18	22	47890	6780	6780	52
Inchinnan 431	40	28	69055	6400	12451	175
Inverkip. 455	23	36	47659	7357	7547	51
Johnstone: High. 397	50	50	77995	10672	10672	45
Johnstone: St Andrew's Trinity 250	34	37	45507	5550	5550	138
Johnstone: St Paul's, ... 657	78	33	73462	12030	12030	52
Kilbarchan: East 414	44	41	59253	9737	9737	248

Congregation . . . . Com	Eld	G	In 03	Ass	Gvn	–18
Kilbarchan: West 505	45	35	103363	20913	18913	70
Kilmacolm: Old. 868	72	–	108811	34560	35320	100
Kilmacolm: St Columba 581	36	21	99064	17080	17080	56
Langbank 165	12	–	36734	1464	1464	12
Linwood 500	46	38	54662	9750	9750	166
Lochwinnoch. 165	12	–	33196	–	–	149
Neilston. 692	45	36	–	12730	12730	90
Paisley: Abbey. 802	58	–	93514	21580	21580	119
Paisley: Castlehead 302	35	16	56348	8300	8300	34
Paisley: Glenburn 327	26	18	45038	–	–	45
Paisley: Laigh Kirk 579	90	66	69770	13330	13330	55
Paisley: Lylesland 480	58	57	79441	14690	14690	45
Paisley: Martyrs' 536	58	25	–	13488	13488	180
Paisley: Oakshaw Trinity. 851	95	60	120516	27967	28183	104
Paisley: St Columba Foxbar. 265	31	33	43485	1116	1188	140
Paisley: St James' 384	33	25	50490	6510	6510	23
Paisley: St Luke's 299	34	30	60949	9130	9130	14
Paisley: St Mark's Oldhall 639	63	116	101530	22420	22420	210
Paisley: St Ninian's Ferguslie 65	–	6	7835	–	–	–
Paisley: Sandyford (Thread Street) 333	23	24	52654	7640	7640	146
Paisley: Sherwood Greenlaw 797	101	60	113044	22060	22060	160
Paisley: Wallneuk North 546	58	–	71421	12490	13490	123
Port Glasgow: Hamilton Bardrainney 462	21	17	42918	4670	4670	74
Port Glasgow: St Andrew's 714	65	54	–	14899	14899	266
Port Glasgow: St Martin's 181	17	–	20359	–	–	45
Renfrew: North 709	66	36	83408	16730	16730	180
Renfrew: Old. 696	49	67	76533	16740	16740	73
Renfrew: Trinity 412	34	78	65759	10710	10710	–
Skelmorlie and Wemyss Bay 417	28	–	59451	9020	9020	55

16. Glasgow

Banton. 83	12	–	17421	–	–	39
Twechar. 77	12	–	12304	–	–	5
Bishopbriggs: Kenmure 366	26	55	72684	13970	14300	140
Bishopbriggs: Springfield 974	60	78	95031	20580	20580	249
Broom 942	66	59	136795	49150	37552	95
Burnside-Blairbeth 741	61	85	180245	48100	48101	299
Busby 408	45	40	62305	12000	12000	25
Cadder. 960	91	66	138424	38440	38940	273
Cambuslang: Flemington Hallside 207	13	21	35697	–	–	54
Cambuslang: Old. 426	55	35	72850	16000	16000	25
Cambuslang: St Andrew's 447	44	17	74203	16000	16000	46
Cambuslang: Trinity St Paul's 336	24	–	73184	13840	14940	52
Campsie 333	24	26	56082	3900	3900	110
Chryston 852	48	30	142399	32580	32780	95
Eaglesham. 725	57	70	102158	28000	28000	250
Fernhill and Cathkin 330	22	40	40800	3000	3000	82
Gartcosh 160	9	14	19468	–	–	78

Congregation	Com	Eld	G	In 03	Ass	Gvn	–18
Glenboig	159	8	14	13175	–	–	10
Giffnock: Orchardhill	566	60	32	177408	46000	46000	335
Giffnock: South	997	93	60	150645	49000	50000	173
Giffnock: The Park	334	27	–	52818	6130	6130	100
Greenbank	1130	85	57	192382	71500	71501	374
Kilsyth: Anderson	470	24	60	83981	11066	12566	144
Kilsyth: Burns and Old	512	38	48	65098	7172	7172	112
Kirkintilloch: Hillhead	173	14	20	17545	–	–	13
Kirkintilloch: St Columba's	604	52	42	84536	18630	18830	110
Kirkintilloch: St David's Memorial Park	803	61	47	97993	24750	24750	148
Kirkintilloch: St Mary's	809	60	78	114082	22180	22180	260
Lenzie: Old	516	47	–	73274	13670	13670	64
Lenzie: Union	876	88	89	152066	39160	39516	320
Maxwell Mearns Castle	343	36	–	139441	27819	27819	110
Mearns	849	48	–	126181	35500	35700	67
Milton of Campsie	377	38	36	45009	3608	3608	142
Netherlee	882	78	64	185381	53000	53000	204
Newton Mearns	783	57	26	123720	30000	30000	190
Rutherglen: Old	426	35	–	54526	6930	9016	60
Rutherglen: Stonelaw	481	47	71	113053	27630	22104	103
Rutherglen: Wardlawhill	402	37	53	45979	8370	8370	143
Rutherglen: West	515	30	29	63293	10400	10400	125
Stamperland	460	40	35	76109	18910	18910	150
Stepps	387	27	21	43855	6430	6430	105
Thornliebank	253	18	51	51181	3750	3750	21
Torrance	293	17	–	52893	3600	3600	135
Williamwood	569	71	43	116322	31320	33840	241
Glasgow: Anderston Kelvingrove	143	21	15	13686	–	–	10
Glasgow: Baillieston Mure Memorial	606	37	106	82657	17510	17510	320
Glasgow: Baillieston St Andrew's	427	30	48	59647	9110	9110	117
Glasgow: Balshagray Victoria Park	306	36	21	73479	16650	16650	86
Glasgow: Barlanark Greyfriars	164	14	25	29732	–	100	150
Glasgow: Battlefield East	177	13	36	44471	3650	3650	6
Glasgow: Blawarthill	209	28	55	–	–	–	97
Glasgow: Bridgeton St Francis in the East	110	18	11	–	–	–	14
Glasgow: Broomhill	671	63	70	128543	32710	32710	70
Glasgow: Calton Parkhead	186	15	13	18557	–	400	15
Glasgow: Cardonald	541	56	102	118924	30200	34061	157
Glasgow: Carmunnock	380	30	34	55260	12000	12000	40
Glasgow: Carmyle	136	7	30	22688	1860	1860	42
Glasgow: Kenmuir Mount Vernon	174	10	42	48003	4680	4680	91
Glasgow: Carntyne Old	161	18	15	33663	6170	6170	84
Glasgow: Eastbank	170	17	30	29083	4880	4880	25
Glasgow: Carnwadric	168	19	30	25361	–	620	24
Glasgow: Castlemilk East	172	13	18	28869	–	–	24
Glasgow: Castlemilk West	149	28	30	22734	–	–	46
Glasgow: Cathcart Old	364	44	53	57630	11970	11970	310
Glasgow: Cathcart Trinity	638	66	78	158150	33908	34408	117

Congregation .... Com	Eld	G	In 03	Ass	Gvn	–18
Glasgow: Cathedral (St Mungo's or High). . 425	52	–	81366	16390	16390	19
Glasgow: Colston Milton................ 139	17	–	28127	–	–	75
Glasgow: Colston Wellpark 202	18	–	30978	–	–	59
Glasgow: Cranhill 47	10	–	9150	–	–	20
Glasgow: Croftfoot 385	47	38	70815	14069	14189	101
Glasgow: Dennistoun Blackfriars 156	25	24	38724	3024	3124	11
Glasgow: Dennistoun Central 280	25	22	50055	6000	6000	205
Glasgow: Drumchapel Drumry St Mary's . . 143	11	–	10564	–	–	18
Glasgow: Drumchapel St Andrew's 466	40	–	51629	8173	8173	30
Glasgow: Drumchapel St Mark's.......... 82	–	15	11389	–	–	–
Glasgow: Easterhouse St George's and St Peter's...................... 51	8	–	–	–	–	–
Glasgow: Eastwood................... 401	55	52	76082	14597	14597	28
Glasgow: Gairbraid 248	22	21	38155	–	–	22
Glasgow: Gardner Street 45	7	–	49639	5430	8430	14
Glasgow: Garthamlock and Craigend East... 85	10	–	–	–	–	80
Glasgow: Gorbals 123	10	12	24274	–	–	8
Glasgow: Govan Old.................. 187	34	23	37444	6666	6666	45
Glasgow: Govanhill Trinity 139	18	35	29437	–	34	6
Glasgow: High Carntyne 485	33	85	78720	14300	14300	113
Glasgow: Hillington Park 434	28	65	65275	13607	13682	120
Glasgow: Househillwood St Christopher's. . 127	10	26	18017	–	33	94
Glasgow: Hyndland................... 285	43	37	89161	17480	17480	51
Glasgow: Ibrox 236	20	33	44442	5780	9780	49
Glasgow: John Ross Memorial (for the Deaf)...................... 74	8	–	–	–	–	–
Glasgow: Jordanhill................... 693	80	33	147900	42000	42500	273
Glasgow: Kelvin Stevenson Memorial..... 189	34	18	37333	3440	3440	142
Glasgow: Kelvinside Hillhead 190	28	–	60412	12870	12870	71
Glasgow: King's Park 863	78	71	142429	36500	36500	335
Glasgow: Kinning Park 188	14	21	32780	3150	3150	25
Glasgow: Knightswood St Margaret's 658	30	48	52413	9207	9207	92
Glasgow: Langside 260	38	40	34646	3000	3131	116
Glasgow: Lansdowne 120	15	–	13368	–	–	3
Glasgow: Linthouse St Kenneth's 150	17	21	25877	–	200	60
Glasgow: Lochwood 80	6	12	13573	–	–	91
Glasgow: Martyrs', The................ 127	4	–	–	–	–	5
Glasgow: Maryhill.................... 214	21	17	36204	2740	2928	89
Glasgow: Merrylea 490	76	55	88312	18710	18710	160
Glasgow: Mosspark................... 234	33	50	57727	10550	14212	–
Glasgow: Mount Florida 292	33	65	79499	20410	13900	150
Glasgow: New Govan 132	17	23	28974	5470	5470	83
Glasgow: Newlands South.............. 684	83	39	140823	46700	34000	50
Glasgow: North Kelvinside 71	3	24	34068	2363	2363	30
Glasgow: Partick South 249	33	35	63950	5071	5071	180
Glasgow: Partick Trinity 217	28	–	64881	6530	6530	50
Glasgow: Penilee St Andrew's........... 172	26	–	35665	3050	3050	30
Glasgow: Pollokshaws................. 181	27	28	43254	1620	1620	61

Congregation	Com	Eld	G	In 03	Ass	Gvn	–18
Glasgow: Pollokshields	361	43	78	109061	24110	24110	44
Glasgow: Possilpark	193	19	20	27956	1430	1430	47
Glasgow: Priesthill and Nitshill	189	18	22	30699	–	25	35
Glasgow: Queen's Park	301	28	39	82272	12375	12375	71
Glasgow: Renfield St Stephen's	191	27	34	66148	10480	11680	40
Glasgow: Robroyston	23	–	–	3037	–	–	14
Glasgow: Ruchazie	79	10	–	14692	–	–	14
Glasgow: Ruchill	121	28	–	42241	2710	2710	25
Glasgow: St Andrew's East	144	22	31	39409	–	100	90
Glasgow: St Columba	145	15	18	39150	–	–	47
Glasgow: St David's Knightswood	537	32	55	106234	17600	17950	77
Glasgow: St Enoch's Hogganfield	206	11	56	37739	3850	7350	30
Glasgow: St George's Tron	444	30	–	219791	58150	58150	60
Glasgow: St James' (Pollok)	187	27	24	55180	2574	2574	60
Glasgow: St John's Renfield	466	54	–	143378	29040	29040	140
Glasgow: St Luke's and St Andrew's	80	9	13	–	–	–	150
Glasgow: St Margaret's Tollcross Park	153	4	–	30963	–	150	57
Glasgow: St Nicholas' Cardonald	388	38	19	59903	7500	7950	53
Glasgow: St Paul's	73	6	–	–	–	–	30
Glasgow: St Rollox	126	10	–	21167	–	–	41
Glasgow: St Thomas' Gallowgate	42	7	–	9446	–	100	10
Glasgow: Sandyford Henderson M'r'l	198	27	16	98553	20306	20306	20
Glasgow: Sandyhills	367	32	55	70117	12850	12850	113
Glasgow: Scotstoun	288	21	–	62455	10810	10810	52
Glasgow: Shawlands	509	32	57	99249	32000	10000	70
Glasgow: Sherbrooke St Gilbert's	420	53	39	104151	29100	29100	130
Glasgow: Shettleston Old	277	27	27	45100	4301	4301	80
Glasgow: South Carntyne	97	11	–	25894	–	453	66
Glasgow: South Shawlands	231	25	–	55180	8424	8424	150
Glasgow: Springburn	340	41	27	61025	11310	11310	105
Glasgow: Temple Anniesland	484	40	50	74973	18060	18344	95
Glasgow: Toryglen	129	11	30	19146	–	–	35
Glasgow: Trinity Possil and Henry Drummond	138	6	–	47097	1936	1936	50
Glasgow: Tron St Mary's	144	16	–	14516	–	–	140
Glasgow: Victoria Tollcross	158	10	30	32852	–	–	61
Glasgow: Wallacewell	171	18	22	34990	–	–	101
Glasgow: Wellington	297	42	–	75851	17800	17800	20
Glasgow: Whiteinch	35	–	–	35941	–	–	30
Glasgow: Yoker	133	11	11	14630	–	–	2

17. Hamilton

Airdrie: Broomknoll	410	41	41	54960	11682	11682	60
Calderbank	143	10	23	17895	1700	1700	25
Airdrie: Clarkston	460	42	30	63944	12440	18087	150
Airdrie: Flowerhill	808	65	32	93624	15156	15156	215
Airdrie: High	431	31	–	46779	5104	5104	33
Airdrie: Jackson	350	48	26	58726	9210	9210	117

Congregation	Com	Eld	G	In 03	Ass	Gvn	–18
Airdrie: New Monkland	392	32	33	46377	7170	21723	–
Greengairs	200	7	–	20195	1860	1860	–
Airdrie: St Columba's	247	11	11	21740	–	–	68
Airdrie: The New Wellwynd	757	83	47	90980	18140	18140	–
Bargeddie	167	11	–	55264	5000	11641	21
Bellshill: Macdonald Memorial	315	24	25	40257	5640	5685	20
Bellshill: Orbiston	261	22	18	16738	2180	2180	8
Bellshill: West	827	65	44	64026	12250	12250	83
Blantyre: Livingstone Memorial	296	18	25	34254	4275	1710	–
Blantyre: Old	388	26	22	68863	12300	12300	68
Blantyre: St Andrew's	301	27	25	59250	11660	11660	58
Bothwell	565	54	47	108470	23840	23840	97
Caldercruix and Longriggend	221	12	19	46022	7502	7502	22
Carfin	62	7	–	7330	1150	1150	–
Newarthill	472	23	28	46877	7080	7080	–
Chapelhall	301	21	35	33548	2651	2651	108
Chapelton	203	15	30	22724	3872	3872	33
Strathaven: Rankin	596	60	34	70841	17030	17030	206
Cleland	238	14	14	27944	–	–	26
Coatbridge: Blairhill–Dundyvan	436	31	29	56173	7546	7546	7
Coatbridge: Calder	477	37	50	45799	8630	8630	–
Coatbridge: Clifton	268	22	23	41627	5571	5571	10
Coatbridge: Middle	413	36	48	47937	5830	6285	168
Coatbridge: Old Monkland	352	19	39	39111	3157	9516	12
Coatbridge: St Andrew's	714	68	52	81581	17090	17090	200
Coatbridge: Townhead	370	24	37	42478	5710	6173	75
Dalserf	275	23	23	56736	9240	9240	119
East Kilbride: Claremont	800	89	48	95222	18010	26910	290
East Kilbride: Greenhills	190	14	35	22546	–	–	12
East Kilbride: Moncrieff	952	80	56	91382	24540	24540	306
East Kilbride: Mossneuk	283	22	–	31022	–	–	229
East Kilbride: Old	690	68	84	82907	16220	16220	119
East Kilbride: South	411	46	49	90000	17650	17650	50
East Kilbride: Stewartfield	–	–	–	5773	–	–	–
East Kilbride: West	684	37	77	59663	10070	10510	195
East Kilbride: Westwood	776	50	140	76217	15030	15030	36
Glasford	195	12	24	16277	2560	2560	22
Strathaven: East	317	32	35	42468	7590	7590	30
Hamilton: Burnbank	146	18	–	27479	4810	3889	7
Hamilton: North	165	34	29	31310	5760	5760	18
Hamilton: Cadzow	806	69	76	90588	19370	19370	180
Hamilton: Gilmour and Whitehill	212	25	–	32786	2898	2898	86
Hamilton: Hillhouse	482	44	33	92386	14740	17737	51
Hamilton: Old	713	70	49	121217	27920	27920	125
Hamilton: St Andrew's	370	32	30	56582	11000	11100	37
Hamilton: St John's	632	61	55	105404	22340	22340	98
Hamilton: South	313	36	29	53851	6760	6760	103
Quarter	88	13	21	16539	2187	2187	10

Congregation . . . . Com	Eld	G	In 03	Ass	Gvn	–18
Hamilton: Trinity 331	29	–	43539	3800	1900	127
Hamilton: West 392	33	–	62546	12850	12850	30
Holytown 350	22	28	44867	4928	4928	80
Kirk o' Shotts 225	10	11	23510	–	–	20
Larkhall: Chalmers 233	18	32	–	3310	3310	40
Larkhall: St Machan's 607	57	49	74007	20210	20210	109
Larkhall: Trinity 343	25	47	43416	5250	5250	129
Motherwell: Crosshill 533	59	61	72673	13750	13750	133
Motherwell: Dalziel St Andrew's 652	80	63	101662	27240	59020	200
Motherwell: Manse Road 259	34	25	42717	7803	7803	34
Motherwell: North 228	33	40	43912	4800	4800	150
Motherwell: St Margaret's 389	15	29	45748	3520	–	177
Motherwell: St Mary's 1007	107	105	101445	21820	21820	235
Motherwell: South Dalziel 442	63	65	80596	15100	15939	120
Newmains: Bonkle 195	17	–	26916	6530	6530	22
Newmains: Coltness Memorial 246	31	29	39606	8980	8980	55
New Stevenston: Wrangholm Kirk 204	13	28	34833	3474	3474	56
Overtown 296	31	47	40127	3105	3105	63
Shotts: Calderhead Erskine 622	41	51	67829	8272	8272	192
Stonehouse: St Ninian's 439	39	36	66259	10040	10040	45
Strathaven: Avendale Old and Drumclog . . . 817	67	75	–	28220	28220	232
Strathaven: West 259	19	39	46457	4320	4320	–
Uddingston: Burnhead 285	24	17	42226	4170	5454	85
Uddingston: Old 711	65	81	108292	18680	18680	86
Uddingston: Park 212	21	33	64121	9600	10090	54
Uddingston: Viewpark 480	35	32	70375	12100	12400	300
Wishaw: Cambusnethan North 568	43	–	69744	15466	15466	172
Wishaw: Cambusnethan Old and Morningside 573	52	19	70912	13040	13040	200
Wishaw: Chalmers 501	29	36	52592	10330	17956	45
Wishaw: Craigneuk and Belhaven 229	27	27	50165	7520	7520	24
Wishaw: Old 385	38	–	38951	6182	6182	97
Wishaw: St Mark's 518	37	57	63401	10630	10630	212
Wishaw: Thornlie 266	27	48	49554	4199	4286	25

18. Dumbarton

Alexandria 473	35	26	59613	11400	11400	53
Arrochar 60	11	17	19218	–	200	60
Luss 85	9	17	27447	–	–	42
Baldernock 233	21	–	45233	5202	5202	14
Bearsden: Killermont 648	55	67	133190	32950	34210	81
Bearsden: New Kilpatrick 1766	140	134	258658	98930	98930	170
Bearsden: North 677	75	71	98690	28150	28650	80
Bearsden: South 979	83	44	151981	40270	40270	80
Bearsden: Westerton Fairlie Memorial 501	52	54	81516	18350	18350	62
Bonhill 931	62	–	61462	13700	13700	150
Cardross 478	36	36	86437	23370	23370	70
Clydebank: Abbotsford 356	25	39	52925	8110	8110	26
Clydebank: Faifley 245	25	49	34176	–	–	20

Congregation . . . . Com	Eld	G	In 03	Ass	Gvn	–18
Clydebank: Kilbowie St Andrew's 330	24	43	42043	6280	6280	157
Clydebank: Radnor Park 264	36	36	48594	5990	5990	9
Clydebank: St Cuthbert's 142	17	29	23970	1000	1000	–
Duntocher 344	35	30	47391	1168	1168	–
Craigrownie. 239	25	22	30981	5570	5570	25
Rosneath: St Modan's 190	12	34	27090	2900	2917	6
Dalmuir: Barclay 331	16	47	40015	6300	6300	12
Dumbarton: Riverside 769	76	88	98086	20260	22906	88
Dumbarton: St Andrew's 163	27	16	31370	–	–	14
Dumbarton: West Kirk. 366	45	28	–	8300	8300	13
Garelochhead. 163	16	–	47953	5876	5876	96
Helensburgh: Park 497	46	39	79140	19760	20004	40
Helensburgh: St Columba 613	48	42	84194	17040	17040	102
Helensburgh: The West Kirk 659	53	57	107562	31350	31350	30
Jamestown. 437	22	25	45313	9030	9030	12
Kilmaronock Gartocharn 272	11	–	25826	–	–	18
Milngavie: Cairns 760	49	–	97849	26300	26300	66
Milngavie: St Luke's 435	39	50	69168	13580	13580	43
Milngavie: St Paul's. 1164	94	116	190679	49370	49370	212
Old Kilpatrick Bowling 310	27	39	49487	7430	3570	151
Renton: Trinity 319	28	–	32355	1710	1710	12
Rhu and Shandon 323	26	56	72012	14040	14580	24

19. Argyll

Appin 94	12	24	16040	–	–	10
Lismore. 57	8	14	8863	–	–	12
Ardchattan. 174	12	10	17599	–	400	14
Ardrishaig 192	27	33	37455	3520	3520	52
South Knapdale 37	6	–	4669	561	–	8
Bute United. 703	35	33	75325	17875	18121	33
Campbeltown: Highland 498	31	30	48833	6788	6788	25
Campbeltown: Lorne and Lowland 957	45	66	72466	13570	13570	251
Coll. 15	3	–	2266	–	–	–
Connel. 157	23	30	41144	–	–	25
Colonsay and Oronsay. 15	2	–	3595	–	–	5
Kilbrandon and Kilchattan. 96	14	–	23926	–	468	44
Craignish. 40	5	–	7874	–	–	–
Kilninver and Kilmelford 57	6	–	8831	–	–	–
Cumlodden, Lochfyneside and Lochgair . . . 112	11	14	20633	–	–	24
Dunoon: St John's 268	31	35	37418	5470	5470	31
Sandbank. 161	12	–	12746	2244	2444	14
Dunoon: The High Kirk. 444	39	34	59713	8979	8979	–
Innellan. 152	–	18	24947	–	–	–
Toward 113	9	–	14403	–	–	11
Gigha and Cara 44	7	–	11422	–	–	5
Glassary and Kilmartin and Ford 128	11	14	19117	–	–	10
Glenaray and Inveraray 132	13	12	21742	–	–	12
Glenorchy and Innishael 87	8	–	13642	–	–	34

Congregation	Com	Eld	G	In 03	Ass	Gvn	–18
Strathfillan	53	5	–	9695	–	–	–
Iona	24	4	–	4802	–	–	3
Kilfinichen and Kilvickeon and the Ross of Mull	33	9	–	8343	–	107	8
Jura	38	7	–	11295	–	–	25
Kilarrow	104	12	15	23485	–	–	18
Kilmeny	48	6	–	9660	–	–	14
Kilberry	13	5	–	1296	–	–	4
Tarbert	171	16	32	30679	–	–	10
Kilcalmonell	65	9	16	7889	–	–	6
Skipness	29	2	–	6968	–	–	11
Kilchoman	82	7	–	9864	684	684	21
Portnahaven	17	–	13	6835	390	390	–
Kilchrenan and Dalavich	32	5	9	8235	–	–	–
Muckairn	142	17	14	18825	–	500	6
Kildalton and Oa	121	15	16	29017	–	–	25
Kilfinan	29	5	8	4072	–	762	–
Kyles	191	16	31	26668	–	500	15
Killean and Kilchenzie	191	–	19	29880	–	–	42
Kilmodan and Colintraive	137	11	17	20421	–	–	20
Kilmore and Oban	679	70	51	89255	15426	15618	40
Kilmun	119	11	24	14849	–	500	7
Strone and Ardentinny	134	12	13	15612	–	350	8
Kirn	356	29	28	78403	9317	9317	60
Lochgilphead	225	20	13	24928	–	–	11
Lochgoilhead and Kilmorich	119	13	20	24096	–	100	5
Mull, Isle of, Kilninian and Kilmore	39	5	–	9917	–	–	–
Salen and Ulva	33	7	–	9561	–	–	10
Tobermory	89	14	–	14856	–	–	–
Torosay and Kinlochspelvie	29	6	–	6365	–	–	5
North Knapdale	81	11	–	31767	–	–	7
Rothesay: Trinity	493	44	44	53710	6500	6500	98
Saddell and Carradale	239	16	29	27541	–	617	18
Southend	255	14	22	27985	–	75	–
Strachur and Strachlachlan	153	15	19	29338	–	–	17
Tiree	123	–	22	23680	–	–	–
22. Falkirk							
Airth	185	9	21	40662	2948	2948	9
Blackbraes and Shieldhill	197	13	18	21831	–	–	25
Bo'ness: Old	541	44	39	56464	7326	7326	79
Bo'ness: St Andrew's	581	32	–	63504	10220	10220	140
Bonnybridge: St Helen's	635	24	34	46651	5460	5460	40
Bothkennar and Carronshore	312	28	8	34323	–	–	34
Brightons	781	42	61	107979	19830	20889	250
Carriden	562	50	22	50428	7330	7330	30
Cumbernauld: Abronhill	315	34	37	48365	–	–	350
Cumbernauld: Condorrat	496	37	44	58659	8860	8860	190

Congregation	Com	Eld	G	In 03	Ass	Gvn	–18
Cumbernauld: Kildrum	442	37	–	35443	4455	4455	194
Cumbernauld: Old	492	39	–	54272	8180	8180	172
Cumbernauld: St Mungo's	358	31	–	48629	3773	3773	130
Denny: Dunipace	439	34	25	50972	6130	6130	72
Denny: Old	487	50	18	60892	11792	11792	100
Denny: Westpark	744	66	44	75495	14360	14360	109
Falkirk: Bainsford	346	15	–	38976	4240	4240	88
Falkirk: Camelon Irving	308	13	15	38246	–	–	25
Falkirk: Camelon St John's	366	22	25	61422	7007	7007	12
Falkirk: Erskine	562	53	38	77138	14980	17080	36
Falkirk: Grahamston United	523	50	43	72331	15170	15236	80
Falkirk: Laurieston	264	20	31	37114	5380	5380	29
Redding and Westquarter	157	13	41	21968	2464	2464	24
Falkirk: Old and St Modan's	1064	73	27	102112	16960	10960	75
Falkirk: St Andrew's West	620	47	33	–	25718	25718	56
Falkirk: St James'	287	28	16	40059	4420	4606	82
Grangemouth: Dundas	314	23	–	32521	2610	2610	7
Grangemouth: Kerse	619	60	27	51746	5870	5870	160
Grangemouth: Kirk of the Holy Rood	696	50	–	48843	9380	9380	82
Grangemouth: Zetland	946	66	73	96025	19260	19260	116
Haggs	327	31	18	45542	4330	4773	80
Larbert: East	657	42	42	81033	12780	12780	153
Larbert: Old	712	43	18	91905	18290	18290	120
Larbert: West	558	46	35	65305	12100	12100	171
Muiravonside	255	22	22	36436	–	–	10
Polmont: Old	566	32	63	65201	13981	14147	65
Slamannan	254	9	–	–	–	–	6
Stenhouse and Carron	642	43	33	68972	9850	9850	33

23. Stirling

Aberfoyle	130	10	17	19140	–	500	20
Port of Menteith	72	8	7	12647	–	1000	14
Alloa: North	293	21	25	52507	6010	6010	29
Alloa: St Mungo's	707	53	47	66801	14160	14160	19
Alloa: West	236	15	32	44140	3000	3000	10
Alva	618	51	32	60723	9640	9640	105
Balfron	200	20	20	59413	10110	10110	22
Fintry	166	11	17	16836	2920	2920	12
Balquhidder	99	4	–	16031	1700	1700	6
Killin and Ardeonaig	164	12	17	33404	1705	3255	30
Bannockburn: Allan	526	36	20	56269	6424	6424	120
Bannockburn: Ladywell	665	46	25	–	3600	3600	11
Bridge of Allan	820	57	89	112916	24360	24360	75
Buchanan	112	8	29j	24243	2667	2667	–
Drymen	311	23	j	53109	6974	6974	10
Buchlyvie	242	15	21	26843	3040	3040	20
Gartmore	83	11	–	15696	2453	2453	14
Callander	698	40	54	100066	22520	22520	120

Congregation	Com	Eld	G	In 03	Ass	Gvn	–18
Cambusbarron: The Bruce Memorial	422	22	–	40856	2970	2970	20
Clackmannan	539	42	40	70421	16220	16280	36
Cowie	153	12	10	14360	486	540	–
Plean	294	8	–	15195	600	600	–
Dollar	692	46	54	98564	17950	17950	142
Glendevon	58	5	–	–	528	528	–
Muckhart	153	12	–	–	4499	4499	24
Dunblane: Cathedral	1088	90	82	173389	54800	54914	253
Dunblane: St Blane's	426	45	30	92251	17790	17958	27
Fallin	273	9	–	42666	–	–	85
Gargunnock	210	13	–	20118	2552	2552	22
Kilmadock	210	11	–	11452	330	630	20
Kincardine-in-Menteith	113	8	–	9185	627	627	15
Killearn	596	43	52	67154	13779	13779	72
Kippen	314	25	24	29757	4122	4122	34
Norrieston	154	9	18	15748	1523	1523	20
Lecropt	281	14	32	45201	3586	3586	12
Logie	602	58	61	89460	18020	18129	65
Menstrie	426	30	26	55262	10461	10461	24
Sauchie and Coalsnaughton	886	36	32	59155	11430	11430	18
Stirling: Allan Park South	278	45	48	45239	7117	7117	31
Stirling: Church of the Holy Rude	278	36	–	39594	4939	17939	26
Stirling: North	562	41	24	54000	9922	9922	186
Stirling: St Columba's	585	65	–	84623	19150	19150	92
Stirling: St Mark's	325	11	–	35111	2453	2453	2
Stirling: St Ninian's Old	838	53	–	84870	13695	13695	45
Stirling: Viewfield	511	32	37	59001	13460	13512	25
Strathblane	379	26	38	55340	8000	8000	42
Tillicoultry	902	59	47	87356	17440	17738	112
Tullibody: St Serf's	632	26	22	66540	7568	7968	46

24. Dunfermline

Congregation	Com	Eld	G	In 03	Ass	Gvn	–18
Aberdour: St Fillan's	408	30	–	55176	11010	11010	40
Beath and Cowdenbeath: North	215	13	21	43607	–	–	48
Cairneyhill	233	26	–	24271	3971	3971	45
Limekilns	360	54	–	68191	14240	14540	25
Carnock and Oakley	235	21	18	47747	4468	4468	28
Cowdenbeath: Trinity	429	25	26	47766	1718	1718	59
Culross and Torryburn	316	21	–	37806	3519	1065	9
Dalgety	673	45	41	94464	18315	18315	59
Dunfermline: Abbey	806	60	–	119859	21802	21802	200
Dunfermline: Gillespie Memorial	409	71	22	105709	17850	17850	93
Dunfermline: North	230	17	–	34111	–	–	15
Dunfermline: St Andrew's Erskine	283	24	14	27445	1903	1903	14
Dunfermline: St Leonard's	545	43	43	67616	11460	11460	109
Dunfermline: St Margaret's	432	51	37	47480	8162	8162	30
Dunfermline: St Ninian's	364	34	55	41719	–	3600	21
Dunfermline: Townhill and Kingseat	433	32	41	61878	7744	7744	40

Congregation	Com	Eld	G	In 03	Ass	Gvn	–18
Inverkeithing: St John's	193	21	19	28943	3729	4085	91
North Queensferry	89	8	–	15387	1860	2275	–
Inverkeithing: St Peter's	323	8	–	24666	1965	1965	20
Kelty	383	29	53	50553	6149	6149	106
Lochgelly: Macainsh	399	34	–	29823	–	–	7
Ballingry and Lochcraig	126	–	–	14300	–	–	–
Lochgelly: St Andrew's	347	–	–	29825	–	–	–
Rosyth	345	26	–	37611	–	–	12
Saline and Blairingone	257	14	20	44966	6940	7040	26
Tulliallan and Kincardine	600	51	80	50229	6354	6555	35

25. Kirkcaldy

Auchterderran: St Fothad's	434	28	18	37388	5840	5840	27
Kinglassie	196	13	–	–	2600	2748	10
Auchtertool	87	6	–	6960	1734	1734	7
Kirkcaldy: Linktown	428	41	31	51337	7140	7475	27
Buckhaven	257	32	14	26429	2889	4289	16
Burntisland	663	48	53	55948	9140	9290	42
Denbeath	92	5	24	7910	–	–	6
Methilhill	175	31	37	19258	–	200	–
Dysart	401	40	18	48073	6700	6700	23
Glenrothes: Christ's Kirk	374	28	67	45159	–	–	25
Glenrothes: St Columba's	653	36	27	57327	8580	8637	86
Glenrothes: St Margaret's	434	31	40	55118	8830	8830	–
Glenrothes: St Ninian's	324	41	12	56761	6952	6952	28
Innerleven: East	219	8	26	24521	–	289	50
Kennoway, Windygates and Balgonie: St Kenneth's	765	49	72	81872	14710	14710	124
Kinghorn	410	31	34	59138	8600	8600	30
Kirkcaldy: Abbotshall	748	64	–	71841	14400	15060	25
Kirkcaldy: Pathhead	578	50	62	71304	13000	13100	177
Kirkcaldy: St Andrew's	303	24	33	43070	6020	6345	21
Kirkcaldy: St Bryce Kirk	859	69	40	74597	20450	20450	36
Kirkcaldy: St John's	417	50	60	61114	11520	11520	20
Kirkcaldy: Templehall	364	23	19	50869	6853	10853	15
Kirkcaldy: Torbain	278	28	28	37056	–	50	25
Kirkcaldy: Viewforth	377	14	–	32846	4419	4419	76
Thornton	247	9	–	20073	2130	2130	66
Leslie: Trinity	372	24	33	25434	720	–	10
Leven	894	51	41	–	14088	15471	84
Markinch	661	38	53	56968	9030	9030	58
Methil	403	24	37	37398	1656	1777	5
Wemyss	196	14	31	28116	588	588	16

26. St Andrews

Abdie and Dunbog	181	18	–	14183	1440	1440	–
Newburgh	290	18	–	28214	2940	–	21
Anstruther	377	21	–	44778	3870	4773	32

Congregation	Com	Eld	G	In 03	Ass	Gvn	–18
Auchtermuchty	326	24	21	34035	1215	972	22
Balmerino	164	20	16	24599	3608	3608	19
Wormit	304	23	59	29953	5577	5577	38
Boarhills and Dunino	176	9	j	14311	2720	2720	–
St Andrews: Martyrs'	404	30	38j	39722	6690	6690	–
Cameron	100	13	15	14461	2629	2629	23
St Andrews: St Leonard's	664	58	32	98170	22517	22517	51
Carnbee	108	12	19	13292	1958	1958	8
Pittenweem	319	20	38	29619	4334	4334	10
Cellardyke	316	20	46	35222	4800	4800	7
Kilrenny	117	11	20	19360	3280	3280	30
Ceres and Springfield	385	28	25	30120	11686	11686	20
Crail	455	36	39	42088	8360	8360	35
Kingsbarns	111	11	–	15426	2110	2110	–
Creich, Flisk and Kilmany	123	12	16	23724	3124	3124	–
Monimail	132	14	–	20176	3938	3938	27
Cupar: Old and St Michael of Tarvit	644	44	21	–	19270	19270	58
Cupar: St John's	839	43	60	64791	12529	12579	59
Dairsie	141	9	21	14734	1940	1940	6
Kemback	114	7	18	12290	2684	2684	–
Strathkinness	150	14	15	18607	3036	3036	–
Edenshead and Strathmiglo	235	13	21	23588	1155	1155	11
Elie	394	30	66	75830	15114	15114	25
Kilconquhar and Colinsburgh	210	17	–	29018	4720	4720	16
Falkland	344	22	10	30234	6655	6655	35
Freuchie	252	17	21	26269	5490	5490	8
Howe of Fife	819	46	–	59317	10065	10065	40
Largo and Newburn	287	17	–	32134	7860	7860	15
Largo: St David's	199	17	59	–	5577	–	16
Largoward	79	6	–	13118	572	572	15
St Monans	324	15	49	48472	6550	6550	60
Leuchars: St Athernase	516	31	36	44304	4873	4873	–
Newport-on-Tay	432	37	–	68713	13160	13160	88
St Andrews: Holy Trinity	659	27	58	47158	11160	11280	11
St Andrews: Hope Park	809	93	56	113233	31780	38088	40
Tayport	479	31	25	43307	6320	6320	50

27. Dunkeld and Meigle

Congregation	Com	Eld	G	In 03	Ass	Gvn	–18
Aberfeldy	270	16	20	39373	4212	4312	124
Amulree and Strathbraan	21	3	–	2191	700	700	–
Dull and Weem	91	10	17	12859	1700	1700	18
Alyth	815	37	40	69990	10950	10950	66
Ardler, Kettins and Meigle	494	23	49	38651	6440	6440	28
Bendochy	88	9	–	14103	1449	1449	4
Coupar Angus: Abbey	405	34	28	49431	3751	3751	125
Blair Atholl and Struan	180	17	20	16256	190	190	15
Tenandry	74	9	9	14242	200	200	9
Blairgowrie	1000	54	52	80333	13000	14000	24

Congregation	Com	Eld	G	In 03	Ass	Gvn	–18
Braes of Rannoch	33	9	j	12655	–	600	–
Foss and Rannoch	138	18	23j	22773	–	300	20
Caputh and Clunie	212	30	15	21737	3127	3127	10
Kinclaven	168	20	13	19155	2470	2470	6
Dunkeld	409	36	30	63332	16250	16250	39
Fortingall and Glenlyon	56	7	–	12577	1100	1100	3
Kenmore and Lawers	99	9	16	24258	1199	1199	15
Grantully, Logierait and Strathtay	175	15	10	32008	1199	1199	28
Kirkmichael, Straloch and Glenshee	152	15	13	14054	950	1451	15
Rattray	554	22	26	–	5490	4941	15
Pitlochry	531	51	31	75682	13710	13710	38

28. Perth

Congregation	Com	Eld	G	In 03	Ass	Gvn	–18
Abernethy and Dron	262	18	15	20587	2000	2000	8
Arngask	151	13	24	16517	2440	2813	–
Almondbank Tibbermore	352	20	38	32958	–	800	40
Ardoch	165	10	33	25095	–	2750	23
Blackford	83	–	–	12379	–	–	–
Auchterarder	723	45	59	74414	17250	17119	33
Auchtergaven and Moneydie	533	22	39	34475	4250	4250	105
Cargill Burrelton	359	19	35	41238	3300	3300	17
Collace	138	10	15	17059	3810	3810	12
Cleish	244	16	20	48756	8800	8800	–
Fossoway: St Serf's and Devonside	222	18	–	33298	6460	6460	–
Comrie	501	32	34j	62544	10240	11056	12
Dundurn	60	7	j	11065	1694	1694	–
Crieff	1036	50	50	100134	15500	15500	68
Dunbarney	578	29	62	48395	9823	9822	50
Forgandenny	92	8	9	12236	1800	1800	11
Errol	312	14	19	30957	5220	5220	24
Kilspindie and Rait	69	4	–	–	1010	1010	6
Fowlis Wester	125	13	–	14408	1227	1227	–
Madderty	106	14	10	14071	1003	1203	18
Monzie	105	10	–	15140	1003	1003	–
Gask	126	12	12	9886	–	500	–
Methven and Logiealmond	370	31	25	24338	–	–	–
Kinross	681	33	29	66210	13068	13068	65
Muthill	331	22	17	30640	2727	30	35
Trinity Gask and Kinkell	60	5	–	7253	720	720	3
Orwell	363	23	26	34436	4433	4665	15
Portmoak	154	13	–	20176	3800	3953	9
Perth: Craigie	732	32	40	60432	10670	10670	36
Perth: Kinnoull	436	30	37	54894	11280	11280	33
Perth: Letham St Mark's	690	41	34	70035	4100	4100	90
Perth: Moncrieffe	193	15	–	9072	–	500	257
Perth: North	1433	111	29	190925	55500	56063	–
Perth: Riverside	62	–	–	–	–	2500	100
Perth: St John the Baptist's	786	46	–	75522	17140	17140	–

Congregation	Com	Eld	G	In 03	Ass	Gvn	–18
Perth: St Leonard's-in-the-Fields and Trinity	637	70	38	90080	19050	19050	30
Perth: St Matthew's	984	60	45	94601	16120	16120	60
Redgorton	157	11	18	14295	1265	1265	37
Stanley	289	17	30	25776	5120	5120	24
St Madoes and Kinfauns	337	23	33	30895	–	–	30
St Martin's	204	8	16	9959	1500	1125	10
Scone: New	612	46	62	60340	11780	11780	45
Scone: Old	735	47	36	53969	9690	10690	47
The Stewartry of Strathearn	547	38	35	51169	2750	2744	32

29. Dundee

Congregation	Com	Eld	G	In 03	Ass	Gvn	–18
Abernyte	96	9	–	10684	1570	1570	–
Inchture and Kinnaird	252	27	–	22351	3357	2000	40
Longforgan	238	22	21	29017	6020	6020	13
Auchterhouse	160	17	21	22115	3970	4070	19
Murroes and Tealing	312	18	22	26724	2388	2388	19
Dundee: Balgay	567	50	35	59620	9630	9630	75
Dundee: Barnhill St Margaret's	874	72	51	105325	25550	25550	53
Dundee: Broughty Ferry East	609	49	36	65585	16110	16110	45
Dundee: Broughty Ferry St Aidan's	644	52	58	64838	11770	11770	30
Dundee: Broughty Ferry St James'	246	14	34	42604	6750	7850	42
Dundee: Broughty Ferry St Luke's and Queen Street	529	53	55	80495	15609	15609	–
Dundee: Broughty Ferry St Stephen's and West	373	23	–	36524	4620	4620	12
Dundee: Camperdown	209	20	19	24777	–	500	12
Dundee: Chalmers Ardler	249	21	26	63466	9119	9119	180
Dundee: Clepington	306	22	–	29859	3996	2432	10
Dundee: Fairmuir	238	16	14	24348	2739	2739	60
Dundee: Craigiebank	368	10	25	46199	9350	6339	207
Dundee: Douglas and Angus	362	–	20	30682	3437	3437	–
Dundee: Downfield South	454	30	30	60559	9700	9833	221
Dundee: Dundee (St Mary's)	692	69	37	97761	23470	23470	21
Dundee: Lochee Old and St Luke's	258	22	24	34482	2691	2691	4
Dundee: Lochee West	546	42	20	36501	4212	7813	80
Dundee: Logie and St John's Cross	453	22	34	91190	17680	17680	53
Dundee: Mains	234	12	–	22330	–	–	28
Dundee: Mains of Fintry	164	8	–	50090	6310	4310	25
Dundee: Meadowside St Paul's	554	47	35	51279	14010	14010	84
Dundee: Menzieshill	474	–	–	42964	–	955	–
Dundee: Mid Craigie	54	3	–	5330	–	–	5
Dundee: St Andrew's	813	75	43	–	13760	13860	40
Dundee: St David's High Kirk	607	60	64	52065	7130	7130	92
Dundee: Steeple	350	35	–	93319	15380	15380	34
Dundee: Stobswell	611	47	–	63535	12650	12650	23
Dundee: Strathmartine	597	–	40	52591	9070	9170	–
Dundee: Trinity	722	46	38	40224	5530	5530	109

Congregation	Com	Eld	G	In 03	Ass	Gvn	–18
Dundee: West	496	30	31	70407	11322	11322	–
Dundee: Whitfield	–	–	–	10634	–	–	–
Fowlis and Liff	163	11	8	16246	2250	2250	20
Lundie and Muirhead of Liff	355	28	–	31342	5291	5359	20
Invergowrie	480	47	59	58664	6057	6172	105
Monifieth: Panmure	457	39	32	51404	6600	6850	56
Monifieth: St Rule's	758	30	56	54831	8393	8393	21
Monifieth: South	426	20	43	42508	4257	3477	148
Monikie and Newbigging	270	11	–	21435	–	–	–

30. Angus

Congregation	Com	Eld	G	In 03	Ass	Gvn	–18
Aberlemno	200	12	–	–	1650	1650	14
Guthrie and Rescobie	220	8	18	19119	1730	1730	10
Airlie Ruthven Kingoldrum	162	14	–	–	869	869	20
Glenisla Kilry Lintrathen	167	14	12	24275	3894	4484	–
Arbirlot	230	13	–	17817	4190	4190	15
Carmyllie	142	8	5	14281	3498	3498	10
Colliston	223	9	12	16013	3090	3090	15
Arbroath: Knox's	428	30	38	30105	6030	6030	12
Arbroath: St Vigeans	652	51	32	47227	10570	10570	38
Arbroath: Old and Abbey	856	45	52	76002	10590	10590	80
Arbroath: St Andrew's	797	55	25	81109	15334	15334	150
Arbroath: West Kirk	1098	93	52	73768	15268	15268	85
Barry	299	18	16	30530	1911	2911	12
Carnoustie	581	48	39	64766	12716	12884	22
Brechin: Cathedral	1042	42	17	65835	7106	7284	32
Brechin: Gardner Memorial	678	31	14	45015	8110	8110	9
Carnoustie: Panbride	769	40	–	53260	9930	9930	67
Dun	86	7	j	–	979	979	9
Hillside	434	28	35j	35173	3693	3693	–
Dunnichen, Letham and Kirkden	467	23	25	37932	–	5410	20
Eassie and Nevay	63	9	9	7585	990	900	–
Newtyle	307	15	22	27064	2860	2600	25
Edzell Lethnot	420	27	46	29906	8640	8640	–
Fern, Careston and Menmuir	135	10	–	11862	2091	2091	6
Glenesk	60	4	–	–	1098	–	17
Farnell	109	8	–	6911	1120	1120	5
Montrose St Andrew's	457	24	27	30165	5900	5900	13
Forfar: East and Old	1459	47	62	94693	16030	16030	116
Forfar: Lowson Memorial	1080	43	29	60734	11737	11737	129
Forfar: St Margaret's	1048	41	30	68760	16690	16865	20
Friockheim Kinnell	241	17	25	19224	1350	1422	4
Inverkeilor and Lunan	204	11	17	17486	2600	2600	6
Glamis, Inverarity and Kinettles	504	34	25	34785	4670	4670	23
Glens, The and Kirriemuir: Old	1204	106	47	135804	26818	26818	90
Inchbrayock	230	10	–	32278	5340	5920	2
Montrose: Melville South	374	19	–	33543	7440	7440	–
Kirriemuir: St Andrew's	402	27	49	46252	6922	6922	23

Congregation	Com	Eld	G	In 03	Ass	Gvn	–18
Oathlaw Tannadice	174	7	–	11793	1305	1545	15
Montrose: Old	643	42	43	99204	16350	16350	125

31. Aberdeen

Congregation	Com	Eld	G	In 03	Ass	Gvn	–18
Aberdeen: Beechgrove	614	76	50	113177	25320	25320	–
Aberdeen: Bridge of Don Oldmachar	252	5	–	81879	–	1000	230
Aberdeen: Cove	90	10	–	–	–	–	36
Aberdeen: Craigiebuckler	886	58	62	75247	18370	18370	230
Aberdeen: Denburn	402	39	21	36326	4050	4050	18
Aberdeen: Ferryhill	530	68	31	60114	12030	12030	46
Aberdeen: Garthdee	307	20	20	28817	–	–	20
Aberdeen: Gilcomston South	268	27	–	109505	23580	23580	53
Aberdeen: Greyfriars John Knox	571	40	36	45536	7870	7025	21
Aberdeen: High Hilton	602	51	44	93043	16819	16819	70
Aberdeen: Holburn Central	492	50	20	57534	10840	10840	14
Aberdeen: Holburn West	584	51	28	101503	29260	29260	40
Aberdeen: Mannofield	1753	120	79	163836	47130	62130	214
Aberdeen: Mastrick	522	27	16	45862	5900	3005	88
Aberdeen: Middlefield	184	9	–	12477	–	220	–
Aberdeen: New Stockethill	65	–	–	11055	–	–	7
Aberdeen: North of St Andrew	510	54	35	66901	15000	15000	11
Aberdeen: Northfield	349	18	22	22283	3710	3230	18
Aberdeen: Queen's Cross	678	52	34	131781	35860	38860	40
Aberdeen: Rosemount	148	20	11	28336	270	270	–
Aberdeen: Rubislaw	682	87	51	127222	35120	36120	105
Aberdeen: Ruthrieston South	675	44	64	63605	10030	11030	87
Aberdeen: Ruthrieston West	425	42	27	54275	7348	7348	16
Aberdeen: St Columba's Bridge of Don	444	31	–	103271	14160	14160	85
Aberdeen: St George's Tillydrone	177	10	18	17374	–	–	11
Aberdeen: St John's Church for Deaf People	106	7	–	–	–	–	2
Aberdeen: St Machar's Cathedral	650	47	–	102860	22242	22242	50
Aberdeen: St Mark's	564	67	31	68487	14010	12764	69
Aberdeen: St Mary's	526	46	23	37769	6496	6496	9
Aberdeen: St Nicholas Uniting, Kirk of	654	63	26	89484	8973	8973	8
Aberdeen: St Nicholas Kincorth, South of	504	35	39	50637	7570	7570	25
Aberdeen: St Ninian's	340	23	23	52370	3987	3987	50
Aberdeen: St Stephen's	295	28	21	52541	6200	6200	–
Aberdeen: Summerhill	217	22	–	26558	–	–	12
Aberdeen: Torry St Fittick's	584	30	34	46077	5247	5397	8
Aberdeen: Woodside	397	35	29	43110	4370	4490	–
Bucksburn Stoneywood	597	25	29	43781	5950	5950	15
Cults: East	358	34	17	46566	6840	–	30
Cults: West	608	41	26	93224	24660	24660	37
Dyce	1382	76	47	77037	13440	13440	275
Kingswells	514	42	24	43814	3700	3700	39
Newhills	988	42	81	90767	17810	18235	255
Peterculter	829	51	34	78593	11750	11750	310

Congregation . . . . Com	Eld	G	In 03	Ass	Gvn	–18
32. Kincardine and Deeside						
Aberluthnott 235	9	15	15147	3180	2891	6
Laurencekirk 538	15	46	27409	4785	4785	17
Aboyne – Dinnet 475	16	29	45922	7260	7260	30
Arbuthnott 125	7	8	10881	1540	1540	–
Bervie 562	25	49	48746	6367	7367	60
Banchory-Devenick and						
Maryculter/Cookney 408	19	14	32951	2925	2925	33
Banchory-Ternan: East 1201	64	46	81520	14280	14280	80
Banchory-Ternan: West 682	40	35	93628	14170	16558	74
Birse and Feughside 308	28	20	34420	5430	2670	43
Braemar 110	9	18j	21974	2345	2345	10
Crathie 173	18	j	31286	6320	6320	–
Cromar 273	13	–	21103	–	–	16
Drumoak and Durris 488	25	51	52168	1380	1380	67
Glenmuick (Ballater) 367	27	36	36888	4630	4630	18
Kinneff 180	7	–	6801	1060	1060	–
Stonehaven: South 321	26	18	45666	4790	4790	10
Mearns Coastal 401	18	20	27866	2565	1909	4
Mid Deeside 856	46	26	53652	7500	7500	50
Newtonhill 407	20	19	26399	2695	2388	200
Portlethen 512	18	–	42315	10630	10630	190
Stonehaven: Dunnottar 900	40	38	70399	11840	11840	–
Stonehaven: Fetteresso 956	40	48	119506	16960	16960	80
West Mearns 616	25	60	41787	7040	7040	20
33. Gordon						
Barthol Chapel 101	8	10	9242	1133	1133	20
Tarves 513	32	33	37941	5418	5418	25
Belhelvie 470	37	18	51135	5593	5593	55
Blairdaff 106	12	–	12800	1280	1280	12
Chapel of Garioch 316	22	18	37580	2420	2420	37
Cluny 211	12	12	25871	2123	2123	7
Monymusk 133	7	7	17608	1251	1251	26
Culsalmond and Rayne 244	7	–	8847	300	124	10
Daviot 171	9	–	15880	1740	1740	9
Cushnie and Tough 302	19	11	30691	–	1600	24
Drumblade 131	9	10	6700	1840	1840	10
Huntly Strathbogie 818	46	25	57408	8383	8383	89
Echt 302	16	14	20949	2420	2612	13
Midmar 172	12	–	13855	2222	2222	12
Ellon 1828	94	31	134465	22520	22520	–
Fintray and Kinellar 193	11	13j	12632	875	875	11
Keithhall 77	8	j	5795	876	876	–
Foveran 388	21	–	36077	2190	2190	36
Howe Trinity 720	34	51	50558	6404	6404	43
Huntly Cairnie Glass 859	31	39	41106	4950	4950	22
Insch-Leslie-Premnay-Oyne 604	–	46	39620	7570	7570	50

Congregation	Com	Eld	G	In 03	Ass	Gvn	–18
Inverurie: St Andrew's	1786	44	75	98931	19370	19370	20
Inverurie: West	778	62	42	70342	10460	10460	80
Kemnay	669	38	–	43014	7998	8614	152
Kintore	862	51	39	63137	18620	22620	66
Meldrum and Bourtie	556	31	44	52390	4580	4580	50
Methlick	399	20	31	45152	3100	3100	–
New Machar	532	26	33	52206	6237	6237	80
Noth	377	14	–	20414	–	–	24
Skene	1596	96	56	107142	20800	20800	210
Udny and Pitmedden	549	–	15	54317	7900	10840	–
Upper Donside	466	20	–	30122	978	1007	20

34. Buchan

Congregation	Com	Eld	G	In 03	Ass	Gvn	–18
Aberdour	154	8	11	9839	702	702	20
Pitsligo	159	13	–	–	1587	1587	65
Sandhaven	92	8	–	9676	675	675	32
Auchaber United	182	14	12	13933	891	891	20
Auchterless	245	18	17	24766	2046	2116	2
Banff	895	39	35	70195	15440	16080	127
King Edward	182	16	13	15217	3795	3795	10
Crimond	292	9	11	21083	200	200	16
Lonmay	181	14	9	9849	899	899	54
St Fergus	217	9	18	8531	200	200	14
Cruden	509	34	28	50270	5680	5680	56
Deer	948	31	21	40031	5450	5504	31
Fordyce	536	32	27	43084	5940	6155	38
Fraserburgh: Old	918	58	81	122733	31030	31030	208
Fraserburgh: South	344	21	27	39780	3883	4031	86
Inverallochy and Rathen: East	93	9	–	17208	2380	2380	–
Fraserburgh: West	707	47	–	50293	8700	9060	48
Rathen: West	113	8	–	8638	790	790	–
Fyvie	420	27	40	36422	6064	6064	32
Rothienorman	197	10	15	10912	946	946	–
Gardenstown	71	11	30	45413	2772	2937	60
Longside	578	29	–	45679	4560	4810	153
Macduff	904	43	63	78876	16520	17434	112
Marnoch	405	20	13	26839	2689	2689	25
Maud and Savoch	270	16	21	19731	770	770	24
New Deer: St Kane's	491	20	16	34777	7073	7073	123
Monquhitter and New Byth	399	20	11	19244	2500	2500	15
Turriff: St Andrew's	564	27	12	46746	4527	4527	30
New Pitsligo	367	11	–	19658	1113	1113	14
Strichen and Tyrie	647	20	44	31429	3434	3434	16
Ordiquhill and Cornhill	164	11	13	12971	326	326	14
Whitehills	319	18	39	30215	2910	2910	23
Peterhead: Old	524	39	36	54999	7560	7560	95
Peterhead: St Andrew's	611	41	33	50289	7620	7742	30
Peterhead: Trinity	388	29	20	22022	20889	20889	16

Congregation . . . . Com	Eld	G	In 03	Ass	Gvn	–18
Turriff: St Ninian's and Forglen 1027	43	59	64071	12007	12182	108

35. Moray

Aberlour 384	25	32	35285	3588	3588	32
Alves and Burghead 170	17	41	22576	–	–	20
Kinloss and Findhorn 92	16	11	12091	–	300	9
Bellie. 398	15	33	38795	7515	7515	36
Speymouth 239	13	21	16089	2365	2365	13
Birnie 227	17	23	18124	1370	1370	8
Pluscarden. 125	12	16	–	2210	2210	25
Buckie: North 613	43	82	49199	8260	8510	45
Buckie: South and West. 341	31	33	35874	6290	6290	195
Enzie. 114	11	17	15380	737	737	10
Cullen and Deskford 418	33	50	31125	6340	6340	30
Dallas 60	7	14	8206	1890	1890	16
Forres: St Leonard's 342	28	48	60263	8976	8976	25
Rafford 81	5	16	10335	1804	1804	–
Duffus, Spynie and Hopeman 394	42	32	48126	6479	6479	21
Dyke 167	15	17	20982	3420	3420	38
Edinkillie. 92	13	–	19434	2484	2484	13
Elgin: High 787	53	41	77815	16335	16335	54
Elgin: St Giles' and St Columba's South 1528	102	55	139600	23590	23590	187
Findochty 55	14	16	21192	550	550	42
Portknockie. 106	9	35	20458	750	982	44
Rathven. 111	12	26	17618	1073	1073	9
Forres: St Laurence 639	39	37	64889	13464	13464	25
Keith: North, Newmill, Boharm and Rothiemay 706	42	56	104601	13794	14169	170
Keith: St Rufus, Botriphnie and Grange. . . . 1094	55	35	64585	8605	8600	91
Knockando, Elchies and Archiestown 276	16	14	16192	1155	1400	5
Rothes. 320	20	23	26019	3770	3770	32
Lossiemouth: St Gerardine's High 408	21	39	51982	8840	8840	24
Lossiemouth: St James' 345	22	39	45163	5229	5229	32
Mortlach and Cabrach 446	26	42	21644	–	–	6
St Andrew's-Lhanbryd and Urquhart 516	28	32	47846	8415	8623	36

36. Abernethy

Abernethy 166	15	–	35873	2882	2882	51
Cromdale and Advie 104	2	–	12041	714	830	9
Alvie and Insh. 73	6	–	21122	2673	2673	9
Boat of Garten and Kincardine 99	10	17	19674	–	–	10
Duthil 72	10	14	8852	–	–	15
Dulnain Bridge 43	6	–	10216	883	883	6
Grantown–on–Spey. 287	18	29	39531	5013	5013	8
Kingussie 130	16	–	22406	–	–	28
Laggan 40	5	–	11970	–	–	–
Newtonmore 91	15	–	22381	–	–	–

Congregation . . . . Com	Eld	G	In 03	Ass	Gvn	–18
Rothiemurchus and Aviemore 96	5	–	18134	–	–	13
Tomintoul, Glenlivet and Inveraven. 183	15	5	13003	–	–	16

37. Inverness

Ardclach 39	3	–	1746	–	–	5
Auldearn and Dalmore 77	8	15	10698	–	–	20
Ardersier. 74	13	15	18944	–	–	23
Petty 72	11	9	18009	–	200	28
Cawdor 176	14	–	24092	–	2000	–
Croy and Dalcross. 54	12	15	8966	–	199	4
Culloden: The Barn 365	30	27	61725	10741	10741	85
Daviot and Dunlichity 61	7	–	16017	–	–	–
Moy, Dalarossie and Tomatin 39	4	10	8983	–	100	15
Dores and Boleskine 107	7	–	16759	–	1374	16
Inverness: Crown. 806	95	68	115624	22250	22250	228
Inverness: Dalneigh and Bona 293	21	34	74637	12056	12056	67
Inverness: East 322	42	20	117345	26750	26750	165
Inverness: Hilton 277	11	31	–	–	–	114
Inverness: Inshes 158	17	–	76542	13840	13840	27
Inverness: Kinmylies 172	12	–	38455	–	–	50
Inverness: Ness Bank 625	69	34	93187	16643	16643	135
Inverness: St Columba High 253	30	23	51878	10210	10360	–
Inverness: St Stephen's 411	41	–	–	12130	12130	68
Inverness: The Old High 169	29	–	–	8334	8334	24
Inverness: Trinity. 393	38	31	60307	11322	11322	112
Kilmorack and Erchless. 147	16	22	36552	–	–	35
Kiltarlity 49	7	–	14736	–	–	14
Kirkhill 73	5	13	20431	–	–	–
Nairn: Old 922	67	39	91113	18320	18320	2
Nairn: St Ninian's 283	17	32	41917	2574	2574	22
Urquhart and Glenmoriston 139	7	4	48983	5470	5470	32

38. Lochaber

Acharacle 35	3	–	16158	–	–	8
Ardnamurchan. 20	4	–	6951	–	–	10
Ardgour. 51	8	13	14759	–	–	1
Strontian 23	3	9	–	–	–	2
Arisaig and the Small Isles 63	8	18	13320	–	–	15
Duror 45	8	14	13030	–	100	12
Glencoe: St Munda's 71	8	18	16719	–	80	12
Fort Augustus 76	7	17	16392	–	66	6
Glengarry 40	8	11	10760	–	–	12
Fort William: Duncansburgh 307	23	27	52050	7510	7880	83
Kilmonivaig 79	8	12	16159	4895	6256	12
Fort William: MacIntosh Memorial 210	26	21	46602	5100	5100	26
Kilmallie. 161	20	25	–	6630	6645	23
Kinlochleven. 74	7	21	17510	–	100	14
Nether Lochaber 57	7	–	13477	–	–	24

Congregation	Com	Eld	G	In 03	Ass	Gvn	–18
Mallaig: St Columba and Knoydart	97	6	–	23996	–	–	–
Morvern	53	4	9	12167	–	85	6

39. Ross

Alness	118	13	–	33213	–	–	28
Avoch	30	6	12	15512	2050	2450	8
Fortrose and Rosemarkie	139	11	–	29398	5230	5230	8
Contin	60	11	–	15884	–	2000	6
Cromarty	73	6	14	18135	–	–	45
Dingwall: Castle Street	140	17	27	43287	4720	4720	12
Dingwall: St Clement's	255	27	26	52519	4626	4626	40
Fearn Abbey and Nigg	113	16	28	–	220	–	16
Tarbat	69	11	–	15605	220	528	6
Ferintosh	209	24	37	47419	2524	2636	30
Fodderty and Strathpeffer	158	16	24	30748	–	537	24
Invergordon	181	13	–	46129	6120	6120	34
Killearnan	146	20	–	27328	1430	2530	26
Knockbain	76	10	–	17543	715	895	10
Kilmuir and Logie Easter	72	10	19	27963	–	–	11
Kiltearn	81	5	5	27767	–	–	26
Lochbroom and Ullapool	54	5	12	29799	–	6	25
Resolis and Urquhart	99	10	–	24143	–	–	9
Rosskeen	142	12	20	41001	–	1000	31
Tain	172	12	26	44972	6920	6920	15
Urray and Kilchrist	119	16	22	38996	–	968	25

40. Sutherland

Altnaharra and Farr	37	–	–	11220	–	–	15
Assynt and Stoer	26	2	–	14926	–	–	24
Clyne	101	12	–	20149	–	–	26
Creich	41	4	–	10997	–	–	12
Rosehall	24	4	–	6799	–	170	5
Dornoch Cathedral	374	36	46	83939	12820	12820	50
Durness and Kinlochbervie	40	3	11	24292	–	–	10
Eddrachillis	19	2	–	15507	–	–	8
Golspie	100	24	18	25378	–	–	15
Kildonan and Loth Helmsdale	44	4	19	15083	–	–	–
Kincardine Croick and Edderton	79	11	17	23191	–	–	37
Lairg	53	7	22	25585	–	–	31
Rogart	29	5	11	11377	–	–	7
Melness and Tongue	56	7	9	13979	–	–	7

41. Caithness

Berriedale and Dunbeath	17	2	–	6206	–	–	6
Latheron	20	1	–	7681	–	–	7
Bower	34	4	7	10209	–	–	–
Watten	47	5	–	11855	–	–	25
Canisbay	43	4	20	12016	–	–	12

Congregation	Com	Eld	G	In 03	Ass	Gvn	–18
Keiss	28	2	13	10256	–	–	–
Dunnet	22	–	9	–	–	–	–
Olrig	61	5	10	11514	–	–	12
Halkirk and Westerdale	89	6	15	15662	–	–	45
Lybster and Bruan	43	8	74	17184	–	–	5
Reay	37	5	10	8867	–	–	–
Strathy and Halladale	24	5	17	8907	–	–	–
Thurso: St Peter's and St Andrew's	249	24	50	–	6875	6875	55
Thurso: West	286	28	42	46591	4590	4590	33
Wick: Bridge Street	181	10	14	31761	3445	3445	7
Wick: Old	239	43	38	56615	6410	6410	28
Wick: Pulteneytown and Thrumster	240	13	25	–	8710	256	275

42. Lochcarron – Skye

Applecross, Lochcarron and Torridon	84	5	16	31887	–	300	18
Bracadale and Duirinish	86	9	–	25124	–	–	64
Gairloch and Dundonnell	103	5	–	57108	5192	5442	35
Glenelg and Kintail	54	10	–	19811	–	300	25
Kilmuir and Stenscholl	82	9	–	34319	–	750	45
Lochalsh	88	10	29	36390	–	2582	60
Portree	137	8	–	53092	3586	3586	48
Snizort	88	11	–	46624	2233	2233	54
Strath and Sleat	187	16	29	64618	8646	8646	69

43. Uist

Barra	27	3	–	9091	–	–	–
Benbecula	67	11	17	27216	–	–	22
Berneray and Lochmaddy	57	4	16	21175	–	–	15
Carinish	81	8	21	34675	–	–	35
Kilmuir and Paible	21	4	–	29080	–	–	8
Manish-Scarista	45	4	–	30192	–	–	15
South Uist	59	12	12	17921	–	–	8
Tarbert	164	16	–	70618	12240	12240	45

44. Lewis

Barvas	93	12	–	49638	3322	3322	–
Carloway	42	1	–	26596	–	700	32
Cross Ness	49	8	–	36179	–	–	26
Kinloch	46	8	–	27331	–	–	27
Knock	79	5	–	44125	–	–	35
Lochs-Crossbost	21	2	–	20893	–	–	30
Lochs-in-Bernera	31	4	–	16662	–	–	–
Stornoway: High	252	17	–	103714	21920	21920	90
Stornoway: Martin's Memorial	122	9	17	55964	6149	6149	73
Stornoway: St Columba	131	13	38	67845	10960	10960	98
Uig	45	6	–	22060	–	–	18

Congregation . . . . Com	Eld	G	In 03	Ass	Gvn	–18
45. Orkney						
Birsay, Harray and Sandwick 386	32	55	35616	2588	2588	30
Deerness 97	9	–	9967	–	–	12
Holm 132	8	14	11782	–	–	16
St Andrew's 84	9	8	8356	–	–	5
Eday 6	1	6	1801	–	–	–
Stronsay: Moncur Memorial 69	9	22	9034	–	–	14
Evie 48	3	–	7024	855	855	–
Firth 121	7	19	20505	2950	3335	24
Rendall 56	4	17	7846	460	460	17
Flotta 27	4	–	3400	–	–	–
Hoy and Walls 71	11	13	4820	–	50	6
Kirkwall: East 507	47	42	50999	9396	16613	62
Kirkwall: St Magnus Cathedral 826	74	39	66325	14930	15032	40
North Ronaldsay 17	2	–	1350	–	–	–
Sanday 97	9	15	9273	–	–	16
Orphir 129	12	18	18863	–	90	10
Stenness 90	10	13	14936	–	143	4
Papa Westray 10	3	–	3881	–	40	–
Westray 72	14	26	18899	–	630	35
Rousay 29	4	9	2557	–	–	–
Shapinsay 66	8	–	6041	–	–	8
South Ronaldsay and Burray 188	10	13	17840	–	–	12
Stromness 402	24	30	45824	5280	5280	70
46. Shetland						
Burra Isle 46	7	28	8384	–	–	14
Tingwall 172	19	29	28085	–	90	45
Delting 103	8	–	15196	–	–	22
Northmavine 84	10	–	8814	–	–	14
Dunrossness and St Ninian's inc. Fair Isle . . . 69	17	–	12207	–	200	24
Sandwick, Cunningsburgh and Quarff 142	11	32	23417	–	–	51
Fetlar 20	5	–	–	–	–	–
Unst 134	11	26	16808	–	–	–
Yell 135	11	32	12037	–	–	–
Lerwick and Bressay 528	37	–	61494	9970	9970	37
Nesting and Lunnasting 42	5	20	7831	–	–	–
Whalsay and Skerries 245	18	20	23841	–	–	12
Sandsting and Aithsting 54	10	–	9033	–	50	45
Walls and Sandness 48	11	14	7946	–	–	12
47. England						
Corby: St Andrew's 328	23	29	63841	1782	1782	15
Corby: St Ninian's 340	22	11	37821	5010	6696	12
Guernsey: St Andrew's in the Grange 241	22	–	41995	5687	6007	13
Jersey: St Columba's 143	24	–	56980	4757	4757	44
Liverpool: St Andrew's 41	5	7	18654	2080	2080	7
London: Crown Court 291	44	11	80652	18330	18330	25
London: St Columba's 1453	60	–	187459	61220	61220	82
Newcastle: St Andrew's 115	18	6	–	3047	3047	19

INDEX OF MINISTERS

NOTE: Ministers who are members of a Presbytery are designated 'A' if holding a parochial appointment in that Presbytery, or 'B' if otherwise qualifying for membership.

'A-1, A-2' etc. indicate the numerical order of congregations in the Presbyteries of Edinburgh, Glasgow and Hamilton.

Also included are:

(1) Ministers who have resigned their seat in Presbytery (List 6-H)

(2) Ministers who hold a Practising Certificate (List 6-I)

(3) Ministers serving overseas (List 6-K)

(4) Auxiliary Ministers (List 6-A)

(5) Ministers ordained for sixty years and upwards (List 6-Q)

(6) Ministers who have died since the publication of the last *Year Book* (List 6-R)

NB *For a list of the Diaconate, see List 6-G.*

Name	Location	Name	Location	Name	Location
Abeledo, B.J.	G'ock/Paisley 14B	Andrews, J.E.	West Lothian 2A	Baxter, R.F.	Edinburgh 1B
Acklam, C.R.	West Lothian 2A	Annand, J.M.	Annandale/Eskdale 7B	Bayne, A.L.	Edinburgh 1A-5
Adams, D.G.	Dunfermline 24A	Arbuthnott, Mrs J.	List 6-I	Beaton, D.	Lochcarron/Skye 42B
Adamson, H.	Irvine/K'marnock 11A	Archer, N.D.C.	List 6-I	Beattie, J.A.	Glasgow 16B
Aitchison, J.W.	Aberdeen 31B	Armitage, W.L.	Edinburgh 1A-48	Beattie, W.R.	List 6-I
Aitken, A.J.	Glasgow 16B	Armour, C.	List 6-R	Beattie, W.G.	Hamilton 17B
Aitken, A.R.	Edinburgh 1B	Armstrong, W.R.	G'ock/Paisley 14A	Beattie, W.G.	Aberdeen 31B
Aitken, E.D.	Stirling 23B	Arnott, A.D.K.	St Andrews 26A	Beautyman, P.H.	Edinburgh 1A-26
Aitken, E.R.	List 6-I	Atkins, Mrs Y.E.S.	List 6-I	Beck, J.C.	List 6-H
Aitken, F.R.	Ayr 10A	Auld, A.G.	Edinburgh 1B	Beckett, D.M.	Edinburgh 1B
Aitken, I.M.	Aberdeen 31A	Austin, G.	Moray 35A	Beebee, G.W.	England 47A
Aitken, J.	List 6-I			Bell, C.J.G.	Ross 39A
Albon, D.W.	West Lothian 2A	Baigrie, R.A.	Edinburgh 1B	Bell, D.W.	Buchan 34B
Alexander, D.N.	G'ock/Paisley 14B	Bailey, W.G.	List 6-H	Bell, G.K.	Glasgow 16A-59
Alexander, E.J.	Glasgow 16B	Baillie, D.	Dum'/K'cudbright 8B	Bell, I.W.	G'ock/Paisley 14A
Alexander, Miss H.J.R.	List 6-I	Bain, B.	Perth 28A	Bell, J.L.	Glasgow 16B
Alexander, I.W.	Edinburgh 1B	Bain, J.	Edinburgh 1A-12	Bell, Mrs M.	G'ock/Paisley 14A
Alexander, J.S.	St Andrews 26B	Baird, G.W.	Hamilton 17B	Bell, R.P.	Ayr 10A
Alexander, W.M.	Aberdeen 31B	Baird, K.S.	Edinburgh 1A-40	Bennett, A.	St Andrews 26B
Allan, A.G.	Glasgow 16B	Baker, Mrs C.	Ayr 10A	Bennett, A.G.	Melrose/Peebles 4A
Allan, J.B.	List 6-R	Balfour, T.	List 6-H	Bennett, D.K.P.	Dum'/K'cudbright 8B
Allan, R.T.	Falkirk 22A	Ballantyne, S.	Aberdeen 31B	Benson, J.W.	Stirling 23B
Allen, M.A.W.	Glasgow 16A-13	Ballentine, Miss A.M.	W' Lothian 2A	Benzie, I.W.	Ardrossan 12A
Allen, Ms V.L.	Angus 30A	Banks, J	Ayr 10B	Berrill, P.A.D.	Kincard'/Dee' 32A
Allison, A.	Dunfermline 24A	Barber, P.I.	Edinburgh 1A-27	Bertram, T.A.	Perth 28B
Allison, Ms M.M.	Glasgow 16A-85	Barbour, R.A.	Dunkeld/Meigle 27B	Best, E.	St Andrews 26B
Allison, R.N.	G'ock/Paisley 14A	Barclay, I.C.	Aberdeen 31A	Beveridge, S.E.P.	Annan'/Eskdale 7B
Almond, D.	Annan'/Eskdale 7A	Barclay, N.W.	Falkirk 22A	Bews, J.	St Andrews 26B
Alston, W.G.	Glasgow 16A-107	Barclay, S.G.	Irvine/Kilmarnock 11A	Bezuidenhout, L.C.	Dum'/K'cudbright 8A
Amed, P.	Moray 35A	Bardgett, F.D.	List 6-I	Bicket, M.S.	Angus 30A
Anderson, A.F.	Edinburgh 1A-30	Barge, N.L.	Glasgow 16A-42	Billes, R.H.	Moray 35A
Anderson, C.M.	Glasgow 16B	Barr, A.C	Glasgow 16B	Birch, J.	Glasgow 16A-11
Anderson, D.	Lochaber 38B	Barr, G.K.	Perth 28B	Bircham, M.F.	Perth 28A
Anderson, D.M.	Lochaber 38B	Barr, G.R.	Edinburgh 1A-18	Bird, J.W.	List 6-R
Anderson, D.P.	Argyll 19A	Barr, J.	Ayr 10B	Birnie, C.J.	Buchan 34B
Anderson, J.F.	Aberdeen 31A	Barr, T.L.	Perth 28B	Birrell, Mrs I.	Perth 28A
Anderson, J.W.	Angus 30B	Barrett, L.	Dundee 29B	Birrell, J.M.	Perth 28B
Anderson, K.G.	Perth 28A	Barrie, A.	Falkirk 22A	Birse, G.S.	Ayr 10A
Anderson, R.	Glasgow 16A-54	Barrie, A.P.	Hamilton 17A-43	Birss, A.D.	G'ock/Paisley 14A
Anderson, R.A.	West Lothian 2A	Barrington, C.W.H.	Edinburgh 1A-2	Bjarnason, S.	Abernethy 36A
Anderson, R.J.M.	Moray 35A	Barron, Mrs J.L.	Dundee 29A	Black, A.G.	Lothian 3B
Anderson, R.S.	Edinburgh 1B	Bartholomew, D.S.	Dum'/K'cud' 8A	Black, A.R.	Irv'/K'marnock 11A
Anderson, Mrs S.M.	Irv'/K'nock 11A	Baxendale, Mrs G.M.	G'ock/Paisley 14A	Black, A.T.	Inverness 37B
Andrew, J.	Gordon 33B	Baxter, R.	Kirkcaldy 25A	Black, D.R.	Glasgow 16A-112
Andrew, R.J.M.	Ayr 10B				

INDEX OF PARISHES AND PLACES

NOTE: Numbers on the right of the column refer to the Presbytery in which the district lies. Names in brackets are given for ease of identification. They may refer to the name of the Parish, which may be different from that of the district, or they distinguish places with the same name, or they indicate the first named charge in a union.

INDEX OF FORMER PARISHES AND CONGREGATIONS

The following index updates and corrects the 'Index of Former Parishes and Congregations' printed in the previous edition of the *Year Book*. As before, it contains the names of parishes of the Church of Scotland and of congregations of the Free Church, the United Free Church and the United Presbyterian Church (and its constituent denominations) which no longer have a separate existence, largely as a consequence of union.

It should be stressed that this index is not intended to be a comprehensive guide to readjustment in the Church of Scotland and does not therefore include the names of *all* parishes and congregations which no longer exist as independent entities. Its purpose is rather to assist those who are trying to identify the present successor of some former parish or congregation whose name may no longer be recognisable. Where a connection between the former name and the present name may easily be established, the former name has not been included, as the following examples will illustrate.

- Where all the former congregations in a town have been united into one, as in the case of Melrose or Selkirk, the names of these former congregations have not been included; but in the case of towns with more than one congregation, such as Galashiels or Hawick, the names of the various constituent congregations are listed.
- Where a prefix such as North, Old, Little, Mid or the like has been lost but the substantive part of the name has been retained, the former name has not been included: it is assumed that someone searching for Little Dalton or Mid Yell will have no difficulty in connecting these with Dalton or Yell.
- Where the present name of a united congregation includes the names of some or all of its constituent parts, these former names do not appear in the index: thus, neither Glasgow: Anderston nor Glasgow: Kelvingrove appears, since both names are easily traceable to Glasgow: Anderston Kelvingrove.
- Some parishes and congregations have disappeared, and their names have been lost, as a consequence of suppression, dissolution or secession. The names of rural parishes in this category have been included, together with the names of their Presbyteries to assist with identification, but those in towns and cities have not been included, as there will clearly be no difficulty in establishing the general location of the parish or congregation in question.

Since 1929, a small number of rural parishes have adopted a new name (for example Whitehills, formerly Boyndie). The former names of these parishes have been included, but it would have been too unwieldy to include either the vast numbers of such changes of name in towns and cities, especially those which occurred at the time of the 1900 and 1929 unions, or the very many older names of pre-Reformation parishes which were abandoned in earlier centuries (however fascinating a list of such long-vanished names as Fothmuref, Kinbathock and Toskertoun might have been).

In this index, the following abbreviations have been used:

C of S	Church of Scotland
FC	Free Church
R	Relief Church
RP	Reformed Presbyterian Church
UF	United Free Church
UP	United Presbyterian Church
US	United Secession Church

Name no longer used	Present name of parish
Abbey St Bathan's	Kirk of Lammermuir
Abbotrule	charge suppressed: Presbytery of Jedburgh
Aberargie	charge dissolved: Presbytery of Perth
Aberchirder	Marnoch
Aberdalgie	The Stewartry of Strathearn
Aberdeen: Belmont Street	Aberdeen: St Mark's
Aberdeen: Bon Accord	Aberdeen: Denburn
Aberdeen: Carden Place	Aberdeen: Queen's Cross
Aberdeen: Causewayend	Aberdeen: St Stephen's
Aberdeen: East	Aberdeen: St Mark's
Aberdeen: Gallowgate	Aberdeen: St Mary's
Aberdeen: Gilcomston St Colm's	Aberdeen: Denburn
Aberdeen: Hilton	Aberdeen: Woodside
Aberdeen: King Street	Aberdeen: North of St Andrew
Aberdeen: Melville	Aberdeen: Queen's Cross
Aberdeen: Nelson Street	Aberdeen: North of St Andrew
Aberdeen: North	Aberdeen: North of St Andrew
Aberdeen: Pittodrie	Aberdeen: St Mary's
Aberdeen: Powis	Aberdeen: St Stephen's
Aberdeen: Rutherford	Aberdeen: Rosemount
Aberdeen: South (C of S)	Aberdeen: South of St Nicholas, Kincorth
Aberdeen: South (FC)	Aberdeen: St Mark's
Aberdeen: St Columba's	Aberdeen: High Hilton
Aberdeen: St Mary's	Aberdeen: St Machar's Cathedral
Aberdeen: St Paul's	Aberdeen: Denburn
Aberdeen: Trinity (C of S)	Aberdeen: Kirk of St Nicholas Uniting
Aberdeen: Trinity (FC)	Aberdeen: St Mark's
Aberdeen: Union	Aberdeen: Denburn
Aberuthven	The Stewartry of Strathearn
Abington	Glencaple
Addiewell	Breich Valley
Afton	New Cumnock
Airdrie: West	Airdrie: New Wellwynd
Aldbar	Aberlemno
Aldcambus	Dunglass
Alford	Howe Trinity
Alloa: Chalmers	Alloa: North
Alloa: Melville	Alloa: North
Alloa: St Andrew's	Alloa: North
Altries	charge dissolved: Presbytery of Kincardine and Deeside
Altyre	Rafford
Alvah	Banff
Annan: Erskine	Annan: St Andrew's
Annan: Greenknowe	Annan: St Andrew's
Arbroath: East	Arbroath: St Andrew's
Arbroath: Erskine	Arbroath: West Kirk
Arbroath: High Street	Arbroath: St Andrew's
Arbroath: Hopemount	Arbroath: St Andrew's
Arbroath: Ladyloan	Arbroath: West Kirk
Arbroath: Princes Street	Arbroath: West Kirk
Arbroath: St Columba's	Arbroath: West Kirk
Arbroath: St Margaret's	Arbroath: West Kirk
Arbroath: St Ninian's	Arbroath: St Andrew's
Arbroath: St Paul's	Arbroath: St Andrew's
Ardallie	Deer
Ardwell	Stoneykirk
Ascog	The United Church of Bute
Auchindoir	Upper Donside

Name no longer used	Present name of parish
Auchmithie	Arbroath: St Vigean's
Auldcathie	Dalmeny
Aultbea	Gairloch and Dundonnell
Ayr: Cathcart	Ayr: St Columba
Ayr: Darlington New	Ayr: Auld Kirk of Ayr
Ayr: Darlington Place	Ayr: Auld Kirk of Ayr
Ayr: Lochside	Ayr: St Quivox
Ayr: Martyrs'	Ayr: Auld Kirk of Ayr
Ayr: Sandgate	Ayr: St Columba
Ayr: St John's	Ayr: Auld Kirk of Ayr
Ayr: Trinity	Ayr: St Columba
Ayr: Wallacetown South	Ayr: Auld Kirk of Ayr
Back	charge dissolved: Presbytery of Lewis
Badcall	Eddrachillis
Balbeggie	Collace
Balfour	charge dissolved: Presbytery of Dundee
Balgedie	Portmoak
Baliasta	Unst
Ballachulish	Nether Lochaber
Ballater	Glenmuick
Balmacolm	Howe of Fife
Balmullo	charge dissolved: Presbytery of St Andrews
Balnacross	Tarff and Twynholm
Baltasound	Unst
Banchory-Ternan: North	Banchory-Ternan: West
Banchory-Ternan: South	Banchory-Ternan: West
Bandry	Luss
Bara	Garvald and Morham
Bargrennan	Penninghame
Barnweil	Tarbolton
Barrhead: Westbourne	Barrhead: Arthurlie
Barrock	Dunnet
Bedrule	Ruberslaw
Beith: Hamilfield	Beith: Trinity
Beith: Head Street	Beith: Trinity
Beith: Mitchell Street	Beith: Trinity
Belkirk	Liddesdale
Benholm	Mearns Coastal
Benvie	Fowlis and Liff
Binny	Linlithgow: St Michael's
Blackburn	Fintray and Kinellar
Blackhill	Longside
Blairlogie	congregation seceded: Presbytery of Stirling
Blanefield	Strathblane
Blantyre: Anderson	Blantyre: St Andrew's
Blantyre: Burleigh Memorial	Blantyre: St Andrew's
Blantyre: Stonefield	Blantyre: St Andrew's
Blyth Bridge	Kirkurd and Newlands
Boddam	Peterhead: Trinity
Bonhill: North	Alexandria
Bothwell: Park	Uddingston: Viewpark
Bourtreebush	Newtonhill
Bow of Fife	Monimail
Bowmore	Kilarrow
Boyndie	Whitehills
Brachollie	Petty
Braco	Ardoch
Braehead	Forth

Name no longer used	Present name of parish
Brechin: East	Brechin: Gardner Memorial
Brechin: Maison Dieu	Brechin: Cathedral
Brechin: St Columba's	Brechin: Gardner Memorial
Brechin: West	Brechin: Gardner Memorial
Breich	Breich Valley
Bridge of Teith	Kilmadock
Brora	Clyne
Buccleuch	Ettrick and Yarrow
Burnhead	Penpont, Keir and Tynron
Cairnryan	charge dissolved: Presbytery of Wigtown and Stranraer
Cambuslang: Rosebank	Cambuslang: St Andrew's
Cambuslang: West	Cambuslang: St Andrew's
Cambusmichael	St Martin's
Campbeltown: Longrow	Campbeltown: Lorne and Lowland
Campsail	Rosneath St Modan's
Canna	Mallaig St Columba and Knoydart
Carbuddo	Guthrie and Rescobie
Cardenden	Auchterderran St Fothad's
Carlisle	The Border Kirk
Carmichael	Cairngryffe
Carnoch	Contin
Carnousie	Turriff: St Ninian's and Forglen
Carnoustie: St Stephen's	Carnoustie
Carrbridge	Duthil
Carruthers	Middlebie
Castle Kennedy	Inch
Castleton	Liddesdale
Caterline	Kinneff
Chapelknowe	congregation seceded: Presbytery of Annandale and Eskdale
Clatt	Noth
Clayshant	Stoneykirk
Climpy	charge dissolved: Presbytery of Lanark
Clola	Deer
Clousta	Sandsting and Aithsting
Clova	The Glens and Kirriemuir: Old
Clydebank: Bank Street	Clydebank: St Cuthbert's
Clydebank: Boquhanran	Clydebank: Kilbowie St Andrew's
Clydebank: Hamilton Memorial	Clydebank: St Cuthbert's
Clydebank: Linnvale	Clydebank: St Cuthbert's
Clydebank: St James'	Clydebank: Abbotsford
Clydebank: Union	Clydebank: Kilbowie St Andrew's
Clydebank: West	Clydebank: Abbotsford
Coatbridge: Cliftonhill	Coatbridge: Clifton
Coatbridge: Coatdyke	Coatbridge: Clifton
Coatbridge: Coats	Coatbridge: Clifton
Coatbridge: Dunbeth	Coatbridge: St Andrew's
Coatbridge: Gartsherrie	Coatbridge: St Andrew's
Coatbridge: Garturk	Coatbridge: Calder
Coatbridge: Maxwell	Coatbridge: St Andrew's
Coatbridge: Trinity	Coatbridge: Clifton
Coatbridge: Whifflet	Coatbridge: Calder
Cobbinshaw	charge dissolved: Presbytery of West Lothian
Cockburnspath	Dunglass
Coigach	charge dissolved: Presbytery of Lochcarron-Skye
Coldstone	Cromar
Collessie	Howe of Fife
Corgarff	Upper Donside
Cortachy	The Glens and Kirriemuir: Old

Name no longer used	Present name of parish
Coull	Cromar
Covington	Cairngryffe
Cowdenbeath: Cairns	Cowdenbeath: Trinity
Cowdenbeath: Guthrie Memorial	Beath and Cowdenbeath: North
Cowdenbeath: West	Cowdenbeath: Trinity
Craggan	Tomintoul, Glenlivet and Inveraven
Craig	Inchbrayock
Craigdam	Tarves
Craigend	Perth: Moncreiffe
Cranshaws	Kirk of Lammermuir
Crawford	Glencaple
Crawfordjohn	Glencaple
Cray	Kirkmichael, Straloch and Glenshee
Creetown	Kirkmabreck
Crofthead	Fauldhouse St Andrew's
Crombie	Culross and Torryburn
Crossgates	Cowdenbeath: Trinity
Cruggleton	Sorbie
Cuikston	Farnell
Culbin	Dyke
Cullicudden	Resolis and Urquhart
Cults	Howe of Fife
Cumbernauld: Baird	Cumbernauld: Old
Cumbernauld: Bridgend	Cumbernauld: Old
Cumbernauld: St Andrew's	Cumbernauld: Old
Dalgarno	Closeburn
Dalguise	Dunkeld
Daliburgh	South Uist
Dalkeith: Buccleuch Street	Dalkeith: St Nicholas Buccleuch
Dalkeith: West (C of S)	Dalkeith: St Nicholas Buccleuch
Dalkeith: West (UP)	Dalkeith: St John's and King's Park
Dalmeath	Huntly Cairnie Glass
Dalreoch	charge dissolved: Presbytery of Perth
Dalry: Courthill	Dalry: Trinity
Dalry: St Andrew's	Dalry: Trinity
Dalry: West	Dalry: Trinity
Denholm	Ruberslaw
Denny: Broompark	Denny: Westpark
Denny: West	Denny: Westpark
Dennyloanhead	charge dissolved: Presbytery of Falkirk
Dolphinton	Black Mount
Douglas	The Douglas Valley Church
Douglas Water	The Douglas Valley Church
Dowally	Dunkeld
Drainie	Lossiemouth St Gerardine's High
Drumdelgie	Huntly Cairnie Glass
Dumbarrow	charge dissolved: Presbytery of Angus
Dumbarton: Bridgend	Dumbarton: West
Dumbarton: Dalreoch	Dumbarton: West
Dumbarton: High	Dumbarton: Riverside
Dumbarton: Knoxland	Dumbarton: Riverside
Dumbarton: North	Dumbarton: Riverside
Dumbarton: Old	Dumbarton: Riverside
Dumfries: Maxwelltown Laurieknowe	Dumfries: Troqueer
Dumfries: Townhead	Dumfries: St Michael's and South
Dunblane: East	Dunblane: St Blane's
Dunblane: Leighton	Dunblane: St Blane's
Dundee: Albert Square	Dundee: Meadowside St Paul's

Name no longer used	Present name of parish
Dundee: Baxter Park	Dundee: Trinity
Dundee: Broughty Ferry Union	Dundee: Broughty Ferry St Stephen's and West
Dundee: Chapelshade (FC)	Dundee: Meadowside St Paul's
Dundee: Downfield North	Dundee: Strathmartine
Dundee: Hawkhill	Dundee: Meadowside St Paul's
Dundee: Lochee East	Dundee: Lochee Old and St Luke's
Dundee: Lochee St Ninian's	Dundee: Lochee Old and St Luke's
Dundee: Martyrs'	Dundee: Balgay
Dundee: Maryfield	Dundee: Stobswell
Dundee: McCheyne Memorial	Dundee: West
Dundee: Ogilvie	Dundee: Stobswell
Dundee: Park	Dundee: Stobswell
Dundee: Roseangle	Dundee: West
Dundee: Ryehill	Dundee: West
Dundee: St Andrew's (FC)	Dundee: Meadowside St Paul's
Dundee: St Clement's Steeple	Dundee: Steeple
Dundee: St David's (C of S)	Dundee: Steeple
Dundee: St Enoch's	Dundee: Steeple
Dundee: St George's	Dundee: Meadowside St Paul's
Dundee: St John's	Dundee: West
Dundee: St Mark's	Dundee: West
Dundee: St Matthew's	Dundee: Trinity
Dundee: St Paul's	Dundee: Steeple
Dundee: St Peter's	Dundee: West
Dundee: Tay Square	Dundee: Meadowside St Paul's
Dundee: Victoria Street	Dundee: Stobswell
Dundee: Wallacetown	Dundee: Trinity
Dundee: Wishart Memorial	Dundee: Steeple
Dundurcas	charge suppressed: Presbytery of Moray
Duneaton	Glencaple
Dunfermline: Chalmers Street	Dunfermline: St Andrew's Erskine
Dunfermline: Maygate	Dunfermline: Gillespie Memorial
Dunfermline: Queen Anne Street	Dunfermline: St Andrew's Erskine
Dungree	Kirkpatrick Juxta
Duninald	Inchbrayock
Dunlappie	Brechin: Cathedral
Dunning	The Stewartry of Strathearn
Dunoon: Gaelic	Dunoon: St John's
Dunoon: Old	Dunoon: The High Kirk
Dunoon: St Cuthbert's	Dunoon: The High Kirk
Dunrod	Kirkcudbright
Dunsyre	Black Mount
Dupplin	The Stewartry of Strathearn
Ecclefechan	Hoddam
Ecclesjohn	Dun
Ecclesmachan	Strathbrock
Ecclesmoghriodan	Abernethy and Dron
Edinburgh: Abbey	Edinburgh: Greenside
Edinburgh: Abbeyhill	Edinburgh: Holyrood Abbey
Edinburgh: Arthur Street	Edinburgh: Kirk o' Field
Edinburgh: Barony	Edinburgh: Greenside
Edinburgh: Belford	Edinburgh: Palmerston Place
Edinburgh: Braid	Edinburgh: Morningside
Edinburgh: Bruntsfield	Edinburgh: Barclay
Edinburgh: Buccleuch	Edinburgh: Kirk o' Field
Edinburgh: Cairns Memorial	Edinburgh: Gorgie
Edinburgh: Candlish	Edinburgh: Polwarth
Edinburgh: Canongate (FC,UP)	Edinburgh: Holy Trinity

Name no longer used	Present name of parish
Edinburgh: Chalmers	Edinburgh: Barclay
Edinburgh: Charteris Memorial	Edinburgh: Kirk o' Field
Edinburgh: Cluny	Edinburgh: Morningside
Edinburgh: College	Edinburgh: Muirhouse St Andrew's
Edinburgh: College Street	Edinburgh: Muirhouse St Andrew's
Edinburgh: Cowgate (FC)	Edinburgh: Muirhouse St Andrew's
Edinburgh: Cowgate (R)	Edinburgh: Barclay
Edinburgh: Cowgate (US)	Edinburgh: Mayfield Salisbury
Edinburgh: Dalry	Edinburgh: St Colm's
Edinburgh: Davidson	Edinburgh: Stockbridge
Edinburgh: Dean (FC)	Edinburgh: Palmerston Place
Edinburgh: Dean Street	Edinburgh: Stockbridge
Edinburgh: Fountainhall Road	Edinburgh: Mayfield Salisbury
Edinburgh: Grange (C of S)	Edinburgh: Marchmont St Giles
Edinburgh: Grange (FC)	Edinburgh: St Catherine's Argyle
Edinburgh: Guthrie Memorial	Edinburgh: Greenside
Edinburgh: Haymarket	Edinburgh: St Colm's
Edinburgh: Henderson (C of S)	Edinburgh: Craigmillar Park
Edinburgh: Henderson (UP)	Edinburgh: Richmond Craigmillar
Edinburgh: Hillside	Edinburgh: Greenside
Edinburgh: Holyrood	Edinburgh: Holyrood Abbey
Edinburgh: Hope Park	Edinburgh: Mayfield Salisbury
Edinburgh: Hopetoun	Edinburgh: Greenside
Edinburgh: John Ker Memorial	Edinburgh: Polwarth
Edinburgh: Knox's	Edinburgh: Holy Trinity
Edinburgh: Lady Glenorchy's North	Edinburgh: Greenside
Edinburgh: Lady Glenorchy's South	Edinburgh: Holy Trinity
Edinburgh: Lady Yester's	Edinburgh: Greyfriars Tolbooth and Highland
Edinburgh: Lauriston	Edinburgh: Barclay
Edinburgh: Lochend	Edinburgh: St Margaret's
Edinburgh: Lothian Road	Edinburgh: Palmerston Place
Edinburgh: Mayfield North	Edinburgh: Mayfield Salisbury
Edinburgh: Mayfield South	Edinburgh: Craigmillar Park
Edinburgh: McCrie	Edinburgh: Kirk o' Field
Edinburgh: McDonald Road	Edinburgh: Broughton St Mary's
Edinburgh: Moray	Edinburgh: Holy Trinity
Edinburgh: Morningside High	Edinburgh: Morningside
Edinburgh: New North (C of S)	Edinburgh: Marchmont St Giles
Edinburgh: New North (FC)	Edinburgh: Greyfriars Tolbooth and Highland
Edinburgh: Newington East	Edinburgh: Kirk o' Field
Edinburgh: Newington South	Edinburgh: Mayfield Salisbury
Edinburgh: Nicolson Street	Edinburgh: Kirk o' Field
Edinburgh: North Morningside	Edinburgh: Morningside United
Edinburgh: North Richmond Street	Edinburgh: Richmond Craigmillar
Edinburgh: Pleasance (FC)	Edinburgh: Muirhouse St Andrew's
Edinburgh: Pleasance (UF)	Edinburgh: Kirk o' Field
Edinburgh: Prestonfield	Edinburgh: Priestfield
Edinburgh: Queen Street (FC)	Edinburgh: St Andrew's and St George's
Edinburgh: Queen Street (UP)	Edinburgh: Stockbridge
Edinburgh: Restalrig (C of S)	Edinburgh: St Margaret's
Edinburgh: Restalrig (FC)	Edinburgh: New Restalrig
Edinburgh: Rosehall	Edinburgh: Priestfield
Edinburgh: Roxburgh	Edinburgh: Kirk o' Field
Edinburgh: Roxburgh Terrace	Edinburgh: Kirk o' Field
Edinburgh: South Morningside	Edinburgh: Morningside
Edinburgh: St Bernard's	Edinburgh: Stockbridge
Edinburgh: St Bride's	Edinburgh: St Colm's
Edinburgh: St Columba's	Edinburgh: Greyfriars Tolbooth and Highland

Name no longer used	Present name of parish
Edinburgh: St David's (C of S)	Edinburgh: Viewforth
Edinburgh: St David's (FC)	Edinburgh: St David's Broomhouse
Edinburgh: St James' (C of S)	Edinburgh: Greenside
Edinburgh: St James' (FC)	Edinburgh: Inverleith
Edinburgh: St James' Place	Edinburgh: Greenside
Edinburgh: St John's	Edinburgh: Greyfriars Tolbooth and Highland
Edinburgh: St Luke's	Edinburgh: St Andrew's and St George's
Edinburgh: St Matthew's	Edinburgh: Morningside
Edinburgh: St Oran's	Edinburgh: Greyfriars Tolbooth and Highland
Edinburgh: St Oswald's	Edinburgh: Viewforth
Edinburgh: St Paul's	Edinburgh: Kirk o' Field
Edinburgh: St Stephen's (C of S)	Edinburgh: Stockbridge
Edinburgh: St Stephen's (FC)	Edinburgh: St Stephen's Comely Bank
Edinburgh: Tolbooth (C of S)	Edinburgh: Greyfriars Tolbooth and Highland
Edinburgh: Tolbooth (FC)	Edinburgh: St Andrew's and St George's
Edinburgh: Trinity College	Edinburgh: Holy Trinity
Edinburgh: Tynecastle	Edinburgh: Gorgie
Edinburgh: Warrender	Edinburgh: Marchmont St Giles
Edinburgh: West St Giles	Edinburgh: Marchmont St Giles
Eigg	Arisaig and the Small Isles
Eilean Finain	Ardnamurchan
Elgin: Moss Street	Elgin: St Giles and St Columba's South
Elgin: South Street	Elgin: St Giles and St Columba's South
Ellem	Kirk of Lammermuir
Elsrickle	Black Mount
Eshaness	Northmavine
Essie	Noth
Essil	Speymouth
Ethie	Inverkeilor and Lunan
Ettiltoun	Liddesdale
Ewes Durris	Langholm, Ewes and Westerkirk
Falkirk: Graham's Road	Falkirk: Grahamston United
Farnua	Kirkhill
Ferryden	Inchbrayock
Fetterangus	Deer
Fettercairn	West Mearns
Fetternear	Chapel of Garioch
Finzean	Birse and Feughside
Fochabers	Bellie
Forbes	Howe Trinity
Fordoun	West Mearns
Forfar: South	Forfar: St Margaret's
Forfar: St James'	Forfar: St Margaret's
Forfar: West	Forfar: St Margaret's
Forgan	Newport-on-Tay
Forgue	Auchaber United
Forres: Castlehill	Forres: St Leonard's
Forres: High	Forres: St Leonard's
Forteviot	The Stewartry of Strathearn
Forvie	Ellon
Foula	Walls and Sandness
Galashiels: East	Galashiels: St Ninian's
Galashiels: Ladhope	Galashiels: St Aidan's
Galashiels: South	Galashiels: St Aidan's
Galashiels: St Andrew's	Galashiels: St Ninian's
Galashiels: St Columba's	Galashiels: St Ninian's
Galashiels: St Cuthbert's	Galashiels: St Aidan's
Galashiels: St Mark's	Galashiels: St Ninian's

Name no longer used	Present name of parish
Galashiels: Trinity	Galashiels: St Aidan's
Galtway	Kirkcudbright
Gamrie	charge dissolved: Presbytery of Buchan
Garmouth	Speymouth
Gartly	Noth
Garvell	Kirkmichael, Tinwald and Torthorwald
Garvock	Mearns Coastal
Gatehouse	Anwoth and Girthon
Gauldry	Balmerino
Gelston	Buittle and Kelton
Giffnock: Orchard Park	Giffnock: The Park
Girvan: Chalmers	Girvan: North (Old and St Andrew's)
Girvan: Trinity	Girvan: North (Old and St Andrew's)
Glasgow: Abbotsford	Glasgow: Gorbals
Glasgow: Auldfield	Glasgow: Pollokshaws
Glasgow: Baillieston Old	Glasgow: Baillieston St Andrew's
Glasgow: Baillieston Rhinsdale	Glasgow: Baillieston St Andrew's
Glasgow: Balornock North	Glasgow: Wallacewell
Glasgow: Barmulloch	Glasgow: Wallacewell
Glasgow: Barrowfield (C of S)	Glasgow: Bridgeton St Francis in the East
Glasgow: Barrowfield (RP)	Glasgow: St Luke's and St Andrew's
Glasgow: Bath Street	Glasgow: Renfield St Stephen's
Glasgow: Battlefield West	Glasgow: Langside
Glasgow: Bellahouston	Glasgow: Ibrox
Glasgow: Bellgrove	Glasgow: Dennistoun Blackfriars
Glasgow: Belmont	Glasgow: Kelvinside Hillhead
Glasgow: Berkeley Street	Glasgow: Renfield St Stephen's
Glasgow: Bluevale	Glasgow: Dennistoun Central
Glasgow: Blythswood	Glasgow: Renfield St Stephen's
Glasgow: Bridgeton East	Glasgow: Bridgeton St Francis in the East
Glasgow: Bridgeton West	Glasgow: St Luke's and St Andrew's
Glasgow: Buccleuch	Glasgow: Renfield St Stephen's
Glasgow: Burnbank	Glasgow: Lansdowne
Glasgow: Calton New	Glasgow: St Luke's and St Andrew's
Glasgow: Calton Old	Glasgow: Calton Parkhead
Glasgow: Calton Relief	Glasgow: St Luke's and St Andrew's
Glasgow: Cambridge Street	Bishopbriggs: Springfield Cambridge
Glasgow: Candlish Memorial	Glasgow: Govanhill Trinity
Glasgow: Cathcart South	Glasgow: Cathcart Trinity
Glasgow: Central	Glasgow: St Luke's and St Andrew's
Glasgow: Cessnock	Glasgow: Kinning Park
Glasgow: Chalmers (C of S)	Glasgow: St Luke's and St Andrew's
Glasgow: Chalmers (FC)	Glasgow: Gorbals
Glasgow: Claremont	Glasgow: Anderston Kelvingrove
Glasgow: College	Glasgow: Anderston Kelvingrove
Glasgow: Cowcaddens	Glasgow: Renfield St Stephen's
Glasgow: Cowlairs	Glasgow: Springburn
Glasgow: Crosshill	Glasgow: Queen's Park
Glasgow: Dalmarnock (C of S)	Glasgow: Calton Parkhead
Glasgow: Dalmarnock (UF)	Rutherglen: Old
Glasgow: Dean Park	Glasgow: New Govan
Glasgow: Dennistoun South	Glasgow: Dennistoun Blackfriars
Glasgow: Dowanhill	Glasgow: Partick Trinity
Glasgow: Dowanvale	Glasgow: Partick South
Glasgow: Drumchapel Old	Glasgow: Drumchapel St Andrew's
Glasgow: East Campbell Street	Glasgow: Dennistoun Central
Glasgow: East Park	Glasgow: Kelvin Stevenson Memorial
Glasgow: Edgar Memorial	Glasgow: St Luke's and St Andrew's

Name no longer used	Present name of parish
Glasgow: Eglinton Street	Glasgow: Govanhill Trinity
Glasgow: Elder Park	Glasgow: Govan Old
Glasgow: Elgin Street	Glasgow: Govanhill Trinity
Glasgow: Erskine	Glasgow: Langside
Glasgow: Fairbairn	Rutherglen: Old
Glasgow: Fairfield	Glasgow: New Govan
Glasgow: Finnieston	Glasgow: Anderston Kelvingrove
Glasgow: Garnethill	Glasgow: Renfield St Stephen's
Glasgow: Garscube Netherton	Glasgow: Knightswood St Margaret's
Glasgow: Gillespie	Glasgow: St Luke's and St Andrew's
Glasgow: Gordon Park	Glasgow: Whiteinch
Glasgow: Govan Copland Road	Glasgow: New Govan
Glasgow: Govan Trinity	Glasgow: New Govan
Glasgow: Grant Street	Glasgow: Renfield St Stephen's
Glasgow: Greenhead	Glasgow: St Luke's and St Andrew's
Glasgow: Hall Memorial	Rutherglen: Old
Glasgow: Hamilton Crescent	Glasgow: Partick South
Glasgow: Highlanders' Memorial	Glasgow: Knightswood St Margaret's
Glasgow: Hyndland (UF)	Glasgow: St John's Renfield
Glasgow: John Knox's	Glasgow: Gorbals
Glasgow: Johnston	Glasgow: Springburn
Glasgow: Jordanvale	Glasgow: Whiteinch
Glasgow: Kelvinhaugh	Glasgow: Anderston Kelvingrove
Glasgow: Kelvinside Botanic Gardens	Glasgow: Kelvinside Hillhead
Glasgow: Kelvinside Old	Glasgow: Kelvin Stevenson Memorial
Glasgow: Kingston	Glasgow: Carnwadric
Glasgow: Lancefield	Glasgow: Anderston Kelvingrove
Glasgow: Langside Avenue	Glasgow: Shawlands
Glasgow: Langside Hill	Glasgow: Battlefield East
Glasgow: Langside Old	Glasgow: Langside
Glasgow: Laurieston (C of S)	Glasgow: Gorbals
Glasgow: Laurieston (FC)	Glasgow: Carnwadric
Glasgow: London Road	Glasgow: Bridgeton St Francis in the East
Glasgow: Lyon Street	Glasgow: Renfield St Stephen's
Glasgow: Macgregor Memorial	Glasgow: Govan Old
Glasgow: Macmillan	Glasgow: St Luke's and St Andrew's
Glasgow: Milton	Glasgow: Renfield St Stephen's
Glasgow: Netherton St Matthew's	Glasgow: Knightswood St Margaret's
Glasgow: New Cathcart	Glasgow: Cathcart Trinity
Glasgow: Newhall	Glasgow: Bridgeton St Francis in the East
Glasgow: Newton Place	Glasgow: Partick South
Glasgow: Nithsdale	Glasgow: Queen's Park
Glasgow: Old Partick	Glasgow: Partick Trinity
Glasgow: Paisley Road	Glasgow: Kinning Park
Glasgow: Partick Anderson	Glasgow: Partick South
Glasgow: Partick East	Glasgow: Partick Trinity
Glasgow: Partick High	Glasgow: Partick South
Glasgow: Phoenix Park	Glasgow: Springburn
Glasgow: Plantation	Glasgow: Kinning Park
Glasgow: Pollok St Aidan's	Glasgow: St James' Pollok
Glasgow: Pollok Street	Glasgow: Kinning Park
Glasgow: Polmadie	Glasgow: Govanhill Trinity
Glasgow: Queen's Cross	Glasgow: Ruchill
Glasgow: Renfield (C of S)	Glasgow: Renfield St Stephen's
Glasgow: Renfield (FC)	Glasgow: St John's Renfield
Glasgow: Renfield Street	Glasgow: Renfield St Stephen's
Glasgow: Renwick	Glasgow: Gorbals
Glasgow: Robertson Memorial	Glasgow: The Martyrs'

Name no longer used	Present name of parish
Glasgow: Rockcliffe	Rutherglen: Old
Glasgow: Rockvilla	Glasgow: Possilpark
Glasgow: Rose Street	Glasgow: Langside
Glasgow: Rutherford	Glasgow: Dennistoun Central
Glasgow: Shamrock Street	Glasgow: Renfield St Stephen's
Glasgow: Shawholm	Glasgow: Pollokshaws
Glasgow: Shawlands Cross	Glasgow: Shawlands
Glasgow: Shawlands Old	Glasgow: Shawlands
Glasgow: Sighthill	Glasgow: Springburn
Glasgow: Somerville	Glasgow: Springburn
Glasgow: Springbank	Glasgow: Lansdowne
Glasgow: St Clement's	Glasgow: Bridgeton St Francis in the East
Glasgow: St Columba Gaelic	Glasgow: New Govan
Glasgow: St Cuthbert's	Glasgow: Ruchill
Glasgow: St Enoch's (C of S)	Glasgow: St Enoch's Hogganfield
Glasgow: St Enoch's (FC)	Glasgow: Anderston Kelvingrove
Glasgow: St George's (C of S)	Glasgow: St George's Tron
Glasgow: St George's (FC)	Glasgow: Anderston Kelvingrove
Glasgow: St George's Road	Glasgow: Renfield St Stephen's
Glasgow: St James' (C of S)	Glasgow: St James' Pollok
Glasgow: St James' (FC)	Glasgow: St Luke's and St Andrew's
Glasgow: St John's (C of S)	Glasgow: St Luke's and St Andrew's
Glasgow: St John's (FC)	Glasgow: St John's Renfield
Glasgow: St Kiaran's	Glasgow: New Govan
Glasgow: St Mark's	Glasgow: Anderston Kelvingrove
Glasgow: St Mary's Govan	Glasgow: New Govan
Glasgow: St Mary's Partick	Glasgow: Partick South
Glasgow: St Matthew's (C of S)	Glasgow: Renfield St Stephen's
Glasgow: St Matthew's (FC)	Glasgow: Knightswood St Margaret's
Glasgow: St Ninian's	Glasgow: Gorbals
Glasgow: St Peter's	Glasgow: Anderston Kelvingrove
Glasgow: Steven Memorial	Glasgow: Ibrox
Glasgow: Strathbungo	Glasgow: Queen's Park
Glasgow: Summerfield	Rutherglen: Old
Glasgow: Summertown	Glasgow: New Govan
Glasgow: Sydney Place	Glasgow: Dennistoun Cental
Glasgow: The Park	Giffnock: The Park
Glasgow: Titwood	Glasgow: Pollokshields
Glasgow: Tradeston	Glasgow: Gorbals
Glasgow: Trinity	Glasgow: St Luke's and St Andrew's
Glasgow: Trinity Duke Street	Glasgow: Dennistoun Central
Glasgow: Tron St Anne's	Glasgow: St George's Tron
Glasgow: Union	Glasgow: Carnwadric
Glasgow: Victoria	Glasgow: Queen's Park
Glasgow: Wellfield	Glasgow: Springburn
Glasgow: Wellpark	Glasgow: Dennistoun Cental
Glasgow: West Scotland Street	Glasgow: Kinning Park
Glasgow: White Memorial	Glasgow: Kinning Park
Glasgow: Whitehill	Glasgow: Dennistoun Blackfriars
Glasgow: Whitevale (FC)	Glasgow: St Thomas' Gallowgate
Glasgow: Whitevale (UP)	Glasgow: Dennistoun Central
Glasgow: Wilton	Glasgow: Kelvin Stevenson Memorial
Glasgow: Woodlands	Glasgow: Wellington
Glasgow: Woodside	Glasgow: Lansdowne
Glasgow: Wynd (C of S)	Glasgow: St Luke's and St Andrew's
Glasgow: Wynd (FC)	Glasgow: Gorbals
Glasgow: Young Street	Glasgow: Dennistoun Blackfriars
Glen Convinth	Kiltarlity

Name no longer used	Present name of parish
Glen Ussie	Fodderty and Strathpeffer
Glenapp	Ballantrae
Glenbervie	West Mearns
Glenbuchat	Upper Donside
Glenbuck	Muirkirk
Glencaple	Caerlaverock
Glendoick	St Madoes and Kinfauns
Glenfarg	Arngask
Glengairn	Glenmuick
Glengarnock	Kilbirnie: Auld Kirk
Glenluce	Old Luce
Glenmoriston	Fort Augustus
Glenprosen	The Glens and Kirriemuir Old
Glenrinnes	Mortlach and Cabrach
Glenshiel	Glenelg and Kintail
Glentanar	Aboyne – Dinnet
Gogar	Edinburgh: Corstorphine Old
Gordon	Monquhitter and New Byth
Graemsay	Stromness
Grangemouth: Grange	Grangemouth: Zetland
Grangemouth: Old	Grangemouth: Zetland
Greenloaning	Ardoch
Greenock: Augustine	Greenock: Cartsdyke
Greenock: Cartsburn	Greenock: Cartsdyke
Greenock: Crawfordsburn	Greenock: Cartsdyke
Greenock: Gaelic	Greenock: St Luke's
Greenock: Greenbank	Greenock: St Luke's
Greenock: Martyrs'	Greenock: St George's North
Greenock: Middle	Greenock: St George's North
Greenock: Mount Park	Greenock: Mount Kirk
Greenock: Mount Pleasant	Greenock: Mount Kirk
Greenock: North (C of S)	Greenock: Old West Kirk
Greenock: North (FC)	Greenock: St George's North
Greenock: Sir Michael Street	Greenock: Ardgowan
Greenock: South	Greenock: Mount Kirk
Greenock: South Park	Greenock: Mount Kirk
Greenock: St Andrew's	Greenock: Ardgowan
Greenock: St Columba's Gaelic	Greenock: Old West Kirk
Greenock: St Mark's	Greenock: St Luke's
Greenock: St Thomas'	Greenock: St George's North
Greenock: The Old Kirk	Greenock: St Luke's
Greenock: The Union Church	Greenock: Ardgowan
Greenock: Trinity	Greenock: Ardgowan
Greenock: Union Street	Greenock: Ardgowan
Greenock: West	Greenock: St Luke's
Gress	Stornoway: St Columba
Guardbridge	Leuchars: St Athernase
Haddington: St John's	Haddington: West
Hamilton: Auchingramont North	Hamilton: North
Hamilton: Avon Street	Hamilton: St Andrew's
Hamilton: Brandon	Hamilton: St Andrew's
Hamilton: Saffronhall Assoc. Anti-B.	Hamilton: North
Hardgate	Urr
Hassendean	Ruberslaw
Hawick: East Bank	Hawick: Trinity
Hawick: Orrock	Hawick: St Mary's and Old
Hawick: St Andrew's	Hawick: Trinity
Hawick: St George's	Hawick: Teviot

Name no longer used	Present name of parish
Hawick: St George's West	Hawick: Teviot
Hawick: St John's	Hawick: Trinity
Hawick: St Margaret's	Hawick: Teviot
Hawick: West Port	Hawick: Teviot
Hawick: Wilton South	Hawick: Teviot
Haywood	Forth
Helensburgh: Old	Helensburgh: The West Kirk
Helensburgh: St Andrew's	Helensburgh: The West Kirk
Helensburgh: St Bride's	Helensburgh: The West Kirk
Heylipol	Tiree
Hillside	Unst
Hillswick	Northmavine
Hilton	Whitsome
Holywell	The Border Kirk
Hope Kailzie	charge suppressed: Presbytery of Melrose and Peebles
Horndean	Ladykirk
Howford	charge dissolved: Presbytery of Inverness
Howmore	South Uist
Huntly: Princes Street	Huntly: Strathbogie
Inchkenneth	Kilfinichen and Kilvickeon and the Ross of Mull
Inchmartin	Errol
Innerwick	Dunglass
Inverallan	Grantown-on-Spey
Inverchaolain	Toward
Inverkeithny	Auchaber United
Inverness: Merkinch St Mark's	Inverness: Trinity
Inverness: Queen Street	Inverness: Trinity
Inverness: St Mary's	Inverness: Dalneigh and Bona
Inverness: West	Inverness: Inshes
Irving	Gretna, Half Morton and Kirkpatrick Fleming
Jedburgh: Abbey	Jedburgh: Trinity
Jedburgh: Blackfriars	Jedburgh: Trinity
Jedburgh: Boston	Jedburgh: Trinity
Johnshaven	Mearns Coastal
Johnstone: East	Johnstone: St Paul's
Johnstone: West	Johnstone: St Paul's
Kames	Kyles
Kearn	Upper Donside
Keig	Howe Trinity
Keith Marischal	Humbie
Keith: South	Keith: North, Newmill, Boharm and Rothiemay
Kelso: East	Kelso: North and Ednam
Kelso: Edenside	Kelso: North and Ednam
Kelso: St John's	Kelso: North and Ednam
Kelso: Trinity	Kelso: North and Ednam
Kennethmont	Noth
Kettle	Howe of Fife
Kilbirnie: Barony	Kilbirnie: Auld Kirk
Kilbirnie: East	Kilbirnie: St Columba's
Kilbirnie: West	Kilbirnie: St Columba's
Kilblaan	Southend
Kilblane	Kirkmahoe
Kilbride (Cowal)	Kyles
Kilbride (Dumfries and Kirkcudbright)	Sanquhar
Kilbride (Lorn)	Kilmore and Oban
Kilbride (Stirling)	Dunblane: Cathedral
Kilchattan Bay	The United Church of Bute
Kilchousland	Campbeltown: Highland

Name no longer used	Present name of parish
Kilcolmkill (Kintyre)	Southend
Kilcolmkill (Lochaber)	Morvern
Kildrummy	Upper Donside
Kilkerran	Campbeltown: Highland
Kilkivan	Campbeltown: Highland
Killintag	Morvern
Kilmacolm: St James'	Kilmacolm: St Columba
Kilmahew	Cardross
Kilmahog	Callander
Kilmarnock: King Street	Kilmarnock: Howard St Andrew's
Kilmarnock: Portland Road	Kilmarnock: Howard St Andrew's
Kilmarrow	Killean and Kilchenzie
Kilmichael (Inverness)	Urquhart and Glenmoriston
Kilmichael (Kintyre)	Campbeltown: Highland
Kilmoir	Brechin: Cathedral
Kilmore	Urquhart and Glenmoriston
Kilmoveonaig	Blair Atholl and Struan
Kilmun: St Andrew's	Strone and Ardentinny
Kilpheder	South Uist
Kinairney	Midmar
Kincardine O'Neil	Mid Deeside
Kincraig	Alvie and Insh
Kinedar	Lossiemouth: St Gerardine's High
Kingarth	The United Church of Bute
Kininmonth	charge dissolved: Presbytery of Buchan
Kinkell	Keithhall
Kinloch	Caputh and Clunie
Kinlochewe	Applecross, Lochcarron and Torridon
Kinlochluichart	Contin
Kinlochrannoch	Foss and Rannoch
Kinneil	Bo'ness: Old
Kinnettas	Fodderty and Strathpeffer
Kinnoir	Huntly Cairnie Glass
Kinrossie	Collace
Kirkandrews	Borgue
Kirkapol	Tiree
Kirkcaldy: Abbotsrood	Kirkcaldy: St Andrew's
Kirkcaldy: Bethelfield	Kirkcaldy: Linktown
Kirkcaldy: Dunnikeir	Kirkcaldy: St Andrew's
Kirkcaldy: Gallatown	Kirkcaldy: Viewforth
Kirkcaldy: Invertiel	Kirkcaldy: Linktown
Kirkcaldy: Old	Kirkcaldy: St Bryce Kirk
Kirkcaldy: Raith	Kirkcaldy: Abbotshall
Kirkcaldy: Sinclairtown	Kirkcaldy: Viewforth
Kirkcaldy: St Brycedale	Kirkcaldy: St Bryce Kirk
Kirkcaldy: Victoria Road	Kirkcaldy: St Andrew's
Kirkchrist	Tarff and Twynholm
Kirkconnel	Gretna, Half Morton and Kirkpatrick Fleming
Kirkcormick	Buittle and Kelton
Kirkdale	Kirkmabreck
Kirkforthar	Markinch
Kirkhope	Ettrick and Yarrow
Kirkintilloch: St Andrew's	Kirkintilloch: St Columba's
Kirkintilloch: St David's	Kirkintilloch: St Columba's
Kirkmadrine (Machars)	Sorbie
Kirkmadrine (Rhinns)	Stoneykirk
Kirkmaiden	Glasserton and Isle of Whithorn
Kirkmichael	Tomintoul, Glenlivet and Inveraven

Name no longer used	Present name of parish
Longformacus	Kirk of Lammermuir
Longnewton	Ancrum
Longridge	Breich Valley
Longtown	The Border Kirk
Luce	Hoddam
Lude	Blair Atholl and Struan
Lumphanan	Mid Deeside
Lumphinnans	Beath and Cowdenbeath: North
Lumsden	Upper Donside
Luncarty	Redgorton
Lund	Unst
Lynturk	Cushnie and Tough
Mailor	The Stewartry of Strathearn
Mainsriddle	Colvend, Southwick and Kirkbean
Maryburgh	Ferintosh
Marykirk	Aberluthnott
Maryton	Inchbrayock
Meadowfield	Caldercruix and Longriggend
Meathie	Glamis, Inverarity and Kinnettles
Megget	Ettrick and Yarrow
Melville	charge suppressed: Presbytery of Lothian
Memus	The Glens and Kirriemuir: Old
Methil: East	Innerleven: East
Mid Calder: Bridgend	Kirk of Calder
Mid Calder: St John's	Kirk of Calder
Midholm	congregation seceded: Presbytery of Jedburgh
Migvie	Cromar
Millbrex	Fyvie
Millerston	charge dissolved: Presbytery of Glasgow
Millport	Cumbrae
Milnathort	Orwell
Minto	Ruberslaw
Monecht	charge dissolved: Presbytery of Gordon
Monifieth: North	Monikie and Newbigging
Montrose: Knox's	Montrose: Melville South
Montrose: St George's	Montrose: Old and St Andrew's
Montrose: St John's	Montrose: Old and St Andrew's
Montrose: St Luke's	Montrose: Old and St Andrew's
Montrose: St Paul's	Montrose: Melville South
Montrose: Trinity	Montrose: Old and St Andrew's
Monzievaird	Crieff
Moonzie	charge dissolved: Presbytery of St Andrews
Morton	Thornhill
Mossbank	Delting
Mossgreen	Cowdenbeath: Trinity
Motherwell: Brandon	Motherwell: Crosshill
Motherwell: Cairns	Motherwell: Crosshill
Moulin	Pitlochry
Mount Kedar	Ruthwell
Mow	Morebattle and Hownam
Moy	Dyke
Moyness	charge dissolved: Presbytery of Moray
Muckersie	The Stewartry of Strathearn
Muirton	Aberluthnott
Murthly	Caputh and Clunie
Musselburgh: Bridge Street	Musselburgh: St Andrew's High
Musselburgh: Millhill	Musselburgh: St Andrew's High
Nairn: High	Nairn: St Ninian's

Name no longer used	Present name of parish
Peterhead: East	Peterhead: St Andrew's
Peterhead: South	Peterhead: St Andrew's
Peterhead: St Peter's	Peterhead: Trinity
Peterhead: West Associate	Peterhead: Trinity
Pettinain	Cairngryffe
Pitcairn (C of S)	Redgorton
Pitcairn (UF)	Almondbank Tibbermore
Pitlessie	Howe of Fife
Pitroddie	St Madoes and Kinfauns
Plockton	Lochalsh
Polmont South	Brightons
Poolewe	Gairloch and Dundonnell
Port Bannatyne	The United Church of Bute
Port Ellen	Kildalton and Oa
Port Glasgow: Clune Park	Port Glasgow: St Andrew's
Port Glasgow: Newark	Port Glasgow: St Andrew's
Port Glasgow: Old	Port Glasgow: St Andrew's
Port Glasgow: Princes Street	Port Glasgow: St Andrew's
Port Glasgow: West	Port Glasgow: St Andrew's
Port Sonachan	Glenorchy and Inishail
Port William	Mochrum
Portobello: Regent Street	Edinburgh: Portobello Old
Portobello: Windsor Place	Edinburgh: Portobello Old
Portsoy	Fordyce
Prestonkirk	Traprain
Prinlaws	Leslie Trinity
Quarrier's Mount Zion	Kilmacolm: St Columba
Raasay	Portree
Rathillet	Creich, Flisk and Kilmany
Rathmuriel	Noth
Redcastle	Killearnan
Restenneth	Forfar: East and Old
Rhynd	Perth: Moncreiffe
Rhynie	Noth
Rickarton	charge dissolved: Presbytery of Kincardine and Deeside
Rigg	Gretna, Half Morton and Kirkpatrick Fleming
Rigside	The Douglas Valley Church
Rinpatrick	Gretna, Half Morton and Kirkpatrick Fleming
Roberton	Glencaple
Rosehearty	Pitsligo
Rossie	Inchture and Kinnaird
Rothesay: Bridgend	The United Church of Bute
Rothesay: Craigmore High	Rothesay: Trinity
Rothesay: Craigmore St Brendan's	The United Church of Bute
Rothesay: High	The United Church of Bute
Rothesay: New	The United Church of Bute
Rothesay: St James'	Rothesay: Trinity
Rothesay: St John's	The United Church of Bute
Rothesay: West	Rothesay: Trinity
Rutherglen: East	Rutherglen: Old
Rutherglen: Greenhill	Rutherglen: Old
Rutherglen: Munro	Ritherglen: West
Ruthven	Huntly Cairnie Glass
Saltcoats: Erskine	Saltcoats: New Trinity
Saltcoats: Landsborough	Saltcoats: New Trinity
Saltcoats: Middle	Saltcoats: New Trinity
Saltcoats: South Beach	Saltcoats: St Cuthbert's
Saltcoats: Trinity	Saltcoats: New Trinity

408

INDEX OF SUBJECTS

INDEX OF ADVERTISERS